Bottom Line's
BIG
FAT
BOOK OF
FREE
MONEY
FOR EVERYONE

By Matthew Lesko

Bottom Line
BOOKS
www.BottomLineSecrets.com

Bottom Line's Big Fat Book of Free Money For Everyone

By Matthew Lesko and Mary Ann Martello

Published by arrangement with Information USA, Inc., P.O. Box E, Kensington, MD 20895
{www.lesko.com}

Bottom Line® Books
First Edition

ISBN 0-88723-340-6

Bottom Line® Books publishes the opinions of expert authorities in many fields.
The use of a book is not a substitute for legal, accounting, health or other professional services.
Consult competent professionals for answers to your specific questions.

Government programs, scholarship offers, contact information, telephone numbers and web sites listed in
this book are accurate at the time of publication, but they are subject to frequent change.

Bottom Line® Books is a registered trademark of Boardroom® Inc.
281 Tresser Boulevard, Stamford, CT 06901

Printed in the United States of America

TABLE OF CONTENTS

FEDERAL MONEY FOR HOUSING AND REAL ESTATE 298

FREE SCHOLARSHIPS.. 412

INTRODUCTION

Who would not love to get a grant? Everyone says that grants are so hard to get, but that is silly! Millions of people get grants every year, so why don't you? You don't get them because you have no idea where they are, and you don't know what to do when you find them! So, that is why I am here. I am going to tell you where all the grants are, what to do when you find them, and how to get them.

Next year, over three million people are going to get grants. I am sorry, not three million — 30 million! What the heck is a zero when it is government work? Thirty million people every year are getting grants and free money. That is why you should be getting one too. If you want to know about them, you have got to put in some effort.

Over $1.1 trillion in grants is given out every year. That is a trillion dollars! Do you know what a trillion is? No? Neither do I! Remember when Rockefeller was the vice president and running for president? Now, there was a guy throwing around a trillion. He probably knew what a trillion dollars was! But you and I don't know. A million dollars, a billion dollars, and now this is a trillion!

Look at this — about nine million new cars are sold every year at the average price of about $20,000. I did a little research and found out that comes to $180 billion worth of cars. So, if one trillion dollars is given out in grants each year, that is over six times the amount of all the new cars sold every year. That is a heck of a lot of money. That is why you have to know about grants.

Millions are spent every year on advertising and salesmen around the country are trying to get you to buy a car. We see ads for automobiles all over the place. Every time you turn on the TV, open a newspaper, a magazine or look at a billboard, you are likely to see an ad for an automobile. But there is never going to be advertising for grants. That is why, as a result, you have got to do the work. You are the one that is going to have to go out there and do something to find these grants. They are not going to come and hit you in the face by themselves.

Where the Grants Are

There are two major sources for grants. One source is foundations and nonprofit organizations. These are those little funny people that love to give away money, like Bill Gates, who have foundations. There are literally thousands of people like him that give out money. And they give out collectively every year about $27 billion.

The government gives over a trillion dollars. If nonprofit organizations and foundations are giving out $27 billion, and the government is giving over a trillion, we are talking about 40 or 50 times to one. So, the government gives out 40 times more money than all the foundations and nonprofit organizations out there. These are your two sources for grants, the nonprofit organizations and foundations, and the federal government. And remember, the federal government gives out 40 times more money! And that is what I know better than anyone.

Writing or Not Writing a Proposal

Half the federal budget is grants or other forms of free money that goes to individuals. There are two different kinds of grants. There are grants where you have to write a big proposal. You have to write some kind of paper, describing everything you are going to do. We will talk about how to get through that process later. There is no magic to doing a proposal; it is just a bigger bureaucratic hurdle to go through for you.

And there are other grants where you do not have to write a proposal. You just have to know about the program and fill out a page or two application to get the money. Technically this is a separate kind of grant. They are both free money in that you do not have to it pay back.

When you talk about grants, many people think of research scientists and filling out 500-page applications. We will talk about that too, but I am also going to tell you about the other kind where you just fill out a page or two, a short form, or a little government document and wow, you get a grant. There are also nonprofit organizations that offer grants that do not require complicated forms.

Who Gets the Money

Who gets all this money? Well, it goes to people. Remember, 30 million people every year get this money. All kinds of organizations — nonprofit organizations, government organizations — are giving out this money. I can categorize who gets grants. One category is people who have needs. People who might have trouble paying their bills. There are grants out there to help you pay them.

If you have trouble paying a health bill, a heating bill or a phone bill, or just need extra money (yes there is grant money for people who don't have a lot of money and just need extra money), there are two programs you should know exist. They are not major ones, but extremely important. Take out a pencil and paper, and write these down. I found out about these recently, and people should know about them. Even if you are not in the category yourself where you need this information or help, you may have relatives, friends, a senior citizen, or know someone who has a disability, who may benefit from this wonderful grant program. The program gives you $1,000 extra a year.

This is from the U.S. Department of Health and Human Services, and is money back to you. You can call the Department right now and get over $1,051 extra a year. There is an income limitation of around $15,000 for this program. If you are a senior, then you are probably not making that much. I have seen studies that show three million seniors are eligible for this program and do not apply. Also, people with disabilities are eligible. If this specific program is not for you, you should still know about it so you can help get this money for other people, their loved ones, or that little old lady down the street.

The way to find out about this program is to contact the U.S. Department of Health and Human Services. Actually, it is run through Medicare. It is {www.medicare.gov} on the web, or 800-MEDICARE. You are looking for the Medicare premium deductions, called the Qualified Medicare Beneficiaries Plan. There are a couple of names for it. The program gives Medicare Part B premiums back to people who need this kind of income, and many people are not applying for it.

There is another program that many people do not know exists through the Social Security system that gives you an extra $6,000 of spending money. This is called the Supplemental Security Income (SSI). If you have a problem with either of these programs, you can contact your congressman's or senator's office and they will help you learn more. These are important programs for people who are in need.

I want to make sure that more people know about these programs. When you learn this information, you not only help yourself getting grant money to do the things you want to do in life, but you help other people. That is what is so important. When you empower yourself with the information, help, and grant money available, (you can't spend

$1.1 trillion on yourself), you can start helping other people. Knowing about these two programs can help you help others.

97.5% Of Grants are From the Government

We are talking about $1.1 trillion. We have 40 to one government money, so nonprofits and foundations give out less than 2.5%, and the rest is government money. The only program the government really advertises is the lottery program. That is why most people looking for money to do things they really want to do are going to play the Lotto, and that is a government program! They go and spend money at 7-Eleven to buy a lottery ticket hoping to get money from a government program. And what have you got, one in a million chance of getting that money? That is nonsense, isn't it?

One in a million chance for you to get money? The last time I looked, lotteries only gave out about $20 billion or so. We are talking about a trillion dollars a year from the government, and not one in a million chance. I will show you programs where two out of every three people who apply for the money get it.

Two out of every three people get money to start a business. A million people a year get money from the government to start or stay in a business. It is not one in a million like the lottery. It is one million people getting money for business each and every year!

The lottery is advertised so that is why we know about the program, and we are all standing in line trying to buy a Lotto ticket. But nobody knows about these other programs because THESE PROGRAMS ARE NOT BEING ADVERTISED! I am going to tell you about these programs and how to find them.

Grants Go To People Who Help Themselves and the Country

The biggest category of people who get grants are people who want to solve problems. Do you have an idea? Do you want to solve a problem? Do you want to create jobs, or just get yourself a better job? These are people like you who want to do something in the world. They want to contribute to society, and that is how a lot of this money is used.

Want to get a better education? Want to create a business? Even though it sounds selfish, by helping yourself, you are helping society!

These grant programs fund real things that society wants and needs. Foundations and government offices have this money waiting to solve problems in society and provide things that society needs. Society needs more educated, energetic and problem-solving people. People that are going to create jobs. People that are going to create new inventions in their life. This money is there to help citizens do these kinds of things.

To me the lottery is welfare, because it is the only government program that encourages you to go sit on the beach. I do not want my taxes to pay for people to sit on the beach for the rest of their lives. I want people to get money in order to make themselves and the country better. If you are out there creating a better society, then that is a society I am living in too. So, then I will have better people around me, better tools, and a better and safer society. That is the purpose of these programs.

There are government grant programs that fund solutions to all kinds of strange problems. There are programs where they give money to teenagers to start a business. Other programs fund building a golf course or tennis court in your backyard. "Not enough tennis courts in people's backyards," does not sound like a big problem to me but for some reason, some bureaucrat thought there was. Actually, the politicians make the laws, and it is the bureaucrats that have to enforce and carry them out.

Programs that put tennis courts in the backyard are really for people in rural areas. Apparently we have a problem in our society where rural development is an issue because the farming society is not what it used to be. So, we have programs to give these ex-farmers money to go into the resort business. You can put a resort in your backyard where 40 acres of corn used to be.

You do not have to understand the reasons why these programs were instituted, but just know that they exist. These programs are there for you to do something in your life! What is important about this is that the programs are for the average Joe. I grew up in a little town called Wilkes Barre, Pennsylvania, and I used to think that anybody who got something from the government was either rich and took a congressman and senator to lunch, or real poor and on some kind of funny program that you were embarrassed to mention.

But that is not true. This money is for people who have the perseverance to go out and get it. The rich do it, the poor do it, and the middle class does it. If 30 million people are getting this money, they cannot all be rich because there are not 30 million rich people in this country. The money goes to people who know about it and go through the effort to get it.

I know a fellow named James Freericks, who got a half a million dollars from government grants to travel around the world! He was an ordinary kind of guy in his early thirties or so, and wound up with a half a million dollars by learning to use the system to travel around the globe.

I live and work in Maryland, and found that my state gives out grants to businesses all over the state. Actually, there is a company called Snyder Seed Company that got a $200,000 grant to work on rodent repellent made out of hot chili peppers. How would you like $200,000 to take your chili peppers and try to turn them into rodent repellant?

I do not know why the government does it. Maybe they are looking for better ideas. I am sure there is some rationale behind it, but mine is not to reason why. Mine is to tell you about these programs so more people apply for them. I hope to get a better group of people applying, so the government will have a better choice of who gets the money.

Tori Stewardson lives in Virginia, and got $15,000 as a 40-year old woman who never finished college. She found a government program that gave her a $15,000 grant to finish her college degree because she was suffering from low self-esteem. Now, would you ever think of calling the government and looking for the government's low self-esteem program? No!

We live in a society where the answers are all out there. I wear the question mark suits because I believe that we can get the answer to anything we want in life. The problem is, we do not know the right questions to ask, and that is what I am trying to help you to do, to show you what questions to ask.

Did you ever see that online brokerage company, Ameritrade, advertised on TV? They are rich, making a lot of money. Well, they got a million dollar grant to open up an office in Annapolis. Would you ever think, "I will start a big business, and I have a lot of money but maybe I will see about some more free money!" Well, there it is.

I found a company in California called Beneficial Design who got $50,000 to develop a website on hiking trails. Are you a hiker? Wouldn't you love to spend the next year developing a website on hiking trails? This guy out in California found a program that gave him $50,000 to do that.

Speaking of hiking trails, I am looking for hiking boots because this summer I am taking part in a government program. I am going to Alaska with my family. My wife and I, and our two teenage boys, are flying to Alaska and are going to work on a government program doing an archaeological dig with Indians! How incredible is that? I would get bored sitting on the beach for two weeks. This is just one example of other types of programs that are out there for you.

Ritz Camera is another big company. They got a $75,000 grant for hiring new employees in Kansas. So, if you are a small business and are going to hire a new employee, find out about the grant money. If Ritz Camera is getting

$75,000, then maybe if you only hire one employee, you could get $2,000, but what the heck? That is free money in the bank for you.

Amazon.com received a $1.5 million grant because they decided to open up a distribution center in Kansas. Did you ever order books from Amazon? They have distribution centers all over the country.

What happens is the state government, the local government, the county government, and the city government are all trying to attract business to the area. So, they give big and small businesses special business incentives, and grant money to come and put the business there. If Amazon.com is cashing in on this, why shouldn't you?

Arlene Fink got $100,000 from the government to work on a better way of letting the elderly know they have a drinking problem! I don't understand it, but I guess there is a problem in the community that some seniors are drinking too much. So, she got $100,000 to develop pamphlets, as well as a program to help them.

How about this? A woman up in Alaska got $200,000 to buy a fishing boat. Did you see *Perfect Storm*? I was thinking about that with these women fishermen. You can get a grant to be in the fishing business in Alaska.

Brett Stern, a fellow I know in New York state, got over $200,000 from the government to work on his invention — $200,000! He is a young boy, a couple of years out of college. He designed a sewing machine that puts together fabric that you do not have to sew. It works with synthetic fabric that will fuse together when it reaches a certain temperature. Throw away your sewing machines.

My dad had a garment factory in Wilkes Barre, Pennsylvania, and women used to sit there sewing all day. This way, they would not have to do it. The machine would just melt the material together.

Or how about this? Len Osbourne was a bouncer in Colorado, making $7 an hour in a nightclub. He was a big guy suited for this work but his career was not going anywhere. He went to the government and they gave him a $10,000 grant to take a computer course. He did not have a college degree. After he completed the 5-month computer course, he was able to get a job earning $50,000 a year with benefits.

He went from being a bouncer at $7 an hour, to making $50,000 a year with benefits on a grant from the government after five months. You are improving yourself and you are improving society, whether it is designing a new gizmo that will put fabric together, or getting a better job, or hiring employees. These programs are there to solve problems in our society, and that is the purpose of the grants.

Or, they are there to solve problems in your family. A woman by the name of Dorothy Heart from Texas called me, and said her daughter had a hospital bill of $40,000! The daughter was a single mom, struggling, and could not pay the bill. Hospitals always want their money now, as many are in financial trouble. Well, Dorothy found a program that gave her daughter the grant money so that she did not have to pay this hospital bill, $40,000! This kind of money is out there.

My Entire Family Gets Grants and I Make A Lot of Money

My wife runs a tutoring service in our neighborhood. We live in a neat community and a lot of the kids have trouble in grade school. Her tutoring service is all volunteers, and it has been going for about 5 years. She got a $4,000 grant from a local organization, and she did not have to fill out much paperwork at all.

That is exactly what I mean. My wife was trying to solve problems in the community and there are organizations that have money to invest in that issue. People who have money want to solve problems. It is a basic human instinct, but you have to know the system to get it and that is what I am trying to do here by showing you the ropes, and giving you the tools to find this kind of money.

As teenagers, my kids got a $10,000 grant. That is right, a $10,000 grant as teenagers. Now, you and I as adults are probably thinking, "Why the heck did they give them that? Why don't they give it to somebody worthwhile like me?" My boys were working on an anti-smoking program for kids, trying to get teens not to smoke. They found this money at the state level — $10,000. They did not line their pockets, but they learned a great deal from the process!

They got devices that you blow into and it shows how bad your lungs are affected by smoke. They went all around the county into the cafeterias during lunch hour and had kids blow into these machines. It is a great way for smokers and those living with smokers to visually see the effects on their lungs. It was a very successful campaign. My boys learned a lot about getting grants, as well as solving problems in the community. This is what this country is about.

I talked to a guy in Washington, Raymond Whitfield. He is 68 years old, and he got a $20,000 grant from the government to go back and get his master's degree. Twenty thousand dollars at 68 years old! So you old farts out there saying, "Nobody is going to give me money to do anything," nonsense! The government cannot discriminate. Raymond at 68 years old got $20,000 to do something he had always wanted to do, and you can too.

Ronald Olszewski of Alabama got a $500 grant to fix up his car. Did you ever think there were grants to fix up your car? Well, there are. You just have to know how to look, and look deep enough to find it. Sure, the car dealer is not going to say anything. There is not going to be a big sign at the car dealer saying, "Free grants. Come fix your car here."

How about a grant to buy a house? Sandie Dotson in Houston got $3,500 to cover closing costs to buy a new home. Three thousand five hundred dollars is not much towards a house, but for a lot of people, that will stop them from home ownership because they do not have the extra money for closing costs.

Or how about this? Linda Jacobs-Holcomb got a $5,000 grant for speech therapy for her child. Would you ever think that, "My child needs therapy, and I can't afford it," and that you could possibly get a grant of $5,000 for it? You can. You just have to know where to look. You have to go through the effort. You cannot knock on one door and expect to get $100,000 by next Tuesday. That one door is probably going to say no, and so you have got to go to the next door and then to the next door. You need to keep going until you get it. It is like getting a job. When you are job hunting, you do not go to one company and say, "Hey, are you hiring today?" If they say no, you do not go home and wait for them to change their mind. You go to the next door, and the next door and the next door. That is what you need to do.

The rich and famous use a lot of this free grant money. This is my biggest frustration in life. If I see the wealthy taking advantage of all these programs then people like you should be doing so too. If people like Ritz Camera, Amazon.com and Ameritrade are getting all this money, why don't you? These rich people hire someone to go and find this money for them. I was one of those guys. I would charge $100 an hour to find money programs for rich people. But what I found was that if a kid like me from Wilkes Barre can find this stuff, anyone can. I want to give you the tools to find it.

George W. Bush Got A $200 Million Grant For His Baseball Team

Just look at the people in the White House today. Do you know how George Bush became a millionaire? That is right, he is a millionaire now in addition to being the President. We all heard that he was more or less a ne'er do well, and was a mediocre student, just like me. The only real money he made was with his baseball team. He found $600,000 to invest in a baseball team in Texas and became the managing partner. As the head of the team, he got the government to give him $200 million to build a brand new baseball stadium.

What happens when you get $200 million for free to build a nice stadium for your team? The value of George's investment soared from $600,000 to about $12 million in a few years. He knew the system, and he got that government money to make him wealthy.

Dick Cheney was even better at it than George W. was. He got literally billions and billions of dollars in government money. He ran a Texas energy company called Halliburton. He got $1.5 billion from a government office called the Export-Import Bank that helped his business sell overseas. He also got another two or three **billion** dollars in contracts from the government. Government contracts are also money you do not have to pay back; you just have to do the work. This is another wonderful source of money.

The two people in the White House today are heroes to at least half of our society who voted for them, and they lived off government contracts and government grants. I am trying to get everybody to be aware of this. We have 30 million people a year who are cashing in on these things. You can, too. You could get grants to pay for your doctor bills, your telephone bills, your heating bills, your food bills — there are even grants around the country that if you have trouble paying for your mortgage, they pay it for you!

Grants To Pay Your Mortgage

That is right. If you lose your job, would you ever think of asking the government to pay your mortgage? Probably not, but there are programs like this. There are grants that pay for storm windows, automobile repairs, dance classes, childcare, prescription drugs — there are even grants to help you adopt a child. And there are even grants from organizations that are set aside just for grandmas!

Cheri Olssen in Nebraska got $4,500 to help pay for a truck to start a recycling business. Here is a woman who wanted to start a recycling business but was short on cash. She needed an extra four or five grand to buy a truck to start the business, and she got it. She said she did not need a grant writer and believes that anybody can do it. This is a little old lady out there in Nebraska who is telling you straight from her heart that she did not need a grant writer and that anybody can get a grant.

And the people running big organizations are not all the brightest crayons in the box. How many people have you worked for that were not very bright? I know I have worked for a bunch in my life. Nobody has any magic in this world. The magic is inside you. You have got to bring it out of yourself. You have got to go through the work and have the perseverance to get it, and that is all it is. It is a matter of perseverance and focus, and I want to help you through the process.

I Have the Qualifications to Help You Get A Grant

Why should I be the one to give you the tools you need to get a grant? Because I have been doing this for a long time. I am 58 years old, so I am certainly old enough. I have been researching money programs for over 25 years. I am not aware of anyone in the country who has more credentials on this subject than I. But I am biased, so do not trust me.

I started a business back in 1975 that helped companies get money and information from Washington. I started in a one-bedroom apartment in Washington, DC, right near the famous Watergate, home to the break-in that led to Nixon's impeachment. Those of you who are old enough will know what I am talking about.

I had a little one-bedroom condominium and no money, and was doing research for fat cats. They would call me and want to know where they could get money to increase the size of their businesses. I would find the money programs and free information that they would use to make billion-dollar decisions. I went from me, a phone, a desk, and no money in a one-bedroom apartment to about 30 or 40 people down on K Street. And I did it in about 3 years.

After a while I got a little tired of helping the rich people. I grew up in a place called Wilkes Barre, Pennsylvania. I did not know anything about Washington. My clients made me smart. They would call and say things like, "We want to know where the money is." And I would go get it. I would do research on anything because I wanted desperately to get paid. I could not believe I was able find all this information, but then I started thinking that it was not really satisfying work. I found that these people would get this money with or without me. They could hire somebody else. If I charged $100 an hour, and was not around, they would hire some lawyer at $200 an hour to do the same kind of work I was doing.

Then I had a chance to write a book. There was an article written about me in *Parade* magazine back in the early '80s. I used to live off publicity then because I did not have any advertising money. A literary agent called me after seeing the *Parade* article and said, "You should write a book about what you know." I said, "Write a book, like a real book with New York publishers and everything?" He said, "Yeah!" I told him, "But I flunked English in college. I'm no writer. I couldn't write a book." He said. "That doesn't matter." And it is true — it did not matter. I wound up with two *New York Times* bestsellers. And since then, I have written over 100 books. Two of my books were awarded Best Reference Book of the Year by the American Library Association.

I wrote a syndicated column for the *New York Times*. That is right — the *New York Times*, this schmuck who flunked English in college. I thought you had to go to Harvard to write for the *New York Times*. I also wrote a column for years for *Good Housekeeping* magazine. I am living a life that I had no idea was possible. I thought someone else did all this stuff. But no — you do not need credentials to do anything in our society. Look at George Bush! He cannot even speak well, had terrible grades, and he is the president! So forget about credentials. Just go out and do your dream.

Since 1975 I have been working on how to get money, help, and information in this society. That is what these credentials show, and that is what I believe in, helping fat cats, poor cats, middle class cats, everybody. I have sold millions of books on this subject. I also know that people have a fascination with grants. That is why I want to tell you the ins and outs of getting a grant. The fat cats get the grants. I have gotten them for the fat cats. Other people have gotten them for the fat cats. But grants are for everybody, over one trillion dollars' worth.

You Can Do It Without Me and My Books

Companies like Procter & Gamble would call me and want to look for money programs. I didn't know where they were. I would just make 100 phone calls to find them. They were paying me $100 an hour, so I did not care how long it took. And I would eventually find them. You do not need my books. I believe the only thing you need is to believe that the help is there. If you believe it is there, you will go out and get it. It takes time, but in our society everybody is short on time. I hope what I am doing for you will cut down the time that it takes you to find this information. There is no magic in me. I am just digging ditches, finding the information that can benefit you. You could do it without my experience and learn it all yourself. It will just take you a little longer.

In most households it takes two busy people working to make ends meet in our society. It used to be that yuppies like me would go to the grocery store, buy food, bring it home and cook it. Now, because of the lack of time, I want to go to the grocery store and get food that is already cooked, so it takes me less time. The service economy is big because we are all trying to save time. That is where the future of our society is. It is in selling services to each other that will save us time.

More Than Grant Money: Loans, Contracts and Venture Capital

I am going to tell you about grants. But as you go through this process and start looking for grants, you are going to come across other kinds of money. It is important to know about these and not dismiss these sources just because they are not grants. If you have a project you want to do, you may think that the only way you are going to get it done is if somebody gives you a chunk of free money to do it. There may be other alternatives that are just as good and will get the project done. Life is all about having an objective and figuring out the best way — maybe not the most perfect way, but a way to get it done.

We do not live in a society that is perfect. Nothing is perfect. Look at all the junk you and I buy. The important thing is getting it done. Keep your ears open for other kinds of money, because you are going to run into them and you may want to use them. You may be saying, to yourself, "I do not want anything to do with loans, because I do not want to be burdened with debt." Listen, if a loan is the only way that you are going to get the thing done, it is very important to do it. And by the way, the government has very interesting loans. The government has some loans you do not have to pay back! How do you like that? I don't know why they call them loans then, right? But they do!

I know a lady who got a loan for $30,000 to help her pay for a house. But if she stayed there for five or ten years, she did not have to pay it back. That is a nice loan, right? So, don't dismiss loans.

How about low interest loans? You may be saying, "I can't afford it," or, "I have bad credit. Nobody is going to give me a loan because I have bad credit." No! Actually many of these loans, particularly from nonprofit and government organizations, are for people who cannot get loans anywhere else.

A lot of people are looking for grants because they say, "Nobody is going to lend me $100,000 to start my business or go to school because I have bad credit." Or, "I don't have collateral." You are thinking of banks, and these loans do not come from banks. The loans from nonprofits and government organizations are really for people who cannot get loans anywhere else. You may be in that category. Keep your antenna open for any kind of money. You may run into loan programs while you are looking for a grant. Put that loan aside because maybe at the end of your search you may want to revert back to the loan because it is not such a bad deal after all. Or maybe you need $100,000 for a project and you only find $50,000 worth of grants. In cases like this, you can use a $50,000 loan to make up the difference.

Government contracts are another big source of cash. I spoke earlier of Dick Cheney getting two billion dollars' worth of contracts. If you are a small business selling a service or product you may be saying to yourself, "If only I had $50,000, then I can go advertise my services so that everybody would know I am here and would come and buy my product." It is easy to see how you would think that this would be the answer to your prayers.

You can do something better and safer. If you have advertising money, you really do not have any idea if your advertising is going to work. Like all those dot.com businesses that spent millions on Super Bowl ads only to go out of business. Instead, you can go to a government office that will help you get a $50,000 contract. That is exactly what you are in business to do — get work. And the government buys more of anything than anyone else in the world. One year the government even spent $30,000 on a freelance priest.

Once you learn to get one contract, then you can get another. And that could grow to Dick Cheney, where he got $2.3 billion of contracts. It is not like getting grants where you may only get one.

Another source of money that we are going to talk about is venture capital. It's like grants in that it's money you don't pay back. But it's like getting married. You get a partner. That is the bad side. But again, if you just want to get your project going, the important thing is to get it started. So what if you have a partner for a while. Learn the process and get the experience so that you do it the way you really want to do it next time.

Another source of money is a tax credit. Tax credits are very important. You are going to pay taxes, right? Well, the government has tax credits they give to do things, like hiring employees and training them, investing in certain industries or fixing up certain buildings.

Loan guarantees are another source. If you find a bank that says they will give you money but, "Do you have a rich uncle who can co-sign for you?" You are in luck because the government offers that service too.

Remember the important thing is that you are going to follow your dream, and you want to get it done, no matter what. It is taking your dream and doing it so you can go on to the next dream, because that one is going to be better!

Grants For Business

I get calls all the time telling us, "I want to start a business. I went down to the Small Business Administration and I asked them for grants. The person there said, 'There are no such things as grants for business. Have you been listening to that Lesko guy? He is just full of poppycock.'" The person at the Small Business Administration (SBA) is right; I am right and everybody is right. That is what is so neat about the world. We all have a piece of us that is right, and we all probably have a piece of us that is wrong.

It is true. I am a salesman so I can over-blow a story to get my point across. That is one of my faults and I understand that. They are right, because the Small Business Administration does not have grant money for businesses. People think that if they start a business and they are looking for money, that they should go to the Small Business Administration. I guess they are a great group, but that is really not the only place for a business to get money. You may or may not want to use them, and they do have a lot of programs. They are mostly loan programs. The Small Business Administration does not have grants, but that does not say that that is the only place for money. The Small Business Administration is a major source, true, but it is not everything. There are grants for businesses, but you have to look elsewhere.

One source of business grants is local and state governments. They can offer grants up to $500,000 if you start or expand a business in their area. If your company was hurt by imports, you can apply for grants up to $700,000. These grants are not from the Small Business Administration. If you are in business and you want a grant, they are out there. It just takes effort to find them. And it is unlikely that the Small Business Administration even knows about these. It is impossible for any one person or office to know everything. I don't even know everything.

Just think, there are three million people that work for the government. So, if you are going to go to one government office and ask them about all of the programs, they are not going to know everything. They barely know what is in their office!

There are only four of us that live in my house — my wife and my two kids. I do not even know what they are doing most of the time, and they live with me! So how the heck is a government employee going to know what every other government employee is doing? They cannot. That is why it takes effort on your part to find these things.

Grants For Paul Newman, Women and To Train Employees

Here is another grant program for business — $100,000 to sell your goods and products overseas! You know who used that once? Paul Newman. He saw me on a TV show in Connecticut. He called my office and all the ladies were so excited. He would not let us call him back, but he did call again. And as a result he found that government money to help sell his salad dressing overseas — $100,000.

There is a $5,000 grant for women who want to start businesses in North Dakota. Maybe they are just looking for women in North Dakota! You have no idea what is out there until you start looking. The Office of Economic Development in your state government is where you begin your search.

Found a way to save energy? There are grants that give you up to $425,000 as a business if you have a product that actually saves energy. Maybe it is a new Venetian blind that does not let in as much heat from your window. Maybe it is a new fuel-efficient carburetor. These are grants to develop your ideas into a big business.

Almost every business has employees, and almost every state now has grant money for you to train them. You can get $25,000 to upgrade the skills of your employees. If your employees do not know Excel, Access or some other computer program, go to your state government. Most every state in our country now has grant-training money to get your employees more efficient on the job, so we as a country can be more competitive. That is the name of the game. If your business is more competitive, then the country is more competitive, and we have a better society.

Or, is your business going to create new jobs? How about $10,000 for every job you create? State and local governments also give out grant money like this.

Or how about $30,000 to reduce wood waste? I am not sure what this is, but if you are manufacturing something out of wood, and you want to cut down on your waste, a $30,000 grant would be a welcome addition to help you accomplish this.

How about $100,000 just to develop a new product? There are state governments that want your business to grow by developing new products. If your business grows, then you hire new people and pay more taxes. So, they give out grants hoping they will get back the money in taxes when your business grows.

How about a $5,000 grant to travel overseas looking for business? Maybe you want to sell cowboy boots to France. American culture is big in Europe, and you can get a $5,000 grant (most of these are from the state government) to travel to France to find customers. The government wants you to sell goods and services overseas. That means more money, a bigger customer base for our products, and that means our economy will grow.

How about this? There are other states that will give you a $15,000 grant just to prepare a business plan to start a business in a small town. The government is very concerned that small towns are dying in this country. There is a lot of economic development help and incentives for people to start businesses in small towns. One state will give you $15,000 just to think about starting a business in a small town. How do you like that? You don't even have to start a business. You just have to think about it and do a business plan.

There are other states that will give you $10,000 for every new job you create. So, if you hire somebody for $20,000-30,000, the government will give you $10,000 in return. You get a one-third discount on that employee. That is an extra 10 grand in your pocket that you do not have to pay that employee.

If you hire somebody with a disability, there are programs that will give you $4,000. Or, if you have a disability and want to start a business, there are grants for your business start-up. They want to make you more productive, and will give you up to $15,000.

How about $100,000 to market your invention? Or how about this, there are some programs for businesses that get grants to work on better ideas. You can get up to a half million dollars. Then they have other programs to give you a $5,000 grant to work on the proposal to get a half million-dollar grant to work on your invention. Which means you can get a grant in order to get another grant!

Or how about a grant of $20,000 to start a daycare center in your business? Maybe you have a little recording studio and you start hiring people. All these people you hire have little kids at home and they want to be near them. Make your employees happy and get a grant from the government to put a daycare center in your business. Moms are happy because they can take a break, see the kid, and they are not anxious or worried about what the child's doing.

So, there are grants out there for businesses. It is just not going to be the obvious places, and they are not at the Small Business Administration. I often see that any time the government opens up an office to solve a problem and it stays there long enough, it almost becomes the last place to go, sort of like the Small Business Administration. They have been there to the end of time. They do good work, but you get caught up in the voicemail and bureaucracy.

If you want to start a business, start at your state and county economic development office. Did you ever see the environmental poster that says "Think global, act local?" It is the same way in getting money from the government. It is all federal and foundation money, but you want to start locally. Start by finding those local organizations that may be able to help you with your project. They are probably getting all their money from a federal or national office anyway.

A Government Contract is Money You Don't Have To Pay Back

Don't forget government contracts. Maybe you have a service — a dog-walking service, a writing service, or you are a freelance artist. How are you going to sell your artwork as a freelance artist sitting in the middle of Iowa? You may be saying to yourself, "If I only had a $50,000 grant, I could sell my artwork." Here is another way. The government has offices that will get you freelance artwork contracts that you can to do right in Iowa on your kitchen table. You can be making $100,000 a year designing brochures for the Dept. of Agriculture.

All you need to be in business is a business card and maybe a few samples. You do not need a big office. You do not need staff. To be in business, you just have to say, "I'm in business."

Or, you can sell somebody else's products. If you think something is sellable, like my books, you can sell it. If you think the government should buy my books, I will sell them to you at a big discount, and you in turn can sell them at the regular price to the government, or to anyone else for that matter. You figure out who in the government buys my kind of books, hook up with a contract, and I will give you 40 percent or more of the sale. See? That is what I mean. And all you need is a business card and a phone, and you are in business.

I really believe that business is easy and very basic. I have an MBA in computer science, and was starting businesses back in the '70s. I had a computer software company back in the '70s that failed. I must have been the only person in the world who had a computer business that failed! I was starting businesses and failing back then, because I had an MBA. I was doing things they taught me in school, like getting business plans, proper accounting, the lawyers, the big office, the furniture, the power drapes, and the power business cards. And when my business failed, I looked around to see who the winners were. It was the people I bought the drapes from, the accountants, the lawyers, and anyone else I gave money to.

The third business I started, I said I do not need accountants. They are not critical to my success, particularly for a small business. The critical thing to your success is YOU and your time. If you are spending time at meetings picking out designer business cards or discussing tax strategies, you are wasting time because those decisions are not critical to your success. The critical thing to your success is getting the customer. Everything else in a business is detail. If you keep a checkbook, then you are an accountant. Money in, money out, and if you have none left, you are broke. That is all you have to know about accounting.

If you get an accountant, they are going to make it so complicated for you that you will need another accountant to understand what the accountant is doing. You do not have to do that. You just have to go and get customers. Concentrate all your time in getting customers. A business card and a phone is all you need. And the government will help you get customers.

I have a huge list of everybody who got a government contract last year. There are millions of businesses every year that are taking advantage of this opportunity. A lawn and tree service in Nebraska got $40,000 of gardening services from the government. Do you like to do gardening work? Why not get a $40,000 contract from the government to do gardening? Somebody's got to do those plants, and it might as well be you. All you need is a shovel or some tools to do it. Or, you can borrow the tools from the friend once you get the contract. Or you can get a contract, and with a contract in hand, any bank will lend you the money to purchase the tools.

Dell Computer Company, now they are no dummies. They sold almost a half a billion dollars of computers to the government last year. The government buys more of anything than anybody else in the world.

There is an organization right here in Washington that got almost $200,000 worth of writing services from the government. Writing! For all that nonsense and bull that comes out of Washington, somebody has got to put all that stuff on paper. The bureaucrats don't really do much themselves. They usually hire contractors to do all the real work.

Want to sell milk? The government recently spent $1 million for milk from a dairy farm in South Carolina.

Copying services is another item. One government office spent $186,000 for freelance copying services. So start looking for a cheap copying machine.

Do you like to make pasta? Last year the government bought $681,000 of macaroni from a company called Pasta USA in Spokane, Washington. You have to really like pasta to make that much of it. But look at all the dough it is bringing in.

I told you earlier that the government even spent $30,000 on a freelance priest. H. Ross Perot is a zillionaire because he found out how to get government contracts. He started his business in his home with $25,000 he got from his wife. Eventually he sold the business to General Motors for a zillion dollars. And when he left General Motors he started another business getting government contracts. It's like when they asked the famous bank robber, Willy Sutton, why he robbed banks, he said, "Because that is where the money is!"

My sister has a little art framing business. She gets about $300,000-400,000 worth of government contracts, just putting frames on artwork. That's a nice business. If you like framing go to the government. My sister's no dummy. I used to call her a dummy a lot when we were young, but she too knows where the real money is.

Government Venture Capital

Government contracts are important. If you have a business and are looking for grants, look for these too. The same holds true with venture capital. I did not know that the government even had venture capital. You probably got some office supplies from Staples. They got $1.5 million in venture capital from the government. That is money they did not have to pay back, but the government shares in the profits. Staples had to give up some of their business for the money, but what the heck? The important thing is to get it done. If it takes being in partnership with somebody, you do it.

Callaway Golf, maker of the famous Big Bertha drivers, got millions in venture money from the government. Their clubs swept the golf industry by storm. These are clubs that can cost $1,000.

Apple Computer and Federal Express also received venture capital money from the government to start their businesses. Intel, the largest manufacturer of computer chips got around $300,000 in the beginning from the government's venture capital.

Mother's Work, the maternity clothes stores for professional pregnant women got $500,000 in government venture capital to help start their business.

Free Cash In Tax Credits

When you are looking for business money, don't forget tax credits. These are business friendly tax credits for companies and for individuals at both the state and federal level.

You can get $2,500 for hiring certain employees in certain zip codes. That is right. Just because your employee is from a certain place, you can get real money in the form of a tax credit. How about a $5,000 tax credit if you provide long-term care insurance for your employees? Or, a million dollar tax credit if you are going to expand your business? Or how about this — a $100,000 tax credit if you donate something to a nonprofit organization? Or, if you hire somebody with a disability, you can get a $2,500 tax credit. Or, you can get a half a million-dollar tax credit if you invest in solar energy or you purchase an electric vehicle. So, maybe the next vehicle that you purchase for your business, get an electric vehicle.

Remember, all the money programs for your business may be grants. Grants are available and they are at the federal level, but they are more likely to be at the state or local level.

Also remember the venture capital, contracts, and tax credits. The most important thing is for you to get out there and just get the darn thing done!

You May Not Need As Much Money As You Think You Do

We think we want lots of money, right? "If I only had a million dollars, I could do this." "Oh, if I only had $10 million, I could do that." "If I had a half a million dollars, I could do this." When I see studies of businesses and why they went out of business, they all say, "Lack of adequate financing." That is a copout. Sure, if somebody threw lots of money at you, maybe you could stay around longer. But the real trick in life is how to do it with less money than you think you need. These are the kind of people who are the survivors in our country. The survivors are not the ones that have millions and millions of dollars to do anything they want in life. With lots of money it is hard to create anything new. All you do is learn how to buy things.

We all yell at Congress because they seem to be throwing money at all the problems we have in our society and they always seem to want to spend more. We seem to do the same in our personal lives, right? We say to ourselves, "I can't go back to school because I don't have a lot of money." "I can't start a business because I don't have a lot of money." Gosh, we sound just like Congress when you have those kinds of feelings. You can do what you want to do in life and you just may not need as much money as you thought you did.

You can start a business nowadays with just a phone, a desk and a business card. How much money is that going to take? A hundred bucks? Fifty bucks? Twenty bucks? So, $200 and you are in business, and you go and get customers. That is it. If you don't have money, then think of another way to do it, or think of a way to do it with less money. There are other solutions. You are just not thinking. The biggest obstacle to success in life is our own mind.

When I started my business, I used to think the same thing. I would dream about all the things I could have been doing if I only had a lot of money. I started with a phone, a desk and a couple of thousand bucks. I used to put little one-inch ads in the *Wall Street Journal* because I was trying to sell research to businesses. In one-inch ads, I could not say a whole lot, but that was all I could afford. I got crazy people calling or writing letters in crayon on napkins and stuff like that.

Then I had a brainstorm. How do I get publicity without buying advertising? How can I get my name out to people without spending money? And that is what you see now. You see this idiot on TV, acting like a madman. I quickly found out that if you are an idiot and crazy, they will put you on TV! It does not matter what you say.

The way I did it was to publish a free newsletter. I said that if businesses wanted to know how to get free information for their business, subscribe to my free newsletter. And the *Wall Street Journal* wrote an article about my free newsletter, as did others.

Then I was getting legitimate inquiries on business stationery, like Citicorp Bank, who later became a client. They wrote for my free newsletter and wanted to know how to get free information so their business would be successful. I got a $3,000 contract from them. I figured out how to be in the *Wall Street Journal* for free. Now, if I had a million dollars, I would be spending more time writing a bigger ad because I would have an advertising agency, right? And if the next ad didn't work, I'd buy a bigger one, because I would have the money to say it louder.

But if you do not have money, you get smarter. You learn how to do it cheaper, and that is what you have to do to survive. Anybody can spend money, but can you get that business without spending the money? That is the key to success.

When I was going on TV and selling my books, I figured TV was pretty boring. I wondered who was watching? Most people have the TV on while they are doing something else. Then I thought, if I got on the *Today Show* and they said, "Next is Matthew Lesko to talk about the government," people are likely to say, "I don't want to know about the government." And they would likely go into the kitchen or bathroom and start doing something else.

My theory is, I have got to get you out of the bathroom. So, I go on TV and start jumping around and screaming. Then you come out of the bathroom and say, "What is that idiot talking about?" Now I have got your attention. Maybe I can teach you something. I used to be a professor, teaching computer science to adult students. They had been working all day and then would come to class. I knew if I could not keep them awake at night, I would never teach them anything! That is the same thing with TV. If I cannot keep you awake, I cannot teach you anything.

Then I saw the reason why they invited me back on TV shows. It was not because I sounded smart or I knew what I was saying. They wanted me because I acted like an idiot! This was entertainment. It was not what I said, but how I said it. And you know that when we see things, it is how people do things we remember and not really what they are saying. You have to play into that and use it. That is what I did.

You have to find out how to get customers with as little money as possible. Anybody can do it with a lot of money. That is why you should not stop your dream simply because you don't have all the money you thought you need. Find out how to do it with little money. Once you do, you will become smarter and stronger.

So many friends of mine, who had millions from venture capital companies, went out of business during the first downturn in society. And do you know why they went out of business? Because they only knew how to do it with a lot of money. When they did not have the money any more, they did not know how to survive.

I am going to be doing what I do for a long time because I can do it with no money or with lots of money. I don't care how much I have. I will find out how to get a customer with $0 in my bank account because that is the way I started. This is how you become a stronger individual. You become a stronger member of society. Anybody can spend money. You have to learn how to do it without the money.

This is true not only in business but also in all areas of society. It is easy to say, "I can't go back and get an advanced degree to better my family and myself, because I will need $300,000 to live in the style to which I have become accustomed." You are not going to grow unless you learn how to sacrifice for a few years. If you are in your thirties, forties or even fifties don't forget you are likely to live 40, 50 or 60 more years. I am going to be 60 soon and I figure I have at least 30 more years. You have got to think long-term.

$600,000 From a $16,000 Investment

A friend who works with me was once a welfare mom. She had four kids and was raising them by herself. The best job that she could get in those days was $25,000 to $30,000 a year. She knew that if she got an education she could better herself. It took her almost 10 years to get her undergraduate and graduate degree. Her first job after graduation earned her $50,000 a year.

She went from making $30,000 to $50,000 and it is not going to stop there. So what if she has $16,000 of college loans. It is stupid to go into debt to take a cruise, but not to invest in your education. It is always worth investing in yourself. It is your best chance of earning more money.

In the first year after graduation she made an extra $20,000. She will make at least $20,000 more each year for the rest of her life. And this is the result of only a $16,000 investment. In 30 years, she will make at least an extra $600,000. An investment of $16,000 turned into $600,000, just because she invested in that education. You will never get that at the bank, stock market or anywhere else.

Doing things with less money takes some imagination and some brain squeezing and stretching. You have to get out and try as many things as possible to see what works. You have to go and do things and have a belief that you can.

Maybe you can only get a grant for $10,000, but school is going to cost $20,000. You have to get out there and keep looking. Take another a step. Try it again, and again, and again.

Change the World Without Winning The Lottery

I was talking to a woman the other day who thinks she is going to get a great deal of money from a big Wall Street deal. She has an inside scoop on an IPO independent offering. This has turned her from a woman who never had a lot of money to a woman now dreaming of becoming a millionaire. She does not have a nickel of the money yet, but she has spent weeks dreaming about what she will do with all the money. Her kids are gone and she works hard at her job. She thinks she wants to use some of the money to help latchkey kids.

I asked why, and she said because her kids were latchkey kids. She was a single mom much of her life, raising her children. She now feels that those kids that do not have parents at home after school need more help, and she wants to do something for them. Instead of figuring out a way to work on the problem now, she believes that this goal can only be accomplished with a windfall of money.

When she was talking to me about it, she was crying. That is the neatest thing in life, to find something you are passionate about, that really moves you emotionally, so that you can put your whole heart and soul into it. That is what I do with my work, and I hope I can help people find things that they have passion for in life. That is when work is not work and you are doing what you want to do and love doing it. I have not worked in 30 years. I just do stuff that I love to do.

When she talked about this, she had so much passion. But then I said, "What are you going to do if you don't get the money?" She said, "Then I won't be able to do it." That is when I got angry. "What do you mean? You have found something that you have so much passion for, and you are only going to do it if you get a million dollars?" What a waste — what a waste of her, what a waste to society, what a waste for everyone. I said, "You can do it without a million dollars!" She told me that she did not know anything about doing it. And I said why don't you just go to the schools in your area and say, "Hey, can I use one of your classrooms after school?" Arrange volunteers to come in and help with the kids, all for free. Do it all on a volunteer basis.

She said, "Is that the way to do it?" I said, "I don't know the way to do it! I am just guessing. Maybe you go to the school board and talk to them. Who the heck knows?" She was trying to think of the perfect way to do it by sitting there in the restaurant guessing. You don't know! You have got to put your foot out the door and ask somebody, and then if that does not work you try something else. If that person tells you that you are stupid, you try something else until it is not so stupid any more.

The biggest problem is that you do not know until you take that first step. It is sort of like painting a canvas. I am not a painter so I really do not know what the heck I am saying. But I am sure that when artists paint or use any kind of art medium, they have only a vague idea of what they want to do. Once they have put the first brush stroke on the painting, something else comes to their mind. This brush stroke leads to another brush stroke, and this thing becomes different from their original idea. All our lives are that way. What you originally thought — you will go to school, get married, etc. — does not happen exactly, because something is in your way and changes your direction.

Yogi Berra said, "When you come to a fork in the road, take it." You do not know where you are going, but you have got to get out there and take that first step, in order to decide about the second. The more education we get in the country, the more we want to know what the last step is going to be before we even take the first step. We want to know what the bottom line is before we take the first step. You cannot. You have to take the first step and see what happens, and then take the next one.

It is so hypercritical when these bank people want business plans from you. They are not business plans; they are fairy tales. It is your best guess, but it is a guess. You thought through it, but that is never going to happen. As soon as you take your first step, as soon as you open that first day of business, everything changes. The environment changes every second, every day. By writing a business plan, you are sitting there in a cocoon saying what is going to happen.

I was reading the other day that when Einstein was a kid in school his father went to the headmaster to inquire about his prospects. Einstein had trouble reading, and did not even read at nine years old. Everybody thought he was mentally handicapped. His father asked the headmaster for advice on what kind of careers Einstein should pursue. Einstein's headmaster, the teacher who should know Einstein's intellectual ability better than anybody else said, "Don't worry. It doesn't matter what career he goes into, because he is going to be lousy at everything."

Einstein! His teacher told him he would be lousy at everything. What do experts know? They don't know. They are wrong most of the time. Weather reports? People spend gazillions of dollars and they cannot tell you if it is going to rain this afternoon. It is the best guess, but it is all we have got.

You know what is best for you. You have to get out there and take that first step. And there is a way to do it without having a gazillion dollars. Want to make a change in the world? You do not need a million dollars. You just have to start doing it. Find the stuff that you have passion for and you will not need as much money as you think you do!

Examples of starting a business with no money

I want to give you some examples of starting a business with no money. Last week I was in Detroit. The local NBC affiliate station pulled me in to act like a trained clown at the mall while they did cut-ins for the local promotion. At the mall every hour on the hour, I spoke to a couple of hundred people, gave out free books, answered their questions, and it was great fun. I did this for eight or ten hours. People said, "Gosh, how could you do that all day long?" I love doing what I do. Actually, I got up at four o'clock in the morning, got on a plane, got to the mall in Detroit, worked all day, eight or ten hours, got on a plane coming back and got home at one or two o'clock in the morning. And I still had energy so I started working when I got home. That is the key. If you love what you are doing, you have got energy to do it all the time.

While I was at the mall in Detroit, people were asking me how to get money to start their businesses that they wanted to do. The more I heard about the businesses, I said, "Okay, you can go out and try to get a lot of money by looking for grants, loans or whatever. And remember I can personally identify about 100 to 150 grant programs for businesses, but a lot of business money is in the way of loans, venture capital, tax credits and contracts."

During this day I found a couple of good examples of how people could actually achieve their dream without even getting the money to do it. So many people wanted to be in the real estate business. They wanted to be real estate investors. "If I only had $100,000 I could go and buy property, fix it up and be this real estate entrepreneur." They have probably been watching infomercials late at night on TV, like mine.

Real Estate Tycoon With No Money Down Or Up Front

If you do not have the money, or if you do not want to spend all the time looking for the money, there are other options. To get in the real estate business, one of the ways to do this is to become a real estate information broker. I do not mean a real estate broker, but a real estate information broker. You could start a business that just gets information for people who want to buy and sell real estate. You are doing the legwork for them, and charge a fee because you work for people who have money and are looking for investments. By doing this, first of all, it costs no money to start that kind of business. With a phone, a desk and a business card, you are an information broker.

Now all you have to do is find the people who are looking to invest in real estate, and you work for them. You charge them by the hour — $25 an hour, $50 an hour, whatever the heck you can get away with to start a business. By doing that, you will learn more about that business than by going to school or even investing your own money. You are going to fail a lot in the beginning. That is what life is all about — failing and learning. So, this is a way to learn the business without failing with your own money. You fail with somebody else's money.

Also, by being an information broker your clients can eventually become your partners. You could manage their property for them for a piece of the action. There are all kinds of services you can provide. If you start a service business nowadays in this country, you are probably not going to go broke. The most important thing that people are trying to buy now is time. Nobody has time to do anything. So, if you have money to invest in real estate, you are probably lacking the time to find the properties to make those investments.

You can begin to sell your time and immediately be in the real estate business. Instead of waiting two to six months looking for the money you may or may not get, you can be in business by the end of the day.

No Money Down Beauty Salon

Here is another example. A lady came to me and said, "I want to get money to start a full-service salon and day spa where I would make money by renting out space in the spa to hairdressing people, manicurists and massage therapists, because that is how a lot of these businesses run." They make money by just leasing out the space and taking a piece of the profits.

I said, "Okay, that sounds like an interesting business." Personal care businesses are going to be growing in the future. We all want to take better care of ourselves, particularly as the baby boomers all grow older. An aging population means an increasing vanity factor. But I said, "Here is another way to do that business without money."

It seems to me that to do that business, you need a lot of money to either buy a building, or to lease space, lease the equipment, buy the equipment and all that. Then go out and find people to set up shop in your facility so that you make money together with them. It seems that the easy part of that business is buying a building or buying equipment. There are a lot of people who will be glad to take your money to invest in real estate or sell you equipment.

It seems the key to the business is finding people that will go into your shop and be contractors or partners for you. If that is the key for you and your business, it must be the key for every other beauty salon business. So, here is an opportunity that I would see in this kind of industry. If you did not find all the money you needed to start up that full-service beauty salon and day spa, you could be a talent broker for other beauty salons and day spas.

In other words, you can manage the problem of finding manicurists, hairdressers or massage therapists for beauty salons. All you need is a phone, a desk and a business card and you can start contacting existing beauty salons right now. Call them and say, "Hey, if you want to set up a manicurist in here, I will get the people. I will find them and manage them." And you do it all for a piece of the action.

If the manicurist is making $30,000 a year, I do not know how the arrangement works, but maybe the owner gets 50 percent and you get 10 percent — some kind of middleman fee. That was how it works with my agent who sells my books to people in New York. They get 15 percent of what I get, and all they do is make the deal. And that is what you could do. You could make the deal. You really take the headache from the owner of finding and managing people.

Maybe they are set up just for haircutting. Now they want to offer more services, but do not have the time or the energy to find and manage the people. That is what you could do, and do it for a fee. And again, all you need is a phone, a desk and a business card, and you are in business! There is always more than one way to skin a cat to make things happen.

Get Equipment For Your Business With No Money

Another guy came to me and said, "If I could get $100,000, I could start a van business immediately. There is so much money out there driving for the elderly." I guess Detroit is full of senior citizens. He works for another company now that provides this service, and said it is very easy to get contracts and all he needs is money to buy a van.

You can go out and search for the money. But I bet there is another way of doing this. If you can get a contract that easily, then you can start a business right now. You go out and borrow, or rent someone else's van for the day, for the week, or whatever. There are a lot of people who will rent you vans. If you can go and get a little contract for $5,000 to shuttle people around, you can lease a van from somebody for a week or whatever the contract is worth until you build up some money to buy your own vans. If you know how to get that contract for that money, you are already in business. Anyone can get a van; the magic is getting the business.

If you knew somebody who wanted to buy 25 hours of recording facilities and you did not have one set up in your basement already, you could find one. I am sure somebody is sitting around the city with recording time that is not being used. You could make a deal. Maybe you will not make as much money as you would if you had your own recording studio, but you would not have to invest in your own studio and that is the way to learn the business.

If you keep learning how to get contracts for customers, eventually you will be able to afford your own recording studio. You might make more profit in the beginning because you will not be paying off your equipment. So, it is a way to be in the business without having to soak a lot of money into it. If you could find out how to get those contracts, whether it is for driving senior citizens or for getting recording business, then that is the key to success. When you have some money in the bank and some steady clients you can start investing in your own equipment.

There was another fellow who came up to me and said that he was cleaning buildings at night but was a little smarter than the average cleaner-upper so he wanted to start his own business. He believed he needed a lot of money to do this. I said, "No, you don't. You don't need money. What you need is a broom, some cleaning equipment, and a vacuum cleaner." And he said, "I have to know how to get contracts and stuff like that." I said, "No, you just have to go out and ask for the business."

Go print business cards with Joe's Cleaning Service on them. Call on 50 small businesses and tell them, "If someone's cleaning your office now, I will clean it for 25 percent less." And you will, because you want that business. You will be working out of your basement so you will not have as big an overhead as an established business. You are probably doing it all yourself with just a few friends. You will be able to do it better and cheaper than anybody else. That is how you get a contract.

If you want to go to a big General Motors and do all of General Motors' cleaning, sure, you need an organization. You will fill out 50 pages of contracts so all the people in suits feel safe. You probably need to get bonded because the suits get worried. And you say you don't know how to get bonded? Don't worry about it. Worry about it only if you have an opportunity to get a big contract. You go after the small businesses where people have other concerns. I have somebody cleaning my offices now and pay them around $70 a week. They come in for a couple of hours and clean. I never asked them for anything. I just give them money. They look nice, work well and everyone is happy.

If you are doing business with big boys, you will need all that nonsense. Actually, when you get bigger, you could get that nonsense for free. Do you want to know how to get bonded or fill out a 50-page contract? Right in your area, there are government offices called Small Business Development Centers. It is not the SBA (Small Business Administration); this is a state office called Small Business Development Center that the SBA helps finance. They will sit down with you for free and help you do the contracts, and get you the free legal help to do it.

Or, if you want to get bonded and your bank will not help you, they have special programs in the government now to help you get bonded as a small business. But truthfully, you do not have to do anything complicated until the client says, "We won't do this unless you are bonded." Then you go out and figure it out. But don't sit there ahead of time thinking, "What happens if they ask me if I am bonded?" "What happens if they ask me, where's the official contract?"

Forget it! Go and get the business. If somebody says that you have to be bonded, then you figure out how to do it. That is the time when you really have to do it. Why waste all your time if you don't have to. Believe me, if you call on 50 small businesses, you will be lucky if one or two ask you for anything complicated. They just want their place cleaned. There are lots of opportunities out there, but they are not in the obvious places. You can always go to a lawyer before you start your business to talk about these concerns. But, if you do, believe me, they are going to scare the pants off of you. It's like talking to insurance salesmen. They can always scare you into paying for more insurance than you ever need. Why worry about being sued, if you don't even have any business, or money. When you get lots of money, then you can worry about those things.

Actually, my philosophy, too, is that you do not have to even file with the government. But you don't ignore the tax man. You never mess around with taxes. There is a tax form called a Schedule C, which lets your small business file taxes very easily. If you are starting a small business, particularly without any money like I am suggesting, it is going to take those bureaucrats three years to find you. Why waste your time? In three years, you may be out of business, and if you are not, fine. You will pay the $50 fine or whatever it is because you did not file on time. Big deal. And if you last three years, you are in good shape.

So, the most important thing is to conserve your energy and just keep looking for customers. That is the most critical part of doing any business.

Isn't It A Lot Of Paperwork?

A lot of people say, "Hey, Lesko — isn't it a lot of paperwork to get money from the government or other places?" And the answer is yes, it could be. But who cares? Who cares if it takes you a night to fill out the paperwork, or a week, two weeks, a month, or if it is one page or 1,000 pages? Where else are you going to get $1,000 to do something, or $100,000 — or a quarter of a million dollars?

What about the last week, the last month? What did you do that month? So many people say it makes them stop. It becomes an insurmountable hurdle. It is an excuse not to do something because they have to fill out some 20-page form. And that's not always true. There is a program, if you want to start a business that only has two pages to fill out, and you get $150,000. So, the paperwork should not stop you.

Sure, some of the complicated grant proposals may take 20 or 30 pages, and it could take you a couple of weeks to complete. But again, if you are getting $100,000 or a quarter of a million dollars to work on your invention, that is worth the effort. You have to do it. Remember, with every hurdle in life, you have to figure out a way over it, around it or through it. If you do not, you are out of the game, and you should not have started the game in the beginning.

How Long Does It Take To Get The Money?

How long does it take to get the money? Well, that is another question where the answer is, it depends. I know some micro-loan programs at the state level that say they guarantee an answer within two weeks. Other programs could take a few months. And there are other programs where they only give the money out once a year, so if you miss that cycle, you have got to wait until the next year. But again, just like the question on the amount of paperwork there is — who cares how long it takes?

There are some emergency funds that you can get very quickly, but most of the money that you want to use to change your life is not going to happen very quickly. You have to allow weeks or even months for this money. You may not even get approved the first time. You may do something wrong and have to file the form again. But again, who cares how long it takes?

I talked to this couple down in Florida who started a hairdressing salon and got $100,000 from the government to help them. They said it took them a few nights in front of the television filling out the forms. That was pretty neat. In a few nights, they got it done, and it was no problem at all. Is it going to take so long to get the money you are not going to apply? Nonsense! If that is your attitude, then do not do anything. Just sit home and be content with what you have now, because you never know how long it is going to take.

That should not stop you from doing anything. That is just another one of those hurdles that the bureaucrats are going to put in front of you to see if you are big enough to get through it, around it, or over it. These are little dragons that you have to slay to get to your quest, and your quest is getting that money or doing what you really want to do in life. And whether it takes a few extra days, a few extra weeks or even a few extra months, who cares? You have got the rest of your life to live. The important thing is that you are working on a mission to change the rest of your life!

Do You Have To Be Poor To Get Money?

Are there income requirements for this money? People ask me that question all the time. "Do I have to be rich?" "Do I have to be poor?" "Do I have to be on welfare?" "Do I have to be a millionaire, like Dick Cheney?" Again, like all the answers to these questions, it really depends. I estimate there are 15,000 money programs that give out money to people to do the things they want, and every program has a different requirement so I cannot really say. Some you do have to be rich, because they want to make sure that you pay some of that money back if it is a loan or a loan guarantee. Some programs you have to be poor, because they only give it to people in need, so you cannot have a high income.

But even for those programs where you have to be poor, listen to this — if you are a woman entrepreneur and want to get money for your business, the government considers you needy if you have $750,000 in the bank. You are almost a millionaire, and the government considers you needy.

Do not let that be a hurdle for you. You would be surprised at who the government thinks are needy. "I make too much money and I cannot get money to buy a house from the government." Nonsense. I have seen housing programs from the government where they consider you needy if your income is $85,000 a year. Can you believe that? Eighty-five thousand dollars a year and they consider you needy!

How about free prescription drugs? That is a favorite program of mine, and you can make $40,000-50,000 a year or more and get your prescription drugs for free. People believe, "Oh, I have to be destitute to do that." No, you just have to know about the program, and go through the bureaucratic hurdles to get it, but it is there. Actually, some of those programs for prescription drugs have no income requirements. You just have to say that you are having trouble paying for the drugs, and they give them to you.

Just think — rich people like George Bush and Dick Cheney got all that money for their careers and they certainly were not poor. I found a program just for grandmas to do what they really want to do in life. They can get up to $5,000 to work on their dreams.

Do you have to be rich? Do you have to be poor? Again, the real answer is it depends. You find the programs that fit you. For some business programs, you must not have a lot of money; other programs for business are just set aside for people who have no money.

It is the same way for housing. Some want you to have a lot of money, and others do not. Also some programs are just for people who cannot get money anywhere else. That is the important thing. A lot of government programs are really set up for people who cannot get money. So, if you are rich, have a friendly banker, or rich relatives, a lot of programs do not want to help you because you have another place to get it. Many of these programs are set up for people who cannot get money anywhere else.

I have a kid going to college, studying engineering, and I am paying almost nothing. I make good money, and I found government programs that will pay almost all of his college education. It is just amazing.

There are people that say, "I cannot get money to go back to school because I make too much money." You are just looking at the major programs. Any time you go and talk about anything, people usually talk about the general programs. The opportunities are in those nuggets that a lot of people do not know exist. So, if you talk to your college counselor about financial aid, they will tell you about the major programs. But the opportunities are in those non-major programs as well. They are the ones that take effort and work to find.

You have got to do the work, because the government is not going to come and hit you on the head to tell you about these programs. You have got to get out and find them yourself!

Getting Money To Buy Or Fix Up A House

Everybody seems to either want a bigger house, a first house, their third house, or fix up an existing house. Every year over 4 million people are getting government money for housing through dozens of programs that real estate brokers are likely to not know even exist!

There are three major levels of programs — the federal programs, state programs, and local programs with a couple of nonprofits thrown in on top of that. Even if you do not have my books, you can go to your library and look up the federal programs. Or, you can call the U.S. Department of Housing and Urban Development. They will send you information about all the federal programs.

On the federal level, there are four areas: the U.S. Department of Housing and Urban Development, the U.S. Department of Agriculture for housing in smaller towns, the Veterans Administration (if you are a vet), and also the U.S. Department of Energy. They have programs to help make your house more energy-efficient. Collect all those and then go to your state capital.

Every state capital has what is called a Housing Commission. You can call your state capital information operator and say, "I am looking for the state housing commission." They will hook you up with an office there. You can have them send you information on their programs. Then you go to your city. Your city has a housing office and there will be programs in the city, and also the county. Actually, more action is happening at the county and local level than even at the state and federal level, particularly for new homebuyers and renters.

Houston has a program where they will give you $3,500 to help with down payment and closing costs. So many organizations, local municipalities, and state governments have money to get people into houses. If you buy a house, they think you will be a better member of society because you actually own a piece of it. You want to protect your home and you are going to work hard to pay the mortgage because you like having your own house.

Iowa has a program that gives you five percent of the mortgage in grant money to use for the down payment and closing costs. So, whatever your mortgage is, they will kick in five percent of your total mortgage and give you that as a grant.

In Minneapolis, you can get $4,000 at zero percent interest. Why do they sell zero percent interest? They do not want to charge you money. They are really not there to make money out of that money. They are there to make sure that you buy a house. You do not even have to pay back that $4,000 until you sell your house. In this society, any house by the time you buy it and sell it is going to go up in value at least $4,000 and that is where you get the money to pay the city.

Louisiana has a program where they give you $10,000 at zero percent interest, and no payments for 20 years. Even the car dealers do not say that. "Don't make a payment for next year." This is 20 years, zero percent interest, so it is wonderful money.

Los Angeles has a program where you can get two percent for closing costs. Whatever the value of the house is, they will give you two percent for closing costs, plus they will give you an extra $30,000 loan with no payments for 30 years. So, you are getting a grant, plus a loan for $30,000 that you do not have to pay back.

Missouri has a program. If you have $750 in your pocket, they will get you a house. That is all you need — $750. So go to your favorite uncle and get $750, and you are in business.

That is how this system works. Again, it takes effort. Remember when you call these housing authorities, you are not going to make one phone call and get a check in the mail for $100,000 for your home. Some are loans, and some are insured loans. There are grants out there and housing that needs rehab where you can get a good deal.

Houses For $1

The government has a program called Houses for a Dollar. The official name is the Urban Homesteading Act. These are rundown houses where if somebody does not pay their mortgage, the government gets that house. It sits and usually deteriorates. Eventually somebody says, "We better get rid of this eyesore," and they have some kind of lottery where for a dollar you buy a ticket. Maybe one in 10 people will get a house, and those are not bad odds. It is a wonderful deal. Then when you get the house, they will give you a low interest loan to fix it up. There are so many couples I know who found these kinds of homes. Isn't that remarkable? A house for a dollar!

I remember I was on a national TV program talking about that government program, the Urban Homesteading Act. They were forcing me to the wall, saying that, "We want to know a phone number where our audience can call." I had the main number in Washington for running the program, but what I did not know was that the program is really run by 170 offices around the country. I gave the main number of the office in Washington, and that whole office is just run by two people — the director of the program and the secretary. And they got 10,000 calls that day because I was on a national TV show. They got thousands and thousands of letters. They called me right away, complaining. When I do things like that, I say, "I will send somebody down and help answer your phones, mail or anything else you need." They usually back off, but I actually helped them. I answered a bunch of the mail, because if I caused the problem I feel the obligation to correct it.

When I do that to bureaucrats, they know they are in business to get the message out. They do not have a way as big as I do sometimes to get it out, and they really have to handle the volume. There are a lot of bureaucrats that do not like me too much, but on the other side I have got bureaucrats that call and say, "Hey, why don't you talk about my program? My program is more important than this program, and people should know about it."

I had a call from an office that gave money to people to start day care centers, and they could not give away all their money, and the year was running out. They called and asked me to talk about this money so people would come and apply for it. These poor bureaucrats could not make quota.

And that is what happens with all the bad publicity in the government offices, the best people do not apply, or the money does not get used well because not enough good people are applying.

If the bureaucrats have better people to choose from, then somebody's brother-in-law won't be hijacked off the street and the money shoved down their throat, which I am sure happens in these agencies. See, if the bureaucrat does not get rid of all their money this year, they will not get it next year.

Government Considers You Needy At $80,000 Per Year

Also on housing, remember that you do not have to be destitute to get money to buy or build a house with government money. For some of these programs as I mentioned earlier, you can be making over $80,000 a year and the government considers you needy, and that you need financial help to buy a house.

It sounds ridiculous but you cannot possibly know all the rules and all the regulations. I don't, and I have been doing this for 25 years. I am surprised every day.

I have found special money programs just to paint your house. Here is a program that I did not even know existed. The government will pay your mortgage! Who would ever think that the government would pay your mortgage?

Actually, they do it through nonprofit organizations. If you have trouble paying your mortgage, have been in the house for a couple of years and lose your job, do not call the Credit Doctor.

The Government Will Pay Your Mortgage

The U.S. Department of Housing and Urban Development has set up nonprofit organizations around the country that will help you with the mortgage. They will contact the bank, or wherever you owe that money, and work it out with them. Some of these people even have money to pay your mortgage five, six, or seven months while you are in between jobs. That is why I wear the question mark suit. Would you ever think of asking a government office to pay your mortgage? Well, it is there, and that is what is important.

If you are looking for your first house to buy, you may be able to take a free class from the government, and get up to $1,000 as a down payment because you took the class. You take something for free and they give you free money because you did something for free. It is bizarre. What they are doing is trying to encourage, particularly first-time homebuyers, to be knowledgeable about what they are doing. That is why they entice people into taking this class. It is just a short course to learn about home buying and money management. Then they give you grant money towards a down payment. What a deal!

Again, my question mark suit — you do not know the questions to ask. The answers are easy. It is asking the right question that is hard.

$10,000 Grant To Fix Up Your Home

Here is a wonderful program I found for seniors to fix up a house. You can get up to $10,000 to fix up a house if you are over 62 years of age. A woman who works at the IRS came to see me when I was giving a speech at a local library, and asked me this question. Her mom lived in Pennsylvania and needed a new roof. Because she was a good daughter, she was going to pay for it.

I said, "Here, try this program." This is a woman who works in the government and has been there many, many years, and she did not even know about the program. It is impossible to know everything. You cannot know what is in another agency. You do not even know what is in your own office. So, she found out about the program and got $7,000 for her mom to put a new roof on her house. That is wonderful. That is what this money is for, for people to solve problems in life.

This is not welfare money. To me, the only real welfare money we have is the lottery. The lottery is welfare money because they want you to pay taxes. Play the lottery, and you are really giving more taxes to the government because all the lotteries are government programs. It is a way for them to collect taxes. Then they say, "You may win the lottery. You have one in a million chance of winning, and then you can go sit on the beach for the rest of your life."

What is more welfare than giving somebody money to go sit on the beach for the rest of their life? I do not want people to sit on the beach. I want them to be out there making society better for me, you and the rest of the world. That is what these programs are set up to do. It is for you to have a better life, make society better, get that education, improve the world, or to start that business we need.

$15,000 To Fix Up Your Home

Do you want to fix up your house? There is money to do that. Again, most of the fix-up money is not only at the federal level, but the state and local level as well. In Greensboro, you can get an $8,500 grant to fix your home from the city.

In Minneapolis, there is $15,000 at zero percent interest and no payments until you sell your house to fix it up. So, are you going to go to the bank and get $15,000 to put on that deck in the back, or do you go to the government and get zero percent interest which you do not have to pay until you sell your house? What a deal!

How about Baton Rouge, Louisiana? Up to a $20,000 grant to fix up your home! How much will you have to work to make $20,000? Come to the bottom line. Maybe a third of it goes in taxes, so that means you have got to make $30,000 for you to get $20,000. That is maybe a whole year's income for most of us. And here is what you could get for free from the government to fix your home.

So housing help is at the federal, state, county, as well as city levels, and remember to get a list of all of the programs. The way to work with government agencies is not to call them and say what you want to do. You call them and get the information about what they have. When you get that, you take the literature home, read about the programs, and then call the bureaucrats back and tell them what they have. "Hey, you have this program here. I want to apply for it." That is how you deal with the bureaucracy. Get their paper, call them back, and tell them what they have.

Getting Money For College

There is lots of money out there for college. Actually, just in the government alone, there are 470 programs worth over $33 billion. Then you have the private sector, which has some money, but not a whole lot compared to the government sector. So, you are talking about $35 billion or so, just for students. That is every year.

The government level consists of federal, state and also some local money. But the two major areas are federal and state. You can get a four-year college degree, a junior college degree, graduate school, professional school, or just take a short course at a technical school. You can even get money to pay an artist to teach you at home. Education and training is hot in this country, and the government, the politicians and the think tanks all realize that for us to succeed as a society, more of us have to get better trained. It now takes brainpower to succeed.

I am 58-years old, and grew up mostly in the '50s and '60s, and went on to college. Those kids that went to work in the factories made a heck of a lot more money than I did when I got out of college, even four years later. At that time you could work for General Motors, a steel factory or in the transportation industry and make $50,000-100,000 a year, just with manual labor. They were wonderful jobs, and you only needed a high school education to get them.

But it is not that way any more. Those jobs have been shrinking in the last 20 or 30 years, and are going away in our society. All the manual labor jobs have gone overseas. We have just become eggheads, so all the jobs now require brainpower and not muscle power. So, you have got to have that education and training to get the brainpower to compete for good jobs in our society if you are going to succeed. And this is how our country is going to succeed. The bigger our brainpower, the better we will be able to compete internationally or globally. That is why it is important. You can never stop learning.

Going To College At 60

The programs I am going to talk about for education are for every age group. It does not matter how old you are. You can be 16 and going to college or attending training programs. Or, you could be 60 or 106! Remember, the government cannot discriminate with age. Actually, right now there are something like 350 universities and colleges around the country where you can go to school for free or next to nothing, just because you are 55 or 60. That is right. At 55 or 60, you can go back and take a computer course or a poetry course — or become a doctor or a lawyer! By the time you hit 60, living until you are 80 or 90 is going to be nothing. So you are a doctor for another 20 years, or a lawyer. Do the things you really want to do.

I even think retirement is a passe idea in our society. That is from the industrial age. You worked in a factory or manual labor all your life, and in your sixties you don't want to do that any more. You want to retire and sit on your butt somewhere. But now with brainpower, and particularly if you are doing the things you love to do, you want to stay contributing all your life. And you can do that.

It does not take manual labor. No matter how much energy you have, you still have to have that brain working. You could be teaching for the rest of your life. You could be counseling. You could be writing. You could be on the net if you want and contributing to our society, and doing it into your eighties or nineties.

I work with a college counselor now. This guy is 92 years old. He just came back from a national tour on his new book about colleges. The guy's terrific — 92 years old and still contributing. And I am paying him good money, and others are too.

You could be like that, but you have got to get that education and training. Find out where it is and get the money. You can get money at any age. Many people who are 35 or 40 are thinking about a new career. You started to become a lawyer and now you would rather be a French chef. Or, maybe you were a clerk typist or a legal secretary and now you want to become a lawyer. You can do those kinds of things in our society.

Actually, there are more people on the college campuses today over 35 than there are 18 and 19-year olds. That is a clue. If you are not thinking about it now, you should think about it soon.

See The Book I Copied From

When you look at federal programs, you can look at my book or the book I copied from in your library called the *Catalog of Federal Domestic Assistance*. Actually, my first *New York Times Bestseller* was from that book. I did not write a lick. This was 20 years ago. I found that at the Government Printing Office they had this book called the *Catalog of Federal Domestic Assistance*. I got so excited about it. Here was one book that had all the government programs to do anything.

So, what I did was I found a publisher in New York. Actually, I found an agent and a publisher in New York, and they gave me a few thousand dollars to write that book. I flunked English in college so I am not this big wordsmith. I got the Catalog from the Government Printing Office and I literally cut and pasted that book. Nothing in the government is copyrighted, so it was not plagiarism. I sent it to the people in New York and it was funny but they took a half a year or a year to edit this thing. The government just spent millions of dollars editing it. Those snobs in New York wanted to do it "their way."

When the book was published, I went on talk shows and it became a *New York Times Bestseller*. You can get better information than the experts themselves. Instead of buying it from my book, you can go right to the Catalog. Cut out the middleman, and get the best stuff.

If you do not think my book has the most up-to-date information, go there. You will see programs, and they are all in funny places. At the U.S. Department of Housing and Urban Development, you can get $15,000 for graduate students to study housing related topics. All the graduates complain that there is no money for graduate education, because they look at two or three major government programs and they forget about the others.

Do you want a job in law enforcement? There is a program in the Justice Department that is run through the state governments that will pay you for a four-year college degree in any area of law enforcement as long as you say that when you graduate you will work in law enforcement somewhere. If you want to become a cop, a lawyer, a DNA specialist and work on the OJ trial, anything at the federal or state level, you can get that money.

Or here is $5,000 to become a librarian from the Department of Education. That is right. The Department of Education — do you want to study library science? That is where it is.

Or, how about community planning? The Department of Housing and Urban Development has $11,000 for you to study community planning. See, it is all kinds of funny stuff.

How about $800 from the Department of Energy to attend a conference because you are an engineering student? Here is my idea. If you are an engineering student going to college up in the Northeast in the cold winter months, find a conference during winter break out in California. You get $800 to fly out there, attend a conference, and then you sit on the beach for the rest of the break and look at the girls. That is the way to use it.

How about $14,000 for a graduate degree in foreign languages? Or there is money at the Department of Defense to get your graduate degree in mathematics.

How about $2,500 for a degree in history from the National Endowment of the Humanities? Do you want to become a nurse, a nurse practitioner, or study child development or violence training? You can get up to $30,000 to do that from the Department of Health and Human Services.

Your State Has Money For College and Artists

There are all these programs in healthcare, criminal justice, or housing and they are all at the federal level. That is just one place you have got to look, because what you want to do next is go to the state level. You need to call your state office of higher education. Every state has one, and they will have a half a dozen to a dozen programs at the state level. That is one of the programs my engineering major son has gotten. He gets $3,000 as long as he says when he graduates he will work in engineering in the state of Maryland for a year. For every year they give him money, they want him to work for a year in the state. That sounds fair enough. He will probably wind up working in Maryland anyway, so it is a great deal.

In other states, you can get $1,000 towards your tuition if you join the Air National Guard or other weird things, like if you are a descendant of the Confederate Army and live in Florida, they give you $150. Or you could get $5,000 to study accounting at any university in New York. Or, receive $1,500 to become a music teacher in Tennessee. Go to the state level and they will send you a listing of the programs. Get the applications and fill them out. There is no magic to these things, and then you are on your way.

Also at the state level is money for artists. You could be a tap dancer, a choreographer, a singer, a storyteller, an arts teacher, a printmaker, a writer — even a poet. These are all at your state arts council. Every state government has an arts council, which gives out up to $180 million every year. These are usually for short-term projects.

I actually talked to a piano player in Ohio. He is in one of my infomercials. He was a struggling piano player, and got money from the government to make his CD. He also gives concerts in the state and the government pays him.

If you are a performer you can travel overseas and perform. The U.S. Department of State will send your group to China, Japan or Yugoslavia or somewhere else to show them American art and music.

Go to your state capital and ask for the state office. It is usually called the state council for the arts. Get their programs. You could be a weaver and get $2,000 to work on your project. It is given out all the time.

Actually, if you are an artist, another neat thing is that the government buys art. You could be a freelance artist, drawing brochures for the EPA on your kitchen table, and getting government contracts, so that is another way to get paid for your art. They need more graphic design, so maybe you can make $50,000 creating pamphlets and information booklets.

A writer is the same way. Where are more words written anywhere else than in the government? All the government produces is words. If you are a writer or an editor, look at these government contracts and find out how you can get a piece of the action.

The other place for money for higher education is through nonprofits. There are thousands and thousands of scholarships out there. They are real, and take effort. You could go on the web or to the library and find a lot about them. We even have them in our books.

What is the key to getting all this money? It is a numbers game. You are not going to go to the financial aid office and apply to one or two places, and expect to get everything you want. You are going to have to fill out 50 applications, maybe 100. Who cares? Once you fill out one or two, they are all the same anyway. That is how you get the money. The more applications you fill out, the better the chances you are going to have to get this money. You have heard about scholarships for people with two left ears or whose grandmother was in the Polish navy. That is all real, but you have to go out and search for it. There are already a lot of resources, organizations, and books that will help you identify these.

$8,000 To Train For A New Job

There is another source of money for education and training, and that is training money. There are a lot of training programs at the federal and state level. If you lose a job you could probably get $8,000 to go train to become a French chef or a computer network engineer. A guy called me, who was a bouncer in a club. He got $10,000 to become a computer network engineer. He went from $7 an hour to $50,000 a year. That kind of thing happens. A guy stopped me on the street and said, "Lesko, I got your book." They gave him $8,000 to take a course at George Washington University on how to become an event planner.

There is a lot of training money out there in our society because that is how you succeed in life, it seems. You have got to have those skills and the government is well aware of the need. The government has set up one-stop training information centers in every state, and in every county now, too. To start your quest for this money, the best place to start is your state government. Ask them about the one-stop training centers, and they can give you the local center. Go down, make an appointment and find out about the programs. They are not going to have every program, but they will know most of the programs.

There are 150 training programs, and the biggest problem is that you cannot go to the yellow pages to find out about any of them. That is the pity. The government does not advertise. You cannot look under "Training," or even "Government," to find them. You are going to have to do some work yourself, and the place to start is that one-stop training program in your state capital.

Also for women, every state capital has an office just for women. Call the governor's office and ask for the women's commission for your state. They will know about the training programs just for women. There are a lot of special organizations for women going back into the workforce, and there is special training money just for that situation. Women who want to get training in traditional men's jobs are eligible for special programs.

Women are a little bit more clever at all of this. Women know about the new society because they know they have to get the education, training or have their own business. That is why women start two out of every three businesses today. That is why there are more women on college campuses now than there are men. They know what is happening in our society. The rest of us have to be aware of it, too, and get trained or get that education so that we can continue contributing for the rest of our lives!

Start Your Own Nonprofit

Maybe you want to start your own nonprofit organization. That may be a reality for you. As you look around for grant money to change the world, you find out that a lot of it is for nonprofit organizations. (See "How To Start or Become a Nonprofit Organization" for the mechanics of starting your own nonprofit.)

Well, there are two ways of handling that issue. You can start your own nonprofit organization, or another way to do it is to find an existing nonprofit organization with whom you can work. Are you looking for $100,000 to work with the elderly, youth or to improve the neighborhood, and the people giving out the money say you have to be a nonprofit organization? You can go to your church, community college or any other nonprofit organization and ask them to work with you if you give them a piece of the pie.

Usually what happens is that you can apply for this grant, and give the nonprofit 10, 20 or 30 percent of the money for using their name and having a place to hang your hat. It is often called overhead. They get that to give you a desk there if you get the grant. You work out the deal with the nonprofit that you will only be there if you get the money. That is a normal relationship. Many of these nonprofit organizations work that way. It is not difficult to try to talk them into doing this. It's a win/win situation.

The other alternative is that you start a nonprofit yourself. There is no magic to this either. But like anything else in life, if you talk to an accountant or lawyers, they can complicate the heck out of everything and it can wind up costing you thousands. Or you can do it yourself for approximately $150.

There was a friend of mine who used to work with one of the big online companies, and he always wanted to start his own nonprofit. He wanted to help kids, and was very active in veterans' organizations. Like me, he was a Vietnam vet. He thought, "What this country needs is not veterans who whine about how they were mistreated, but veterans who do something for the community." He went to an attorney and the attorney said, "Yeah, it will cost you $3,000 to become a nonprofit organization." He said, "If I had $3,000 I would do something for the community, and not give it to some attorney to become a nonprofit organization."

I was sitting in his office one day, opened up my book and said, "Here, call this office over at the IRS." The IRS has a special office that just helps people start nonprofit organizations. And actually, they have a special office within that just for veterans' organizations. He called them and they sent him the paperwork. He had it all out on his dining room table and it took a couple of evenings to complete. He filled it all out, sent it in, and of course it was screwed up. The IRS sent it back to him and he made the changes. And with any question he had, he found he had a person at the IRS to call and straighten it out.

Just like taxes. You can worry the heck over it, or just give it your best shot and hope for the best. If you screw up enough, the government will tell you, and then you change it and send it back to them. It still beats paying a couple of grand to some attorney.

When he started his nonprofit he raised $3,000 in his first fundraiser and gave it to the local Ronald McDonald's House in honor of veterans. See, that is what to do with money. Why give it to some attorney or an accountant to become a nonprofit when you can take that same money and do something good with it? That is what a nonprofit is in business to do, and that could be you.

The other hurdle is filing at the state government. Call the state capital operator, ask for the Secretary of State, and then ask them "How do I become a nonprofit organization in the state?" That will cost you usually under $100 to become a nonprofit and you can learn that system too. The important thing is that you did not let a hurdle like $3,000 for some attorney stop you from doing what you want to do, becoming your own nonprofit.

And once you become a nonprofit, the joy is not only finding the money that is out there for you, but it is fun taking advantage of all the other stuff for nonprofit organizations. The government has programs where you could get volunteers to work for you for free. Action does that, Vista, and the White House even has a national service program that sends people to nonprofit organizations to work for free. You could have free employees that are paid by the government to work for you.

Also, you could get free stuff, just because you are a nonprofit organization. You know the drug confiscated limousines that the Justice Department gets from drug runners? Because you are nonprofit, they could give it to you for free. Any surplus government property, you as a nonprofit could get for free. And that is usually run through a state agency of surplus property. The federal government gives it to the state government, which in turn gives it to nonprofit organizations. So, check out how to get free stuff or free property.

I know a woman down in Texas who got an entire air force base for free because she was going to set up a nonprofit radio station. They had an air force base they were not using, so they gave it to this lady because she was a nonprofit organization.

You want to do some volunteer work this summer? Go to your local homeless shelter or your local church. Learn about this system and how to get furniture for them for free from the government because they are a nonprofit organization. But again, you have to know about the program in order to take advantage of it.

Another thing available is art. The National Gallery of Art will send out free art to nonprofits. How about getting a Jeep for your parade, a canon, a tank or the Blue Angels to come and fly over your parade? You can. Put in your request and they will do that for you.

How about if your women's group could get a top-gun pilot to come and speak at a meeting? You can get speakers because you are a nonprofit organization, community group or an association of musicians. Want to know how to write off your summer vacation when you travel? Call the IRS and tell them your association's next meeting, and how you would like an agent to come and talk for free about how to write off your summer vacation. Because you are a nonprofit, they will, and that is what is neat in this country. There are so many goodies out there for nonprofit organizations if you know where to ask.

The Department of Energy has tools for schools. All the surplus equipment they have at the Department of Energy, such as scientific equipment, you can get for free if you are a school. For homeless shelters, there are certain surplus property programs set up just for people who run homeless shelters. Locate a homeless shelter or church in your community with whom you would like to work, and find out how to get the pastor a drug-confiscated limousine or a cigarette boat to run around the local lake.

More importantly, maybe you need a van. Maybe you need new furniture or used computers that are still very good and can be used. You could get equipment that is just a year or two old that is still very usable and worthwhile. You could get it for free because you are a nonprofit organization. A lot of these grants are for nonprofits, but do not let that stop you. You either work with the nonprofit organization or you become your own nonprofit organization and that is easy to do. You have just got to do it!

Develop An Info Tool Kit

Kaboom! Do you hear that? That is the information explosion. You have probably been hearing it for years now. Data, data everywhere and not a thought to think. We are living in this information society. There is more information now than in the history of mankind. Do you realize that in the last 30 years our society has created more information than in the previous 5,000? That is right. You know that. You have seen it. You have seen all the books, magazines and TV stations. Go on the web now and put in a keyword like "back pain," "grant money," or something like that, and you will get a million citations. That is how our society is now and you have to learn how to cope with this information explosion. That is what I want to talk about now.

I have been doing this for about 25 years. I have got an MBA in management information systems, and it was my dream to have some kind of business. I didn't care. I would have sold hot dogs in the park. Actually, back in the '70s, I even had a computer software company that went belly-up. I must have been the only person in the world that had a computer business that failed.

1973 Changed The World Of Information

After you have a lot of failures, what it seems like you do in this country is become a teacher or a consultant. Well, I became both. I became a professor in computer science at a local university, and then I became a consultant to Fortune 500 fat cats. By the way, the mid '70s was a crucial time in our society. Actually about 1973 was when the whole world changed. I really believe that.

Before 1973 whatever happened usually traveled along on a graph on a straight line. Organizations would plot sales for a couple of years and the path would normally continue. To keep things going along that path all you had to do was take care of what was going on inside of your organization.

Then 1973 changed our whole world, and the country has never been the same. We even fell behind countries like Japan and Germany. These people were beating our pants off until the '90s. So, we went through 20 or 30 years where we were not the best. Other people were better, and that is really because we did not know how to handle 1973.

Internal vs. External Information In Organizations

What happened in 1973? That was the time when people realized that information outside their organization was important. The oil embargo happened. We thought we had all the power in the world then all of a sudden, a few Arab states halfway across the world decided to yank up the price of oil and it crippled us. It devastated the whole economy because some little country decided to change their prices, and it brought us to our knees.

That was when we started to realize we could not just take care of what was inside our organization. We had to know what was outside of our organization, and that was how I started this company. Back in 1975, I started a business called Washington Researchers. I wanted to help organizations find out what was going on outside of their company, or outside of their organizations.

The accounting people ruled the companies — payroll, accounts receivable, manufacturing. That was what the executives had to know about in order to survive. Now, in 1973 they had to know more. They had to know what was going on outside of their organization. It was this external information that could hurt them more than the internal information.

The First Information Brokerage Business

That was why I set up a company that was going to get information. I was going to design an external management information system, and was going to get information for all these hotshot executives on what was going on outside of their organization. I said, "Hey, if you plotted and kept up to date on your markets you will succeed. I will prepare monthly reports on what is going on in your markets, and also your competitors."

Not only that, you had to know about legislation because Congress could pass a law and put you out of business. Or, what about the development of new technology that could help you? Gosh, is somebody going to have a new idea, or a new patent that will put you out of business? A good executive, I felt, had to monitor these four areas: markets, competition, legislation and technology.

I was going to go out and save the world, and convince organizations they needed this. I would do these reports every month. Well, it did not really work out that way. I could not convince anybody. Nobody had that kind of foresight. Everybody was fighting fire drills and did not want to get reports that would inundate them with paperwork. Really, they did not even understand me. These were fat cats of big corporations.

So, what I did was offer research. What do you want to know? I will get the information for you on anything you want. What happened was that these fat cats would call me and would want to know mostly about their competitors. They would want to know about getting into new businesses, or getting into new markets.

I started my business with just me, a phone and a desk. I had a little one-bedroom apartment here in Washington, DC, and I ran the whole business. I would be sitting in my underwear most of the time, waiting for the phone to ring. I just had two failing businesses and I was starting a business again. I think if I did not have those two failing businesses, I would not have anywhere near the success I have today. I would have some mediocre business that was just plugging along and getting by. But the failures were the best thing that happened to me.

My 2 Failures

I had a computer business that failed, and another little research company that failed. With an MBA, I would start a business like they taught me in business school. I would go out and get the accountants, the lawyers and the proper tax structure, the power furniture, the power business cards and the power drapes — all this stuff that I thought was necessary in order to succeed. When my companies went out of business, who won? The guy from whom I bought the drapes, the accountants and the lawyers were the winners. They got my money early, and I went out of business. I was SOL.

When I started my third business, I thought as an entrepreneur starting your own business, your most important resource is you. You are doing most everything, so you have to be very critical of how you spend your time. If you are having meetings about picking out drapes for your office, that is a waste of time. If you are having meetings with an accountant, figuring out the right tax structure, and you are not even making money yet, that is a waste of time. Who cares? You are going to pay taxes on what? Nothing.

Identify Your Critical Success Factors

I figured out that an entrepreneur had to focus on the critical success factors of the business. I believe the single critical success factor of any business is customers. If you do not have customers, you have got nothing! You have got zero, zilch, zip, nada. You have got to concentrate on getting customers. The rest will fall into place. If you can keep a checkbook, you are an accountant.

Now I have a big business. Every time I take it to accountants, I get so confused. I have to call them to find out what the heck I am doing. The more I keep to myself and just run it like my checkbook, I know what I am doing and how much money I have. So, I figure I am going to keep it simple and just concentrate on getting customers.

The other thing I learned from failure is that nobody cared if I failed. That was the big thing that used to stop me from doing anything. I used to worry that I was going to fail and people would point at me walking down the street. "Oh, there's Lesko, that failure." That big F on my forehead would be prominent to everyone else.

No One Cares If You Fail

But when I failed I found out that nobody really cared, even my friends and family. Superficially, maybe they cared for a few seconds or minutes, but we are all so involved in our own lives. We really do not care that much about other people. It makes interesting gossip, but they do not really care. That was what used to stop me from doing things — that fear of failure. Once I failed a couple of times and I saw that nobody really cared, that gave me courage. I could not wait to start another business because I felt that the worst that could happen is I fail, and I had already done that a couple of times.

Success Is Having Fun

So the third time I just said this time I am just going to start having fun. That was when it was different. That was when I tried to find out what was unique in me and bring that out so that I was different from everybody else. I was trying to be like everybody else in my other businesses because people were telling me, "This is the way to be successful," so I tried to do that. Then someone else would say, "This is the way to do it," and I would try to be like that.

Nonsense. What people want in this world is something different all the time, not something the same. We already have the same. So, I started trying to have fun, trying to be different, and that was when things started working. Even now, 20 years later after my first success, I still have to fight every day to find out what is unique about me and to keep having that fun. I know the successful part of it is when you are doing what is natural to you.

From 1 to 30 People In 3 Years

That was when it took off! I went from a one-bedroom apartment where my business was just me, a phone and a desk to where I had 30 or 35 people and a big office down on K Street in Washington, DC with all the other mucky-mucks down there trying to get money. And it all happened in about 3 years.

To tell you the truth, you got better service from me when I was in my bedroom. People used to call me, and I was the whole kit and caboodle. It was only me, and I think I charged $25 an hour back then. This was 20 years or so ago. I would work forever for that kind of money.

When I was on K Street, I would hire these people and charge $100 an hour, $200 an hour or whatever I could get, and I had people whose names I did not know working for my clients. It seems like you get diseconomies of scale as you grow bigger. You charge a higher price and give out a worse product. That is why I keep looking for little guys when I need to find some service — a person who owns it, operates it, does everything. If I went to some big company, I would get down to the 15th tier of some person who does not care. You can never find the people because nobody has their heart in it when they are working for somebody else.

Take Heart In Your Failure, Nixon Died A Hero

There are people in life that really should encourage you about failure, people like Richard Nixon. I will never forget when he was thrown out of the White House. Can you imagine anything worse in life than to be thrown out of the White House? Could you imagine calling your mother up and saying, "Mom, they threw me out of the White House"? Nixon was thrown out of the White House, and somehow he redeems himself and dies a hero.

No matter what you do in life, you will never be worse than being thrown out of the White House. So do not worry about failure. When I started this business, I used to put little one-inch ads in the *Wall Street Journal*. I would say things like, "I can get research for you on any topic. Just call me." You cannot really tell your story in a one-inch ad, and that was the problem. I would get all kinds of weird stuff. People would write on napkins in crayon and it was a waste of money.

Little Money Leads To Big Creativity

Having little money is important. You have to be more creative. I took that little money I was using for one-inch ads in the *Wall Street Journal* and decided to come out with a free newsletter on how to get free information. I figured instead of a one-inch ad in the *Wall Street Journal*, if I could get the *Wall Street Journal* to write up about my free newsletter, then I would have the sanction of the *Wall Street Journal* saying, "This guy's a great researcher." I figured they would be more inclined to write up something that was free to their readers.

The hotshots in corporations were what I was after. I figured the *Wall Street Journal* was the place. I only knew about three or four things at the time, so I wrote them up in a four-page newsletter. On page four I put all the stuff that I could do. I am better, faster, cheaper and I will find anything — just call me.

Then these other organizations started writing about my newsletter — the *Wall Street Journal*, the business magazines. For the same price of a one-inch ad, I was able to do this little newsletter and send it out to the media, and they wanted to write about it because they have got to fill those pages with something that hopefully will help their readers. So, a free newsletter on finding free information sounded good, and that was when my phone never stopped ringing. That is what I do now.

It's Not What You Say; It's How You Say It

Again, when I started doing consumer books, I found the same thing. You have got all these talk shows and they are not really talk shows. They are just vehicles for selling stuff. I would say, how do I get on talk shows? TV is really entertainment, so I figured out after I did one talk show that it is not what you say, but how you say it. That is what people buy on TV, how things are done.

When I went out there and showed all my energy, danced around and wore question mark suits, they wanted me on TV. They did not care what I said. They just wanted me there. I was on *Letterman* seven or eight times, *Larry King* about a dozen times. I had a beeper because they would use me when somebody cancelled. I remember I was in Chicago one day and Letterman called me. I think it was Christopher Walken who cancelled at the last minute. He had some film he hated and did not want to plug. If I can get seven minutes on national TV, that is worth tens of thousands of dollars.

I remember being on *Letterman* and thinking okay, I am here acting crazy, plugging my book, and then in the middle of my seven minutes I stop and somebody has a commercial for something for which they probably paid $40,000 or $50,000, maybe more for this one-minute commercial. I am getting seven minutes for free because I am acting like an idiot. So that is a lesson on how to use the system.

This business really taught me not only about that, but more importantly how to get information. When I started this business of getting information for business clients, anything they would ask I would do because I was hungry. I wanted to please them. I wanted to get paid, because the only way I got paid was if I got the information.

Mr. Potato Head

So, I was sitting there and I remember one of my first clients called me. It was a guy who was a friend of a friend who had a million dollars invested in a commodity on the New York Commodities Exchange called Maine Potatoes. I did not know anything about potatoes. I was a city kid. I remember when I came to Washington, a friend of mine had a country house and I went out there to see him for dinner. He sent me out in the backyard to find fresh potatoes for dinner. I was out there about 20 or 30 minutes. I finally came back and said, "I cannot find those potato trees.

Where the heck are they?" I had no idea potatoes grew under the ground. That was how much I knew about potatoes.

So, this potential client called me and he said he had all this money. He was a hotshot MBA from Wharton Business School, the University of Pennsylvania, and he knew that most of the people that invested in the market are really just trying to outguess the other idiots that are in the market. He figured if he had some basic information about the supply and demand of potatoes, he would have an edge on everybody else in this potatoes market.

Potatoes were going crazy at that time, and even the *Wall Street Journal* had front-page articles on the subject. What they normally sell for $15, were now selling for $100. People were making or losing fortunes every day in this thing.

So, he called me up on a Wednesday or Thursday and he said, "Lesko, if you can find in 24 hours what the basic supply and demand for Maine potatoes is, we have a deal because we want to make a trade by the end of the week." In those days I would say yes to anything. I did not know about Maine potatoes, but I only charged him if I got the information. So, we agreed on a couple of hundred bucks or whatever for me to get the information. I said yes and had no idea how much it would cost or how long it would take. But I had nothing else to do in those days. I would have worked for this guy for $25.

I would charge what I thought they would pay. That is why the more success you have, the more confident you are to charge more because they probably will pay it. I said okay, I will get the information in 24 hours. When you have a small business at home and you are waiting for clients, you hang around, watching soap operas, going to the kitchen and waiting for the phone to ring. The days can be real boring.

I Ran My Whole Business On One Book

So, now I had a real client. I used to run my whole business on one book called *The US Government Manual*. I knew nothing about Washington. I did not really know where stuff was, as I never used Washington that much. I would rely on *The US Government Manual* because it had a description of all the agencies.

You cannot find in your phonebook things like the Census Bureau. Nothing is listed by keyword. You cannot look under, "Census." You have to know the organizational structure. You have to know that the Census Bureau is part of the Department of Commerce, so you need to first look under the Department of Commerce in the blue pages, and then see under that a listing for the Census Bureau.

So, I picked up *The US Government Manual*. I looked in the index for potatoes. Nothing there. I thought, oh my gosh, what am I going to do? I turned to the table of contents, which had a listing in alphabetical order of all the major departments and agencies. The first agency right up at top was the U.S. Department of Agriculture. Hey, that sounds logical — agriculture, potatoes — so I called the U.S. Department of Agriculture.

I was trying to pretend that I was this big shot research company and needed this important information. I got on the phone and I said, "Hello, this is Mr. Lesko from Megabuck Research Company. I have a client who has to know about the basic supply and demand of Maine potatoes. Do you have someone there who could help me, sir?"

They said, "We have to put you on hold, Mr. Lesko." Like a good bureaucrat, they put me on hold. They came back and said, "Well, Mr. Lesko, we will have to switch you to Charlie Porter." I said, "Charlie Porter? Why are you switching me to Charlie Porter? Does this guy handle prank calls or something like that? I have got to know about the supply and demand of Maine potatoes in 24 hours for my important client."

He said, "Oh, no. He doesn't handle prank calls. Charlie Porter is our resident economist specializing in the supply and demand of Maine potatoes." I said, "Really? There is a guy there who just studies potatoes?" He said yes. Wonderful.

They switched me over to Mr. Porter and I hear, "Porter here." "Mr. Porter, this is Mr. Lesko and I am from Megabuck Research Company. I have got this client who needs to know the basic supply and demand of Maine potatoes in 24 hours. Could you help me out?"

He comes back with, "Yep, I think so." I am thinking in my mind, is this guy really going to help me? So, I start quizzing him a little bit about his background. "Mr. Porter, before I get into it, my client invests a lot of money and I would like to know a little bit about your background."

15 Years Of Studying Potatoes

So he starts telling me. He is a GS-17. For the last 15 or 16 years of his life he has been studying the supply and demand for potatoes. He has got a bachelor's in economics, and a master's in agricultural economics. He has spent 16 years and been making $70,000-80,000 a year just studying potatoes. I started smelling payday. Porter sounded like he could really help me.

I started getting excited. I said, "Well, Mr. Porter, we can do this. You sound great. How can I get this information?" He said, "Well, you could come down and see me, we could do it over the phone, or I could send you the material — any way you want to do it."

First of all, Mr. Porter did not sound real busy, and I certainly was not busy — this was my only client. So, I made an appointment to go see Charlie the first thing the next morning down at the Department of Agriculture. I was a cab ride away — actually, I rode my bicycle. Trying to find his office was a challenge. There are hundreds of little offices all over — north wing, south wing. I was 10 minutes late for our appointment because I got lost in the maze of all these offices around there.

I finally found his office, and opened the door. It was a little 12 by 12 room with a desk. Charlie was behind the desk. There was another chair in front of the desk, and then all around the walls were bookshelves. There were hundreds of books. I sat down on the chair in front of Charlie's desk, looking and glancing at these bookshelves all over, and I see that every book was about potatoes! I used to think maybe one book was written about potatoes, if you were lucky. Charlie had all these books about potatoes.

Charlie started going on about potatoes. I got there about 9:30 in the morning, and was there for over two and a half hours talking about potatoes. It was amazing. No matter what reference came up, he had a source for it. He would go into his drawers, into his files, and find graphs. He was telling me that he was also a potato statistician where he made potato models. When he said potato models, at first I was thinking of Mr. and Mrs. Potato Head. But no, these were statistical models that he designed that really forecast the supply and demand of Maine potatoes.

He would bring out graph paper, computer models that he generated, and he would put them on the window because he would want to show one graph over another graph. When these two lines crossed, it showed what was going to happen to supply and demand of Maine potatoes. It was just phenomenal.

We started talking about the potato problem in Europe. Everybody was worried. There was a potato shortage in Europe. He got on the phone, and a guy came in the office who was the European potato expert. He was telling us that the scare was just a false alarm because a boat came in just half-loaded with potatoes, or something like that. It was nothing with which to be concerned. It was amazing.

When I found Charlie Porter, the problem was not getting the information — the problem was getting out of his office! I had a feeling that he has been studying potatoes for the last 16 years of his life, and finally somebody asked him what he has been spending a lifetime studying.

His wife is sick of hearing about potatoes, right? Nobody in the government even knows he is there any more, and he just grinds away, studying. He loves potatoes. Who else is going to pay you $60,000-80,000 a year to study potatoes? Only the government, and that is where these people are.

Then he started showing me the statistics that come out every month from the Department of Agriculture, showing the supply and demand of potatoes. It showed you how many potatoes were grown, how many potato chips were made, and even how many Pringles potato chips were made because they make them where they squish up all the potatoes, make them perfect and they spit them back out again in some machine. He said, "If you want to get this information every month for free from the government, go across the hall and talk to the potato statistician." There was a guy across the hall and all he did was count potatoes. I could not imagine this stuff.

So, I thanked Charlie after two and a half hours. I was kind of overloaded on potatoes at that time, but I thought that if I went across the hall and talked to the potato statistician, I could get these statistics every month. I could take the report from the government, put my name on it and sell it to my client every month for a revenue stream. What you are trying to do in business is find out how to get money regularly, and not just once in a while. So, that sounded like a good deal to me.

I went across the hall and there are these two big doors. It was like a whole gymnasium, full of people. Rows and rows of desks, and everybody was behind the desks with calculators. They even had the paper coming out of the calculators. It looked like spaghetti. What was amazing to me when I first came into the room was that they had nameplates, and the first name was Asparagus. I thought that was the guy's name, like Mr. Asparagus. But no, it was the name of their commodity. They had an expert, a statistician for every commodity. The first guy was asparagus and bananas; then celery and carrots. They went down the list.

So, I asked the first guy, where was the potato statistician? It was this huge room and looked like hundreds of people. He said, "You go down this row of people here, turn at the end over there, and you won't miss him because the guy way over in the corner is the potato statistician." It looked like one of those old movies of the insurance company.

I get to the end of the row and turn over to the corner, and there is another row there. I see a guy way at the end, and he was wonderful, too. He showed me how to read those statistics and made me smart so that I could then show my client.

I got home that afternoon, called my client, gave him all this stuff, and it was wonderful. That to me is what information is all about in our society. If you find somebody like that, a person who has spent his life studying something, you do not have to worry about information overload, because you have got somebody who has read all that stuff.

Free Experts: The Key To Information Overload

I sat in that room with Charlie Porter who had read hundreds and hundreds of books on potatoes. I did not have to sit in the library and read all those books. I could ask Charlie, and he could tell me the one book to read. He could tell me what will be in the books next year because he is working on that research today.

That is the power of information in our society. That is how to cope with the information overload, and what I did for years and years, helping Fortune 500 clients. They would call me for anything. Procter and Gamble wanted to start a chain of pasta stores. Well, I found that the government has a pasta expert, who is some guy getting paid $80,000 a year just to study pasta. They would show me free market studies on pasta, what is hot and what is not, as well as what government money programs are available to start pasta stores.

Just think — if you go onto the web and put in "pasta," you are going to get a million citations. You do not know a good one from a bad one. That is why people are important. You find the experts, and the web may be good for that.

I remember doing a market study on Polish golf carts. Actually, my heritage is Czechoslovakian and that is pretty close to Poland, but gosh, I found a Polish golf cart expert in Washington that did a study on Polish golf carts that I got for free.

My brother was in a health food business. I found a free report on the health food industry for him, a market study that was something that could cost you millions of dollars.

I was doing a report for urinal screens. That is right — urinal screens! A client, a chemical company, was thinking about making urinal screens, and I found a government expert on urinal screens! When I was doing the study, the biggest selling brand for urinal screens was called Sweet Pee. How tacky a business is that? The second biggest selling brand was called Super Pee. My business was really answering thousands and thousands of requests like that from clients, and that was what made me smart. Your clients make you smart, no matter what business you are in because you want to please. You want to get the money or whatever it is, and you will do anything to do it. That is what stretches your imagination.

That is why when you get old, rich and comfortable, you are not stretching any more. The most important thing is change. Our society is changing. There are changes running through our society like a freight train, and the change started occurring back in 1973 because we had to know about our outside world. When you make decisions faster, you will get ahead of the game faster.

There Was Life Before Federal Express

Just think, it was not so long ago that Federal Express started. We did not have Federal Express 20 years ago. What was wrong with the mail? It wasn't fast enough, right? So we had Federal Express. Then after Federal Express, overnight was not fast enough, so we have fax machines to get it to you even faster. Email is doing that now, too, or your phone. You want to get information? We used to have phones only at home. Now we have mobile phones so we get information faster and make decisions faster.

All the indications around our society are that change is happening very fast, and you have to know how to deal with that change. There is more information now available in the world than ever before. I mentioned earlier that in the last 30 years we have created more information than in the past 5,000.

So, I believe as citizens, if you want to prosper in this society, want to get the money, information or help you need, you have to learn how to use the tools in our society. You have to understand what is good and bad about each of these tools. I look at the tools like this, and here is where we go for information in my mind. One is the computer. Two is the library and other things in the library — books, periodical stuff. The other thing is media. Then we have experts. We have paid experts and we have free experts. We have the government. We have the nonprofit organizations. We have the telephone, which I think is still a very important tool for information, and your friends, which is another source of information.

Let us run through them again: computer, library, the media, paid experts, free experts, the government, nonprofits, the telephone and your friends.

What Is Bad About Computers And The Internet

Now, the computer I gave you a little hint about before. What is good and bad about computers? Technology is always sold by sizzle. When computers first came out, they were selling personal computers like, "Boy, your kids are not going to go to college unless you have a computer. Life is going to pass you by unless you have a computer."

You can go on the computer and read 500 newspapers. Have you finished the morning newspaper on your front door? No. You do not have time to do that. What are you going to do with 500 newspapers? That is what I mean.

We get sucked up in technology and forget what is really good and bad about that technology. The salesmen sell us the sizzle. The key to buying technology is that the longer you wait, the better and cheaper it is.

Just think, the first piece of technology in our country that was for mass consumption was the automobile. The first automobiles were very expensive, just like the first computers or the first anything in technology. They were very complicated. To get around in this country, you jumped on a horse to get somewhere. Now these complicated automobiles with gas, clutches and all this kind of stuff would make you worry. There was no software for the automobiles — in other words, no roads. If you had a car and you did not have roads, you could not get anywhere. That was like having a computer without software, so it was very difficult.

Also, listen to this — horses were faster than the cars. So why did people buy those first automobiles? Because you had those high-tech junkies who wanted the first of everything. If you waited, until Henry Ford came along and made it cheap, mass-produced, and the infrastructure of the highway system was set up in our country and the cars became easier to use, then automobiles became a good buy.

It was the same way with computers. The first computers were almost like toys. People did not even write letters so they did not have to use word processors. Right now for a computer, the good parts are word-processing. Why you would have a typewriter nowadays is silly; but remember, we used to use typewriters way back when. We did not write that much, so why did we need a computer? You got sucked in anyway.

The other thing is that computers handle large amounts of data. That is what a computer does. They would show these things like, "Balance your checkbook by using a computer." If you did not balance your checkbook by hand, it would take you longer to put it into the computer and balance it. That is until we got the software sophisticated enough and easy enough like Quick Books. It really is easier now, but in the beginning it was not.

You have to evaluate what it is really good for, like the Internet and online databases. If you want to live in a cave and not do anything, that is fine. Most of the stuff on the Internet you could probably get somewhere else, but now it is becoming easier and easier. But in the beginning, it was not.

I bought one of the first PCs. It was almost $10,000. And that was in 1980 dollars. Then it got to about $5,000 and a $1,000 PC was unheard of. That is how much it costs today and they have all of the software. So, the longer you wait for something, the better it is. It was like that ten years ago with the first cell phones. I know people who paid thousands of dollars a month for their cell phones in the beginning, and now for $29.95 you have one. You waited, because that is what the economics of technology is. The longer you wait, the better it is, and the cheaper it will be.

Computers cause as many problems as they solve. You go on the Internet today and you put in a keyword like "money," "grants," or "back pain." You are going to get 5,000 citations. So now you have got a bigger problem than when you started. What are you going to do with 5,000 websites? You do not know a good website from a bad website. Maybe you say the first one is better. Why is that first one better? Do you know why that first one is probably first? Because that first person paid money to have his name come up first. That is the only reason that it is first, and that is how these websites work.

It causes many problems. You have to know when to use a computer as a good tool, and when it is not. To my mind, if you find a Charlie Porter, he knows all the websites. He knows the one website that is good and saves you that problem. That is how to use the computer and use another source to make sure that you have got the right place.

To me, even on the web, the best stuff is really coming from government or nonprofit organizations, besides meeting friends and email. That is separate. But for actually getting information, it is those kinds of things. Also the web is wonderful for getting opinions from people, the forums and things like this. In other words, doctors used to have to wait to go to an annual meeting to find out something. Now, the smart doctors can find answers. They can just put it on a forum and get an answer, the same way you and I can. So, it increases the speed of our society because we get answers quicker. There are a lot of good things on the web and on the computer, but you have to know what is good and bad about it. It does not solve all your problems.

What Is Good About The Library

Also, we have another source — the library. Now, you are thinking, who is going to ever use the library? Well, nobody did much in the past, to tell you the truth. If you were not on the web you could go to your local library and probably get on the web there and they would help. I have been in this business 25 years, even before the web became popular. I used to think that because we live in an information society, the most important building in our community should be the library, right? But no, it is the video store or something like that. You never see big lines waiting to get into the library. You know why? Most libraries grew up handling books, periodicals, publications and things in print. To tell you the truth, things in print are about yesterday.

When I made my first book that became a *New York Times Bestseller*, I copied that whole book from a book that is published in the Government Printing Office. Nothing in the government is copyrighted so it was legal. It is plagiarism but plagiarism is not illegal. I took that, sent it to New York, and they messed around with it for six or eight months before it came out in the bookstore. So, if you got that book, it was out of date.

You could go to the Government Printing Office by the time the book came out and get a newer edition already. The publishing process is long and cumbersome. It is getting faster, and that is what the net is about, too, but when you are buying stuff in print, it is out of date. The answers are changing every day. It is so difficult to keep up. Most of us are looking for information about today and tomorrow. "Where do I get this money?" "What is the best job to get?" "What is the best investment?" These kinds of issues are about what is happening today in our society, not yesterday. Printed material is about yesterday.

It is the same with magazines. I used to write for *Good Housekeeping* magazine. There were two, three and four months from when I wrote the article and the article was printed. That is the problem. We, as consumers, are looking for information about today, when in fact the stuff in books, magazines, periodicals and things like that are about yesterday.

What is good about that, though, is that it is very important because it also finds you sources. If I wrote a book about information and it came out last year, I am probably still keeping up on that information, and keeping up about that topic. Printed material is good for history and also for finding out who the experts are in the field. That is why I go to the library a lot, to look for leads, to look for sources and things like that. We should honor those public libraries. What I want to do and what every library should have is a telephone. You could go there and they could help you find information on the telephone, and not just the web or books. The telephone is important, and we will get to that tool as we go on.

Actually, I worked in a public library for a while down in Orlando. It is one of the richest libraries in the world. I badmouth libraries all the time because they are not keeping up. I said I should put my money where my mouth is and find out from the inside. So, they let me work in this library in Orlando, Florida. It is a rich library because they get a percentage of all real estate taxes. Development was booming in Orlando. I worked there for a couple of weeks, every day helping at the reference desk or whatever. They were really good at solving people's problems concerning local information, like what movie schedules there were, who was your local congressman and things like that. They were terrific.

But to find out what the latest cure to back pain was, they would go to a book that was written a couple of years ago. Now you and I know, every day in the media we find out there is a new cure to this. Things are changing too quickly to find out the latest information if it is published in a book.

Experts Are Wrong: They Can't Keep Up

The other tool is paid experts. If you need something, you go to a paid expert. You call me and want to know about information. I will charge you, as much as I can get. But like me, doctors, lawyers or whatever, most of what we know we learned in the first year in business. Everything I know now, the stories I am telling and the skills I have learned, I developed in the first year of business. I have spent the last 20 years putting different titles on it and saying it differently, trying to package it differently. I have got a business to run and I do not have time to learn any more.

A doctor is the same way. How much time does your doctor spend really learning that new cure to cancer? When was the last time that you spent more than three, four or five minutes with your doctor when he did not have his hand on the doorknob, waiting to go out the door? See, they do not have time any more. It is too tough.

Our society is so complicated now and changes so quickly that the so-called experts cannot keep up. It is impossible, so the experts do not really know. You talk about who is going to win the election before the election. Everybody is guessing. When these paid experts are getting money for something, they have less time to really study because now they are in the business of making money, and that is where their time is spent, making money and not learning, and getting as much leverage out of the little skills they do have.

In An Information Society: Free Is Better

Remember, you do not get what you pay for in our society. That is silly. Experts are there because they are convenient most of the time. You will see an ad for a lawyer. You will not see an ad for the free lawyer; they do not have the money to advertise. You will see ads for doctors nowadays; you will not see the ads for the free medical information because they do not have money to put the ad in the paper.

The bank will have ads about the money they have for sale. That is what banks do; they sell money. The government does not sell you money. They give it away for free, so they do not have ads for it. So, that is important.

To me, free experts are better. Where do the free experts hang out? They are not in clubs like the American Medical Association or the American Bar Association. That is why I could not make a whole lot of money selling research. I could not charge enough. When you sell services in this country, you really have to charge a lot of money. And the only way I feel that people get away with charging a lot of money are those that have good clubs and good unions, like the American Medical Association, the American Bar Association, the researcher's association — a big enough union that we could charge $300 an hour and really make a killing.

The free experts are out there. They are in two places: government and nonprofit organizations. I believe — and I am biased so do not trust me a lot of times, either — the federal government and state government are the largest sources of money, help and information in the world. I have made a career professing this, so again, I am very biased, but I believe it. Almost 35 percent of everything in our society is government. That is about what you pay in taxes. About a third of our income goes to government.

The government does not make stuff. It is not like General Motors, where it is making automobiles. It does not make products. It has two things: information and money. Information is in the form of paper or it is in the form of expertise. I actually went out and counted — in the federal government alone there are almost 700,000 experts, people like Charlie Porter, who are sitting there getting paid to study stuff, everything from broom handles to jelly beans.

Most people think of information in Washington as Pueblo, Colorado. I have made a living out of selling and using government information. I have done this almost my entire adult life, and I have never used Pueblo, Colorado. Pueblo, Colorado is just the tip of the iceberg.

Government Publishes Twice As Much As All Private Publishers

There is another organization in Washington called the National Technical Information Service. This is an organization that collects technical information from various agencies of the government. Every year, they publish 100,000 different titles. All of commercial publishing, all the New York publishers, every publisher in this country, all of them combined publish an average of 50,000 books a year. One little publisher in the government is publishing twice as much as all the private publishers in this country. That is what I mean about the power of information.

The government spends over $3 billion alone to do the census every 10 years, just to count people. We count a lot more than that, but $3 billion. Do you know how much $1 billion is? If you spent $1,000 every day since the day Christ was born, as of today, you would have not spent $1 billion. And we spend $3 billion on the census. We spend almost $2 trillion on the budget in the federal government. It is astounding. That is right, a third of everything.

A lot of people say, "Well, I want to ignore the government. I do not care what the government does as long as it stays away from me!" That is stupid. It is ignoring a third of our society. I live in Washington, DC. Hating the government is sort of like hating the freeways to get somewhere. You hate those freeways. But if I only have two days to get on the beach, am I going to take seven hours going on the small roads because I hate the freeways to get to the Jersey shore for the weekend? No. I am going to get on 95 because it is the fastest way I can use, even though I hate the freeways and they are boring.

That is the same way with the government. You may hate the government, but so many times it is going to be the fastest and best way to get anywhere. The other thing to remember is that you hear all the bad stuff about Washington because we have 6,000 reporters who are sitting at the National Press Building. Their job is to show you how the government screwed up today. You are going to look at the media and see stories about waste, fraud and abuse — "Hammers at the Defense Department for $50,000," or "Fraud at the Department of Housing and Urban Development," "Sex in the White House." Do you think sex is not going on anywhere else? You think that fraud is not going on anywhere else? No. It is just that we live in a society where all this is public.

But do not throw the baby out with the bathwater. There are a lot of tools that you could use that are there. Sure, all that stuff you read is true, but you can go to any organization and find the same. You say that everybody in the government is lazy and shiftless. In any big organization, most of the people are that way. Go to your bank or even the 7-Eleven. You get 20 percent of the people doing 80 percent of the work. That seems to be a basic law of physics in this country.

The government is so powerful. It has all these experts. Where else are you going to find these Charlie Porters or the grant money we are talking about to do anything? That is why the fat cats use this stuff. That is why it is not going to go away. I have been at this for 20-some years, through Republican administrations, Democrat administrations. Ronald Reagan said he was coming to town and he was going to cut the bureaucrats. The government grew under Ronald Reagan. That is the reality of it. It does not go away, no matter what they say. You have got to start learning how to use these things.

It does not solve every problem, but it is an important tool for you to start to use. If you could find an expert who spent their whole life studying a topic, they could tell you the one website to read. They could tell you the one book to read, or whatever it is. They could tell you what is going to be in the book or on the websites next month or next year because they are researching that today. That is what is fun, and what life is all about.

Nonprofit organizations are another great source of information. Say you have a new idea for a teacup, and want to start a teacup business. You can go to Washington and find your Charlie Porter for teacups, plus you can contact a nonprofit association that is an expert in this topic, the National Teacup Manufacturers Association. We are an extremely organized society.

How do you find these associations? There is a book in the library called *Gale Encyclopedia of Associations*. That is one book I wish I wrote. He has been selling that thing for 30 or 40 years. Every library and every big organization buys it because of the power that these associations have.

There is a Barbie doll association for people with Barbie dolls. If you want to invest in Barbie dolls, that is the place you should go first to find out about that investment. They are going to have some of the best information. It may be biased because they are pro-Barbie doll, but where else are you going to get it?

There is a bullfighting association. There is a green olive association. There is a bobsledding association. There is a hearing dog resource center association. Even a parents of murdered children association. Or how about this? A toilet seat manufacturers association. That is right. Remember my urinal screens? There is a urinal screen association, too.

I took a golf lesson this past week with my 16-year old kid who is a gorilla, about six foot two and about 185 pounds. He does not play that much, yet he hits a golf ball a mile.

After we had the lesson, the instructor told me he wanted to start a golf school and he did not know where to go. I said find the golf course manufacturers association, and learn what states and zip codes have the highest concentrations of new golf courses. Where are they building the most new golf courses in this country? That is where you probably want to start a school. You do not want to go where it is all mature market, where the schools and courses have been around forever. You want to go to a place where there are a lot of new players. They are the people who need lessons.

The Government Cured My Back Pain

Associations and the government are both web-oriented. But remember, a lot of the stuff on the web is going to be out of date. So don't stop after just checking their website. You still have to rely on people. I had back pain about 20-some years ago, when I first started this business. I thought the back pain originated from the funny things they made me sleep on in the Navy. I was in the Navy for three years, two months and nine days, but who was counting?

I was going to my doctor, and he was telling me things like, "Oh Lesko, your back pain is not so bad. Everybody has back pain. Come back when we can operate." I would go to another doctor and he would tell me the same thing. "Try this." I go back, "No." "Well, try that." And that is a clue when they say, "Try this." You come back — "Try that." They are guessing.

I took some of my own medicine. I called the National Institutes of Health, and in about three or four phone calls I found this bureaucrat, who specializes in back pain. Here was a guy at the National Institutes of Health literally handing out millions of dollars in back pain research. He was telling me the results of research that were not even published yet. This was about 20-some years ago, and he said that 99 percent of back pain is caused by the way we lead our life. The tension ties the muscles, so it is really a lack of flexibility. He said the YMCA had a back pain course that had a 75 percent cure rate.

So, I went to Georgetown Road in Bethesda to the YMCA. I took a back pain course, and in a couple of sessions my back pain went away. I never have had it again. I just keep doing those exercises. I know friends who later had surgery and are still not cured. You can go to NIH today and get a copy of a report that shows half of back pain surgery is not worthwhile.

If you are arguing with your doctor and he says, "Let's do surgery. We will fix up that back for you," what do you say? You do not know. He has heard everything bad you could say about this, and you cannot argue with him. It is impossible.

"Well, Doctor — do I really need that surgery?" They will say some gobbledygook you will not understand. But here is what you do. You go to the National Institutes of Health. You get this free study that shows half of back pain surgeries that were performed were not worthwhile. You bring that study to your doctor, and put it on her desk. You say, "Hey, how am I different from the people in the study that had the operation and it was not worthwhile?" You have to make that doctor stretch her imagination. That is the only way you are going to get the best.

I feel that you could get better health advice for free than you can from the doctor because doctors cannot keep up on all the new developments. The answers are changing every day. But in a few phone calls, you can find somebody who spent a lifetime studying that topic. They are not out there to make money. They are out there to find the information, and get it out to people.

Remember Charlie Porter? When I found him, the problem was not getting the information. The problem was getting out of his office. You could do that for anything.

Get Better Legal Help Than A Lawyer

Legal problems are another thing. You can look to the government to solve legal problems, too. We live in the biggest democracy in the world, right? And most of us feel that we cannot get any satisfaction because we cannot hire some high-priced lawyer. So, we walk around humble and hoping that nobody will get angry because we cannot hire an attorney to fight for us, right? Nonsense. We should all have access to legal help, and you can. If anybody messes you over in this country, you can get free legal help that is better than anything else you could find.

If you have a problem where your insurance company does not pay a claim, you could hire your attorney, your brother-in-law's attorney or whatever, and he will fight for you. You are going to be fighting the attorneys of the insurance company. Their attorneys do this day in and day out. They know all the loopholes. They know all the answers to any question you are going to ask. You cannot fight that way. All you are going to do is run up an attorney bill.

Here is what I think is better. The government has an office that will fight that insurance company for you. It is at your state capital, and called the Insurance Commissioner's Office. Every state capital regulates all the insurance companies doing business in their state. Their job is to investigate any complaint that you as a consumer have with that insurance company. What is neat about this is that they have to investigate even if you are wrong.

My kid had his car towed away from a department store because he parked there and he went away. It cost him $100 to get his car. He went to the government who came out, investigated the store, went over and talked to the guy, and got my kid's money back. Nobody knew it was my kid. He was 16 years old and was able to accomplish it. Now that is power.

I was so angry at an airline a couple of years ago because it made me late for my kid's soccer game. It was half my fault, but you know how you just want to blow off steam? So I wrote a letter to the government, complaining about the airline. I sent a copy to the airline. I got a $300 check in the mail from the airline as a peace offering. Remember, when the government calls the insurance company and complains, the government can put the insurance company out of business. If it is you and your lawyer, the worst they have to lose is to pay your claim eventually. But if they lose the argument with the government, the government can put them out of business. They have too much to lose to fight the government. It is cheaper for them to pay you off than to argue.

It is the same with me. I sell books in the mail. If our customer service screws up and you contact the U.S. Postal Service about me, I will get a letter from a postal inspector. I will call you personally, and will say, "Keep the books." I do not want to mess with the postal inspector.

When your dry cleaner screws up your question mark suit, or you bring in a sweater and when you bring it home it is the size of a potholder, that dry cleaner is regulated. You do not even have to call the government. You can just go back to the dry cleaner and say, "Hey, I am going to report you to the state licensing office." That small business dry cleaner could lose all his business, and he does not want that to happen. He will make amends, and do what you want.

The Government Has Salami Police

Think about your delicatessen. Do you know the government has salami police? If you go into a delicatessen, buy a pound of salami, bring it home and feel it is a little light, like maybe the deli owner had his thumb on the scale, you can call the Office of Weights and Measures in your state capital. Out come the salami police! They can investigate because you cannot mess with the scales.

The same thing can happen when you pump gas at a gas station. One day it costs you $10 to fill up, and the next day it costs you $15. Maybe they are messing with the pump. That is illegal.

You buy a cord of wood and maybe you do not know what a cord is. Later you find out you got cheated. They will come out and find that person who sold you that wood. You have got to know your rights. Everyone is regulated. When anybody messes you over — your bank, your insurance company, your real estate broker, your doctor, you can get the power back. You can find the office that regulates them, and they will investigate. You do not have to hire attorneys, as you can get it better for free.

I had a guy who owed me some money in a business deal down in Tennessee and he was not paying. So, what I did was call the state Attorney General's Office in Tennessee, and they contacted the business. This small business got a letter from the state Attorney General's Office. "What did you do to this guy in Maryland?" They rolled over and gave me the money. They do not want to mess with the Attorney General, as they can put them out of business. That is the power we all have as citizens of this country.

Another source that we use for information is our neighbors, or our friends. To me, that is so ridiculous. I live in a community that is really in the shadow of the National Institutes of Health. This is where the big research happens in the medical field.

I remember being at a party in my neighborhood, and this one neighbor asked the other neighbor, "Harry, I have hemorrhoids and I am thinking about having an operation. What did you do for your operation?" There he is, asking Harry for advice on his hemorrhoids when he could make a couple of calls and talk to an expert at the National Institutes of Health who spent the last 15 years of his life just studying hemorrhoid operations! You can find out what is good and bad about any hemorrhoid operation from that expert.

Why trust Harry? We have this feeling and maybe it is just a comfort level because somebody else went through it. How much research did Harry really do? You can get better information than Harry, and better information than your doctor.

You can get better legal help than from your lawyer. Maybe somebody made a pass at you at the Christmas party and you are a woman — or you are a guy, whatever. You are wondering if it is sexual harassment or not. What do you do? Do you hire an attorney at $200 an hour to see if it was sexual harassment? No. You can call an 800-number in the government and talk to somebody who wrote the sexual harassment laws. We have an office in the government and all they do is enforce it. If you have a case, they come out and sue the people for you.

I sell on Home Shopping, and one of the lawyers down at Home Shopping was telling me what I could or could not say because the Federal Trade Commission will yell at me. I just called the Federal Trade Commission and talked to the expert who writes these laws. I went back to Home Shopping and said, "Hey, you are full of bubkas. Here is what the Federal Trade Commission says, right from the horse's mouth." You can get better information than anybody in this country. You can get it for free, and it is available to you for the price of a phone call.

How You Treat People Determines Your Success

The problem is it takes a little effort to get it. Besides the web, books, the media, and all these other sources we mentioned, when you start trying to get experts, it is different. You have to learn how to think a little bit differently. The key to getting that kind of help is how you treat those people once you get them on the phone.

This is really the soul of what I am about, I think — how to treat people, how to get this information, how to use all the information sources in our society, and basically how to use people. That is one tool of technology we all know how to use. We all like people, and I think in the information explosion, they are even going to be more important. As you get more and more information, you have to know how to be able to go out and find the people who read all that kind of nonsense, who know what is good and bad about it, know the one website that is of value, know the one book that is going to have your answer. You do not have time to read a million citations on the web. You do not have time to read the 200 books that are written on that subject, because time is becoming very valuable. That is why how you treat people on the telephone, and these experts is an important tool for your survival in an information society, whether it is finding help, money, information or anything you need.

I developed what is called a "seven phone call rule." If you start looking for stuff using the phone, maybe you will find somebody who may be of help. If you are looking for grant money, they will send you one place. If it is not there, they will send you over to another. If it is not there, five calls later you may be back to the same person where you started. You get this bureaucratic runaround no matter what it is.
That is going to happen.

1) *Introduce Yourself Cheerfully:*
You are finally going to get to the person who can help you after an average of seven phone calls. That is my theory. It takes you an average of seven phone calls to find whatever it is you want in this country. It may take 12, or maybe you can do it in one or two with some of my books, but an average of seven phone calls is what it takes.

What happens is that your pressure level builds because you get aggravated that you are not getting what you need and people could not help you. By the time you really get to the person who can help you, you are angry because you have been getting the bureaucratic runaround. You have been on hold and on voice mail for days. This person picks up the phone that can really help you, and what is in the back of your head is all this bad stuff that has happened to you over the last hour or two on the phone. So, that person picks up the phone and you start yelling, "Now listen, you lazy, shiftless bureaucrat. You better help me because my tax dollars pay your salary." Even if you do not say that in those words, it may come out that way. And when it does, you are not going to be the highlight of anybody's day.

Most of these free experts are on the government payroll or in nonprofit organizations, and you are not paying them. So, if you are not paying them, their salary does not depend on how well they help you. They should help because we live in their society where we are trying to help each other, but it really does not work that way. So, you have got to use your personality to make them want to help you. The only thing you have is your personality because you are not going to send them a check or anything else.

In them, in all of us, is the need to want to help somebody else. But again, remember when I told you earlier how giving is very selfish and the problem is trying to find some deserving person? You have got to be this deserving person that they want to help. You are not going to do that by yelling and screaming the first words out of your mouth. The first things out of your mouth are so important. That sets the mood for the whole thing, so you have to be cheerful and nice so that they want to relax, sit back and talk to you.

If you do not create that feeling, remember they could hang up right after you say hello, and just not answer the phone after that. They will get paid the same, whether they answer the phone or not, or if they stay with you for a half hour on the phone. So, that is what you have to do. Somehow you, your personality and voice, have to make them want to spend time with you. You do that by carefully choosing your first words. Be very cheerful in the way you introduce yourself. Also, you have to be open and candid. You do not want to be sneaky. "You do not need to know who I am. I just need to know stuff." If you do not know what you need, say, "I don't know." Or, "My boss is trying to get something." Or, "I am really just trying to find money to do a certain thing. What kinds of programs do you have? I really know nothing about this."

2) *Be Open and Candid:*

Do not pretend that you are something you are not. You have to be open and candid about who you are and what you are doing. You want them to be open with you, and to tell you all about what is going on in their office, what kind of resources they have or what kind of money programs exist. Again, you have to create that feeling of openness by being candid.

3) *Be Optimistic:*

You have to believe in your mind that their office has the help or money you need. If you are not optimistic, and say, "You do not have any money for somebody who wants to open a golf course, do you? You do not have that kind of money, do you?" The easiest thing for them to do is say no. You are happy if they say no because you were looking for the "no" answer. Your implication and the way you phrased the question, they thought you were looking for a no, so they can please you by saying no. You go away, the problem goes away, and you are happy because you got what you expected.

But if you call and say, "Hey listen, I understand you may have this stuff. Are you sure you do not have it around here somewhere?" You have got to make these people stretch their minds, and that is important. Maybe it is across the hall, or maybe it is somewhere else. You have to be optimistic. Your optimism will make them stretch. You can make them think, "Where else can it be if it is not in my area? Maybe it is somewhere else. I have to find out about it for this person on the phone." That is what your optimism can do to these people.

4) *Be Humble and Courteous:*

That is obvious. You do not want to call and say, "I have been looking around for money for a long time now, and I know it is not around but I just want to make sure that you do not have any hiding somewhere." Nobody will want to talk to you. But if you portray yourself as in need of help, are polite, humble and courteous, that is important. Again, you create the atmosphere where they want to help you.

5) *Be Concise:*

Respect people's time. You want to be quick and to the point about what you are seeking. Showing respect for others is an important trait.

6) *Be Conversational:*

In addition to being concise, you want to talk about some other things. If you find the person is a baseball fan, you can talk about baseball. If you find out anything, like they are a Republican, you can mention being anxious for the Republicans to get the Senate back, or something like that. It is important because the more you talk about yourself or other things, the more you show your human side, and the more you show your human side, the harder it is for that person to flunk you. The person has the ability to pass or fail you in this test of getting money or information.

I do not know if you remember when you were in school. Actually, when I taught school, I saw it better. When I was a professor at college, I would have people come and talk to me after class. The smart kids really would not talk about the work; I taught computer science. They would sit in my office and show me pictures of their dog or their mother, and show their personal side. I would get to know them more as an individual. Then when we had the test, it was harder to flunk the person who I knew about their dog, their parents, and their relatives. The person I did not know in class and who had a failing grade made it so easy for me to give them an F.

It is the same way with getting information. Being conversational and talking about other things is important. Also, be complimentary. You do not want to say, "You have got a lousy job. You must be miserable. You do not really know much." If you call and say, "Somebody told me that you are the best person to talk to about how to get money to build a farm house," or something like that, or how to get money to travel overseas. We love to hear that we have the answers. When people say that to me, it goes to my head, and I am a nicer person. It is a natural thing.

7) *Return a Favor:*

If somebody gives you something nice, try to return the favor. I sent free books to a lot of sources that helped me. If you do not return the favor, at least send a thank you note to somebody who helps you. It takes you a minute, and it does not have to be in your word processor or your computer, but just a little handwritten note. These handwritten notes go a lot further in our professional life now than the computer ones.

Reader's Digest sends me letters with the name of my dog on it, and they are just computer-generated letters. But a handwritten note goes a long way. So, how you care for these people that can help you on the phone is really the key to your success at getting information. And it is important because all these information pools we talked about in society all have their value, and you have to know when to use and not use any of them, whether it is the computer, the library, the media, the experts, the government, nonprofit organizations, your friends and the telephone. To me, one of the most important tools we have in our society for coping with this information explosion is the telephone, so do not forget to use the phone!

Other Grants And Freebies

You have been reading about how to get grants for your house, your business and your education. But there are other kinds of money out there. They are not particularly grants sometimes. They call them other things — maybe direct payments, financial help or even services that are worth more than the amount in grants that you could get.

These services and other things are probably even more valuable than the grant money because they are going to solve real problems in your life. The reason you are probably looking for a grant is because you are a little tight for money. I can show you how to get extra money by not paying for things you can get for free.

The first subject is healthcare. Everybody is going to have healthcare problems at some time in their life, and you should not only be thinking of yourself when you think about these programs.

This Book Is Out Of Date

And by the way, remember that everything gets out of date. If I give you a phone number, and you call and get some Chinese laundry, do not worry about it. The organization is still there. It is probably called something else or moved across the street. You may have to do a little work by contacting a government operator or the local information operator. Do not give up, as the program is still there.

These are all very valuable services. I think one of the important things in society is that we are really here to help other people, too. I am going to go over 20 or 30 items that you could really use, either for yourself, someone in your family, or for someone on your street. If you do not need these items right away, you will soon. We are all taking care of aging parents or grandparents, or little kids. Tonight you can begin telling others about the freebies that I am going to show you now.

What gives me the most pleasure in life is that I am able to give somebody a phone number, just a phone number, that they can call to solve a problem. They will get a service for free that would have cost them thousands of dollars. Now they will not have to go and look for a $1,000 or a $2,000 grant, because now they have got it for free, or get a problem solved they never thought could be solved. If you have a question, I will give you a phone number. I love telling people where to go!

Free Prescription Drugs

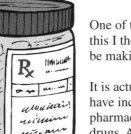

One of the greatest things I have found in healthcare is free prescription drugs. When I found this I thought they would put me on the cover of *TIME* magazine. Do you realize you could be making $40,000 or more in this country and get your prescription drugs for free?

It is actually run through the pharmaceutical companies. Every program is different. Some have income requirements and some have no income requirements, like Merck, the big pharmaceutical company. They have no income requirements at all to get free prescription drugs. All you have to say is you are having trouble paying for your prescription drug. And truthfully, most middle class people have trouble paying for prescriptions. If you get a prescription now, it could be $100 or $200 a month. You could easily be spending $1,000 a year on some medication.

Medicare does not cover prescription drugs for seniors, so they are getting hit hardest. That is why all the politicians are saying, "We are going to start a program for seniors." Well, you do not have to wait that long. You can find out about it now. That is why it is a sin that the politicians and the media show these war stories about seniors eating dog food because they cannot pay for the prescription drugs. It perpetuates the myth that people cannot help themselves, but that is false. I will show you whom to call.

You can call the Pharmaceutical Research and Manufacturers of America at 1-800-PMA-INFO. They will send you a list of all the pharmaceutical companies that run these programs. Or, if you are online (which is how they prefer you view it) you can go to {www.phrma.org} and find the programs there. All you have to do is contact the manufacturer of the drug, tell them your circumstances, ask them about the requirements, and what usually happens is that you have to take a form to your doctor to sign. Your doctor has to sign this because they want to be friends with the doctor, not you. It is the doctor that prescribes the drugs. The doctor signs it and usually in two or three weeks you get the drugs sent to your doctor, and it is free.

I get wonderful phone calls from people all over saying, "Lesko, I took your advice and called. Sure, there is a little bit of paperwork, but now I am saving $100 a month, $200 a month, $300 a month, or thousands of dollars a year." It is not only for you, so look at it for everyone in your household. You have got your kids, your smoking patch, or Prozac. But you have to know about the program to take advantage of it. Put that phone number or put that website on the side and look into it for yourself and everybody else.

Free Healthcare For Kids

Here is free healthcare for kids. We have a program all around the country now that is called the CHIP program. You can be making $37,700 a year and get free healthcare for your children. Maybe you are making $100,000 and do not need this, but you know somebody else that probably cannot afford healthcare. Make sure they know about this program. This could be worth at least $5,000 a year for them or you, and this is why people do not get healthcare in this country. It is too expensive.

To find out about CHIP, just call up your State Department of Health in your state capital. Say you live in Pennsylvania. You call up Harrisburg and ask for the state capital operator. The area code in Harrisburg is 717. So, you find the area code; call 717 and the information operator, 555-1212. You ask for the state capital operator. They will give you another number to call. You call that number and say, "Hey, I want to talk to the information center at the State Department of Health for the state of Pennsylvania," or wherever you live. Then you call and say, "Hey, I want to know about the healthcare program for kids." You can also call toll-free 877-KIDS-NOW or check it out online at {www.insurekidsnow.gov}.

If they do not know about the program, then contact your local congressman's or senator's office. They are the only ones in the system that have a motive to work for you. All the bureaucrats you are going to call get the same paycheck whether they work for you or not, whether they find you the stuff you need or not. But the congressman wants your vote. That is how they get paid. If they get more votes than anybody else, then they keep getting their paycheck. They will do that little favor for you because they know that their phone calls go on different colored pieces of paper.

When they call the government, it is different than you calling the government because they are the ones, the congressmen and senators, who give money to the bureaucrats to run their agencies. That is why these bureaucrats treat congressmen better than you or me.

$6,000 For A Senior or Disabled

Here is another thing that people do not know. Seniors or the disabled can get an extra $6,000 spending money. That is called Supplemental Security Income. Find out if you are eligible, but there is an income limit. Many seniors now are living on very little income. Their house is paid off. They are living on Social Security and maybe a little extra, and a lot of these things are not asset-based. You can call the Social Security Hot Line at 800-772-1213 and ask about Supplemental Security Income (SSI).

You are going to sit on hold, of course. If you call Microsoft, you are going to sit on hold forever. It is like that for everything. Nobody does customer service well. So, the government is not doing it well. I just called Microsoft, and was on hold for 30 minutes. They want to charge me $35 an hour, or $35 a problem, to solve a problem I have with their software. It is bizarre. You have got learn how to use the system. So, that is an extra $6,000 for seniors and people with disabilities.

Many Seniors Can Get $1,000 Now

Here is another freebie that seniors and people with disabilities do not even know exists. I have seen studies that show that three million people are eligible for this money and are not applying for it. It is worth over $1,000 a year. If you have seniors in your family, you could get this money for them. A lot of seniors are afraid of the system. They are not used to voice mail or how to deal with bureaucracies. So take a half hour out of your life, or an hour, whatever it takes, to get on the phone and find that program. It is part of Medicare.

The Social Security seniors are deducted a premium from their check to pay for Medicare Part B. At certain incomes, they do not have to have that deduction, and the government will repay that money to them. It is worth $1,000 a year. So, if you have a senior living on a fixed income of $12,000-$15,000 a year, another $1,000 is serious money and you could get it for them. It is called the Qualified Medicare Beneficiaries Plan. To find out how to get this, call the Medicare Hot Line at 800-MEDICARE, or {www.medicare.gov}. What you are looking for is their free publication that describes these programs — "Guide to Health Insurance for People with Medicare." It shows how to get that deduction for Medicare Part B back for cash in your pocket.

The programs we just talked about can be easily worth $5,000 to $10,000 a year to your family. And I only talked about four items.

$2,500 To Adopt A Child

Or how about this — did you know you could get grants for adoptions? I know so many aging yuppies that are having trouble having kids so they look at adoption. Look for the grants for adoptions. You can get up to $2,500 or more to help you finance an adoption.

A good place to begin your search is with a couple of organizations. One is the National Adoption Information Clearinghouse and they are in Washington, DC. They will help you find the information. Also, use this clearinghouse for any kind of help you need for the adoption process, because the process is not easy. This information could be valuable to you or to someone you know who is considering adoption. That is the goal of my work. Not only do I educate somebody about something, but then they can educate somebody else. That is how we get more leverage on this information and more people get helped in society.

Two other organizations besides the National Adoption Information Clearinghouse are the National Adoption Center in Philadelphia and the National Council for Adoption in Washington DC. Call the information operator, get the phone numbers on these organizations, and call them. You can surf for them on the web and you will probably find the three organizations.

$6,000 Worth Of Free Speech Therapy

Here is a great program for anybody who has young kids in the house before they enter school. If they are having trouble with their speech, you can get up to $6,000 worth of free speech therapy, no matter what income level you are. You could be a millionaire and if your child is having trouble enunciating or you are concerned about their speech patterns, help is available. You need to go to your local school system, and tell them about it. Actually it starts for kids ages two or three years old. It is a wonderful service, but you have got to know about it to take advantage of it.

Like everything in life, people are not going to come over and bang you on the head to tell you about this stuff. You have got to go and find it for yourself. And even the experts won't know it exists. We interviewed doctors all over the country, and ninety-four percent of them did not even now about the free prescription drug program. That is why you cannot even trust the experts.

If your local school board does not know about it, call your congressman's office and tell them to contact the Office of Special Education Programs at the U.S. Department of Education. They will help you.

Free Alcohol And Drug Treatment

Here is an interesting item — free alcohol and drug treatment. There are so many substance abusers in this country now — alcohol and drugs, or other kinds of substances. I do not know the jargon that well, but I do know there is free treatment available. The free treatment is not always easy to find because there is a complex array of places that offer free treatment. But there is a lot of free treatment at the county level through nonprofit organizations, and you may even have to go to another state or another locality to find this kind of help. But it is out there. It may just take a little effort.

There are two organizations that will help you find the free treatment. Do not forget that this is another service that you can use to help someone else. The National Drug and Treatment Routing Service is a special clearinghouse to help you find treatment. The phone number is 1-800-662-HELP. The clearinghouse is part of the National Institutes of Health and their website is {www.niaaa.nih.gov}.

The National Clearinghouse for Alcohol and Drug Abuse is another organization that can help. What is so neat about this country is that not only are there people to help you and give you things for free, but there are other people like this Clearinghouse that help you find the people giving you things for free. The number is 800-729-6686, and their website is {www.health.org}. This is for free alcohol and drug treatment. It could easily cost $5,000-$10,000 for something like that.

See what I mean? Although you may not call them grants, all these free services like free prescription drugs, may be like having an extra $5,000 in your pocket. This is better than a grant.

Free Wheelchairs

How about free wheelchairs? Do you know somebody who needs a wheelchair? The American Cancer Society offers free wheelchairs, as well as the Easter Seals. Look in the phone book for the American Cancer Society and Easter Seals.

Free Mammograms

Free mammogram service is a wonderful program from the Centers for Disease Control out of Atlanta. The program is set up all over the country. Women 40 or 50 years old or more and making $40,000 can get free mammograms, free breast cancer treatment, and free cervical cancer treatment in every state of the country. You can call this number at the Centers for Disease Control, Division of Cancer Prevention: 770-488-4751. The program is also run through your state capital. You can call your state capital operator as I told you earlier, and ask for the State Department of Health. They should know about it. But again, remember that one bureaucrat does not know everything. If you get stuck, call the number above for the Centers for Disease Control.

Other places, such as the American Cancer Society or your local YMCA offer programs. You can also call the National Cancer Institute for any cancer problem. Their number is, 800-4-CANCER. They are a wonderful clearinghouse and counseling service. I helped a friend who had breast cancer. When she called the hotline they were able to identify what stage of breast cancer she really had, and helped her identify the latest procedures for curing that stage of breast cancer. They also told her who were the best doctors in the area to perform that kind of procedure.

When you have a health problem, it is information that gives you the power. Usually the fear we have with health is the fear of the unknown. We may be sitting there with cancer or with whatever ailment we have, and do not know if we are going to die right now or live for 50 more years. We do not know what our chances are and we do not even know if the doctor really knows.

There is a way to get better information than your doctor. Earlier we talked about that and living in the information society. With 1-800-4-CANCER, you can begin the search to get the best information on any aspect of cancer, including free videos on the effects of chemotherapy. As we are living longer, we are going to have more of these kinds of problems in our life and in the lives of our loved ones.

Free Hospital Care

How about free hospital care? So many people go to the hospital and think they can pay for it. They find out later that the insurance company is not going to pay. There are hospitals around the country that have to treat you for free, whether or not you can pay the bill. This is not just emergency rooms, but this is the hospital itself. These are hospitals that got money under a program called the Hill Burton Act. Because they got this government money, they made a promise that they will treat a certain amount of people for free. To find the Hill Burton hospitals in your area call 800-638-0742, and they will give you a listing of hospitals.

This program also includes long-term care facilities. If Grandma wants to go to a nursing home and you know Medicaid will not pay for it because she makes too much or has too much in assets, then check out Hill-Burton. This program is concerned more with a person's income rather than their assets. A lot of elderly do not make a lot of money day by day in income, but they have a lot of assets. So, you may be covered there.

By the way, most hospitals have other kinds of programs if they are not part of Hill Burton. At Johns Hopkins, this woman really had a serious cancer problem and her healthcare did not cover it. She had all these bills at Johns Hopkins, and they were sending out torpedoes from Detroit to try to get the money from this poor lady. I started making some calls for her.

See, people in need do not have the strength to fight for themselves. In the healthcare situation, you have to help other people when they have a problem. You have to sometimes be advocates for other people in the system.

I called the social workers over there and explained the problem, and they could not help. I called all the places I knew, and then I just started calling accounting at Johns Hopkins Hospital up in Baltimore, Maryland. I found this little accountant who found a program to pay this woman's bill. It was $8,000 or $9,000. I talked to her doctor up there; I talked to everybody. No one was helpful until I called deep enough in that bureaucracy at Johns Hopkins to get her bill covered, and it just took a phone call.

That is the power we have in our society. You do not have to take everything at face value. You have the power to change things. You have the power to change no to yes. You do, but it takes perseverance. I do not think no means no in our society any more, except in sexual harassment. It seems like in everything else, there are ways to change that no to a yes. I asked 50 people at Johns Hopkins, how can this woman not pay her bill? Oh, no, no, no! So, I found this little accountant who was able to change it to a yes, and you can do that, too, for other people.

Free Immunizations For Your Kids

How about free immunizations for your kids? This could be worth a couple of hundred bucks. Every kid needs to be protected from chickenpox, polio, diphtheria, mumps, whooping cough, German measles, tetanus, spinal meningitis, and Hepatitis-B. Just call the National Immunization Hot Line, 800-232-2522. Maybe you do not have a kid now, but you will run into somebody with a kid. Then you can say, "Hey, take this number for next time your kid needs an immunization shot." It is part of the Centers for Disease Control and their website is {www.cdc.gov/nip}.

50% Discount On Airfare

How about this? Do you know you can get 50 percent off your airfare if you are going to visit a sick relative? When you call for a reservation and you have got to go see somebody who is sick, ask about bereavement and compassion fares. Call your airline of choice or find out how many airlines are going to your place that your sick friend or relative is. Then call each one of them and ask them about the bereavement and compassion fares. See how low you can go, because they can give you those deals of up to 50 percent discount.

So many people think, "Oh, we just want to solve the problem, so we are getting on the next plane to go and help somebody." No — find out about the discount fares to visit a sick relative. That is a nice little freebie to have.

Insurance Coverage For Workers With A Disability

And do not forget that there is a new law. If you know somebody who has a disability and they are working with their disability, there is a law where they can get cheap health coverage under Medicaid. A 1997 law permits that. Here is a website to find out about it. It is called {www.bazelon.org}. The law is something your local state Department of Health should know.

Healthcare is outrageous. It is funny that so much of us live our life based upon our healthcare coverage. "I cannot take that job because it does not have healthcare." We are not using the best talents or the people in our society because they are making decisions based on if they get healthcare or not. I do not think that is right, but that is another issue.

Free Taxis For Grandma

How about a taxi to get Mom to the doctor? If you are working and Mom calls and says, "I have a doctor's appointment today. Can you drive me to the doctor and back?" "Oh Mom, I can't. I've got meetings. My boss won't let me off to do that." What do you do? You can get a free taxi ride for Mom to go back and forth to the doctor. How do you find out about it? Again, you cannot look in the phone book under "Free Taxi." It is never going to be there. They are going to have all the four taxis that charge a lot of money.

Hotline To Help Your Grandparents

Call the Elder Care Hot Line. The government has set up as part of the Department of Health and Human Services an 800-number to help you with any kind of problem that you have with a senior, either a senior that is living near you or a senior who is living in another state. It is wonderful.

My mom wanted some legal advice. She lives in Florida and I called the Elder Care Hot Line. They hooked me up with somebody in Florida who gave her free legal help. She made an appointment, and in two days, she walked in and talked to this attorney for free about a legal problem. I could not get my attorney to act that fast, and she got it for free. The Elder Care Hotline is at 800-677-1116. Keep that number handy.

Nursing Home Police

If mom is in a nursing home in Arizona, and you talk to her and find she is worried that they are not treating her well, then you can take some action. You call that hot line and find out who will come out and investigate Mom in her nursing home. The nursing home is regulated and you have the right to make sure that they are doing everything on the up and up. The government will send somebody out to make sure they are treating Mom right. That is the power you have, even though you are not in Arizona.

Free Health Insurance Counseling

You can find out about how to get free health insurance counseling. Health insurance is so complicated for seniors or for anybody, but now they have set up a special counseling service for seniors to help them choose the best healthcare. It is a free service.

You can hire a consultant and spend $100 an hour, or call an agent, and talk to someone who is biased. Or you can get the best experts in the world to help you make that kind of decision and get it for free. All these services are worth hundreds, thousands of dollars. They are better than money, because even if you got a grant for $5,000, you would not know about the free health insurance counseling, and would spend maybe $500 asking some expert and not get the best information. The government programs are not in business to sell you something, but they are in business to help you solve that problem.

$20,000 To Buy A Van Or Talking Computer

Do you know somebody who has a disability? There is money available to help them buy a van or a talking computer. More importantly, they also have free services that will send somebody to their house to evaluate what kind of new technology they could use to make their life better because of the disability. Maybe they do not walk as well any more, or are losing their eyesight.

Well, there is so much technology out there to help people with disabilities, and the government has set up an office called the Rehabilitation Engineering and Assistive Technology to help you find out what technology will help you live a better life. These are free consultants to help you. In addition a lot of states also have money, like low-interest loans and grant money, to help you buy this technology to make your life better. Some states even offer free loaner equipment.

You can find this two ways. The phone number in Virginia for the Rehabilitation Engineering & Assistive Technology is 703-524-6686, and the website is {www.resna.org}. They will direct you to your local office, which is usually in your state capital. They will work with you to find what you need.

Discounts On Dental Bills

A lot of people are looking for an inexpensive way to get braces for their kids. Kids, seniors and others are also looking for a better way that they can afford. There are free dental services out there, too. Again, this could save you hundreds or even thousands of dollars. The services vary from location to location. Some are from the state Department of Health. Some are from local dental societies or from dental schools in the area. I used to go to the dental school at Georgetown University to get my teeth fixed. It was a fraction of what it would cost if I went to a private dentist. So, contact your local state Department of Health and start looking.

All this may take a little effort, but who cares if it takes 20 minutes on the phone if you are going to save $1,000 on a dental bill? It is going to take effort, but look at the money you save. Look at the help that is out there. That is what I mean when I say that a lot of this stuff is better than grants. If you are going to spend a couple of days trying to get a grant for $1,000 so you can have dental care, instead spend 20 minutes on the phone and try to find out how to get that dental care for free.

Emergency Rooms Have To Care For You

Also, remember if the emergency room is open, they have to care for you, whether you can afford to pay or not. You are legally responsible for the money, but they have to take care of you and not worry about the bill until after you are okay. Remember that. And if they do not treat you well, you can contact the U.S. government's Centers for Medicare and Medicaid Services, and say you want them investigated.

That is how you get power in the system. If they say, "We can't treat you because you don't have insurance and we're afraid you won't pay," say, "I'm going to report you." Or, you do not have to be that mean about it. You can just say, "Well, I do not think you are treating me fairly, and I am going to contact the Centers for Medicare and Medicaid Services."

The hospitals are afraid of the Centers for Medicare and Medicaid Services. That is where they get all their Medicaid and Medicare money, and most hospitals are living off of government programs. The government pays for half the healthcare in this country. That is why it is strange when people say, "We can't have government financed healthcare," since half of it is financed already.

Free Care By The Best Doctors In The World

You can get healthcare by the best doctors in the world for free. Sam Donaldson, a gazillionaire, had his prostate surgery done for free from the government. Isn't that amazing? One of the richest people in our society has cancer and says, "Where should I get my cancer surgery done? I will go to the government and get it for free." And he did.

The average person would never think of that. The average person does not know about the program. The government gives $18 billion to doctors all over the country to treat conditions for free. Sam knew about it. Actually, I think he has beehives on his ranch out in Oklahoma or Texas, and he gets government money for his beehives. That's another government program.

Tom Brokaw of NBC News, even got money from the government to buy a radio station in North Dakota. See, the rich people use this stuff. But I think that there are more deserving people out there who should get this free cancer treatment rather than Sam Donaldson. But Sam knows about the program and got on the list. How do you find out about the program? It is done in Washington and all around the country.

So, there are a couple of places to look. One is that you can contact the Clinical Center, which is part of the National Institutes of Health. They have hundreds of programs currently underway. So, if they are studying your condition, you can be treated for free because they need you. Some people say you are like a guinea pig, but again, it is the best doctors in the world, and in all medicine. Everybody is guessing, and here you get the best and the latest technology.

To find out about the program call 800-411-1222. That is the Clinical Center, and you can ask about their clinical trials. What are they studying? Maybe you have headaches and they are studying the best treatments for your type of headaches.

I had a missing tooth and they were studying dental implants. I talked myself out of getting a free dental implant though, when I talked about it on *Larry King* and the office got 10,000 calls. They took me off the list.

Clinical trials are occurring all across the United States, not just at NIH. To keep track of them, there is a database where they can search to see who is doing research on your condition. It is called the Computer Retrieval and Information on Scientific Projects, and is from the Office of Reports and Analysis. They have a long website at NIH. It is {http://www-commons.cit.nih.gov/crisp}. They can run a database for you about who in the country is doing research.

To tell you the truth, the last time I talked with the people there, they were not the nicest people in the world. So, you may have to use your personality to get them to like you. But you do have a right to it, so hang in there. If they are mean to you, then call your congressman's office and tell them to call. Make sure they get this for you.

$5 (Or Free) For STD Tests

Here is something you may or may not be interested in. It is $5 for STD tests. These are sexually transmitted diseases. There is an STD Hot Line and they will show you where to get tested. If you are worried about any of this stuff with the AIDS crisis, then call, as they are very confidential and local. For only $5, there is no excuse. The hotline is 800-227-8922.

Free Research On Any Health Topic

How about free health information? As I mentioned earlier, I believe you can get free health information on any topic that is better than your doctor. Remember I found the expert at NIH, spending the last 13 years of his life studying back problems and was able to tell me results of research that was not even published yet.

Here are a couple of places to start to find this information. These are people who will do the research for you to find out who specializes in your condition or treatment. It is free research on any health topic. The first one is the National Health Information Center at 800-336-4797, or on the web at {www.health.gov/nhic}.

The government has one just for women now called the Women's National Health Information Center. It is part of the Centers for Disease Control and can be reached at 800-994-WOMAN or on the web at {www.4women.gov}. And also the National Institutes of Health has an information clearinghouse that will put you in contact with all of their information clearinghouses. NIH has information clearinghouses on everything they are studying, whether it is arthritis, cancer, bone diseases, headaches or anything. You can call their main number and they will put you through to the information clearinghouse. And remember, information clearinghouses are wonderful because they will do the research for you. They will find out who in our society specializes in the information that you want. It is like having your own librarian. Their number is 301-496-4000, and on the web at {www.nih.gov}.

Fight Your Insurance Company For Free

Also, you should be aware of how to fight the healthcare system. There are people out there who will fight for you if your insurance company does not pay a claim. Are you going to hire an attorney to fight that insurance company? Their attorneys are bigger than your attorney, and who knows what is going to happen. You are going to wind up with a big attorney bill.

Instead, you can call your state Insurance Commissioner's office and they will fight that health insurance company for you. I use it all the time. When a health insurance company says, "We are not going to cover you, Lesko," I just tell them, "You are not treating me fair and I am going to call the insurance commissioner." The office is located in your state capital, and again you can find this by contacting your state capital operator. They will investigate your insurance company. You can even be wrong, but they still have to investigate. So, use these to your heart's content. That is why they are there, and they are a way to get power back in the system. You do not have to hire an attorney.

Insurance companies are more afraid of the Insurance Commissioner than they are of you or your attorney. Remember, the worst they lose in arguing with your attorney is that they have to pay your claim. But when they argue with the Insurance Commissioner, the worst they lose is all their business, because the Insurance Commissioner could say, "Okay, you are a bad guy and we will not let you do business in our state." They do not want to mess with it.

Anytime you have a problem, try to find an advocacy group because they have learned the system and how best to fight it. It is like a lawyer who learns the system and fights the same cases over and over. They know the buttons to push, the way to make things happen. And these advocacy groups are usually free to you.

50% Discount On Your Phone Bill

Another incredible thing is that you can get a 50 percent discount on your phone bill. Are you having trouble paying your phone bill? The Federal Communications Commission is making phone companies give you a 50% discount. But the phone company is never going to say, "Hey, here is how to pay only half the price." They are not going to tell you that, so you need to find out for yourself.

Call your phone company and ask them about programs called Link Up America or Life Line program. There are two different programs from the Federal Communications Commission. If they do not know about the programs, find the Federal Communications Commission and ask them. Or again, just call your congressman and ask them to find out about it for you.

$7,000 Grant To Fix Up Your Home

Another program for seniors is that they can get $1,000 to $7,000 to fix up their home. The USDA, the U.S. Department of Agriculture, runs this program. We talked about that earlier. Another program is through Community Connections. For more information about most housing programs, call 800-998-9999.

Go To College For Free At 55

Do you realize that if you are 55 or older you can go back to school for free or next to nothing? Get Grandpa off the sofa. Instead of watching the weather channel all day or whatever he does, tell him that he can go to a local college and study poetry if he wants, or world history. He could even take courses in meteorology. Instead of just sitting there, complaining about the weather, he can go and study it. He will be more fun at Thanksgiving dinners that way, too.

Also, for people 55 or older there is free training. If you lose a job and are over 55, the U.S. Department of Labor has free training. In your state government, you have a state Department of Labor. Ask them about it. If they do not know about it, then go to U.S. Department of Labor in Washington DC, and look for the Division of Older Workers. If you are 50 and older, you are considered an older worker. I am 58 and I qualify for all these programs. So, if I do not sell any more books, I am going to be at the Division of Older Workers.

Free Hearing Aids

How about money to buy hearing aids? The Better Hearing Institute, 1-800-EAR-WELL, has money to help you buy hearing aids. If you know somebody, or you are someone who has trouble financing a hearing aid, there are money programs to assist you. Again, you do not have to get a grant. Here is money for you. On the web, it is {www.betterhearing.org}.

Free Eye Care

Free eye care — if you are over 65 you can get free eye care from the National Eye Care Project by the American Academy of Ophthalmology. Call 1-800-222-3937 and ask about the program. On the web, it is {www.eyecareamerica.org}.

Get Paid As A Volunteer

Seniors can get paid to help in their community. If you are a senior, or know a Grandma, Grandpa, or a lady down the street who does not know what to do with her life, call the National Senior Service Corps. Corps members become mentors, tutors, help in the community, schools, hospitals, and get paid for it. Do something in the community, and keep contributing. The National Senior Service Corps can be reached at 800-424-8867, and on the web at {www.cns.gov}.

Go On A Free Archeological Dig

You know what I am going to do this summer? I am going on a government program with my family. As I said before, I have got two teenage boys, who are now giants, 16 and 19. My wife, the two boys and I are going to Alaska on a free archeological dig with the government. I always wanted to go on an archeological dig. Sure, we have to pay to get there, but if you go to Outward Bound or some other place, they are going to charge you thousands of dollars for something like this. We are going with the best archeologist in the world and are actually working with Native Americans digging around for 500-year-old artifacts. Can you imagine the things we are going to learn? And learn as a family — that is what is so neat.

One year we went and restored historical buildings out in the wilderness in upstate Minnesota. These two programs are part of Passport in Time. Passport in Time is with the Department of Agriculture's Forest Service. The programs are located all over the country. They have a catalog they will send you and you can see all the stuff you can do anywhere in the country. But again, they do not advertise, so find it on the web, or just call the US Department of Agriculture locally and ask for Passport in Time. They can be reached at 800-281-9176 or on the web at {www.passportintime.com}. Get on their mailing list, get their catalog, and have a wonderful time.

After we did the first one in upstate Minnesota, one kid talked about marine biology. I said, "Let's do something in marine biology." I called the state of Maine and said, "Hey, I have got a family here. We want to volunteer and learn something about marine biology." I talked with the Natural Resource Division of the state of Maine. They did not know who I was. I just called out of the blue. See, if you treat people nicely, they start helping you. They found us some place that wanted to use us as volunteers in marine biology.

It was this wonderful museum on the coast of Maine where we went out and gathered specimens. We spent a whole week learning about marine biology. I know more about sea urchins and other sea life than I will ever use. It was an incredible experience, and it was all free. The best things in life are free, and all the best services in life are for free, but you just have to know where to go to get them, and that is what I love doing. I love telling people where to go!

Free Legal Help

We live in the greatest democracy in the world, and most of us walk around afraid that we will not get any justice because we cannot afford some hotshot attorney. But that is silly. You can get better legal help than you can from any lawyer if you learn how to use the system. That is the key.

Fight Insurance Companies Who Won't Pay Your Claim

Let's say your insurance company does not pay a claim, and you call that insurance company up in Hartford, Connecticut. You talk to some bureaucrat in this huge bureaucratic insurance company and they say, "Well buddy, did you see paragraph C, section B? We do not pay claims. We are the premium company. We just like collecting premiums." That is the way a lot of insurance companies work nowadays.

What is your recourse when something like that happens? Well, you know that Uncle So-and-so has a brother-in-law who is a lawyer. You call them and maybe they charge you, or maybe they give you the first hour free and then they charge you $100, $200, $300 an hour, whatever the heck they can charge.

But even if you have the money to afford a lawyer, you are probably not going to win against the insurance company. Their lawyers are better than anybody else's lawyers, because their lawyers do this 24 hours a day. That is all they do. And your brother-in-law, the attorney, how many cases like this does he really get? So, that is why you do not stand a chance against these companies who do it all the time. What happens, too, is that the company does not mind fighting with you because the worst that could happen is they have to pay the claim that they should have paid in the first place.

If you learn how to use the system, and the system is the government, you can call your state capital operator right now. If you are in Maryland, call Annapolis and ask for the state capital operator, and then ask them for the state Insurance Commissioner. Every state has a government-run office that regulates the insurance business in that state. That means that a business has to comply with everything that the government says, and if they screw up, they are out of business. The Insurance Commissioner will investigate your claim whether you are right or wrong. You could be some idiot, completely wrong, but they will contact the insurance company.

The insurance companies do not want to mess with the government. First of all, the insurance company is a big bureaucracy, as is the government with whom they have to deal. For two big bureaucracies to talk to each other it costs them $5,000 just to exchange letters, correspondence and email. It becomes cheaper to pay you off with a couple of hundred bucks, a thousand bucks or whatever you are trying to get. That is why this is a wonderful tool.

My family and I have used this many times. When you contact the insurance company, all you have to say is, "I do not think I am being treated fairly, and I am going to contact the state Insurance Commissioner's office." That is usually enough for them to put you on hold, go in the back room, come back and start making other arrangements that are more pleasing to you.

When they start messing with the government, if they lose, they could lose their whole business. When your lawyer starts messing with their lawyer, the only thing they can lose is the amount of your original claim. Having the government on your side is like calling the same people who brought you Desert Storm to go out and hassle these people for you. These are the most powerful people in the world.

Fight Mail Order and Retail Companies

I sell books through the mail. If we screw up and do not send a refund or our office messes up your order, you could go through our customer service and try to get it settled. But you can contact the U.S. Postal Inspector, because you bought this book through the mail. They will contact us directly. When we get a letter from the Postal Inspector, I will call you personally! I will say to keep the book. I do not want to mess with the Postal Inspector because it will cost me to deal with them, and if I screw up somehow, they could put me out of business.

It is cheaper, easier, and better for me to just make you as happy as possible so that when they contact me I can say, "She's very happy. There's no problem there. Call her and see."

The way to get the upper hand in society is to find a government office that regulates the people who did you wrong.

Credit Card Problems

The problems we have are usually because some big corporation messed us over. For instance, let us look at your credit card bill. "I returned that merchandise and it is still on the bill." You call the bank and they say, "We called the store and they said you did not return it." You do not have to pay it, and that is why I love credit cards.

Call your state Banking Commissioner, as they are the ones who regulate the bank and the credit card industry. They will contact that credit card company for you, and that is how to get justice and satisfaction. There is a 600-pound gorilla now that is fighting for you. The credit card company will just shove the bill right back to the retailer, and it will be their problem and not yours any more.

Over 40 Is Age Discrimination

When I was about 50 I started looking into what things are available for senior citizens. I was trying to figure out when the government actually considers you a senior citizen. Do you know when it is? Forty years old! At 40 years old, the government considers you a senior. Do you know why? Because that is when the age discrimination law starts in our society. So, if you are in the workforce and are over 40, the government considers you an old guy or an old woman, and they will protect you.

If you are an over 40 person looking for a job and you feel they are only hiring younger people, that could be against the law. Or, maybe you got fired and find that the company kept all the young people. That too could be against the law. How do you find out?

Like in most things people say, "Well, I will go to an attorney." You know what? The attorney is going to charge you $100 or $200 an hour to go learn the law for you. Like doctors with medicine, it is hard for attorneys to keep up on all the changes in the law. The law changes every day.

So why pay for an attorney to go learn the current law for you when instead, you can call the government's Equal Employment Opportunity Commission and talk with an attorney who wrote the law, and they are free. If you have a case, they will come and sue the people for you and get you hundreds of thousands of dollars because you were discriminated against.

It is the same way in housing and in sexual harassment. If somebody makes a pass at you at the Christmas party and you are not sure if it is sexual harassment, find out. Do not call an attorney, but instead call the government. And if you do have a possible case, they will come and sue the people for you. Any legal problem you have, do not call attorneys who have to learn the law for you on your nickel. Call an attorney who wrote the law, and they are free.

Free Child Support Enforcement

There are so many ways to get justice, including child support. Do not forget that the government set up child support enforcement offices in every state. Only about half the women in this country who are owed child support get their full amount. That is only 50 percent. If you know somebody who is not getting all their payments or you are one, contact your state department of health and ask about the Child Support Enforcement Office. There is no income requirement. You could be a millionaire, still be owed child support, and they will go chase it down for you. They can go through the Social Security Administration records, the IRS, the Defense Department, the FBI, and the Veterans Administration. They have the authority to use all these databases now to find those deadbeat dads or deadbeat moms, whoever owes child support.

I found a neat organization in Toledo, Ohio, called the Association for Children for Enforcement of Support Locator. This is a clearinghouse that will help you get child support. They know the whole system and they advise you against hiring private people who try to collect the money for you and keep a percentage of it. You could get all of it yourself by going through the public sources. You can reach them at 800-537-7072 or on the web at {www.childsupport-aces.org}.

Muggers' Money

The government also has muggers' money. If you get mugged in this society, there is a crime victims assistance program where they have money, and can pay you for the days lost from work or some other expenditure. It is run through the Justice Department. If your local police department does not know about this, contact the U.S. Department of Justice and ask for the crime victims assistance program. It is a big pot of money out there.

Government Will Fight Your Lawyer, Your Doctor and Your Deli

Money is also set aside for lawyers that run off with your money, as they are regulated, too. Lawyers, doctors, dentists, accountants, every professional is regulated. If you have a lawyer that messes you over, you can contact your state capital. Contact the office that regulates the attorneys and file a complaint. What you need to do to get the attention of some professional is to contact their licensing board because they do not want to have a bad letter on file, or to be investigated by their licensing board. How badly did they really mess you over? Even if you lose, it still looks bad for them.

It is the same way with your doctor's office. Go to the state licensing board and file a complaint. Get satisfaction. Make sure you get these people's attention. When you file a complaint or say you are going to go to the licensing board, you get their attention. That is when you get your phone call returned, and when you get your case reviewed. So, use these.

Every state capital now has a separate pot of money, so if for some reason your lawyer runs off with your money, they can reimburse you from this pot of money. It is nice to know that this kind of money is there, but what is amazing to me is that there is actually a pot of money. Lawyers run off with clients' money so often that they have to set up a fund to cover it.

Even your delicatessen is regulated. If you go to your delicatessen and buy a pound of salami, and the salami seems a little light, like maybe the deli owner had his thumb on the scale, you can call the state capital and ask for the Office of Weights and Measures. They have salami police who come out and buy salami to see if they are messing with the scales. Every commercial scale is regulated, just like the pumps at the gas station. You fill up your gas tank and it costs you $15. You fill it up the next day and it is $20. Somebody may be messing with those pumps. Call the Office of Weights and Measures.

If you buy a cord of wood, and say, "Okay $200 for a cord of wood." But you do not even know what a cord is. Two weeks later, your neighbor says, "That is not a cord of wood. Here is how you measure a cord of wood, and you got screwed." What do you do? You call the Office of Weights and Measures, and they will go find the guy who sold you the wood. That is their job.

The same holds true with hospitals and nursing homes, as they too are all regulated. They get government money from Medicare, Medicaid or whatever, so they must follow certain rules and guidelines. If a hospital messes you over, just call the Department of Health and Human Services in Washington DC. Actually, they have regional offices, too, that will come out and investigate your hospital for cleanliness or treatment issues.

If your mom is in a nursing home down in Arizona, and says, "They are not treating me right. All the food was cold." Do you want to take care of Mom? You call the state capital in Phoenix and ask for the office that regulates nursing homes. They will go and check Mom's nursing home for you. All it costs you is a price of a phone call. You do not have to get on an airplane, go down to Arizona, and check it yourself.

Working Over 40 Hours Could Be Illegal

Are you working more than 40 hours a week and not getting paid time and a half? It could be illegal. How do you get that justice? The Department of Labor in your state capital will investigate your boss, and will do it anonymously. So, if you have any wage or overtime issues and things like that, it is the office of the Department of Labor in your state capital who can help.

Pension Police

Many retirees are worried about their pension, and think maybe they should be getting more. There are pension police — the Pension Benefit Guarantee Corporation in Washington DC. They will investigate that pension plan for you. Here is their 800-number — 800-400-7242, or on the web at {www.pbgc.gov}.

There Is Even IRS Police

And you know what? There are even people who will fight the IRS for you. If you get the runaround from the IRS or they are banging on your door, saying they are going to put a lock around your house for that 13 cents that you owe them from 1972, or they want hundreds of thousands of dollars from you and you cannot pay all that money, Congress has set up special offices that will fight the IRS for you. They are called tax advocate centers, and are wonderful. If you have an argument, they can go right into the computers, correct the information, stop you from getting that mail, and can be an advocate for you.

That is the way Congress set it up. Everyone in Congress believes the IRS has too much authority in this country, so they set up these offices for the taxpayer. It does not matter how rich or poor you are. They will work for you. Look in the blue pages of your phone book under U.S. Department of Treasury and ask for the tax advocate center. It cannot hurt to try. Why hire some attorney at $200 an hour when these people will do it for free!

More Free Money

We all want more money. Here I would like to talk about some little odds and ends that people often ask me when I go around the country. They are little things that I found out over the years. Don't forget, I have been doing this thing for 25 years.

One thing I found recently was that you can get $500 for turning in annoying telephone solicitors. Isn't that neat? There is a rule at the Federal Communications Commission, the FCC, that if one of these annoying people calls you, and you tell them not to call, but they still call you two more times within a 12-month period, you get $500 from them.

Or, if they call you with a prerecorded message to your home, that is against the law. You could get $500 for that. Or, if they call you before 8:00 AM or after 9:00 PM, that is another way for you to get the money. Or, if they send you an unsolicited fax, you get $500 from that.

And here is how to find out how to do this. You can call 888-CALL-FCC, or go to the web at {www.fcc.gov}. When telephone solicitors call me, I just yank their chain. I say, "I would like to talk to your supervisor, because six months ago I told your company that you cannot call me any more, and now under the U.S. Federal Communications Commission Rules, I am able to collect $500 from you." Just knowing the law gives you power over any of these people.

Also, if you owe people money and they are calling you at weird hours, there are laws against that, too. You do not have to put up with obnoxious people on the phone that are bugging you for money. How do you find out about the law? You do not hire an attorney. No, the Federal Trade Commission regulates the law. Call 877-FTC-HELP (toll-free) or on the web go to {www.ftc.gov}. They have free reports on the rules governing debt collection practices, and they also have some great free reports for credit issues.

You see the ads in the paper and on television for the Credit Doctor, who wants $500 from you to fix your credit. There is nothing they can do that you cannot do yourself. There is no magic to this. The Federal Trade Commission has free reports called, "Credit Repair," "Self-Help May Be the Best," "How to Dispute Credit Report Errors," or, "How to Deal with Credit Problems." These are all free, very easy and understandable to read, and are designed to help you deal with any credit problems you have.

I do not know if you have seen the ads for free credit counseling agencies. Be careful. Mostly they are nonprofit organizations, trying to help. But one thing to consider is that the credit card companies may finance them. Anybody who is working with credit card companies will never tell you about your bankruptcy options. They want to make sure the credit card people get their money. Bankruptcy is a legal option in this country and is not reserved just for fat cats. If they do not talk about bankruptcy, you should go somewhere else. You can find out about credit repair and all these issues from the free reports from the Federal Trade Commission.

You can also go to your local county cooperative extension service. They are part of your county government and they too offer free credit counseling services. You can find them in the blue pages of your phone book under "County Government" and then "County Cooperative Extension Services." When you contact them, tell them you need help with credit problems. That is better than the people who will not tell you all the information you need to know.

Every community has a number of nonprofit organizations that can be very helpful in times of need. If you are really stuck, or know somebody who is, these organizations can provide extra spending money, pay some necessary bills, or even help with medical problems.

There was a nanny in my neighborhood, who I met at my kid's school bus stop, and she needed prescription drugs. She actually needed an exam by a doctor in order to get the drugs but she could not afford the exam. I called around to doctors and nobody would help me. Then I called Catholic Charities and talked to a nun there. I explained the problem and within two days they got the examination for the woman. And you do not have to be a Catholic to get this help.

Community Action Agencies and the Salvation Army are also available to solve problems like this in the community. If you cannot find them, contact your local library and they will direct you. They are good places to check if you do not know where to go.

Another thing that could be very rewarding to know is unclaimed property. Mary Ann Martello, the woman who wrote this book with me, got on a website called {www.unclaimed.org} and found over $2,000 of unclaimed money for members of her family. She wrapped up the information as gifts and presented them as presents at Christmas. Being the bearer of good news is great fun.

This is a database of all the unclaimed property available from state governments. Say you moved into town 20 years ago and put down a deposit for the phone company. When you left town you probably forgot to collect your deposit. The money goes into the state government's unclaimed property program.

Or maybe your mom or your grandmother set up a $500 CD in the bank when you were born, and now, 30 years later, it is worth $10,000 and it is sitting in some bank in your old hometown. They do not come and look for you. They give that money to the state government and it sits there waiting for you to come and collect it. I remember years ago looking at California's listing of unclaimed property. They had money there for Bob Hope. You mean the state couldn't find him? Massachusetts had money for the Archbishop of Boston. There is literally billions and billions of dollars sitting in these unclaimed property places.

If you are not online, go to your state capital and ask for the Office of the Secretary of State. They will be able to tell you where in that state they keep the unclaimed property.

Government auctions are another source of incredible bargains. A lot of people always want to know about government auctions. There are a couple of places to look for auctions, as each department handles things differently. The post office has auctions in about eight places in the country — Philadelphia, Atlanta, and a couple of other cities. I used to go to these auctions because they were fun to do. And for $100 I would get 500 stuffed animals, so I would have toys for my kids for the rest of their lives.

The post office also sells a lot of junk that is sold on late-night TV because if you refuse the shipment, the company often does not even want it back. It sits in the back of the post office waiting to be sold at these auctions. Or, it could be that sweater from Aunt Tilly in Seattle that you never received at Christmas time. It may be sitting in the back of the post office, and once a month, they will have an auction to get rid of all that stuff. So, contact your local post office and they will tell you where all the auctions are. They also auction off jeeps, post office vans and other great stuff.

The U.S. Customs Service holds big time auctions that can include jewelry, cars, or even saddles. These are items that are confiscated because they were entering the country illegally. They auction off furs, planes, boats, diamonds, and more. A private organization called EG&G in Fairfax, Virginia runs the auctions for the government. Their phone number is 703-273-7373, or on the web go to {www.treas.gov/auctions/customs} and find out about the auctions there. They are held all over the country and are fun. A lot of people I have met at the auctions just go to them on vacation. It is better than Disneyland for a lot of people.

What people often do is go to these auctions, get all this stuff, and then hold garage sales, selling it to make money. They buy it at one price, and then they sell it at flea markets for a higher price.

The Defense Department is loaded with stuff. They say that things they buy for $1, they sell for two cents. There is an office in Battle Creek, Michigan that runs their auctions. They can be reached at 800-GOVTBUY. On the web, it is {www.drms.com}, the Defense Reutilization Marketing Service. Great bargains on all kinds of things. I've talked to people that got cameras, vehicles, and clothing. Some Army/Navy surplus stores get all their stuff at these auctions which they then sell in their stores.

The IRS has unclaimed money, too — all those unclaimed refund checks. If you fill out your IRS form and you think you owe money but really you are due a refund, you may not be looking for a check. If you move in the meantime, the IRS check is not forwarded. It goes back to the IRS and waits for you to collect it. There is $62 million sitting there for people that do not know they are due a refund. Here is how to find out, 1-800-829-1040. It is worth it to just make a call and see.

Social Security has the same thing. Here is a number if you have an unclaimed social security check — 800-772-1213. If you are a veteran, here is where to find if you have a check sitting there, call 800-827-1000.

So, these are just other sources of more money. Check them out. Give them to other people to use. But most importantly, have fun!

Best Starting Places

I get so many questions. "Where do I start?" "Where do I go?" I cannot cover every possible situation. Even though you may have books of mine and there are thousands and thousands of sources, you are never going to have everything you want.

Here are two places that you could contact when you do not know where to start. The first place is the Federal Information Center. This is an office set up by the government that will actually do for free what I charge lots of money to do. Their job is to find out who in the government could possibly solve your problem, has the information you need, or has the money you want. Remember, no one office is an end-all and be-all, but it is a good place to start. So, start here. The Federal Information Center can be reached at 866-FIRST-GOV (toll-free). Whether it is finding a passport, finding money to go to graduate school, or finding an expert on Maine potatoes, they will help you.

The other good starting point place is your state capital operator. They are located in your state government. Call the information operator in your state capital, and ask for the state capital operator. When you get the state capital operator say, "Hey, I am looking for _____." Toothpaste cleaner, or money to start an aircraft carrier or whatever the heck it is, let them work. They do this all the time, and they know where to get you started. So, the most important thing is that you have a place to start. When you get that place, you ask them. If they do not have the answer, you ask them where else to go. That is what I love doing. I love telling people where to go!

Closing

Thank you for reading this lengthy introduction. It was fun for me to have an opportunity to share what I've picked up in my 25 years of helping other people get money and help.

If you're looking for me or my organization and you need more information, there are two ways to find me. My general 800-number is 1-800-UNCLESAM, and through that number you can find me or we will send you out literature. Or you can contact me on the web at {www.lesko.com}.

Remember, you can't get the magic that is in me. There is separate magic in you, and you have to make sure that you tap into your own magic and share it with the world.

Good luck to you.

Matthew Lesko
Author and Entrepreneur

Notes From Mary Ann

My name is Mary Ann Martello, and I've been co-authoring books with Matthew Lesko for years. If truth be told, Matthew comes up with the title and gets you to buy the book. I fill in the middle with resources that keep you from returning it. It works out great. It has been a wonderful work experience for me. I get paid, plus I get lots of freebies. In fact, if you could see my house, and I am glad you cannot because it is such a mess, you would find drawers and drawers of coloring books, pamphlets, posters and pictures that I got for free. I found free prescription medications for my grandmother, job training for friends, college money for relatives and much more.

What I would like to do is show you the grant possibilities, and then you can take it from there. Grants come in many different shapes and sizes, from $2 million to expand your manufacturing business, down to $100 to pay your heating bill. I know we told you this before, but it is not going to be easy to get a grant. The bigger the grant, the more complicated the forms. But this does not mean that it is impossible to achieve. It just means that it will take some work.

What we discovered from grant recipients is that you need to talk to many different people to uncover grant programs. The way I have always approached research is that I believe that the information or resource I am seeking exists somewhere, and that I just need to talk with the right person.

We talk about the seven phone call rule a lot. We believe it will take seven phone calls to track down that right person. Sometimes it will take less when we are lucky. Unfortunately, there will be no blinking neon sign that says, "Free Money — Come and Get It." Anything worth doing will take some work, right? This is your chance to turn your dreams into reality, so let's go for it.

Finding the grant-making agency is a challenge. For instance, if you want a grant for a business, there are many different places to investigate. You can look at the federal and state governments for assistance, as well as even your county. That is what makes finding the grant a challenge. In addition, resources exist to help you get your ideas and paperwork in order.

The Book We Copy From

A good starting place for the federal money is the *Catalog of Federal and Domestic Assistance*. This manual has over 1,000 pages, providing information on federal funding programs. Your local library will usually have a copy of the publication. An easier way to search it is on the web at {www.cfda.gov}. You can search by keyword to find programs that may apply to you. Each listing provides information on who qualifies for the program, and a contact person for more information.

By writing, phoning or emailing these programs, you may find a winner. And if you do not qualify for their program, they may know of others. Through the catalog you can learn about hundreds of programs. Programs exist to help you start a business in a rural or depressed area, for women to get transportation contracts, and even for low-income people to start their own business.

For instance, inventors and researchers can qualify for the Small Business Innovation Research Program that provides small businesses the chance to explore the commercialization of their product. Past grant winners include businesses that designed a state-of-the-art wheelchair, seedless watermelon, herbal products, as well as others.

The U.S. Department of Energy's Inventions and Innovations Program provides grants to businesses that have an idea or an invention that will save energy. Winners include companies that made more efficient water heaters, solar energy, lighting and insulation.

I even saw where the Office of Environmental Education of the EPA gave a several thousand-dollar grant to a couple of puppeteers to create a play on recycling. Anything is possible. Just try and think of how your business plan or idea might match up with the government agency or office.

The Gateway to Grants From Nonprofits

Another good resource for uncovering federal government money programs is the website called First Gov for Nonprofits, on the web at {www.firstgov.gov/Business/Nonprofit.shtml}. Now, you may be thinking that you are not a nonprofit. So why should you check out this site? I am going to talk later about becoming a nonprofit, but whether you are one now or not, this website is worth a look.

Nonprofit Gateway links you directly to every federal government department's and agency's grant sites. The grant sites outline all the grants available through the department or agency, contact people, eligibility, forms, past awardees and more. It eliminates the need to search each department's website to uncover grant opportunities. The website also provides a directory of the federal government and listings of information services and links. This will give you lots of starting places.

Many agencies have tips on completing proposals, sample forms and more. The purpose of all of this is to make applying for a grant easier and more understandable. What is nice about learning who got grants in the past is that you see what programs or projects were of interest and how much money they were awarded.

A little side note — in our surveys of people who purchased our book, we found that not everyone has access to the web. Check out your local library as many provide Internet access. There are also many free Internet access providers, such as Juno at {www.juno.com}. I did a search and found a site called Internet for Free, which lets you pick your state and area code, and you can find a free Internet access provider. They are at {www.internet4free.net}.

Each department within the federal government has an office called the Office of Small and Disadvantaged Business Utilization — a big name for a small office that is designed to help small businesses learn how to do business with that particular department. But they also may be able to refer you to an office or bureau that handles your business interest. In addition, whether it is selling your product or providing your services, this office can get you started.

Contracts Can Be Better Than Grants

As Matthew always says, "A government contract is better than a grant," because your main objective is to do a business and provide a product or a service.

There are actually offices called Procurement Assistance Centers, whose job is to help small businesses get government contracts with any department bureau or office. These actually were started to help companies get Department of Defense contracts, but have now expanded to include the entire federal government. They are great resources, with offices located throughout the country. They can explain the bidding process, the resources available, and provide information on how the procurement system operates. They can even match your product or service with the appropriate agency, and then help you market your product. All you need to do is start counting your money — not a bad deal.

Your state Department of Economic Development is located in your state capital. This office is designed to help businesses get started or expanded. They can answer all your questions and direct you to other appropriate offices within the state government for more specific business issues, such as licensing or registration. Many states offer special loan or grant programs, some more than others.

They also offer tax incentives, training assistance, and energy evaluations. If you need to get your employees up to speed on the latest computer technology, this office may be able to offer you money to cover the training, or help with reducing the cost.

Lots of Grants for Business

We uncovered several states that offer grants for recycling programs, alternative fuels, or even childcare centers. Iowa will give you $40,000 to recycle tires, and $10,000 to start a business if you have a disability. California has a $50,000 tax credit to start an onsite childcare facility. Minnesota will give you $4,000 for technical assistance to start your business, and Wisconsin has $30,000 to start a rural business. Maybe that bed and breakfast is really within your reach.

Tennessee, Michigan, Rhode Island and many other states want to give you money to train your employees. A majority of states will even give you a tax credit for each new job you create, or if you hire someone trying to get off welfare.

How does London, Paris or Rome sound? If you think overseas may be the ticket for your company, then there is money to attend tradeshows or other resources for exporting your product.

Cheri Olssen said she had a small recycling business where she bought and resold aluminum cans. She stumbled upon a grant offered by the Nebraska Department of Environmental Control. After she completed a simple application, she received a $4,500 grant for a flatbed gooseneck trailer and a truck. Check out your state to see what they can do for you today.

Another resource for money is venture capital. This is what is known as having a silent business partner. Join the likes of Staples, Intel, American Online and thousands of others who have used venture capital to start or expand their businesses.

The SBA licenses small business investment companies who in turn provide venture capital or start up financing for small businesses. You can check them out at the Small Business Administration website at {www.sba.gov}. There are also many different venture capital companies at the state level or in the private sector. Some venture companies' focus on a certain area of a state or the country, as well as have an area of expertise. It is worth investigating to see what money is out there for you.

Located at a more local level, there are sometimes agencies called Economic Development Councils or some other similar name. The mission of these councils is to stimulate the economy of a particular area, and often start up business assistance is included. Your local Chamber of Commerce, business organization or other associations may be able to direct you to those resources.

Free Consulting Help

If you need help writing your business plan and getting all your P's and Q's in order, then visit your local Small Business Development Center. These centers are located in a majority of counties throughout the United States, and are funded through both federal and state monies. The purpose of the centers is to help people write their business plan, and to begin searching for funding, if needed. They are experts in this field, and can help you organize your thoughts and complete a well thought out plan of action.

When Phillip Seahorn wanted to start his Internet marketing business, he went to one of these offices and said he got thousands of dollars worth of free business counseling, and even help with seeking funding for his venture. He had no idea that such an office of help existed and felt that his business would never be this far along without the assistance these people offered.

Having said all that, sometimes you actually need very little to start a business. Matthew started with a desk in his apartment and business cards. My own husband started a business working at night, using our computer in the den. A year later, he has an office and several employees. These offices will help you figure out what the minimum is that you need to get started, and you can grow with your business.

Foundations That Give You Support

I have talked a great deal about business grants, but I want to take a few minutes to discuss grants offered through foundations. If you cannot find what you need through the government, then you can turn to other sources for funds. Foundations made nearly $20 billion in charitable grants last year.

Before approaching foundations as your funding source, there are many issues to consider. Primarily, although there are always exceptions, these foundations provide grants to other nonprofits, not to individuals, with some focusing on a specific geographic area or interest. Probably the largest organization designed to help people learn about grants and grant writing is The Foundation Center. This is a nonprofit center that gathers and disseminates information on foundations. They have an extensive collection of books, documents, reports and publications focused in the grants area, plus knowledgeable staff to assist users in locating information. They have five main offices scattered throughout the US, plus libraries in every state. In addition, they publish funding directories specific to certain fields, such as aging, arts, families, health, higher education and women.

They also offer grant writing classes and other courses to help you in your search. We found several Internet search engines that will help you find a nonprofit organization that meets your needs. You can try {www.idealist.org} and {www.guidestar.org}. Guide Star actually has a searchable database of over 850,000 organizations.

Also, many corporations have foundations that support local projects. When I was trying to get sponsorship for a youth horse show, I found that the new professional hockey team in my town actually had a special office and monies to support just such events. Make sure that the foundation you are contacting matches with what you are trying to do. It will save time on your part and theirs.

I mentioned earlier about becoming a nonprofit. A majority of foundations or organizations, and even government programs award grants only to nonprofits. There are two avenues you can take. One, you can find a nonprofit you can work with to apply for the grant, and then they can be a conduit for the money. Obviously, you need to work with an organization whose goals match with your cause, and who you feel you can trust.

Think of your current membership in various organizations and clubs. What about local service organizations or education institutions? You obviously now will be held accountable to both the grant making agency and the nonprofit.

Start Your Own Nonprofit

The other avenue to take is to become a nonprofit. It is not as difficult as you may imagine. I have a friend named Dan Meeks. He wanted to start a Vietnam vet service organization that would help troubled teens in the area. Dan did what most people would do — he went to a lawyer and was told it would take several thousand dollars to fill out the paperwork.

Since he knew us and had our books, he thought he should be able to apply by himself. He got the forms from the IRS and filled them out as best he could. Then he called the IRS and the guy actually walked him through the rest of the forms. He sent in a check for $150, which was the IRS filing fee and got his nonprofit status without the lawyer's huge fees. Now Dan is able to seek funding from a variety of sources, and fulfill a dream that is important to him.

No More Starving Artists

Do you really need to be a starving artist or to suffer for your art? I do not think so. Heidi Hart, Doug Sharples, Bradley Sowash, David Sovlino, plus hundreds of other artists were able to take advantage of what their state arts councils had to offer in the way of grants.

When we talked with David Sovlino, he said that he followed a simple application process that was pretty straightforward, and then if he had any questions, the council was more than willing to give him a hand. Bradley Sowash had the same experience.

I know a choreographer that got a $10,000 fellowship designed to just free up her time to create new work. Many cities and counties have their own arts councils willing to assist those local artists in the creation and performance of their work. Search for those by contacting your city or county government, as well as your state arts and humanities organizations.

When I did a search for other grants for artists, I found many private arts organizations that offered help. Some provide travel money. Others provide financial assistance to artists in need. Many offer fellowships for artists who work in specific mediums, so that they can create free from external pressures.

Search on the web. Contact arts organizations. Check out arts publications, as well as talk to other artists to learn what is out there. Something that always has intrigued me is that a certain percentage of all federal and state building money must be spent on art. I think it would be interesting to take advantage of that opportunity.

When we searched for grants, we found specific ones for architects, sculptors, writers, vocalists, artists in their mature phase, $5,000 for comic book writers, and even $2,500 for artists who are emerging in their art form. There is something for everyone.

Even though the National Endowment for the Arts gives only limited money directly to individuals, their website links you to any government office that offers some type of arts or community grants, as well as to your state and local arts organization. I saw where there were grants for a sculpture garden, bike paths, and even a collection of oral histories.

Housing Grants

Wouldn't it be great to give Grandma $10,000 to repair her roof, or even get $6,000 for closing costs on your dream home? What about $2,000 for storm windows, or $700 to pay your electric bill?

I talked with the Chandlers who, even though they had some credit problems in the past were still able to get a $3,000 grant for closing costs to buy a new home. They talked about what a relief it was to get the grant, and how they never would have been able to come up with the money for the down payment without help. Sandy Dotson got $3,500 for her closing costs and said it was not hard to apply at all.

How did they get the money? They called around and talked with their local and state housing authorities. A majority of states offer grants or low interest loans to either first-time homebuyers or low-income residents. Just because you owned a home a while ago does not necessarily disqualify you from assistance. We learned that many states say that if you have not owned a home in three years, it means that you can still qualify for the first-time homeowner's help. It also may apply to those who are legally separated or divorced.

Many housing and community development agencies offer housing assistance and home repair programs. If you live in a small town, the U.S. Department of Agriculture's Rural Housing Service offers some grant and loan programs to buy, repair or build housing.

Even the U.S. Department of Housing and Urban Development has a housing repair program, and they offer counseling programs for those in danger of losing their homes. So, if you cannot pay your mortgage, they will help you work it out with your bank so you do not lose your home.

Your state energy office can direct you to heating and weatherization grants, and most utility companies can also offer to help with your bills. You do not need to be a professional grant writer to complete these simple forms. You just have to make a phone call to get the process started.

Grants for Education and Job Training

We sent out an email to people who bought our books and asked them to respond back if they got a grant. My mailbox overflowed with people that got grants to go to school. Ronald King gets money to go to school, plus a voucher for books and money to help with living expenses. Dennis Harwood gets $6,000 a year to go to auto mechanic school part-time at night. His goal is to double his salary. What is interesting is that his wife knew about the program, and once her husband went to school found that the phone kept ringing with other people asking her how he was able to do this. She just assumed everybody knew about the grant programs.

Karen Ladd is a stay-at-home mom with four kids. She wanted to finish her degree so that when her youngest goes to school, she can get a good job. She found out that you can get a federal grant to go to school, and that she can use the money to pay for her online courses she is taking to finish her accounting degree. She said she never would have been able to go to school without the money or the online classes. Many people, like Rebecca Lowers get money from both federal and state governments.

All states have a Department of Higher Education, and most offer some type of assistance programs for residents. You may be able to get grants if you are smart or if you are going into medical or teaching professions, or if you meet some income requirements. It varies state to state, so check it out. There are also millions of dollars worth of federal grant and loan programs. You can contact the U.S. Department of Education or talk with your school or potential university's financial aid office to learn more.

I see in many publications or some of the junk mail I get that companies offer to find scholarships for your kids' college tuition for a fee. My philosophy is that if someone is going to charge me money to do something, then I should be able to do it by myself for less.

A friend was going to spend $300 to have a company find scholarships for her. I went on the web, and by using a variety of search engines found her 30 scholarship programs that met her qualifications. There was no guarantee she would get them, but I did as much as that guy who was going to charge her $300 would do.

There are grants to study overseas, money to learn about history, anthropology, housing issues, hairstyling, gardening and more. There is even money for smart athletes to go to school. Many people have heard Matthew talk about a woman that got money to take computer courses, and that has to be one of the top calls we get in the office. People want to get their Microsoft certification, learn C++ or whatever the latest computer program is. This is not a once in a lifetime incident.

I talked with Len Osborne. Len was the bouncer making $7 an hour and was going to get laid off. He saw Matthew's book and called the state Department of Labor where he was living. He received $1,000 to live on, gas money to get to training, a computer to keep, money for books and took over $10,000 worth of classes so that he could become a Microsoft certified systems engineer. It quadrupled his salary to over $50,000 with benefits. Len says it absolutely works and literally turned his life around.

Ed Blakesley got the same thing when he was collecting unemployment. He says he will be able to make more money than ever before. Will Mosely and Samantha White also were able to get their computer courses paid.

Talk with your local Job Training Partnership Act Office, the Employment Services Office, or even your unemployment or workman's comp officer, if you have one. Most of our success stories people talk about how one person happened to know about a program, and how lucky they felt to get in.

Grants for Your Health

When my grandmother was getting treatment for cancer, the doctors prescribed her medication that was going to cost $200 a month. She was living on a fixed income and really could not afford the bill. The doctor and pharmacist were no help, but we happened to talk with a drug rep who was delivering sample products to a doctor's office. We learned that every drug company has a program to help people get the medications they need if they cannot afford them. It takes one phone call to the drug manufacturer and your doctor needs to sign a form. That is it.

My grandmother got her medications for free, and when we started talking about this program, we helped hundreds of others also take advantage of the service. Karen Moriarty gets $1,000 worth of free medications each year and learned about the program in one of our books. She cannot thank us enough. There are programs out there for health insurance for kids, cheap or free dental care, free mammograms, free hospitalizations and more. It may take a little digging, but these programs exist.

Copies of Grant Applications

I am going to give you two big tips that will help you actually win the grant. Once you have found a grant program that applies to you, if it is offered by a federal or a state agency, you can request a copy of a successful grant application. Most of the agencies have a listing of past awardees and you could submit a Freedom of Information Act request to get a copy of a specific completed application.

This takes a little time and will cost you about $20, but you get a chance to see what a winner looks like. It is very helpful to see how others submitted their proposals and really what a successful application package looks like.

The second tip applies to any grant program. Almost everyone we talked to said that they had many conversations with the grant-making agency. They asked hundreds of questions on how to complete the application and they always found the agencies helpful. Many agencies also let you submit a preliminary application, which they will comment on, and then return to you for completion.

A friend of mine who received a grant to make a CD said that the help the council gave him to complete his proposal was invaluable and made his application a grant winner, rather than a grant loser.

I know I have given you a lot of information and resources to check. It may seem overwhelming. What I find helpful is to make a list of all the possible places to check, even it may seem like a stretch. I always get the name of the person to whom I am talking and use my nicest telephone voice. It tends to make people want to be more helpful. I have had people dig through their desk to find old reports, or gone on hunts to find the right person who I need to talk to because I have treated them with kindness.

When All Else Fails

When all else fails and you are stumped, not knowing where to turn, remember that you have a Representative and Senators in Congress. These people are certainly running for re-election and would love your vote. They all have workers called case managers in their offices, whose job it is to cut through red tape for people, and try to solve constituent problems. If they help you, then you will be sure to tell your family and friends about it, and maybe next election they will win by a landslide.

I have given you as much as I can give you about grant hunting, so happy hunting and follow your dreams.

Mary Ann Martello
Author and Researcher

WRITING YOUR GRANT PROPOSAL

There are lots of places to look for help on the mechanics of grant writing. The library has books, government funding sources publish guidelines, organizations like the Foundation Center (www.fdncenter.org) and the Grantsmanship Center (www.tgci.com) have lots of useful information online, as well as publications you can purchase. A quick search on the Internet turned up 300,000 websites that focus on grants writing!

But before you dive in, you need to ask yourself one question: Is it worth it? The instant answer is, "Of course!" You've already followed your heart instead of your wallet. But remember, you will be persuading someone to give you money, not telling them you have to have it. You'll need to marshal all your resources and be absolutely convinced that you are proposing an important project; otherwise, you'll feel as if you're begging and no one enjoys that. Have you asked yourself, are we the best people to do this job? Could we do a better job teaming up with some other, better-established organization and doing our project under their auspices? Is the service we are proposing needed? If we build it, would anybody come? Is there anybody with money out there who might be willing to back this project financially? What's in it for the organization that gives us the money?

If this is more soul searching than you had planned, you're not ready to start writing a grant proposal. Remember, flawless prose cannot conceal a weak proposal. The writing is easy compared to the thinking process that goes into planning a great project.

Every potential funder's expectations are different, but here are some general tips for how to prepare a convincing and successful grant proposal.

Proposal Writing Tips

Grants are a two-way transaction

In our hurry to explain how very much we need the money for an important project, it is easy to forget this vital fact: grants are a two-way transaction. Your organization gets much-needed funds, but what does the giver get in return? Frame your proposal, and the problem you're addressing, from the funder's perspective instead of your own. Don't devalue your own contribution to the community. What are you giving the funder? A better-educated workforce? A place to go after school that could cut down on the shoplifting and vandalism that is slowly destroying neighborhood businesses? A better image in the community?

Wal-Mart's charitable giving program (www.walmartfoundation.org) is a classic example of philanthropy that serves its stockholders as well as the communities where Wal-Mart does business. Wal-Mart has been accused of building its "big box" stores on the outskirts of small and medium size towns, where its lower prices and all-in-one-place convenience hasten the collapse of smaller, long-established local stores and empty the older downtowns. Wal-Mart's charitable giving for 1999, which totaled almost $164 million, is targeted, in part, to dissolve this image of the bully from out of town. The slogan on their website makes the point succinctly: "Community Programs that work for Wal-Mart, SAM's Club and you. After all, we live here too." Funding decisions for charitable projects are made at the local level by store employees and most of the programs require Wal-Mart associates to volunteer in the fundraising process. When Wal-Mart does support national causes such as United Way, it insists that Wal-Mart's local contribution stays in the community where it was raised. Wal-Mart's generosity creates a better business climate for its stores as well as making a positive impact on the communities where it does business.

Do your homework

Before you put anything in writing, find out everything you can about the company, foundation or government agency you plan to ask for money. Read their printed application guidelines thoroughly. Read their annual reports, which will list grant recipients from previous years. Call previous grant recipients and get their take on working with the organization. Sometimes the granting organization will give you a copy of the form their evaluators use to "grade" the grant applications when they decide how to award the monies. These blank review sheets make a great checklist when it comes time for you to edit your draft proposal.

Cultivate a good relationship with the grant program officer

Most organizations giving grants have one or more employees responsible for collecting the applications and overseeing the process in which a panel of employees, experts, or other consultants decides which applicants will receive funds. Although job titles vary, this person is often called the program officer. Should you send this person a dozen long-stem roses the day after you submit your grant proposal? Absolutely not! Nevertheless, the program officer can be immensely helpful in furthering your success. Remember, reviewers want to see a stack of informative yet concise, appropriate proposals. Your best effort will make the program officer look better. Don't be afraid to ask program officers to clarify details. They will usually supply you with copies of winning proposals from previous years and some will even review your draft proposal and provide helpful comments if you give them plenty of time. There are a few cardinal rules, however; don't ask a question that is clearly answered in the guidelines, and don't expect any hand-holding if you've put off applying until the last minute.

Don't try to fit square pegs into round holes

Your priorities should match those of the organization you are applying to. For example, one local ice cream store was so besieged with requests for donations to everything from soccer clubs to Girl Scout troops to Sunday school picnics that the store finally announced that it would not consider requests for any money that did not contribute to education. Many organizations have very specific agendas, such as the environment, technology in schools, help for the elderly, or arts education, for example. Do some research before you ask.

Sometimes, what you need most is something nobody is interested in funding. Nonprofits that have high-maintenance facilities, such as historical societies or theaters, have a notoriously difficult time getting the money for expensive but necessary upkeep, although lots of companies are willing to fund a specific event that gets their logo in front of the public. Before you begin asking corporate funders for money for a new roof, you should sit down with your organization's budget and make sure you have already sought grants for everything that is likely to be attractive to sponsors.

Consider starting small

If your group is the new kid on the block, you won't have the kind of track record that could reassure potential funders that you'll still be standing there, fiscally sound, at the end of the project. Although there are at least 90 kids in four different schools who desperately need the service you'll provide, your long-term success at funding such a program may depend upon successfully funding and completing a one-year "pilot program" at one school. If you have done a great job on the small scale test run, your credibility will be greater when you go back to ask for money to expand. (However, you may want to reconsider if you are applying to an organization that does not look kindly upon grant recipients returning to ask for money a second time.)

Companies love company

Most corporate givers and philanthropic organizations want to be associated with a group of "good citizen" companies. They probably will want to see their logos with a bunch of other sponsors'. To avoid a sort of chicken-and-egg cycle-we can't sponsor you until we know that other companies are willing to sponsor you-solicit non-monetary contributions first and share that information with potential funders. For instance, if you want money to develop a program that will encourage poor parents to read to their children, you could arrange for a local design firm to create the layout and a local printer to print the workbooks for free before you go to a corporation asking for dollars. Those donated services are essentially "matching gifts" that could be worth thousands of dollars. Submit your proposal to other potential funders as well as your most likely source. It's expected that you will do so and it shows that you are committed to your project. Do notify all potential funders that you are submitting the proposal to other sources.

Proofread, proofread, proofread

Wouldn't it be awful if your proposal was rejected because you added the figures wrong in the budget section? Or you didn't double-space the introduction according to the guidelines? Or you misspelled the foundation chairman's last name in the cover letter? Ask people unfamiliar with the project to read your prose to see if they understand what you're asking for. Make sure that any charts or graphs you use are not so complicated that it will take a reviewer 15 minutes just to decode them.

Write like a reporter

Put the most important elements at the beginning of each section and amplify in subsequent paragraphs. If a reviewer is only going to read the first paragraph of each section, what is the most essential information for her to have when she makes a decision? You can ask program officers about how much time reviewers have to read the applications and

how many they are likely to receive. If you do the math and it looks as if your reviewer will be reading about three 30-page applications an hour, you'll want to get straight to the point in your application.

Don't forget to include an "evaluation" method

At the end of your project, funders will ask, "Was my money well spent?" You'll want to have hard data that demonstrates your success so that you'll have an even stronger proposal the next time you ask for money. If you need to pay a professional to evaluate your project, be sure to put that cost in your budget. A proposal without an effectively designed evaluation is like a science experiment without an explicit method for measuring results. The proposal and the experiment both flunk.

How much money should you ask for?

Don't give a low estimate because it will look as if you haven't planned realistically. Likewise, padding looks like waste and won't go over well. Most grant application guidelines are very specific about how to calculate costs. Also, don't ask a potential sponsor for $20,000 when their history suggests that they seldom give more than $5,000 per grant.

First impressions count, so do your best writing last

The first part of a proposal is almost always a summary or abstract, and you are sometimes limited to as little as 250 to 500 words. Don't write this until you have written everything else in the application. By this time you ought to be really focused and ready to drive home a few key points with a minimum of fluff. Remember, this might be the only section a reviewer reads so it better be good.

Be very specific about how the project will unfold

Be sure to tell what will happen in what sequence. You might want to draw up a timetable, which can make it easy for the evaluator to visualize the process. When you describe what paid or volunteer staff will be working on the project, don't forget to explain how you will free up time for a full-time employee who already has a full plate of responsibilities.

Tell your funders what will happen after the project

Funders will want to know that you have thought ahead to the time after your project is successfully completed. What sort of follow-up activities will take place? Will you need to seek more grant money or will you be able to carry on independently?

Back up any claims with hard facts

Chances are, the facts and figures you need are right in your own organization's records, or can be found by checking with state and local agencies. (This is all the more reason for your organization to keep accurate counts of attendance, volunteer hours, etc.) Use statistics to describe your community, your clientele, and the problem you plan to address. The following statement, written by the fictional, nonprofit Cornbelt Farm Families Association, uses easily obtained numbers to give the background for why it needs funds to offer more computer training classes for adults.

"Although our region of the Eastwest has prospered from the new technological services industries centered around Ourstate University Research Park, the small farm town of Cornbelt has suffered the double loss of declining agricultural produce prices and the closure of the Cleanfast vacuum factory, where at least one member of each of 500 Cornbelt farm families worked to provide a second income. Although the regional unemployment rate averages 5.5 percent, Cornbelt's hovers near 12 percent. Average per capita personal income for the region is $28,500, yet the annual income for Cornbelt Farm Families Association's clients averages $16,000. The drought of 1999 also hurt these families. Crop losses were an estimated $50 million for the Tri-County area.

"As conditions for farm families have worsened, the number of Cornbelt residents seeking computer training at Cornbelt Farm Families Association has increased by 30 percent, from 455 in 1998 to 650 in 2000."

Remember your manners

If you do receive a grant, write a thank you note. If you don't receive a grant, call and politely ask why. You might get answers that will provide you with the keys to writing a successful proposal next year. Some organizations will even provide you with copies of the evaluators' "grade cards," on request; these can provide a gold mine of constructive criticism.

What Information Should You Provide In Your Proposal?

Grant proposals can be short or long (some government-funded programs can easily run to 100 pages of documentation!) and the sections may have different titles, but the following list will give you an idea of the standard components of a proposal and the information they require.

The executive summary or abstract

In one page or less, this section must sum up everything to follow. The writing in this section should be so clear and compelling that the reviewer will want to find out more. If the executive summary is unclear the reviewer may well weed out your proposal without even reading the rest of the application. As noted previously, write this section last.

The statement of need or problem

This section tells why your project should be undertaken. You should set it up so that it leads naturally to the project description in the next section, which will describe how you want to address this need.

✱ Use accurate statistics that support your description of the problem.
✱ Demonstrate that your organization has a thorough understanding of the specific issue, along with the larger social issues that may be contributing factors.
✱ Show that the need or problem, as you have described it, can be at least partially solved.

The project description

This section tells what the grant will be used for. Subsections describe

✱ the objectives (what the results of the project will be);
✱ the methods for meeting those objectives;
✱ staffing (who will do what and how);
✱ how you will evaluate whether you are meeting your objectives.

The budget

This section contains an outline of projected expenses. Be sure to address each of the elements listed in the project description.

Organization information

This section conveys the information that demonstrates your organization's ability to carry out the project successfully. Without deluging the reader with facts and figures, you need to tell

✱ when your organization was founded;
✱ its mission statement (your proposal should be consistent with the mission);
✱ the services your organization provides and the audience it serves;
✱ how your organization is structured;
✱ expertise of key staff members.

Conclusion

Like a talented debater summing up at the end, you want to briefly reiterate your key points. This is the one place in the proposal where it's O.K. to get a little emotional. This might be the spot to share a pithy quote from a client whose life has been changed for the better by your services or an editorial from the local paper that supports your point.

TYPES OF ASSISTANCE AND GRANTS SOURCES
(or where you can find money)

Types of Assistance

You are on the money hunt, but exactly what are you shooting for? When you read grant guidelines or proposal information, you will find a great many new terms. Here are a few basic definitions to help you along.

Grants: Grants are generally considered a desirable form of financial assistance since they represent an outright award of funds and are not required to be repaid.

Project Grants: Grants provided for a fixed period for the development of a specific project or the delivery of specific services or products.

Loans: Since loans must be repaid, they are often viewed by applicants as less desirable than grants. However, with the reduction of federal funds available for grants and the increasing level of competition for such funds, loans are often the only form of assistance available.

Direct Loans: Loans given directly to the applicant for a specific period of time and are needed to be repaid with interest.

Guaranteed/Insured Loans: Programs in which the federal government makes an arrangement with a lender that protects the lender if the person fails to repay or defaults on a loan.

In-Kind Donation (Use of property, facilities, and equipment): Programs that provide the loan of or use of facilities, property, or materials.

Government Grants

Catalog of Federal Domestic Assistance

The best single resource for leads on federal funding programs is published by the federal government and is called the *Catalog of Federal Domestic Assistance*. This manual of more than 1,000 pages provides the most comprehensive information on federal funds, cross-indexed by agency, program type, applicant eligibility, and subject. The Catalog is available in many libraries, and describes federal government programs that provide funds or non-financial assistance to state and local governments, public agencies, organizations, institutions, and individuals. Included are the program's legislative authority, explanations of each program, types of assistance provided, restrictions, eligibility requirements, financial information, application and award procedures, information contacts, and related programs.

The Catalog and some of the other publications listed in this guide are also available as online databases. Such databases can be searched using personal computers with modems, or perhaps by arranging for a search to be conducted at a local library. While not all libraries offer online searching services, many larger public and research libraries do, generally for a fee. If a local library does not have online searching capabilities, library personnel may be able to direct interested parties to outside search services or consultants.

You can purchase a copy of the *Catalog of Federal Domestic Assistance* for $63 by contacting the Superintendent of Documents, U.S. Government Printing Office, P.O. Box 371954, Pittsburgh, PA 15250 or U.S. Government Printing Office, 732 N. Capitol St., NW, Washington, DC 20401, 202-512-1800. You can also find the Catalog in many libraries and you can search it online at {www.cfda.gov}. In addition, you may purchase a copy of the Catalog on CD-ROM. The CD-ROM also contains the Federal Assistance Award Data System (FAADS) database. With this feature, you can check out a specific program to see who received the program funds in the past. This is an incredible feature, as it may help you tailor your proposal accordingly. You can search by program number, keyword, or location. The CD-ROM is available for $54. See "How To Read The Catalog Of Federal Domestic Assistance" on page 86 and "Developing And Writing Federal Government Grant Proposals" on page 93.

Federal Register

Updated information on federal programs and grant awards appears in the daily *Federal Register*, also available from the Government Printing Office. Federal agencies are required to publish description of programs, guidelines, and eligibility requirements in the *Federal Register*. You can purchase a subscription for the *Federal Register* for $764 per year by contacting the Superintendent of Documents, U.S. Government Printing Office, Washington, DC 20402; 202-512-1800. You can also find the *Federal Register* in many libraries and you can view it online at {www.gpoaccess.gov/nara/}.

PREAward and POSTAward Grants

In addition, House offices have access to two databases known as PREAward Grants and POSTaward Grants, available through the House Information Resources/Member Information Network System. (Senate offices have access to these databases via the Senate Library or Senate Reference Center.) These files include current grant availability data from the *Catalog of Federal Domestic Assistance* and the *Federal Register*, as well as reports from federal agencies about grants awarded during the latest four quarters. The databases are available only through congressional offices; requests for a search of these databases may be made through an individual Member of Congress. To contact your Representative, The United States House of Representatives, Washington, DC 20515; 202-224-3121; {www.house.gov}; and Your Senator, U.S. Senate, Washington, DC 20510; 202-224-3121; {www.senate.gov}.

How To Read
The Catalog Of Federal Domestic Assistance

Program Number, Title, and Popular Name

Each program in the Catalog is preceded by a five-digit program identification number. The first two digits identify the Federal department or agency that administers the program, and the last three digits are assigned in numerical sequence. Thus, program number 10.500 is administered by the Department of Agriculture, 11.500 by the Department of Commerce, 12.500 by the Department of Defense, 93.500 by the Department of Health and Human Services, and so on. (In the numerical sequence of program numbers, some numbers do not appear due to program deletions or consolidations. To accommodate users' systems and records, the numbers are not reassigned to other programs but are reserved for the reinstated programs.)

Program Title:

The program title is the descriptive name given to a program. The popular name, which is less descriptive than the program title, is the name by which the program is commonly known. Not all programs have one.

Objectives:

This is a brief statement of what the program is intended to accomplish along with the goals toward which the program is directed.

Eligibility Requirements:

Applicant Eligibility

This section indicates who can apply to the Federal government for assistance and the criteria the potential applicant must satisfy. For example, individuals may be eligible for research grants, and the criteria to be satisfied may be that they have a professional or scientific degree, 3 years of research experience, and be a U.S. citizen. Universities, medical schools, hospitals, or State and local governments may also be eligible. Where State governments are eligible, the type of State agency will be indicated and the criteria that they must satisfy. Certain programs in the Catalog (e.g., the Pell Grant program that provides grants to students) involve intermediate levels of application processing, i.e., applications are transmitted through colleges or universities that are neither the direct applicant nor the ultimate beneficiary. For these programs, the criteria the intermediaries must satisfy are also indicated, along with intermediaries who are not eligible.

Beneficiary Eligibility

This section lists the ultimate beneficiaries of the program, the criteria they must satisfy, and who specifically is not eligible. The applicant and beneficiary will generally be the same for programs that provide assistance directly from a Federal agency. Financial assistance, however, that passes through State or local governments will have different applicants and beneficiaries since the assistance is transmitted to private sector beneficiaries who are not obligated to request or apply for the assistance.

Credentials/Documentation

This is a brief description of the credentials or documentation required prior to, or along with, an application for assistance. The eligibility factors that must be proven, certified, or established are indicated in this section. This section also indicates whether OMB Circular No. A-87 requirements, "Cost Principles Applicable to Grants and Contracts with State and Local Governments," are applicable. In cases in which specific Federal circulars or other regulatory requirements are not applicable to the program, disclaimer statements may be included referencing the requirements(s) from which the program is excluded.

Application And Award Process

Preapplication Coordination

This section indicates whether any prior coordination or approval is required with governmental or nongovernmental units prior to the submission of a formal application to the Federal funding agency. For example, programs may require: State agency approval prior to the submission of an application to a Federal agency; The submission of environmental impact information as required by the National Environmental Policy Act of 1969, or other types of requirements.

Application Procedure

This section discusses the basic procedural steps required by the Federal agency in the application process, beginning with the lowest level (e.g., State and local government units, institutions or organizations) and ending eventually with the Federal government. Each program indicates where applications are to be submitted. Numerous programs in the Catalog require the standard application forms in OMB Circular No. A-102. Other applications may be in the form of a written request to the funding agency stating the need for assistance and requesting available services, or a formal proposal prepared in response to an announcement in the Federal Register or the Commerce Business Daily. Also indicated in this section is guidance concerning the applicability of OMB Circular No. A-110, "Grants and Agreements with Institutions of Higher Education, Hospitals, and Other Nonprofit Organizations." When specific Federal circulars or other regulatory requirements are not applicable to the program, disclaimer statements may be included referencing the requirements(s) from which the program is excluded.

Award Procedure

This section lists the basic steps for awarding assistance, beginning with the organizational components of the Federal Agency that has final approval authority for the application and ending with the lowest level at which Federal resources are expended. Also indicated is whether assistance passes through the initial applicant for further distribution by intermediate level applicants to groups or individuals in the private sector. Accepted applications are evaluated by the headquarters, regional, local, or district office to determine the feasibility of the proposed project to include consistency with Federal and individual agency policies concerning its scope and purpose. Grant payments may be made by letter of credit, advance by Treasury check, or reimbursement by Treasury check. Awards may be made by the headquarters office directly to the applicant, an agency field office, a regional office, or by an authorized county office.

Deadlines

When available, this section indicates the deadlines for applications to the funding agency in terms of the date(s) or between what dates the application should be received. Reference is made to new applications, continuations, renewals, and supplementals. Application deadline information is indicated in the agency's program guidelines, or announced in the *Federal Register*. Where not available, applicants should contact the funding agency for deadline information.

Range of Approval or Disapproval Time

This section gives a representative range of time required for the application to be processed (in days or months) at the Federal level.

Appeals

In some cases, there are no provisions for appeal. Where applicable, this section discusses appeal procedures or allowable rework time for resubmissions. Appeal procedures vary with individual programs and are either listed in this section or are documented in the relevant Code of Federal Regulations (CFR).

Renewals

This section discusses whether renewals or extensions of applications are available and indicates the appropriate procedures. In some instances, renewal procedures may be the same as the application procedure, e.g. for projects of a non-continuing nature renewals will be treated as new, competing applications; for projects of an ongoing nature, renewals may be given annually.

Criteria for Selecting Proposals

This section indicates the criteria used by the Federal grantor agency to evaluate proposals and the criteria used to award funds for projects.

Examples of Funded Projects

This section indicates the different types of projects that have been funded in the past. Only projects funded under Project Grants or Direct Payments for Specified Use are listed here. The examples give potential applicants an idea of the projects that may be accepted for funding.

Range of Assistance Given

This section lists the representative range (smallest to largest) of the amount of financial assistance available. These figures are based on funds awarded in the past fiscal year and the current fiscal year to date. Also indicated is an approximate average amount of awards that were made in the past and current fiscal years.

Related Programs

This section lists programs in the Catalog that are closely related based on objectives and program uses. Applicants should also refer to these programs, as they may provide additional assistance in a related area of interest.

Program Accomplishments

This section briefly describes the accomplishments of the program using quantitative data, focusing on program output, results achieved, or services rendered during the past fiscal year, the current fiscal year, and projections for the next fiscal year.

Financial And Administrative Information

Federal Agency

The Federal agency is the Federal department, agency, commission, council, or instrumentality of the government, and the primary organizational sub-unit (the administering office) that has direct operational responsibility for managing a program.

Types of Assistance

This section indicates the form in which the assistance is transmitted from the Federal government and is initially received for use or distribution by the applicant. See also Types of Assistance.

Obligations

The dollar amounts listed in this section represent obligations for the past fiscal year, estimates for the current fiscal year, and estimates for the budget fiscal year as reported by the Federal agencies. In each succeeding edition of the Catalog, the dollar amounts are revised to reflect changes that may result from supplemental appropriations or amendments. Each program indicates what the obligation figures represent in terms of the type of assistance provided. Obligations for nonfinancial assistance programs indicate the administrative expenses involved in the operation of the program as an indication of the magnitude of the services being provided, or the items involved in obligations.

Budget Account Number

This 11-digit budget account identification code represents the account that funds a particular program. The code is consistent with the code given for the program area as specified in Appendix III of the Budget of the United States Government.

Authorization

This section lists the legal authority on which a program is based (acts, amendments to acts, Public Law numbers, titles, sections, Statute Codes, citations to the U.S. Code, Executive Orders, Presidential Reorganization Plans, and Memoranda from an agency head).

Regulations, Guidelines, and Literature
This section lists the title, number, and price of guidelines, handbooks, manuals, and other officially published information pertinent to a program. Code of Federal Regulations (CFR) citations are also listed.

Information Contacts

Regional or Local Office
This section lists the agency contact person, address, and phone number of the Federal Regional or Local Offices to

be contacted for detailed information regarding the program such as: current availability of funds and the likelihood of receiving assistance within a given period; preapplication and application forms required; whether a preapplication conference is recommended; assistance available in preparation of applications; whether funding decisions are made at the headquarters, regional, or local level; application renewal procedures (including continuations and supplementals) or appeal procedures for rejected applications; and recently published program guidelines and material. For many programs in the Catalog, this section suggests consulting Appendix IV for these offices.

Headquarters Office
This section lists names and addresses of the office at the headquarters level with direct operational responsibility for managing a program. A phone number is provided in cases in which a Regional or Local Office is not normally able to answer detailed inquiries about the program. Also listed is contact information for persons who can provide additional information. If the departmental or agency Internet site is known, it is shown as a link.

Assistance Considerations

Formula and Matching Requirements
This section indicates the formula and matching requirements prescribed in the allocation of funds or maintenance of effort requirements. A formula may be based on population, per capita income, and other statistical factors. Applicants are informed about any matching requirements to be met.

In general, the matching share represents that portion of the project costs not borne by the Federal government. Usually, a minimum percentage for matching share is prescribed by program legislation, and matching share requirements are included in the grant agreement. Attachment F of OMB Circular No. A-102 sets forth the criteria and procedures for matching requirements, including those made in cash or in-kind. Cash contributions represent the grantees' cash outlay, including the outlay of money contributed to the grantee by other public agencies, institutions, private organizations, or individuals. When authorized by Federal regulation, Federal funds received from other grants may be considered as the grantees' cash contribution. In-kind contributions represent the value of noncash contributions provided by the grantee, other public agencies and institutions, private organizations, or individuals. In-kind contributions may consist of charges for real property and equipment, and value of goods and services directly benefiting and specifically identifiable to the grant program. When authorized by Federal legislation, property purchased with Federal funds may be considered as grantees' in-kind contribution. Maintenance of effort (MOE) is a requirement contained in certain legislation, regulations, or administrative policies that a grantee must maintain a specified level of financial effort in a specific area to receive Federal grant funds, and that the Federal grant funds may be used only to supplement, not supplant the level of grantee funds. Programs that have MOE requirements and have total allocations over $100 million (current fiscal year) will have the following statement in this section: "This program has maintenance of effort (MOE) requirements, see funding agency for further details."

Length and Time Phasing of Assistance
This section indicates the time period during which the assistance is normally available, any restrictions on the time permitted to use the funds awarded, if any, and the timing of disbursement of the assistance, e.g. lump sum, annually, quarterly, or as a required.

Uses and Use Restrictions

This section describes the potential uses for the assistance provided to meet stated objectives, and the specific restrictions on the use of funds. The section cites one or more applications depending on the nature of a particular program. Since this section translates objectives into the uses of a program, users may develop a clearer understanding of the program's objectives.

Post Assistance Requirements

Reports

This section indicates whether program reports, expenditure reports, cash reports, or performance monitoring is required by the Federal funding agency, and specifies the time intervals (monthly, annually, etc.).

Audits

This section discusses audits required by the Federal agency. The procedures and requirements for State and local governments and nonprofit organizations and institutions are set forth in OMB Circular No. A-133.

These requirements pertain to awards made within the respective State's fiscal year - not the Federal fiscal year, as some State and local governments may use the calendar year or other variation of time span designated as the fiscal year period, rather than that commonly known as the Federal fiscal year (from October 1st through September 30th).

Records

This section indicates the record retention requirements and the type of records the Federal agency may require. Not included are the normally imposed requirements of the General Accounting Office.

Foundation Grants

If you can't find what you need through the government, then you can turn to other sources for funds. Private foundations are nonprofit entities that are managed by a board of trustees and directors. When you think of these foundations, you usually think of the Ford or Rockefeller Foundations. These were established by wealthy families, and are designed to support a variety of humanitarian causes. They receive their monies from a principle fund or endowment. More than two-thirds of foundations are Family foundations that are influenced or managed by the founding donor or donor's family. Another type of foundation, called a Community Foundation, receives their monies from a variety of donors in a specific area and the focus is to support charitable activities in their area. In 1998, foundations made nearly $19.5 billion in charitable grants.

Before approaching these foundations as your funding source, there are many issues to consider. Primarily these foundations provide grants to other nonprofits, not to individuals. Some foundations fund a specific focus area, such as the arts, children, or housing. Other considerations have to do with the geographic area. Foundations may fund projects nationally or internationally, but some only support projects in a particular state or region. It is generally good to identify state or local foundations, as they may have a greater interest in local problems. Also, the type of support varies. Foundations may supply grants for scholarships, building funds, or seed money. Foundations often have specific funding cycles to consider and strict eligibility requirements. Planning ahead is the key.

As most of their funds go to nonprofits, individual grant seekers may have difficulty receiving funds from private foundations. You must look carefully at the foundation's guidelines to see if you meet the requirements. Obviously, major foundations would be overwhelmed sifting through thousands of individual donor requests. In addition, there are strict regulations regarding record keeping and other financial issues that foundations must follow. Other nonprofits are familiar with these and compliance is easier.

Find A Nonprofit To Work With

You may want to consider an affiliation with a tax-exempt organization. The organization would be the fiscal sponsor, which means that they would receive the grant funds, and then disperse them to your project. Think of your current membership in various organizations or clubs. What about local service organizations or educational institutions? Think of organizations that offer programs similar to yours or organizations that may gain some benefit by supporting yours. All of these are potential partners in your endeavor. Many organizations or community colleges would like the good public relations your project would generate. It is imperative that if you choose to affiliate with an organization, that the organization be a tax-exempt organization designated as such by the Internal Revenue Service. You should see that they have 501(c)3 status. The main purpose of establishing an affiliation is to open the doors to more funding opportunities. The tax exempt status will allow the organization to receive monies from foundations, as well as offer a tax deduction to those who donate to the organization. When you form an affiliation with an organization, there are several things to consider and that should be settled in some form of a letter of agreement.

- how long will this relationship last?
- who is responsible for the record keeping the funding organization will require?
- how much autonomy will you be allowed? Remember, your project will be a reflection on the affiliation organization, as well as on yourself.
- if your project involves music, writing, video, art, etc., who will own the copyright to these works?
- how will the financial arrangement be handled?
- what other types of support can they offer you?

The Foundation Center

The Foundation Center is a nonprofit organization which gathers and disseminates factual information on foundations. The Center's libraries in New York City, Atlanta, San Francisco, Cleveland, and Washington, DC, contain copies of foundations' tax returns, extensive collections of books, documents, and reports about the foundation field, and current files on the activities and programs of about 50,000 U.S. foundations, plus knowledgeable staff to assist users in locating appropriate information.

The Foundation Center also publishes funding directories specific to certain fields, such as: aging; arts and culture; children, youth, and families; health; higher education; international programs; libraries and information services; religion; women and girls; and elementary and secondary education.

In addition, the Center has established cooperating reference collections in each state, where Center publications and information on foundations in the immediate state or region can be consulted. A list of cooperating libraries housing these regional collections appears in most of the Center's publications.

It is a good idea to look for foundations close to home; they are more likely to have a greater interest in local problems than would larger foundations with a national focus. Foundation Center resources are a good starting point for identifying likely funding sources. The next step is to learn more about these foundations by obtaining copies of their annual reports and/or grants guidelines. Some may be available at the Foundation Center's cooperating libraries. Grantseekers will need to find out whether their projected proposals match the foundation's areas of interest and geographic guidelines, whether the proposal is within the foundation's budgetary constraints, and whether the foundation normally funds the type of project being considered. For further information, contact the Foundation Center, 79 Fifth Avenue, New York, NY 10003; 800-424-9836: 212-620-4230; {http://fdncenter.org}.

Developing and Writing
Federal Government Grant Proposals

PART ONE:
Developing A Grant Proposal

Preparation

A successful grant proposal is one that is well prepared, thoughtfully planned, and concisely packaged. The potential applicant should become familiar with all of the pertinent program criteria related to the Catalog program from which assistance is sought. Refer to the information contact person listed in the Catalog program description before developing a proposal to obtain information such as whether funding is available, when applicable deadlines occur, and the process used by the grantor agency for accepting applications. Applicants should remember that the basic requirements, application forms, information, and procedures vary with the Federal agency making the grant award. Individuals without prior grant proposal writing experience may find it useful to attend a grantsmanship workshop. A workshop can amplify the basic information presented here. Applicants interested in additional readings on grantsmanship and proposal development should consult the references listed at the end of this section and explore other library resources.

Initial Proposal Development:
Developing Ideas for the Proposal

When developing an idea for a proposal it is important to determine if the idea has been considered in the applicant's locality or state. A careful check should be made with legislators and area government agencies and related public and private agencies which may currently have grant awards or contracts to do similar work. If a similar program already exists, the applicant may need to reconsider submitting the proposed project, particularly if duplication of effort is perceived. If significant differences or improvements in the proposed project's goals can be clearly established, it may be worthwhile to pursue Federal assistance.

Community Support

Community support for most proposals is essential. Once a proposal summary is developed, look for individuals or groups representing academic, political, professional, and lay organizations that may be willing to support the proposal in writing. The type and caliber of community support is critical in the initial and subsequent review phases. Numerous letters of support can be persuasive to a grantor agency. Do not overlook support from local government agencies and public officials. Letters of endorsement detailing exact areas of project sanction and commitment are often requested as part of a proposal to a Federal agency. Several months may be required to develop letters of endorsement since something of value (e.g., buildings, staff, services) is sometimes negotiated between the parties involved. Many agencies require, in writing, affiliation agreements (a mutual agreement to share services between agencies) and building space commitments prior to either grant approval or award. A useful method of generating community support may be to hold meetings with the top decision makers in the community who would be concerned with the subject matter of the proposal. The forum for discussion may include a query into the merits of the proposal, development of a contract of support for the proposal, generation of data in support of the proposal, or development of a strategy to create proposal support from a large number of community groups.

Identification of a Funding Resource

A review of the Objectives and Uses and Use Restrictions sections of the Catalog program description can point out which programs might provide funding for an idea. Do not overlook the related programs as potential resources.

Both the applicant and the grantor agency should have the same interests, intentions, and needs, if a proposal is to be considered an acceptable candidate for funding.

Once a potential grantor agency is identified, call the contact telephone number identified in Information Contacts and ask for a grant application kit. Later, get to know some of the grantor agency personnel. Ask for suggestions, criticisms, and advice about the proposed project. In many cases, the more agency personnel know about the proposal, the better the chance of support and of an eventual favorable decision. Sometimes it is useful to send the proposal summary to a specific agency official in a separate cover letter, and ask for review and comment at the earliest possible convenience. Always check with the Federal agency to determine its preference if this approach is under consideration. If the review is unfavorable and differences cannot be resolved, ask the examining agency (official) to suggest another department or agency which may be interested in the proposal. A personal visit to the agency's regional office or headquarters is also important. A visit not only establishes face-to-face contact, but also may bring out some essential details about the proposal or help secure literature and references from the agency's library.

Federal agencies are required to report funding information as funds are approved, increased, or decreased among projects within a given State depending on the type of required reporting. Also, consider reviewing the Federal Budget for the current and budget fiscal years to determine proposed dollar amounts for particular budget functions. The applicant should carefully study the eligibility requirements for each Federal program under consideration (see the Applicant Eligibility section of the Catalog program description). The applicant may learn that he or she is required to provide services otherwise unintended such as a service to particular client groups, or involvement of specific institutions. It may necessitate the modification of the original concept in order for the project to be eligible for funding. Questions about eligibility should be discussed with the appropriate program officer. Deadlines for submitting applications are often not negotiable. They are usually associated with strict timetables for agency review. Some programs have more than one application deadline during the fiscal year. Applicants should plan proposal development around the established deadlines.

Getting Organized to Write the Proposal

Throughout the proposal writing stage keep a notebook handy to write down ideas. Periodically, try to connect ideas by reviewing the notebook. Never throw away written ideas during the grant writing stage. Maintain a file labeled "Ideas" or by some other convenient title and review the ideas from time to time. The file should be easily accessible. The gathering of documents such as articles of incorporation, tax exemption certificates, and bylaws should be completed, if possible, before the writing begins.

REVIEW

Criticism

At some point, perhaps after the first or second draft is completed, seek out a neutral third party to review the proposal working draft for continuity, clarity, and reasoning. Ask for constructive criticism at this point, rather than wait for the Federal grantor agency to volunteer this information during the review cycle. For example, has the writer made unsupported assumptions or used jargon or excessive language in the proposal?

Signature

Most proposals are made to institutions rather than individuals. Often signatures of chief administrative officials are required. Check to make sure they are included in the proposal where appropriate.

Neatness

Proposals should be typed, collated, copied, and packaged correctly and neatly (according to agency instructions, if any). Each package should be inspected to ensure uniformity from cover to cover. Binding may require either clamps or hard covers. Check with the Federal agency to determine its preference. A neat, organized, and attractive proposal package can leave a positive impression with the reader about the proposal contents.

Mailing

A cover letter should always accompany a proposal. Standard U.S. Postal Service requirements apply unless otherwise indicated by the Federal agency. Make sure there is time for the proposals to reach their destinations. Otherwise, special arrangements may be necessary. Always coordinate such arrangements with the Federal grantor agency project office (the agency which will ultimately have the responsibility for the project), the grant office (the agency which will coordinate the grant review), and the contract office (the agency responsible for disbursement and grant award notices), if necessary.

PART TWO:
Writing The Grant Proposal

The Basic Components of a Proposal

There are eight basic components to creating a solid proposal package:

- The proposal summary;
- Introduction of organization;
- The problem statement (or needs assessment);
- Project objectives;
- Project methods or design;
- Project evaluation;
- Future funding;
- The project budget.

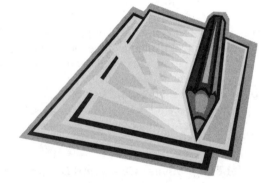

The following will provide an overview of these components.

The Proposal Summary:
Outline of Project Goals

The proposal summary outlines the proposed project and should appear at the beginning of the proposal. It could be in the form of a cover letter or a separate page, but should definitely be brief - no longer than two or three paragraphs. The summary would be most useful if it were prepared after the proposal has been developed in order to encompass all the key summary points necessary to communicate the objectives of the project. It is this document that becomes the cornerstone of your proposal, and the initial impression it gives will be critical to the success of your venture. In many cases, the summary will be the first part of the proposal package seen by agency officials and very possibly could be the only part of the package that is carefully reviewed before the decision is made to consider the project any further.

The applicant must select a fundable project that can be supported in view of the local need. Alternatives, in the absence of Federal support, should be pointed out. The influence of the project both during and after the project period should be explained. The consequences of the project as a result of funding should be highlighted.

Introduction: Presenting a Credible Applicant or Organization

The applicant should gather data about its organization from all available sources. Most proposals require a description of an applicant's organization to describe its past and present operations. Some features to consider are:

- A brief biography of board members and key staff members;
- The organization's goals, philosophy, track record with other grantors, and any success stories.

The data should be relevant to the goals of the Federal grantor agency and should establish the applicant's credibility.

The Problem Statement: Staffing the Purpose at Hand

The problem statement (or needs assessment) is a key element of a proposal that makes a clear, concise, and well supported statement of the problem to be addressed. The best way to collect information about the problem is to conduct and document both a formal and informal needs assessment for a program in the target or service area. The information provided should be both factual and directly related to the problem addressed by the proposal. Areas to document are:

- The purpose for developing the proposal.
- The beneficiaries - who are they and how will they benefit.
- The social and economic costs to be affected.
- The nature of the problem (provide as much hard evidence as possible).
- How the applicant organization came to realize the problem exists and what is currently being done about the problem.
- The remaining alternatives available when funding has been exhausted. Explain what will happen to the project and the impending implications. Most importantly, explain the specific manner through which problems might be solved. Review the resources needed, considering how they will be used and to what end.

> **There are eight basic components to creating a solid proposal package**

There is a considerable body of literature on the exact assessment techniques to be used. Any local, regional, or state government planning office, or local university offering course work in planning and evaluation techniques should be able to provide excellent background references. Types of data that may be collected include: historical, geographic, quantitative, factual, statistical, and philosophical information, as well as studies completed by colleges, and literature searches from public or university libraries. Local colleges or universities that have a department or section related to the proposal topic may help determine if there is interest in developing a student or faculty project to conduct a needs assessment. It may be helpful to include examples of the findings for highlighting in the proposal.

Project Objectives: Goals and Desired Outcome

Program objectives refer to specific activities in a proposal. It is necessary to identify all objectives related to the goals to be reached and the methods to be employed to achieve the stated objectives. Consider quantities or things measurable and refer to a problem statement and the outcome of proposed activities when developing a well stated objective. The figures used should be verifiable. Remember, if the proposal is funded, the stated objectives will probably be used to evaluate program progress, so be realistic. There is literature available to help identify and write program objectives.

Program Method and Program Design: A Plan of Action

The program design refers to how the project is expected to work and solve the stated problem. Sketch out the following:

- The activities to occur along with the related resources and staff needed to operate the project (inputs).
- A flow chart of the organizational features of the project. Describe how the parts interrelate, where personnel will be needed, and what they are expected to do. Identify the kinds of facilities, transportation, and support services required (throughputs).
- Explain what will be achieved through 1 and 2 above (outputs); i.e., plan for measurable results. Project staff may be required to produce evidence of program performance through an examination of stated objectives during either a site visit by the Federal grantor agency and/or grant reviews which may involve peer review committees. It may be useful to devise a diagram of the program design. For example, draw a three column block. Each column is headed by one of the parts (inputs, throughputs, and outputs), and on

the left (next to the first column) specific program features should be identified (i.e., implementation, staffing, procurement, and systems development). In the grid, specify something about the program design, for example, assume the first column is labeled inputs, and the first row is labeled staff. On the grid, one might specify under inputs five nurses to operate a child care unit. The throughput might be to maintain charts, counsel the children, and set up a daily routine; outputs might be to discharge 25 healthy children per week. This type of procedure will help to conceptualize both the scope and detail of the project.

- Wherever possible, justify in the narrative the course of action taken. The most economical method should be used that does not compromise or sacrifice project quality. The financial expenses associated with performance of the project will later become points of negotiation with the Federal program staff. If everything is not carefully justified in writing in the proposal, after negotiation with the Federal grantor agencies, the approved project may resemble less of the original concept. Carefully consider the pressures of the proposed implementation, that is, the time and money needed to acquire each part of the plan. A Program Evaluation and Review Technique (PERT) chart could be useful and supportive in justifying some proposals. Highlight the innovative features of the proposal which could be considered distinct from other proposals under consideration.
- Whenever possible, use appendices to provide details, supplementary data, references, and information requiring in-depth analysis. These types of data, although supportive of the proposal, if included in the body of the design, could detract from its readability. Appendices provide the proposal reader with immediate access to details if and when clarification of an idea, sequence, or conclusion is required. Time tables, work plans, schedules, activities, methodologies, legal papers, personal vitae, letters of support, and endorsements are examples of appendices.

Evaluation: Product and Process Analysis

The evaluation component is two fold: (1) product evaluation; and (2) process evaluation. Product evaluation addresses results that can be attributed to the project, as well as the extent to which the project has satisfied its desired objectives. Process evaluation addresses how the project was conducted, in terms of consistency with the stated plan of action and the effectiveness of the various activities, within the plan.

Most Federal agencies now require some form of program evaluation among grantees. The requirements of the proposed project should be explored carefully. Evaluations may be conducted by an internal staff member, an evaluation firm or both. The applicant should state the amount of time needed to evaluate, how the feedback will be distributed among the proposed staff, and a schedule for review and comment for this type of communication. Evaluation designs may start at the beginning, middle, or end of a project, but the applicant should specify a start-up time. It is practical to submit an evaluation design at the start of a project for two reasons:

- Convincing evaluations require the collection of appropriate data before and during program operations; and,
- If the evaluation design cannot be prepared at the outset, then a critical review of the program design may be advisable.

Even if the evaluation design has to be revised as the project progresses, it is much easier and cheaper to modify a good design. If the problem is not well-defined and carefully analyzed for cause and effect relationships, then a good evaluation design may be difficult to achieve. Sometimes a pilot study is needed to begin the identification of facts and relationships. Often a thorough literature search may be sufficient.

Evaluation requires both coordination and agreement among program decision makers (if known). Above all, the Federal grantor agency's requirements should be highlighted in the evaluation design. Also, Federal grantor agencies may require specific evaluation techniques such as designated data formats (an existing information collection system) or they may offer financial inducements for voluntary participation in a national evaluation study. The applicant should ask specifically about these points. Also, consult the Criteria For Selecting Proposals section of the Catalog program description to determine the exact evaluation methods to be required for the program if funded.

Future Funding: Long-Term Project Planning

Describe a plan for continuation beyond the grant period, and/or the availability of other resources necessary to implement the grant. Discuss maintenance and future program funding if the program is for construction activity. Account for other needed expenditures if the program includes purchase of equipment.

The Proposal Budget: Planning the Budget

Funding levels in Federal assistance programs change yearly. It is useful to review the appropriations over the past several years to try to project future funding levels (see the Financial Information section of the Catalog program description).

However, it is safer never to anticipate that the income from the grant will be the sole support for the project. This consideration should be given to the overall budget requirements, and in particular, to budget line items most subject to inflationary pressures. Restraint is important in determining inflationary cost projections (avoid padding budget line items), but attempt to anticipate possible future increases.

Some vulnerable budget areas are: utilities, rental of buildings and equipment, salary increases, food, telephones, insurance, and transportation. Budget adjustments are sometimes made after the grant award, but this can be a lengthy process. Be certain that implementation, continuation, and phase-down costs can be met. Consider costs associated with leases, evaluation systems, hard/soft match requirements, audits, development, implementation, and maintenance of information and accounting systems, and other long term financial commitments.

A well prepared budget justifies all expenses and is consistent with the proposal narrative. Some areas in need of an evaluation for consistency are:

- The salaries in the proposal in relation to those of the applicant organization should be similar;
- If new staff persons are being hired, additional space and equipment should be considered, as necessary;
- If the budget calls for an equipment purchase, it should be the type allowed by the grantor agency;
- If additional space is rented, the increase in insurance should be supported;
- If an indirect cost rate applies to the proposal, the division between direct and indirect costs should not be in conflict, and the aggregate budget totals should refer directly to the approved formula; and
- If matching costs are required, the contributions to the matching fund should be taken out of the budget unless otherwise specified in the application instructions.

It is very important to become familiar with Government-wide circular requirements. The Catalog identifies in the program description section (as information is provided from the agencies) the particular circulars applicable to a Federal program, and summarizes coordination of Executive Order 12372, "Intergovernmental Review of Programs" requirements in Appendix I [not available online]. The applicant should thoroughly review the appropriate circulars since they are essential in determining items such as cost principles and conforming with Government guidelines for Federal domestic assistance.

Guidelines And Literature

United States Government Manual
Superintendent of Documents
U.S. Government Printing Office
Washington, DC 20401

OMB Circular Nos. A-21, A-87, A-102, A-110, A-122, and A-133, and Executive Order 12372:
Publications Office
Office of Administration
725 17th Street, NW
Washington, DC 20503

Government Printing Office (GPO) Resources

The government documents identified above as available from the GPO can be requested (supply the necessary identifying information) by writing to:

Superintendent of Documents
Government Printing Office
Washington, DC 20401

Regional and Federal Depository Libraries

Regional libraries can arrange for copies of Government documents through an interlibrary loan. All Federal Depository Libraries will receive copies of the Catalog directly. A list of depository and regional libraries is available by writing:

Chief
Library Division
Superintendent of Documents, Stop SLL
Washington, DC 20401

How To Find Nonprofit Organizations

The Foundation Center is not the only resource for finding nonprofits. One unbelievably info packed location to find nonprofit organizations is Idealist, {www.idealist.org}. This site is maintained as a project of Action Without Borders, a self-described "global coalition of individuals and organizations working to build a world where all people can live free, dignified and productive lives." It is not associated with any specific nation or government.

Idealist has an enormous searchable database, including a list of 37,000 nonprofit and worldwide community organizations from 165 countries. The nonprofit groups run the gamut from children's relief services to the arts to environmental concerns to drug recovery programs. Also available at Idealist is a Nonprofit Career Center. Here you may search for a job in your chosen nonprofit field, look for fellowships in public service, obtain information regarding academic programs geared to students interested in nonprofit organizations as a career, and find many volunteer opportunities available both here and abroad. The career center also allows you to post an opportunity that your organization may have to fill.

In addition to the aforementioned information, Idealist has listings of many of the resources available to groups that maintain nonprofit status. Every imaginable business service is listed here including grant writing, insurance, accounting, video production, marketing, graphic design and public relations. For more information, contact Action Without Borders, 79 Fifth Ave., New York, NY 10003; 212-843-3973; {www.idealist.org}.

Known as "The donor's guide to the charitable universe," GuideStar, {www.guidestar.org}, is a veritable Mecca of nonprofit information. Its searchable database has 850,000 (not a typo!) organizations listed for the United States. In addition to the plethora of listed nonprofits, GuideStar also offers help to those organizations, including how to file tax documents properly and successfully. GuideStar's website is maintained by a group called Philanthropic Research, Inc., (PRI) which serves to encourage all types of philanthropic work. Any group with nonprofit status can be listed at GuideStar free of charge. As with Idealist, GuideStar also offers a link to information regarding volunteering, jobs, careers, and how to make donations and give online. The Nonprofit HelpCenter is also available to help groups register online, so that they too, can be listed among the extensive group of GuideStar's database. Contact GuideStar, 427 Scotland St., Williamsburg, VA 23185; 757-229-4631.

The Foundation Center is an online "gateway to philanthropy on the World Wide Web." Along with a large database of philanthropic organizations, including links to funding groups and corporate and private foundations, there are links and information on how to write a proposal, how to establish a nonprofit organization, tax info and how to receive grants for individuals. There is also an extensive library, which has large excerpts from appropriate publications about nonprofits. Many of the books are available for sale online as well. Also available for purchase are CD-Roms and a huge selection of books and directories of nonprofits. Some of these directories are categorized by location, while others are listed by topic, such as Health, and the Arts. The list of resources is seemingly endless. A printable digest from The Foundation Center entitled Philanthropy News Digest is also accessible from this website and contains articles on a large variety of subjects relating to charitable works and organizations. There is also a large searchable database, The Foundation Directory Online, available by subscription, for $195 annually. The directory is updated quarterly. For further information, contact the Foundation Center, 79 Fifth Avenue, New York, NY 10003; 800-424-9836; 212-620-4230; {http://fdncenter.org}.

The Internet Nonprofit Center is operated by The Evergreen State Society located in Seattle, Washington. Their website has a Locator Search feature which provides the name and location of nonprofits. Search at {www.nonprofits.org}. For more information, contact the Evergreen State Society, P.O. Box 20682, Seattle, WA 98102; 206-329-5640; {www.nonprofits.org}.

The Council on Foundations assists foundations to help them grow and work effectively. Their website {www.cof.org} has links to community foundations and to member foundations and corporate giving programs. For more information, contact Council on Foundations, 1828 L St., NW, Washington, DC 20036; 202-466-6512; {www.cof.org}.

Here is your chance to use the IRS. The IRS has a database of over 1,000 tax-exempt organizations from which you can access a wealth of priceless information. You may access this database through the website. In order to understand the codes in these files, you will also have to download the Instructions Booklet, which is available on the same link. This information is also available on CD-ROM and includes more financial information per organization than the Internet data. Ask for the Statistics of Income (SOI) samples of Forms 990 and 990-EZ. Contact Internal Revenue Service, P.O. Box 2608, Washington, DC 20013; 202-874-0700; {www.irs.gov/charities/index.html}.

In addition the Exempt Organizations Technical Division of the IRS publishes the Cumulative List of Organizations that includes a complete listing of names and addresses of exempt organizations. To order this subscription for $160 contact the Superintendent of Documents, U.S. Government Printing Office, Washington, DC 20401; 202-512-1800; {www.gpoaccess.gov}. Don't forget to check with your state registration office for nonprofits. See "How To Start Or Become A Nonprofit Organization" on page 102.

Corporate Grants

Within the past decade, as government funding on the federal, state, and local levels has declined, there has been a steady increase in grant seekers pursuing corporate support. Many corporations provide funds for local projects in areas where they have their headquarters or plants, or sponsor projects which somehow enhance their corporate image. Corporate foundations operate a little differently than private foundations, as they can often respond quicker to your requests and don't have the regulations that private foundations must follow. In addition, corporations will often also offer in-kind contributions, such as equipment, use of facilities, or expertise to assist you in your project. Information on corporate foundations and direct corporate giving is listed at the Foundation Center website at {http://fdncenter.org/funders}.

HOW TO START OR BECOME A NONPROFIT ORGANIZATION

Don't be Afraid...Read on!

Sound impossible? No way! Yes it can be bureaucratic and there's some red tape you'll have to wade through, but if you are a qualifying type of organization, getting nonprofit status is definitely the way to go, especially if you want to get grants from funding groups. Attaining nonprofit status for yourself as a group or organization may be critical in order to receive those grants that you are hoping will fund you, and it will only cost you a couple hundred dollars! Many grants are only available to nonprofits. So don't wince at the mention of what may sound like an overwhelming and daunting task. Dive in! It may be easier than you think.

First and foremost in establishing or creating a nonprofit is filing for Federal and state nonprofit tax status. Nonprofit status is not available to individuals, only to organizations, so your group must be incorporated or exist as an association or trust. To help you determine if your organization may qualify for tax-exempt status, or to find out what you will need to do in order to qualify, request Publication 557 from the local office of the Internal Revenue Service. This publication takes you step-by-step through the filing process, and contains instructions and checklists to help you provide all of the necessary information required to process your application the first time around. The fee to become exempt can be as low at $150! The IRS has even established a hotline at 877-829-5500 staffed with experts on completing the forms and can help you with any questions you may have. They can't make it any easier for you! You can also check out any questions you may have at {http://www.irs.gov/charities/index.html}.

Most organizations seeking tax-exempt status from the Federal government must use either; Form 1023, Application for Recognition of Exemption Under Section 501(c) (3) of the Internal Revenue Code; Form 1024, Application for Recognition of Exemption Under Section 501(a) or for Determination Under Section 120. The forms will ask you to provide the following information:

* A description of the purposes and activities of your organization
* Financial information, and if you have not yet begun operation, a proposed budget, along with a statement of assets and liabilities (if you have any)
* Information on how you intend to finance your activities, through fundraisers, grants, etc.

Another great feature available directly from the IRS is the Tax-Exempt Organization Tax Kit. Basically it's a packet that contains all the necessary forms for filing for exemption status, all informational publications and even forms for filing your tax return, the various versions of Form 990, Return of Organization Exempt from Income Tax. These publications are downloadable, grouped together at the IRS website, within the Tax-Exempt section. They are also available by calling 800-TAX-FORM, toll-free.

Critical when filing for tax-exempt status, obviously, is to have an organization that has a darned good reason for asking for exemption. The IRS has separated the classifications of acceptable organizations into ten groups within which your potential organization may fall, thus possibly qualifying for exemption.

* Charitable Organizations
    - Charitable
    - Religious
    - Educational
    - Scientific

    - Literary

* Social Welfare Organizations
    - Civic Leagues
    - Community Organizations

* Labor and Agricultural Organizations
  - Labor Unions
  - Farm Bureaus

* Social Clubs
  - Hobby Clubs
  - Country Clubs

* Business Leagues
  - Trade Associations
  - Chambers of Commerce
  - Real Estate Boards

* Fraternal Societies
  - Lodges and Similar Orders and Associations

* Veteran's Organizations
  - Posts or organizations of past or present members of the Armed forces of the United States

* Employees' Associations
  - Voluntary employees' benefit associations
  - Local associations of employees

* Political Organizations
  - Campaign committees
  - Political parties
  - Political action committees

* Other Tax-Exempt Organizations
  - Miscellaneous qualifying organizations

The organization must also have an Employer Identification Number (EIN), be in the process of applying, or apply directly while applying for exemption status. Form SS-4, Application for Employer Identification Number, gives detailed instructions on obtaining an EIN over the phone. The form is downloadable from the IRS web site. Once you have your EIN enter it into your application or exemption form. Please note that the correct IRS contact information for all exempt organizations seeking an EIN is below.

EIN Operations   800-829-4933
Holtsville   {www.irs.gov}
NY 00501   Fax: 631-447-8960

The applications require detailed financial status. If it is a new organization, current financial statements must be provided along with projected budgets for the coming two years. Organizations in existence three years or more also must provide current information as well as detailed info from the last two years. Once you have submitted the necessary forms and fees, and all goes well, a ruling or determination letter should be on its way to you in no time.

To receive help and information directly from the IRS, contact your local office listed in the government pages of your telephone book or contact:

Exempt Organizations Technical Division
Internal Revenue Service
U.S. Department of Treasury
1111 Constitution Ave., NW   877-829-5500
Washington, DC 20224   {www.irs.gov}

Once you are granted tax-exempt status, you must move on to the task of filing new forms to account for your tax year. And careful, detailed accounting is a must. Filing your organization's Form 990, the IRS nonprofit tax return, requires some rigorous financial reporting. As a nonprofit organization, you must report carefully the following:

1. An object revenue & income statement, with particular categories specified (rental revenue),

2. A balance sheet, with particular categories specified like cash, accounts receivable, accounts payable (salaries, postage etc.),

3. A statement of functional expenses, in which all expenses are allocated to program services, fundraising, or operations,

4. A report of expenses segregated by individual program service (educational mailings, a seminar program),

5. A support schedule that details the organization's sources of revenue, with particular categories specified (charitable donations, membership fees, investment income).

Never fear! While it may sound confusing and tedious, there is hope! Luckily there is accounting software available to help you with your reporting. Sort of like Turbo Tax for nonprofits, these available software systems, if set up appropriately, can make your IRS reporting pretty easy. Thank goodness!

Although we do not recommend any particular accounting software, a simple internet search turned up a wealth of software systems. Here is a sampling of what we found:

- NfpAccounting.com, 7050 Friars Rd., Suite 203, San Diego, CA 92108; 619-275-0907; {www.nfpaccounting.com}.

- CYMA Systems, 2330 W. University Dr., Suite 7, Tempe, AZ 85281; 800-292-2962; {www.cyma.com}.

- Araize, 130 Iowa Lane, Suite 102, Cary, NC 27511; 919-319-1770; {www.araize.com}.

- ACI Associates, Inc., 5732-D Industry Lane, P.O. Box 1144, Frederick, MD 21702; 800-966-6725; {www.automationc.com}.

- SunGard Bi-Tech, 890 Fortress St., Chico, CA 95973; 530-891-5281; {www.bi-tech.com}.

- Fund E-Z Development Corporation, 106 Corporate Park Drive, White Plains, NY 10604; 914-696-0900; {www.fundez.com}.

- Intuit Fundware, 6430 S. Fiddlers Green Circle, Ste 500, Greenwood Village, CO 80111; 800-551-4458; {http://publicsector.intuit.com}.

- MIP, 313 East Anderson Lane, Suite 120, Austin, TX 78752; 800-647-3863; {www.mip.com}.

There are many advantages to becoming a nonprofit organization. An obvious one is getting reduced rates on things like postage. But the United States Postal Service may not consider your group a nonprofit just because you have tax-exempt status. There are many rules, regulations and restrictions. For example, nonprofits must fall into categories somewhat like the IRS categories listed above, and then they must file Form 3624 in order to have their request processed. The acceptable categories are: religious, agricultural, educational, labor, scientific, veterans, philanthropic and fraternal. For more information, forms for application and all the Post Office rules, visit the USPS website, {www.usps.com} and search the Postal Explorer, for "nonprofit."

Another thing that some nonprofits are able to do is set up lobbying groups. Again, there can be substantial red tape involved. You must file forms with the IRS and be of a particular nature to qualify. Basically, nonprofits may lobby if they are publicly funded in some way, educational or hospital medical research organizations, or organizations supporting government schools. Any group lobbying in any inappropriate way will not be permitted to do so. If it goes beyond the limits and lobbying is substantial, (this is usually determined by proportion of moneys spent), the organization is likely to lose its Federal tax-exempt status.

State Registration

As with any filing of a tax application or return, when you send in something to the Federal government, you need to notify your state government as well. Although it is the IRS that gives you the authority to raise money as a tax-exempt organization, your state government will want to know about the proposed activities of your organization. Relevant information that your state will be interested in includes:

* The name and address of registrant
* The purpose of the nonprofit
* Any articles of incorporation
* The names and addresses of any board of directors

In existence is something known as the Unified Registration Statement, (URS) which serves as a kind of standard form that most of the states in the country accept as the ample documentation to register within said state as a nonprofit organization. The state will also want to know how much of a tax-exempt contribution you expect to attain over the course of a year. Some states have maximum amounts before you must register, while others have no minimum. Some states' fees are based upon the amount of contributions, and some are flat fees. The usual fee for filing this information with most states is minimal, usually from $30.00 to $50.00, with some states requiring no fee, and others going much higher. Contact the appropriate state corporation office, listed on pages 121–129 to obtain the necessary forms, and see the state listings below for more specific state-by-state information. The state will also require an annual financial report, and most will accept a completed Federal IRS report.

Don't forget that state and Federal laws are not the only ones to which nonprofit organizations are subject. Governments of smaller jurisdictions, such as counties, cities, municipalities, small towns, and really any form of governmental authority, can and do implement laws that may be stricter or at least different than their superior governments. Such an authority may require organizations to register specifically within their jurisdiction, in addition to all other state and Federal registrations. Any soliciting organizations, no matter where they are based, that make charitable solicitations to residents of these jurisdictions, and don't adhere to the local law and its associated regulations, may be subject to legal action by that jurisdiction's governmental authority.

State Registration Requirements

Alabama
Office of the Attorney General
Consumer Affairs Section
11 South Union St.
Montgomery, AL 36130
334-242-7300
800-392-5658
www.ago.state.al.us

Registration Requirements
State form or URS
IRS Determination Letter
Articles of Incorporation or charitable organizational
    charter
$25 Registration fee

Organizations exempt from registration:
Educational institutions and their authorized and
    related foundations;
Religious organizations;
Political organizations;
Fraternal, patriotic, benevolent, social, educational,
    alumni, heath care foundation, historical and
    civil rights organizations, including fraternities
    and sororities;
Civic leagues and civic organizations, which solicit
    solely from their own membership;
Any charitable organization which does not intend to
    solicit and receive and does not actually receive
    contributions in excess of $25,000 during the
    fiscal year, provided all of its fundraising

functions are carried on by persons who are unpaid for their services;

Persons requesting any contributions collected for the relief of a specific named individual if all contributions do not exceed $10,000 and are turned over to the named beneficiary;

Any post, camp, chapter of a bona fide veteran's organization, or organization of volunteer firefighters, ambulance companies, or rescue squads and affiliates of those organizations, whose fundraising is done by unpaid volunteers

Annual Reporting Requirements
Due within 90 days of fiscal year end
Annual written report in required format
Annual $25 filing fee
IRS 990 or financial report
Registration renewal required annually on or before September 30th

Alaska
Attorney General
Alaska Department of Law
1031 W. 4th Ave., Suite 200
Anchorage, AK 99501-1994
907-269-5135
www.law.state.ak.us

Registration Requirements
State form -(URS not accepted)
IRS Form 990
Audit
Due September 1st

Organizations exempt from registration:
Religious organizations;

Charitable organizations that do not intend to or do not raise or receive contributions, excluding government grants, in excess of $5,000 during a fiscal year;

Organizations that do not receive contributions from more than ten (10) persons during a fiscal year if either, 1) all functions, including solicitation, are carried on by volunteers and/or, 2) an officer or member of the organization is not paid or does not otherwise receive all or part of the assets or income of the charitable organization

Annual Reporting Requirements
There are no annual reporting requirements once an organization is registered.

Arizona
Secretary of State
Charitable Organizations
1700 W. Washington, 7th Floor
Phoenix, AZ 85007-2888
602-542-4285, or toll-free in Arizona, 800-458-5842
www.sos.state.az.us

Registration Requirements
State Form A.R.S 44-6552 - (URS not accepted)
IRS Form 990

Organizations exempt from registration:
A charitable organization that is established and operated within Arizona exclusively for a charitable purpose and that has a board of directors that serves without remuneration, if the solicitations are conducted under any of the following conditions 1) by volunteers who receive no remuneration or 2) by bona fide paid employees or 3) at meetings or assemblies of the membership or with individual members;

Nonprofit hospitals and their foundations;

Nonprofit blood banks and their foundations;

Schools, colleges and universities, their associations and foundations;

Licensed public radio and TV stations that are raising monies for their own operations;

Solicitations solely from private foundations;

Political parties, candidates and campaign committees required to file financial information with election commissions or agencies;

Organizations soliciting contributions not exceeding $25,000

Annual Reporting Requirements
State financial report form

Arkansas
Office of Attorney General
Consumer Protection Division
Fundraiser Registration
323 Center St., #200
Little Rock, AR 72201-2610
501-682-2007, or toll-free 800-482-8982
www.ag.state.ar.us

Registration Requirements
State Registration Form or URS
IRS Form 990, or
IRS Form 990-EZ and AR Attachment to IRS Form 990, or
Annual Report of Charitable Organization
IRS Determination letter

Copy of Irrevocable Consent for Service
No registration fee required

Organizations exempt from registration:
Nonprofits raising less than $25,000 per year with no paid staff or fundraisers;
Religious organizations;
Accredited educational institutions and parent-teacher associations associated with accredited institutions;
Governmental organizations -departments, branches or instrumentality of federal, state and local governments;
Nonprofit hospitals licensed in AR or any other state;
Political candidates and organization - any candidate for national, state, or local office or a political party or other committee required to file information with the Federal Election Commission or any other state election commission;

Annual Reporting Requirements
Due Date on or before May 15th or within 6 months after close of fiscal year
No annual filing fee
IRS 990 -EZ or annual report
Audit required for organizations with gross revenue in excess of $500,000

California
State of California
Office of Attorney General
Registry of Charitable Trusts
P.O. Box 903447
Sacramento, CA 94203-4470
916-445-2021
http://caag.state.ca.us/charities

Registration Requirements
State Form CT-1 or URS
Certificate/Articles of Incorporation
Bylaws
IRS Form 990
IRS Determination Letter

Organizations exempt from registration:
Religious corporations;
Religious organizations;
Government agencies;
Political committees;
Schools and hospitals

Annual Reporting Requirements
Due January 15th
Form RRF-1
$25 for organizations with assets or revenue exceeding $100,000 during fiscal year
IRS 990
Financial Report

Colorado
There is no registration requirement in Colorado at this time.

Connecticut
Office of Attorney General
Public Charities Unit
55 Elm St.
P.O.Box 120,
Hartford, CT 06141-0120
860-808-5318
www.cslib.org/attygenl/

Registration Requirements
State Form CPC-63 or URS
One-time filing fee of $20.00

Organizations exempt from registration:
Nonprofits normally receiving less than $25,000 annually provided organization does not compensate any person primarily to conduct solicitations;
Religious corporations, institutions, and societies;
Parent-teacher associations or accredited educational institution;
Nonprofit hospitals licensed under laws of CT or another state;
Government units or instrumentalities of any state or the United States;

Organizations seeking an exemption must file Form CPC-54, "Claim of Exemption From Registration" (no fee required)

Annual Reporting Requirements
Due Date: Within 5 months of the fiscal year end
Form CPC-60, Annual Report Sheet
IRS Form 990
$25 filing fee
Audit if gross receipts (excluding government grants and fees) exceeds $100,000

Delaware
There is no registration requirement in Delaware at this time.

District of Columbia

Department of Consumer & Regulatory Affairs
941 N. Capitol St. NE
Washington, DC 20002
202-442-8941
http://dcra.dc.gov

Registration Requirements
District form or URS
Certificate/Articles of Incorporation
Bylaws
IRS Form 990
IRS Determination Letter

Organizations exempt from registration:
Organizations receiving less than $1,500 in gross
total receipts in a calendar year, provided
individuals who are unpaid carry out all
functions, including fundraising;
Educational organizations raising money for
educational purposes;
Church or religious corporations or organizations
under the control of a church or religious
corporation;
The American Red Cross;
Organizations where solicitations are made
exclusively among the membership of the
soliciting agency

Please note that exempt organizations are required to
file a claim to that exemption.

Annual Reporting Requirements
Due April 15th
$25 filing fee
Financial report

Florida

Florida Dept. of Agriculture & Consumer Services
The Capitol
Tallahassee, FL 32399-0800
850-488-3022
www.doacs.state.fl.us

Registration Requirements
State form - (URS not accepted)
IRS Form 990 or financial report on state form
IRS Determination letter
Fees range from $10–$400

Organizations exempt from registration:
Anyone soliciting for a named individual, provided
all contributions collected without any
deductions are turned over to the beneficiary;

Charitable organizations, which limit solicitation of
contributions to the membership of the
organization

Annual Reporting Requirements
There is no reporting requirement after registration,
which must be renewed annually.

Georgia

Secretary of State
Securities and Business Regulation
Suite 802, West Tower
2 Martin Luther King Jr. Dr. SE
Atlanta, GA 30334
404-656-3920
www.sos.state.ga.us

Registration Requirements
State Form C100 or URS
IRS Form 990
IRS Determination Letter
$25 Registration fee
Audit if gross revenue over $1,000,000
Financial report reviewed by a CPA for organizations
with revenue between $500,000 and $1,000,000

Organization exempt from registration:
Nonprofit educational institutions;
Professional, business and trade associations that do
not solicit members or funds from the general
public;
Fraternal, civic, benevolent, patriotic and social
organizations if solicitations are carried on by
persons for their services and are confined to
their memberships;
Any solicitations for a named person where all
contributions are turned over to named person;
Charitable organizations whose total gross revenue is
less than $25,000
Any local or state organization of hunters, fishermen
and target shooters having tax-exempt status
Political parties, action committees and candidates
for federal or state office who are required to file
financial information to election commissions;
Publishers of commercial publications that solicit
advertisement and provide a percentage of
revenue for a charitable purpose

Please note that proof of exemption is required.

Annual Reporting Requirements
Due within one year of filing

$25 renewal/filing fee
IRS 990
Financial report required if proceeds are $500,000 or
    more (CPA); independent CPA review required
    for proceeds of $100,000 to $500,000
Audit required if revenue is over $1,000,000

Hawaii
There is no registration required in Hawaii at this
    time.

Idaho
There is no registration required in Idaho at this time.

Illinois
Office of the Illinois Attorney General
Charitable Trusts Bureau
100 W. Randolph Street, 3rd Floor
Chicago, IL 60601
312-814-2595
www.ag.state.il.us/charitable/charity.html

Registration Requirements
State Form CO-1 or URS
Certificate/Articles of Incorporation
Bylaws
IRS Form 990
IRS Determination Letter
Audit if over $150,000 in gross revenue
$15 Registration fee
Financial report on state Form CO-2

Organizations exempt from registration:
Government agencies or subdivisions;
Educational institutions;
Religious organizations

Annual Reporting Requirements
Due within 6 months of close of fiscal year
$15 filing fee ($100 late fee if registration expires)
IRS 990
Financial report on state Form AG990-IL
Audit if revenue over is $150,000 or professional
    fundraiser used

Indiana
There is no registration required in Indiana at this
    time.

Iowa
There is no registration required in Iowa at this time.

Kansas
Secretary of State
First Floor, Memorial Hall
120 SW 10th Avenue
Topeka, KS 66612-1594
785-296-4564
www.kssos.org

Registration Requirements
State Form SC or URS
Certificate/Articles of Incorporation
IRS Form 990
IRS Determination Letter
Audit if contributions exceed $100,000.

Organizations exempt from registration:
Any religious corporation, trust or organization;
Accredited educational institutions or any of their
    foundations;
Any other educational institution confining its
    solicitation to the student body, alumni, faculty
    and trustees;
Fraternal, social, alumni organizations and historical
    societies when solicitation is confined to their
    membership;
Any organization, which does not receive
    contributions in excess of $10,000 per year

Annual Reporting Requirements
Due within 6 months of fiscal year end
$40 filing fee
IRS 990 (or financial report)
Audit if contributions exceed $100,000

Kentucky
Office of Attorney General
Consumer Protection Division
700 Capitol Ave.
Frankfort, KY 40601
502-696-5389
www.law.state.ky.us

Registration Requirements
State form or URS
IRS Form 990

Organizations exempt from registration:
Organization soliciting contributions solely of its
    members and their families;

Religious organizations soliciting funds for religious purposes;

Accredited educational institutions soliciting contributions from alumni, faculty, students and families

Annual Reporting Requirements
Due within 4 1/2 months of fiscal year end
IRS 990, unless no 990 yet filed with the IRS

Louisiana

Dept. of Justice
Public Protection Division
Livingston Building
1885 N. Third St.
Baton Rouge, LA 70802
225-326-6400
www.ag.state.la.us

Registration Requirements
URS
IRS Determination letter
Certificate/Articles of Incorporation
Bylaws
Financial statement
Copies of Contracts with professional solicitors
List of all states where organization is registered
$25 Registration fee

Organizations exempt from registration:
Any charitable organization not utilizing the services of professional fundraisers;

Religious organizations, including exempt from federal income tax under IRS 501(c)(3), if not primarily supported by funds solicited outside its own membership or congregation; Educational institutions recognized or approved by the Louisiana Dept. of Education; Voluntary health organizations organized under Louisiana or federal law.

Annual Reporting Requirements
Due on the anniversary of annual registration
$25 renewal fee
IRS 990

Maine

Department of Prof. & Financial Regulation
Charitable Solicitation Registration
Office of Licensing & Registration
35 State House Station
Augusta, ME 04333-0035
207-624-8603
www.state.me.us/pfr/olr

Registration Requirements
State of Maine Charitable Organization Registration Form or URS
IRS Form 990
IRS Determination Letter
$50 Application fee, $50 registration fee (total: $100)

Organizations exempt from registration:
Organizations that solicit primarily within their membership and where members conduct solicitation activities;

Organizations that do not receive contributions from the public in excess of $10,000 or do not receive contributions from more than 10 people during the calendar year, if fundraising is carried on by volunteers;

Educational institutions registered or approved by Dept. of Education;

Hospitals that are nonprofit and charitable;

Persons soliciting contributions for the relief of any individual specified by name at the time of the solicitation where all contributions go directly to said person for individual's use.

Organizations claiming exemptions must submit a copy of form letter from IRS, any other appropriate financial statements and a $10 fee.

Annual Reporting Requirements
Due by November 30th
Fee: $100, if more than $30,000 raised, then additional $50 filing fee.
IRS 990
Financial Report may be submitted instead of IRS 990
Audit required if gross revenue is more than $30,000

Maryland

Office of the Secretary of State
Charitable Organizations Division
State House
Annapolis, MD 21401
410-974-5534
www.sos.state.md.us

Registration Requirements
State Form COR-92 or URS
Certificate/Articles of Incorporation
Bylaws
IRS Form 990
IRS Determination Letter

Financial review (if revenue is between $100,000 and 200,000)
Audit (if gross income from charitable contributions equals or exceeds $200,000)
Fee ranging from $50-$200

Organizations exempt from registration:
Religious organizations;
Organizations soliciting funds from their own memberships

Please note that organizations claiming exemption must provide evidence of its exemption.

Annual Reporting Requirements
Due within 6 months of fiscal year end
Fees range from $50-$200
IRS Form 990
Financial review (conducted by independent CPA if gross income from charitable contributions is greater than $100,000 but less than $200,000)
Audit (by an independent CPA if gross income from charitable contributions is greater than $200,000)

Massachusetts
The Commonwealth of Massachusetts
Office of Attorney General
Division of Public Charities
One Ashburton Place, Room 1413
Boston, MA 02108-1698
617-727-2200
www.ago.state.ma.us

Registration Requirements
State form Short Form- Schedule A-2 or URS
Certificate/Articles of Incorporation
Bylaws
$50 Registration fee

Organizations exempt from registration:
Religious;
The Red Cross and certain veterans' organizations

Annual Reporting Requirements
Due within 4 1/2 months of fiscal year end
Annual filing fees range from $35-250
IRS Form 990
Financial report - must use MA Form PC
Audit if revenue exceeds $250,000 (over $100,000 and not more than $250,000, CPA review statement required)

Michigan
Department of Attorney General
Charitable Trust Section
P.O. Box 30212
Lansing, MI 48909
517-373-1152
www.michigan.gov/ag

Registration Requirements
State forms or URS
Certificate/Articles of Incorporation
Bylaws
IRS Form 990
IRS Determination Letter

Organization exempt from registration:
Religious organizations with tax-exempt status;
Educational institutions certified by the state board of education;
Veterans groups organized under federal law;
Licensed nonprofit hospitals and their foundations and auxiliaries

Please note that organizations seeking exemption must file a questionnaire before determination of exemption.

Annual Reporting Requirements
Due 30 days prior to registration expiration.
IRS Form 990
Financial Report.
Audit if revenue is over $250,000, financial review required if revenue is between $100,000 and $250,000

Minnesota
Office of Attorney General
Charities Unit, Suite 1400, NCL Tower
445 Minnesota St.
St. Paul, MN 55101
651-296-3353
www.ag.state.mn.us

Registration Requirements
State registration form or URS
Certificate/Articles of Incorporation
IRS Form 990
IRS Determination Letter
$25 Registration fee

Organizations exempt from registration:
Organizations that do not employ paid staff of professional fundraisers and that do not receive or plan to receive more than $25,000 in one year;

Religious organizations exempt from filing IRS Form 990;

Certain educational institutions;

Organizations limiting solicitations to persons who have a right to vote as a member;

Annual Reporting Requirements

Due within 6 months of close of fiscal year

Financial statement (Atty. Gen. Annual Report form)

IRS Form 990, 990-EZ, or 990-PF

Audit if revenue exceeds $350,000. $25 renewal fee

Mississippi

Mississippi Secretary of State

Charities Registration

700 North St., P.O. Box 136

Jackson, MS 39202-0136

601-359-1633 or (toll free) 888-236-6167

www.sos.state.ms.us

Registration Requirements

State forms additional to URS- "Supplement to URS" including Annual Financial Reporting form

IRS Form 990

IRS Determination Letter

Certificate/Articles of Incorporation Bylaws

$50 registration fee

Audit required if gross revenues over $100,000 (or over $25,000, if a professional fundraiser is used), or request for audits may occur on a case-by-case basis for registrants between $25,000 and $100,000.

Organizations exempt from registration:

Accredited educational institutions;

Educational institutions that solicit solely from students, alumni, faculty, trustees and families;

Fraternal, patriotic, social, educational alumni organizations and historical societies when solicitation of contributions is made solely by their membership;

Any charitable organization that does not intend to solicit and receive and does not actually receive contributions in excess of $4,000 provided persons who are unpaid for such services carry on all fundraising functions

Organizations seeking exemption must file Form CE.

Annual Reporting Requirements

Reporting must be done on the URS and by doing so, renew registration and submit financial report simultaneously

Due at anniversary of original registration

$50 filing fee

IRS Form 990

Financial Report

Audit if gross revenues exceed $100,000 (or over $25,000, if a professional fundraiser is used). Audits may be requested on a case-by-case basis for registrants between $25,000-$100,000

Missouri

Missouri Attorney General

207 West High St.

Jefferson City, MO 65102-0899

573-751-3321

www.moago.org

Registration Requirements

State registration Form 1-A or URS

Articles of Incorporation

IRS Form 990

IRS Determination Letter

$15 initial Registration fee, $50 thereafter

Organizations exempt from registration:

Religious organizations;

Educational institutions and their authorized and related foundations;

Fraternal organizations provided solicitations are limited to membership of such organizations;

Hospitals, provided fundraising not done by professional fundraiser;

All 501(c) 3, 501(c) 7 and 501(c)(8) organizations that have obtained and can document such status from the federal government

Annual Reporting Requirements

Due within 2 1/2 months of fiscal year end

$50 annual fee, after initial $15

IRS Form 990

Financial Report

Montana

There is no registration required in Montana at this time.

Nebraska

There is no registration required in Nebraska at this time.

Nevada

There is no registration required in Nevada at this time.

New Hampshire

Department of Justice
Charitable Trusts Unit
33 Capitol St.
Concord, NH 03301-6397
603-271-3591
http://doj.nh.gov

Registration Requirements
State forms or URS
Conflict-of-interest policy
Certificate/Articles of Incorporation
Bylaws
IRS Form 990
IRS Determination Letter
$25 Registration fee

Organizations exempt from registration:
Religious organizations

Annual Reporting Requirements
Due within 4 1/2 months of fiscal year end
Financial report on state Form NHCT-2A or
IRS Form 990 or IRS Form 990-EZ or
     IRS Form 990-PF

New Jersey

N.J. Division of Consumer Affairs
Charities Registration Section
153 Halsey Street, 7th Floor
P.O. Box 45021
Newark, NJ 07101
973-504-6215
www.state.nj.us/lps/ca/charhlp.htm

Registration Requirements
State Form CRI-200, CRI-150I, CRI-300R or URS
Certificate/Articles of Incorporation
Bylaws
IRS Form 990
IRS Determination Letter

Organizations exempt from registration:
Religious organizations;
Educational institutions filing their curricula with the
     Dept. of Education

Annual Reporting Requirements
Due within 6 months of fiscal year end
Filing fees range from $0-$250
IRS Form 990

Financial report certified by authorized officer of
     organization if revenue under $100,000
Audit for revenue $100,000 and over

New Mexico

Attorney General of New Mexico
Registry of Charitable Organizations
111 Lomas Blvd., NW, Suite 300
Albuquerque, NM 87102
505-222-9090
www.ago.state.nm.us

Registration Requirements
State form or URS
Certificate/Articles of Incorporation
IRS Form 990
IRS Determination Letter
Audit if total revenue is in excess of $500,000

Organizations exempt from registration:
Any church or group organized for the purpose of
     worship, religious teaching, or other religious
     activity;
A school, college or other institution with a defined
     curriculum, student body and (faculty,
     conducting classes on a regular basis;
Charitable organizations that receive less than $2,500
     per year in contributions;
Local affiliates of statewide or national organizations
     for which all local fundraising expenses are paid
     by a registered parent organization

Annual Reporting Requirements
Due within 2 1/2 months of fiscal year
IRS Form 990
Financial Report may be submitted instead of 990
Audit if total revenue is in excess of $500,000

New York

Department of Law, Charities Bureau
120 Broadway, 3rd Floor
New York, NY 10271
212-416-8400
www.oag.state.ny.us/charities/role.html

Registration Requirements:
State form CHAR410 or URS
Certificate/Articles of Incorporation
Bylaws
IRS Form 990
IRS Determination Letter

Audit if over $150,000 in revenues (CPA review if between 75,000–$150,000).
$25 Registration fee

Organizations exempt from registration

Religious agencies and organizations and charities operated, supervised, or controlled in connection with a charity organized under the Religious Corporations Law;

Educational institutions confining solicitations to student body, alumni, faculty and trustees and their families;

Fraternal, patriotic, social and alumni organizations and historical societies chartered by Board of Regents when soliciting memberships;

Organization receiving $25,000 or less and not paying professional fundraisers;

Local post, camp, chapter or county unit of a veteran's organization;

Educational institutions or libraries that file annual financial reports with Regents of University of State of New York or with an agency having similar jurisdiction in another state

Please note that even exempt organizations must submit Form CHAR006, which must be filed annually.

Annual Reporting Requirements

Due date 41/2 months after fiscal year end
Fees $10 or $25 depending on revenue generated
IRS Form 990
Financial Report - must be reviewed by CPA if revenue $75,000–$150,000.
Audit if revenue $150,000 and over

North Carolina

Department of Secretary of State
Division of Facility Services/
Solicitations Licensing Section
P.O. Box 29622
Raleigh, NC 27626-0622
919-807-2214
www.secstate.state.nc.us

Registration Requirements

State form- (URS not accepted)
Certificate/Articles of Incorporation
Bylaws
IRS Form 990
IRS Determination Letter
Fees range from $0–$400

Organizations exempt from registration:

Any person that solicits for a religious organization;

Solicitations of charitable contributions by the federal, State or local governments or their agencies;

Any person who receives less than 25,000 in contributions in a calendar year and does not provide compensation to any officer, trustee, organizer, incorporator, fund-raiser or solicitor;

Any educational institution, the curriculum of which, in whole or in part, is registered, approved, or accredited by the Southern Assoc. of Colleges and Schools or an equivalent regional accrediting body, and any foundation or department having an established identity with any of these educational institutions;

Any licensed hospital and any foundation or department having established identity with that hospital if the governing board of the hospital, authorizes the solicitation and receives an accounting of the funds collected and expended;

Any noncommercial radio or television station;

A qualified community trust;

A bona fide volunteer fire department, rescue squad, or emergency medical service;

A YMCA or YWCA;

A nonprofit continuing-care facility

Annual Reporting Requirements

Due within 4 1/2 months of end of fiscal year
Fees range from $50-$200
IRS Form 990 or financial report

North Dakota

Secretary of State
State of North Dakota
Administrative/Licensing Division
600 E. Boulevard Ave., Dept. 108
Bismarck, ND 58505-0500
701-328-3665
800-352-0867 ext. 8-3665
www.state.nd.us/sec

Registration Requirements

State Form SFN 11300 ($25 fee) and SFN 7974 ($10 fee) in addition to URS
State Articles of Incorporation for Nonprofit Form SFN 13003 ($30 fee)
IRS Form 990

Organizations exempt from registration:

A duly constituted religious organization, or any group affiliated with and forming an integral part of that organization that has tax-exempt status from the government of the United States;

Organizations soliciting funds for institutions of higher learning;

Private or public elementary or secondary school;

Charitable organizations using only volunteer unpaid fundraisers and soliciting funds for a political sub-division or other government entity or for a civic or community project with no contributions benefiting any individual;

Candidates for national, state and local elective office or political party or other committee required to file information with the federal or state election commission or similar agency

Annual Reporting Requirements
Due September 1st
$10 filing/renewal fee
Annual report /renewal application on required Form SFN 11302A

Ohio
Office of the Attorney General
Charitable Law Section
150 E. Gay St., 23rd Fl.
Columbus, OH 43215
614-466-3180
www.ag.state.oh.us

Registration Requirements
State forms or URS
Certificate/Articles of Incorporation
Bylaws
IRS Form 990
IRS Determination Letter
Registration fees range from $0-$200

Organizations exempt from registration:
Any religious agencies and organizations, and charities, agencies, and organizations operated, supervised, or controlled by a religious organization;

Any educational institution, when solicitation of contributions is confined to alumni, faculty, trustees, or students and their families;

Any organization that does not receive gross revenue, excluding grants or awards from the government or a 501(c)(3) organization, in excess of $25,000 and does not compensate any person primarily to solicit;

Every person other than an individual, when solicitation of contributions for a charitable

purpose or on behalf of a charitable organization is confined to its members, present and former employees, or present and former trustees

Annual Reporting Requirements
Due within 4 1/2 months of fiscal year end
Fee: $50–$200
IRS Form 990 or financial report (Attorney General's Form)

Oklahoma
Office of the Secretary of State
2300 N. Lincoln Blvd., Suite 101
Oklahoma City, OK 73105-4897
405-521-3912
www.sos.state.ok.us

Registration Requirements
State form or URS
IRS Form 990
IRS Determination letter
Financial statement (SOS Form 0102)
$25 Registration fee

Organizations exempt from registration:
Organizations formed for religious purposes and other organizations directly operated, supervised, or controlled by a religious organization;

Educational institutions which have a faculty and regularly enrolled students, and offer courses of study leading to the granting of recognized degrees when solicitations of contributions are limited to students and their families, alumni, faculty, and trustees;

Fraternal organizations, when soliciting from their own members, and patriotic and civic organizations, when solicitations of contributions are confined to membership of said organization and managed by membership without paid solicitors;

Persons soliciting contributions for the relief of a named person where all contributions are turned over to named beneficiary;

Any organization, which collects from charitable solicitations less than $10,000/year

Annual Reporting Requirements
Due by March 31st or with annual registration renewal
IRS Form 990
Financial report (state form required)

Oregon

Oregon Dept. of Justice
Charitable Activities Section
1162 Court St., NE
Salem, OR 97301-4096
503-378-4400
www.doj.state.or.us

Registration Requirements

State registration Form RF-C or URS
IRS Determination letter
Certificate/Articles of Incorporation
Bylaws
No registration fees required

Organizations exempt from registration:

Cemetery corporations
Child-caring agencies regulated by the Department of
    Human Services
Foreign corporations or foundations making only
    grants or donations in the state of OR
Government agencies or sub-divisions
Post-secondary educational institutions holding no
    property in OR with individual solicitations
    confined to alumni
Religious organizations holding property solely for
    religious purposes

Annual Reporting Requirements

Due within 4 1/2 months of fiscal year end
Form CT-12, CT-12F, or CT-12S
Filing fees from $10–$200
IRS Form 990
Financial Report

Pennsylvania

Department of State
Bureau of Charitable Orgs.
207 N. Office Building
Harrisburg, PA 17120
717-783-1720
www.dos.state.pa.us

Registration Requirements

State forms or URS
IRS Form 990
IRS Determination Letter
Audit required in certain cases
Certificate/Articles of Incorporation
Bylaws
Annual Registration Fees: ($15–$250)

Organizations exempt from registration:

Organizations of law enforcement personnel,
    firefighters, or other persons who protect public
    safety, not benefiting any person outside active
    membership of organization;
Religious institutions and separate groups or
    corporations that form an integral part that are
    tax exempt and primarily supported by fees
    charged for services rendered, government grants
    or contracts, or solicitations from their own
    memberships, congregations, or previous donors;
Accredited educational institutions and any
    associations, foundations and support groups that
    are directly responsible to educational
    institutions;
Hospitals subject to regulation by the Dept. of Health
    or Dept. of Public Welfare and any foundation,
    which is an integral part;
Nonprofit libraries that file an annual fiscal report
    with the state library system;
Senior citizen centers and nursing homes that are
    nonprofit, charitable and tax exempt, and have
    all fundraising activities carried out by
    volunteers;
Organizations raising $25,000 or less annually that
    do not compensate anyone;
Local post, camp, or chapter of any veterans'
    organization chartered under federal law and any
    service foundations recognized in their by-laws.

Annual Reporting Requirements

Due 135 days after end of fiscal year
Fee: $15–$250
IRS Form 990
Financial Report reviewed by CPA if contributions
    $25,000–$100,000
Audit if contributions $100,000 or more

Rhode Island

Department of Business Regulation
Securities Division
233 Richmond St.
Providence, RI 02903
401-222-3048
www.dbr.state.ri.us

Registration Requirements

State form or URS
IRS Form 990
Audit if annual gross budget exceeds $500,000
$75 Registration fee

Organizations exempt from registration:

Religious organizations;

Institutions indirectly affiliated with any religious organization that maintain and operate homes for the aged, orphans or unwed mothers;
Accredited educational institutions;
Organizations raising $25,000 or less in a calendar year, whose fundraising activities are carried on by volunteers;
Nonprofit hospitals;
Organizations soliciting contributions solely from their membership;
Public libraries;
Veteran's organizations and their auxiliaries;
Public art museums

Please note that organizations must file annually for exemptions.

Annual Reporting Requirements
Due on anniversary of registration
$75 filing/renewal fee
IRS Form 990
Financial Report
Audit if proceeds exceed $100,000

South Carolina
Office of the Secretary of State
Public Charities Section
P.O. Box 11350
Columbia, SC 29211
803-734-1790
www.scsos.com

Registration Requirement
State form or URS
IRS Determination letter
$50 Registration fee

Organizations exempt from registration:
Organizations expecting less than $20,000 in contributions, that have no paid staff, and have tax-exempt status;
Veterans' organizations chartered by Congress;
Membership organizations for which there are specific qualifications for joining other than paying dues
Educational institutions
Political subdivisions of the state
Organizations established by persons requesting relief of an individual specified by name

Annual Reporting Requirements
Due within 4 1/2 months of fiscal year

IRS Form 990
Financial Report (may be submitted instead of 990)

South Dakota
There is no registration required in South Dakota at this time.

Tennessee
Secretary of State
Charitable Solicitations
William R. Snodgrass Tower
312 8th Ave. N., 8th Floor
Nashville, TN 37243
615-741-2555
www.state.tn.us/sos/charity.htm

Registration Requirements
State forms SS-6001 or URS, and SS-6002
Certificate/Articles of Incorporation
Bylaws
IRS Form 990
IRS Determination Letter
Audit if gross revenue over $250,000

Organizations exempt from registration:
Churches;
Educational institutions, their booster clubs, parent organizations and affiliated groups;
Volunteer fire departments, rescue squads and local civil defense organizations;
Organizations raising less than $30,000 in gross contributions during their fiscal year

Annual Reporting Requirements
Due within 6 months of fiscal year end
Fees range from $100–$300
IRS Form 990
Financial Report required when revenue is more than $100,000
Audit unless proceeds do not exceed $10,000

Texas
There is no registration required in Texas at this time.

Utah
Department of Commerce
Division of Consumer Protection
160 East 300 South
SM Box 146704
Salt Lake City, UT 84114-6704

801-530-6601
www.commerce.utah.gov/dcp/

Registration Requirements
State form- URS NOT accepted
$100 registration
Certificate/Articles of Incorporation
Bylaws
IRS Form 990
IRS Determination Letter
Audit
Renewal required annually on the 1st of January,
April, July, or October following the completion
of 12 months after initial registration

Organizations exempt from registration:
A solicitation that an organization conducts among its
own bona fide membership exclusively through
the voluntary efforts of other members or
officers of the organization;
A bona fide religious, ecclesiastical, or
denominational organization if 1) the solicitation
is for a church, missionary, religious or
humanitarian purpose and 2) the organization is
a physical place of worship where nonprofit
religious services and activities are regularly
conducted and carried on OR a bona fide
religious group that does not maintain a specific
place of worship, that is not subject to federal
income tax and not required to file an IRS Form
990 under any circumstance OR a separate group
or corporation that is an integral part of an
institution that is income tax exempt and is not
primarily supported by funds solicited outside
its own membership or congregation;
A broadcast media owned or operated by an
educational institution or governmental entity;
Any school or institution of higher learning
accredited by the state or club, parent, teacher,
student organization within and authorized by
the school in support of the operation and
activities of the school;
A volunteer fire department, rescue squad or local
civil defense organization whose financial
oversight is under the control of a local
governmental entity.

Annual Reporting Requirements
Due quarterly during year one 30 days after end of
quarter
Due 30 days after end of fiscal year thereafter
Financial report or IRS Form 990

Vermont
There is no registration required in Vermont at this time.

Virginia
Commonwealth of Virginia
Dept. of Agriculture and Consumer Services
Division of Consumer Affairs
P.O. Box 1163
1100 Bank St.
Richmond, VA 23219
804-786-2373
www.vdacs.state.va.us

Registration Requirements
State Form 102 or URS
Certificate/Articles of Incorporation
Bylaws
IRS Form 990 or audit
IRS Determination Letter
$100 Registration fee

Organizations exempt from registration:
Any accredited educational institutions or related
foundations, and any other educational
institution confining its solicitation of
contributions to its student body, alumni, faculty
and trustees, and their families;
Persons requesting contributions for the relief of any
individual specified by name at the time of
solicitation when all contributions are turned
over directly to named beneficiary;
Charitable organizations that do not intend, in a
calendar year or the three preceding years, to
receive contributions from the public in excess of
$5,000, and all of whose functions are carried
out by volunteers;
Organizations that solicit only within the membership
of the organization;
Organizations that have no office within the
Commonwealth and solicit within the state,
solely by means of telephone, telegraph, direct
mail or advertising in national media and have a
registered chapter, branch or affiliate within the
Commonwealth;
Tax-exempt health care institutions licensed by their
state Dept. of Health or Mental Health and any
supporting organizations;
Civic organizations such as a local service club,
veterans' post, fraternal society or association,
volunteer fire or rescue group, or local civic
league or association operated exclusively for
educational or charitable purposes for the benefit
of the community;

Organizations seeking exemption must file "Forms 100A-100H" as applicable.

Labor unions, associations and organizations with tax-exempt status;

Agencies designated by the Virginia Department for the Aging as area agencies on aging;

Nonprofit debt counseling agencies

Please note that exempt organizations must file appropriate forms and a $10 filing fee.

Annual Reporting Requirements

State Form 102

Due within 4 1/2 months of fiscal year end

Registration renewal fee: $30–$325

IRS 990,990-PF, 990-EZ or certified annual audit or certified treasurer's report where proceeds are less than $25,000

Current list of officers, directors, trustees, and principal salaried staff members

Current copies of contracts with paid fund-raising organizations

Certificate/Articles of Incorporation or amendments to those documents not previously filed;

Bylaws or amendments to that document not previously filed;

IRS Determination letter

Washington

Office of Secretary of State
Charities Program
Dolliver Building
P.O. Box 40234
801 Capitol Way South
Olympia, WA 98504-0234
800-332-4483 (GIVE)
360-753-0863
www.secstate.wa.gov

Registration Requirements

State form or URS
IRS Form 990
IRS Determination letter
$30 Registration fee

Organizations seeking exemption must file an exemption form.

Annual Reporting Requirements

Due within 4 1/2 months of fiscal year end
$10 filing/renewal fee
IRS Form 990
Financial Report

West Virginia

Secretary of State
State Capitol, Building 1, Suite 157-K
1900 Kanawha Blvd. East
Charleston, WV 25305-0770
304-558-6000
www.wvsos.com

Registration Requirements

State form - (URS not accepted)
IRS Form 990
IRS Determination letter
Fees range from $15–$50
Audit if contributions exceed $10,000

Organizations exempt from registration:

Educational institutions, the curriculums of which in whole or in part are registered or approved by the state board of education, either directly or by acceptance of accreditation by an accrediting body and any auxiliary associations, foundations and support groups which are directly responsible to any such educational institutions;

Persons requesting contributions for the relief of any individual specified at the time of solicitation when all of the contributions collected without any deduction are turned over to the named beneficiary;

Hospitals, which are nonprofit;

Organizations which solicit only within the membership of the organization by members thereof: provided that the term "membership" shall not include those persons who are granted membership upon making a contribution as the result of solicitation;

Churches, synagogues, associations or conventions of churches, religious orders or religious organizations that are an integral part of a church, which qualifies as tax exempt under 501(c)(3);

Organizations sponsoring single fund-raising events for a named charitable organization;

Organizations such as local youth athletic organizations, community service clubs, fraternal organizations, volunteer fireman or auxiliaries are exempt if they do not employ a professional solicitor or fund-raiser or do not intend to solicit or receive contributions in excess of $10,000 during the calendar year.

Annual Reporting Requirements

There is no annual reporting requirement other than registration renewal.

Wisconsin

Bureau of Direct Licensing & Real Estate-
  Charitable Organization
Department of Regulation & Licensing
1400 E. Washington Ave.
P.O. Box 8935
Madison, WI 53708-8935
608-266-5511
http://drl.wi.gov/index.htm

Registration Requirements

State forms or URS
Certificate/Articles of Incorporation
Bylaws
IRS Form 990
IRS Determination Letter
Audit if contributions exceed $100,000
$15 Registration fee

Organizations exempt from registration:

Candidate for national, state or local office or a
  political party or other committee or group
  required to file financial information with the
  federal elections commission; Organizations that
do not raise or receive contributions in excess of
  $5,000;
Fraternal, benevolent, patriotic or social
  organizations that solicit contributions solely
  from their membership;
Veteran's organizations;
Nonprofit postsecondary educational institutions;
Organizations soliciting contributions for relief of a
  named individual if all contributions are given to
  the named individual

Annual Reporting Requirements

Due August 1st
$15 filing/renewal fee
IRS Form 990
Financial Report if contributions from exceed $5,000
  organizations must file either
Audit if charitable contributions exceed $100,000

Wyoming

There is no registration required in Wyoming at this
  time.

State Corporation Divisions

Alabama

Division of Corporation, Secretary of State, 11 South Union St., Ste. 207, Montgomery, AL 36106 or P.O. Box 5616, Montgomery, AL 36103-5616, 334-242-5324, Fax: 334-240-3138; {www.sos.state.al.us}. Selected Publications: Guide to Incorporation. Phone Information: 334-242-5324. Office is not completely computerized yet, but can do word search or partial name search by officer, incorporator, or serving agent. Copies of documents on File: Available by written request for $1 per page plus $5 for certified copies. Can provide information over the phone at no cost. Mailing Labels: No. Magnetic Tape: No. Microfiche: No. New Corporate Listings: No.
Custom Searches: Can do word or partial name search. Printout of search results by mail is free. Online Access: Yes. Number of active corporations on File: Figures Not Available

Alaska

State of Alaska, Division of Banking, Securities and Corporation, Corporation Section, P.O. Box 110808, Juneau, AK 99811-0808, 907-465-2530, Fax: 907-465-3257; {www.dced.state.ak.us/bsc}. Selected Publications: None. Phone information: 907-465-2530. Copies of Documents on File: Complete corporate record (Articles of Incorporation, annual report, amendments, etc.) Cost $30, certified copies add $5, list of officers and directors cost $1, Certificate of Status cost $10. Mailing Labels: No. Copy of complete master file excluding officers and directors is priced at $100. Monthly supplements are an additional $10. Microfiche: No, only disk and email. New corporate listings: yes. Custom Searches: yes. Online Access: Yes. Number of active corporations on file: 25,172.

Arizona

Arizona Corporations Division, Records Division, Secretary of State, 1300 W. Washington, Phoenix, AZ 85007 or P.O. Box 6019, Phoenix, AZ 85005, 602-542-3026, Fax: 602-542-3414; {www.cc.state.az.us}. Selected Publications: Sample packet with forms and statutes mailed for $8. Guideline booklets will be available soon. Phone Information : 602-542-3026. Copies of Documents on File: Cost 50 cents per page, $5 for certified copics. Mailing Labels: No. Magnetic Tape: Master File $400, issued monthly. Requester must supply blank tape. Microfiche: All corporations statewide $75. New Corporate Listing: Monthly Listing of New Domestic Companies for

$200 plus $200 for new foreign listings. Custom searches: Yes, request in writing or in person. Can search by company name, agent name or officer name. Online Access. There is a charge for filing online. Available through Information America, Dunn and Bradstreet and other commercial services. Number of corporations on file: 100,000

Arkansas

Secretary of State, Corporations Division, State Capitol Building, Room 256, Little Rock, AR 72201, 501-682-5151, Fax: 501-682-3437; {http://sos.state.ar.us}. Selected Publications: None. Phone Information: 501-682-5151. Copies of Documents on file: Call 501-371-3431 for copies at 50 cents per page plus $5 for certified copies. Domestic companies $50, Foreign companies $300. Mailing labels: No. Magnetic Tape: Master file 2 cents per name. Microfiche: No. New corporate Listing: Statistics only. Custom Searches. Categories include foreign, domestic, profit, and nonprofit corporations. Cost: 2 cents per name, 50 cents per page. Online Access: Yes. Number of active corporations on file: 1,000,000

California

Corporations, Supervisor of Records, Secretary of State, 1500 11th Street, CA 95814-5701, 916-653-6814, {www.ss.ca.gov}. Selected Publications: Corporations Checklist Booklet. Request must be in writing and cost is $5. Phone Information: 916-653-6814. Copies of Documents on File: Articles of Incorporation: cost is $1 for first page, 50 cents for each additional page plus $5 for certified copies, Certificate of status $6, Statement of officers $5 and $10 for certified copies (written requests only). You must pay in advance or send blank check not to exceed $20. Send requests to secretary of state, Attention RIC unit. Mailing Labels: No. Magnetic Tape: Yes, Master copy $17,600 annually. Call 916-653-8905 for information. Hard copy $14,000.13. Microfiche: No. Custom Searches: Computer generated listing of Active Stock ($17,030), Active Non-Stock ($422). Active Non-Stock by Classification $150 per list. Management Services Division, Information Systems Section, 1230 J Street, Suite 242, Sacramento, CA 95814. All orders must be submitted in writing. Basic cost of magnetic tape copy is $1.02 per 1,000 names. Basic cost of same run, for custom search, printed on paper, is $4.13 per

1,000 names. $150 minimum is applied to both. Online Access: Yes. Number of Corporations on File: 2,000,000.

Colorado

Corporate Division, Secretary of State, 1560 Broadway, Suite 200, Denver, CO 80202, 303-894-2200, Fax: 303-869-4864; {www.sos.state.co.us}. Selected Publications: Corporate Guide. Copies of Documents on File: Cost is 50 cents per page, plus $10 for certification. Mailing Labels: No. Magnetic Tape: Available for $500 for complete set of five. Tapes must be purchased individually. Categories: Foreign and Domestic. Microfiche: available at $1 a sheet (includes Summary of Master Computer File, must be purchased in its entirety). New Corporate Listings: Reporting Service costs $200 a year. Weekly list of New Corporations. Written requests only. Custom searches: Yes. Categories: Foreign and Domestic available on a cost recovery basis. The minimum fee is $50. Online Access: Available. Fee is $300 for 3 months or $1,000 per year. Number of Corporations on File: 235,000.

Connecticut

Office of Secretary of State, Division of Corporations, 30 Trinity Street, Hartford, CT 06106; Fax: 860-509-6068; {www.sots.state.ct.us}. Selected Publications: None, but to get a copy of Connecticut General Statutes, call 860-509-6190. Phone Information: 860-509-6001. Copies of Documents on File: Fees are $20 regardless of number of pages, $25 for certified. Written requests only. Mailing Labels: No. Magnetic Tape: Copy of master database of corporations $300. Requester must provide tapes. Microfiche: No. New Corporate Listing: No. Custom Searches: No. Online Access: Yes. Number of Corporations on File: over 200,000

Delaware

Delaware Department of State, Division of Corporations, Secretary of State, P.O. Box 898, Dover, DE 19903, 302-739-3073, Fax: 302-739-3812; {www.state.de.us/corp}. Selected Publications: Incorporating in Delaware. Phone Information: 302-739-3073. Copies of Documents on File: (for domestic only) Available at $1 per page $20 for certification. Short forms $20 and $100 for long forms of good standing. Certificate of incorporation $50 minimum, amendment certificate $100 minimum, change of registered agents $75. Requests may be faxed to 302-739-3812, but written requests are preferred. Requests must be paid for in advance,

add county fee and send a check. Call for number of pages. Documents filed prior to 1983 are not on computer and must be requested in writing. They offer same day or 24-hour expedited services to file or retrieve certified documents. Same day request completed and released by 5pm, when requested by 2pm. Additional fee is $20. Mailing Labels: No. Magnetic Tape: No. Microfiche: No. New Corporate Listings: No. Custom Searches: Yes, domestic corporations only. Number of Active Corporation on File 397,829.

District of Columbia

Corporations Division, Consumer and Regulatory Affairs, 941 N. Capitol NE, 1st Floor, Washington, DC 20002, 202-442-4430, Fax: 202-442-4523; {http://dcra.dc.gov}. Selected Publications: Guideline and Instruction Sheet for Profit, Nonprofit, Foreign, or Domestic. Phone Information: 202-442-9453. Copies of Documents on File: Available for $25 each (all copies certified). Mailing Labels: Will be available in near future. Profit and nonprofit lists updated quarterly. Magnetic Tape: No. Microfiche: No. New Corporate Listings No. Custom Searches: Computer searches on registered agents are available. Online Access: Yes. Number of Active Corporations on File: 50,000.

Florida

Division of Corporations, Secretary of State, PO Box 6327, Tallahassee, FL 32314, 850-488-9000 or 800-755-5111; {www.sunbiz.org}. Selected Publications: Copy of the Law Chapter 607 (corporate law). Forms included. (Publications on laws of nonprofit corporations and limited partnerships also available.) Phone Information: 904-488-9000. Limit of up to 3 inquiries per call. $10 charge to receive hard copy of microfiche on the corporations, no charge for faxing copies. Copy of Documents on File: Available at $1 per page if you do it yourself. Written requests must be paid for in advance: $1 for non-certified annual report; $10 for plain copy of complete file; $8.75 per 8 pages and $1 each additional, for any certified document including complete file. Microfiche: Yes. Contact Frank Reinhart or Ed Bagnell at Anacomp, 850-488-1486. Magnetic Tape: No. New Corporate Listings: No. Custom Searches: 850-488-1486. Online Access: Available through CompuServe, 800-848-8199, address written request to Attn: Public Access, division of Corporations, 904-487-6866. Ask for a CompuServe intro-pak. Charge for connect time online is $24 per hour, plus $12.50 per hour additional corporate access fee. Both are prorated by time used. CompuServe can be contacted directly at Southeastern Information Systems, P.O. Box 6867, Tallahassee, FL 32314, Attn: Keith Meyer, 904-656-4500. As of February, 1992, Anacomp will handle. Contact Eileen Self, 904-487-6073 for service. Number of active Corporations on File: 691,000

Georgia

Division of Business Services and Regulation, Secretary of State, Suite 315, West Tower #2, Martin Luther King Drive, SE, Atlanta, GA 30334, 404-656-2817, Fax: 404-651-9059; {www.sos.state.ga.us}. Selected Publications: None, but information package on how to file sent upon request. Phone Information: 404-656-2817. Copies of Documents on File: Available for a minimum of $10 and all copies certified. Bills will be sent for orders over $10. Mailing Labels: No. Magnetic Tape: No. Microfiche: No. Cost is $1,000 for a one time listing, if you want to receive a monthly or weekly update, cost is $600. Lists are on magnetic tape. Custom Searches: No. Online Access: Yes. Number of Active Corporations on File: 350,000

Hawaii

Business Registration Division, Department of Commerce and Consumer Affairs, 335 Merchant St., Honolulu, HI 96813, PO Box 40, Honolulu, HI 96810, 808-586-2744, Fax: 808-586-2733; {www.state.hi.us/dcca/breg-seu/}. Selected Publications: None. Copies of Documents on File: Available at 25 cents per page, plus $10 per page for certified copies. Expedited service available for $10 fee plus 25 cents per sheet, plus $1 per page. Mailing Labels: No. Magnetic Tape: No. Microfiche: No. New Corporate Listing: Weekly printout available but only for walk-ins. Custom Searches: No. Online Access: Yes. Downloading information from database available through FYI at 808-586-1919. Number of Active Corporations on File: 45,000

Idaho

Corporate Division, Secretary of State, 700 West Jefferson, Room 203, Statehouse, Boise, ID 83720, 208-334-2300, Fax: 208-334-2282; {www.idsos.state.id.us}. Selected Publications: Idaho Corporation Law. Phone Information: 208-334-2300. Copies of Documents on File: Available at 25 cents per page, $2 for certified copies. Mailing Labels: Very flexible and may be combined with custom search. Fee is $10 for computer base, 25 cents for first 100 pages, 10 cents for next 500 pages and 5 cents per page thereafter.

Magnetic Tape: available for $20 per tape if you supply the tape. They will supply diskette for additional $10. Microfiche: Available for $10, 50 cents for each additional copy of same. Custom Searches: Yes. You supply the tapes or they will supply them at cost. New Corporate Listing: No, but published weekly in The Idaho Business Review. Online Access: Available though Data Share program. Call computer department 208-334-5354. Number of Active Corporations on File 200,000

Illinois

Corporations Division, Centennial Building, 501 S. 2nd St., Rm. 350E, Springfield, IL 62706, 217-782-6961, Fax: 217-782-4528; {www.sos.state.il.us}. Selected Publications: Guide for Organizing (Domestic, Nonprofit, or Foreign). Phone Information: 217-782-7880. Copies of Documents on File: available at $5 per page up to first 10 pages; 50 cents for each page thereafter. Mailing Labels: No. Magnetic Tape: Yes. Categories: Domestic and Foreign cost $1,500; Not-for-Profit cost $1,500. You must supply tape. Microfiche: Available for $171. New Corporate Listings: Daily list of newly formed corporations costs $185 per year; Monthly List priced at $105 per year. Custom Searches: No. Other: Certified List of Domestic and Foreign Corporations (Address of Resident Agent included) costs $38 for two volume set. Online Access: Yes.

Indiana

Office of Corporation, Secretary of State, E018, 302 West Washington Street, Indianapolis, IN 46204, 317-232-6576, Fax: 317-233-3387; {www.in.gov/sos}. Selected Publications: Guide Book. Request by calling 800-726-8000. Phone Information: 317-232-6576. Copies of Documents on File: Available at $1 per page and $15 to certify. May pay in advance or be billed. Mailing Labels: No. Magnetic Tape: No. Microfiche: No. New Corporate Listings: Daily Listing is published monthly for $20 a month. Custom Searches: No. Online Access: Yes. Number of Active Corporations on file: 200,000

Iowa

Corporate Division, Secretary of State, Lucas Building, Des Moines, IA 50319, 515-281-5204, Fax: 515-242-6556; {www.sos.state.ia.us}. Selected Publications: Iowa Profit Corporations. Phone Information 515-281-5204. Copies of Documents on File: available at $1 per page; certified copies cost $5. Mailing Labels: No. Magnetic Tape: No. Master file is available on CD-Rom for $200. Microfiche: No. New Corporate Listings: No. Custom Searches: Yes. Searches by name of corporation or partial name. Online Access: Available through Dial Up Program. Contact Sheryl Allen, 515-281-5247. Cost is $175 per year, plus telephone charges. Number of Active Corporations on File: 200,000

Kansas

Corporate Division, Secretary of State, Memorial Hall, 120 SW 10th Ave., Topeka, KS 66612-1594, 785-296-4564, Fax: 785-296-4570; {www.kssos.org}. Selected Publications: None. Will send out forms with instruction sheets. Phone Information: 785-296-4564. Copies of Documents on File: Available at 50 cents per page plus $7.50. Certificate of Good Standing $7.50, Letter of Good Standing $5, Written Record Search $5. Magnetic Tape: Yes. Master file is available. Microfiche: No. Other: New Corporate Listings: No. Custom Searches: Yes, but they cannot search for. Online Access: Available through Info Network Kansas, 785-296-5143. Number of Active Corporations on File: 66,000

Kentucky

Corporate Division, Secretary of State, Room 152, Capitol Building, 700 Capitol Avenue, PO Box 718, Frankfort, KY 40602, 502-564-2848, Fax: 502-564-4075; {www.sos.state.ky.us}. Selected Publications: None. Phone Information: 502-564-2848. Copies of Documents on File: Call 502-564-7330 to obtain number of copies in advance. Cost is 50 cents per page; $5 for certified copies. Computer screen print out is $1. Mailing label: No. Magnetic Tape: No. CD-Rom available for free and they can send it to you for free. Microfiche: No. New Corporate Listings: Available for $50 a month. Custom Searches: Yes, partial name search. Online Access: Yes. Number of Active Corporations on File: 400,000

Louisiana

Corporate Division, Secretary of State, 8549 United Plaza Blvd., Baton Rouge, LA 70809, 225-925-4704, Fax: 225-925-4410; {www.sec.state.la.us}. Selected Publications: Corporate Law Book ($10). Phone Information: 225-925-4704. Copies of Documents on File: Available starting at $15 for certified articles only. Cost for complete file, including amendments is $60. Mailing Label: No. Magnetic

Tape: No. Microfiche: No. New Corporate Listing: Weekly Newsletter at no charge. Requester must supply self-addressed stamped envelope. Custom Searches: Yes, can search by agents and individual names. Online Access: Dial Up Access, 225-922-1475. Cost is $360 per year. Number of Active Corporations on File: 120,000

Maine

Information and Report Section, Bureau of Corporations, Secretary of State, 101 State House Station, Augusta, ME 04333-0101, 207-624-7752, Fax: 207-287-5874; {www.state.me.us/sos/cec/}. Selected Publications: None at this time. Phone Information: 207-624-7752. Copies of Documents on File: Available for $2 per page, plus $5 for certified copies. Mailing Labels: No. Magnetic tape: No. Microfiche: No. New Corporate Listings: Monthly Corporations Listing costs $10. Custom Searches: Yes, by corporation name. Online Access: Yes. Number of Active Corporations on File 46,000

Maryland

Corporate Charter Division, Department of Assessments and Taxation, 301 W. Preston Street, Baltimore, Maryland 21201, 410-767-1330, Fax: 410-333-5873; {www.dat.state.md.us}. Selected Publications: Information Guides for Filing and other issues are available. Phone Information: 410-767-1330. Copies of Documents on File: Available for $1 per page, plus $6 for certified copies. There is a $20 expediting fee. Certificate of good standing $6, Articles of Incorporation $20. Mailing Labels: No. Magnetic Tape: Available on 6 tapes for $75 each. Microfiche: No. New Corporate Listings: Monthly corporate Computer Printout costs $25 a month. Custom Searches: Yes. They can search for names, agents, principal offices, and documents filed by the corporation. Online Access: Yes. Number of Active Corporations on File: 300,000

Massachusetts

Corporate Division, Secretary of State, 1 Ashburton Place, Boston, MA 02108, 617-727-9640, Fax: 617-742-4528 {www.state.ma.us/sec/cor}. Selected Publications: Compendium of Corporate Law ($15). Phone Information: 617-727-9640. Copies of Documents on File: Available for 20 cents per page, $12 for certified copies. Mailing Labels: No. Magnetic Tape: Cost is $300 for copy of master file and record layout. Requester must supply tapes. Microfiche: No. New Corporate Listings:

Semi-monthly filings cost $15; Quarterly Filings cost $50; bi-weekly printout cost $15. Custom Searches: Available on a cost recovery basis. Online Access: Direct Access program. Cost is $149 annually. Connect time is 40 cents per minute. Number of Corporations on File: 375,000

Michigan

Corporation Division, Corporation and Securities Bureau, Michigan Department of Commerce, PO Box 30053, 6546 Mercantile, Lansing, MI 48909, 517-241-6470, Fax: 517-241-0538; {www.michigan.gov/}. Selected Publications: None. Copies of Documents on File: Available at a minimum of $6 for 6 pages or less, $1 for each page thereafter. Certified copies cost $10. (Request a price list.) Mailing Labels: No. Magnetic Tape: No. Microfiche: Available for $145. New Corporate Listings: Monthly Listing ranges at about $100 per month (each month is priced differently). Custom Searches: No. Online Access: Available through KnowX (www.knowx.com), a division of Information America, 800-235-4008. You can pay for these online searches by credit card or prepaid account. Price varies. To view all records of a corporation, $15. Other prices range from $1 to $6. Number of Corporations on File: 251,000

Minnesota

Corporate Division, Secretary of State, 180 State Office Building, 100 Rev. Dr. Martin Luther King Jr. Blvd., St. Paul, MN 55155, 651-296-2803, Fax: 651-297-7067; {www.sos.state.mn.us}. Selected Publications: Guide to Starting a Business in Minnesota. Phone Information: 651-296-2803. Copies of Documents on File: Available for $3 per copy, $8 for certified copies. Request copies by sending a letter, indicating your address or fax number. Mailing Labels: No. Magnetic Tape: Yes, on 9 tapes for $11,250 annually and $710 per month. Microfiche: No. New Corporate Listings: Daily Log costs 25 cents per page. Custom Searches: Available on a cost recovery basis. Categories same as for mailing labels. Online Access: Yes. Number of Corporations on File: 194,500

Mississippi

Office of Corporations, Secretary of State, PO Box 136, Jackson, MS 39205, 601-359-1633 Fax: 601-359-1607; or street address: 700 North St., Jackson, MS 39202; {www.sos.state.ms.us}. Selected Publications: None. Phone Information: 601-359-1633. Copies of Documents on File: $1 per page plus

$10 for certified copies. Mailing Labels: No. Magnetic tape: No. Microfiche: No. New Corporate Listings: No. Custom Searches: Available to limited extent. Printout costs $2 per page. Online Access: Yes. Number of Active Corporations on File: 80,000

Missouri

Corporate Division, Secretary of State, 600 W. Main and 208 State Capitol, PO Box 778, Jefferson City, MO 65102-0778, 573-751-4153, Fax: 573-751-5841; {www.sos.mo.gov}. Selected Publications: Corporation Handbook (free). Phone Information: 573-751-4153. Copies of Documents on File: Available at 50 cents per page plus $10 for certified copies. Mailing Labels: No. Magnetic Tape: No. Microfiche: No. New Corporate Listings: not usually, but can be set up on special request. Custom Searches: Yes, on website. Online Access: Yes. Number of Active Corporations on File: 192,000

Montana

Corporate Division, Secretary of State, Capitol Station, Room 260 Helena, MT 59620, 406-444-3665, Fax: 406-444-3976; {http://sos.state.mt.us/css}. Selected Publications: None. Phone Information: 406-444-3665. Copies of Documents on File: available for 50 cents per page; $3 for certification. Prepaid accounts are available for obtaining certificates and other information. Mailing Labels: No. Magnetic Tape: No. Microfiche: No. New Corporate Listings: No. Custom Searches: No, but can search by name of corporation only. Online Access: Yes. Number of Active Corporations on File: 33,000

Nebraska

Corporate Division, Secretary of State, State Capitol, Lincoln, NE 68509, 402-471-4079, Fax: 402-471-3666; {www.sos.state.ne.us}. Selected Publications: None. Phone Information: 402-471-4079. Copies of Documents on File: Available for $1 per page, $10 for certified copies. Fax your requests and they will bill you, or request over the phone. Mailing Labels: No, but database is available on CD-Rom. Magnetic Tape: Contact Nebraska Online at 800-747-8177. Microfiche: No. New Corporate Listings: Also available through Nebraska Online. Custom Searches: No: Online Access: Yes. Number of Active Corporations on File: 50,000

Nevada

Office of Corporations, Secretary of State, 202 N. Carson St., Carson City, NV 89701,

775-684-5708, Fax: 775-684-5725; {www.sos.state.nv.us}. Selected Publications: Guidelines. Copies of Documents on File: Available for $1 per page, $10 for certified copies. Prepayment required (they will not send a bill). Mailing Labels: No. Magnetic Tape: Copy of master file available, 775-684-5715. Corporations takes 2 tapes which requester supplies. Cost per tape is $25. Microfiche: No. New Corporate Listings: Monthly Listing of New Corporations costs $20 a month. Custom Searches: Yes. Cost determined at time of request. Other: A listing of corporations on file, the "Alpha Listing," which includes names of active and inactive corporations can be fully downloaded for $100. Available on reel tape only. Contact Timothy Horgon. Online Access: Yes. Number of active Corporations on File: 60,000

New Hampshire

Corporate Division, Secretary of State, State House, 107 N. Main St., Concord, NH 03301, 603-271-3244; {http://webster.state.nh.us/sos/corporate/}. Selected Publications: None. Phone Information: 603-271-3246. Copies of Documents on File: Available for $1 per page, plus $5 for certified copies, and $25 expedited services. Annual report can be faxed to you for $10. Mailing Labels: No. Magnetic Tape: No. Microfiche: Complete listing of all registrations. No breakdown by type of entity (updated monthly). Annual Subscription costs $200. New Corporate Listings: Monthly Subscriber List costs $25 plus postage. Custom Searches: No. Online Access: No. Number of Active Corporations on File: 33,000

New Jersey

Commercial Recording Division, Secretary of State, 820 Bear Tavern Road, West Trenton, NJ 08628, (Mailing address: CN 308), 609-292-9292, Fax: 609-530-6433; {www.state.nj.us/treasury/revenue/}. Selected Publications: Corporate Filing Packet. Phone Information: General Information call 609-292-9292; There is a charge for standard information, $15 look-up fee for each verbal or fax request plus $10 expedited service fee. Copies of Documents on File: Available for $1 per page plus $25 for certified copies (except for LLCs and Nonprofit corporations, which cost $15 to certify). Mailing Labels: No. Magnetic Tape: No. Microfiche: No. New Corporate Listings: No. Custom Searches: Yes. Each request is reviewed on individual basis. Requester is billed for computer time. Online

Access: Yes. Number of Active Corporations on File: 436,314

New Mexico

State Corporation Commission, 1120 Paseo De Peralta, PO Box 1269, Santa Fe, NM 87501-1269, 505-827-4502, Fax: 505-827-4387; {www.nmprc.state.nm.us}. Selected Publications: None. Phone Information: 505-827-4504. Copies of documents on File: Available for $1 per page, minimum $10, plus additional $25 for certified copies. Mailing Labels: No. Magnetic Tape: No. Microfiche: No. New Corporate Listings. Yes. Monthly listings available. Requester must send manila self-addressed envelope, with postage worth $1.70 each, for as many listings as you would like. Online Access: Custom Searches: Yes, call their information line, 505-827-4509. They provide free printouts of certificates of good standing, officers and agent names. Number of Active Corporations on File: Over 100,000

New York

New York State, Department of State, Division of Corporations, 41 State Street, Albany, NY 12231, 518-473-2492; Fax: 518-474-4478 {http://www.dos.state.ny.us/corp//corpwww.html}. Copies of Documents on File: Available for $5 per document, $10 for certified copies. To receive copies of documents on file, send in a letter of request. Mailing Labels: No. Magnetic Tape: No. Microfiche: No. New Corporate Listing: Report of Corporations is printed daily and mailed out every other day. It is available in the Daily Report through subscription only, for $125 per year, $75 for 6 months or $40 for 3 months. Online Access: Yes. Number of Corporations on File: 1,200,000

North Carolina

Division of Corporation, Secretary of State, P.O. Box 29622, Raleigh, NC 27626-0622, 919-807-2225, Fax: 919-807-2039; {www.secstate.state.nc. us}. Selected publications: North Carolina Business Corporation Guidelines, North Carolina's Nonprofit Corporation Handbook. Copies of Documents on File: Available for $1 per page, $5 for certified copies. Mailing Labels: No. Magnetic Tape: Available on cost recovery basis. To make a request write Bonnie Elek. Categories: All active corporations, foreign, domestic, nonprofit, and profit. Microfiche: No. New Corporate Listings: Available for $20 per month and issued in hard copy only. Custom Searches: Yes. Categories: Type of Corporation, Professional

Corporations, Insurance Corporations, Banks, and Savings and Loans. Online Access: Available. Number of Active Corporations on File: 400,000

North Dakota

Corporation Division, Secretary of State, Capitol Building, 600 E. Boulevard Ave., Bismarck, ND 58505, 701-328-2900, Fax: 701-328-2992; {www.state.nd.us/sec}. Phone Information: 701-328-2900. Copies of Documents on File: $5, $25 for certified copies, $1 additional for every four pages. Written or phone requests accepted. Fax on demand service will send you the forms you need, 701-328-0120. Mailing Labels: No. Magnetic Tape: No. Microfiche No. New Corporate Listings: Monthly Corporation list costs $35–$37 per month. Custom Searches: No. Online Access: Yes. Number of Active Corporations on File: 22,500

Ohio

Corporation Division, Secretary of State, 30 East Broad Street, Columbus, OH 43215, 614-466-4980, Fax: 614-466-3899; {www.state.oh.us/sos/}. Selected Publications: Corporate Checklist. Phone Information: Corporate Status call 614-466-3910. Available for $1 per page, $5 for certified copies. Mailing Labels: No. Magnetic Tape: Available for $125 for 6,250 corporation names, thereafter the cost is 2 cents per corporate name with a maximum of 25,000 names. Microfiche: No. New Corporate Listing: List is updated daily. $48 flat fee, plus 5 cents a page and 3 cents a line. Depends on how recent or old a list you would like. Custom Searches: Yes. Categories: location (county), Foreign, Domestic, Profit, Nonprofit. Online Access: No. Number of Active Corporations on File: 400,000

Oklahoma

Corporations, Secretary of State, 2300 N. Lincoln Blvd., Oklahoma City, OK 73105, 405-521-3911, Fax: 405-521-3771; {www.sos.state.ok.us}. Selected Publications: Forms and Procedures to Incorporate. Phone Information: 900-733-2424 for record search. Charge is $5 per call. Copies of Documents on File: Available for $1 per page, $10 for certified copies. Mailing Labels: No. Magnetic Tape: $500 per tape. Requester must supply 3490 type cartridges. Microfiche: No. New Corporate Listings: Hard Copy costs $150 a month, with Amendments it is $250 a month plus postage. Custom Searches: Yes, date of incorporation and registered agent information is provided. Online Access: Yes. Number of Corporations on File: 224,159

Oregon

Corporation Division, Secretary of State, 255 Capitol St., NE, Suite 151, Salem, OR 97310-1327, 503-986-2200, Fax: 503-986-2308; {www.filinginoregon.com}. Selected Publications: None. Phone Information: 503-986-2200. Copies of Documents on File: Available for $5 for all documents in a corporation's file except annual report. Annual reports are an additional $5. Certification fee is $15. Business Registry on diskette or email is $15 per month or $150 per year. Mailing Labels: No. Magnetic Tape: Complete master file costs $200. Requester must provide tape. Microfiche: No. New Corporate Listings: Statistical Report of New Corporations is available for $15 per monthly issue. $150 per year. Custom Searches: Yes, minimum charge is $50. Online Access: Yes. Mead Data, Information America and Dunn and Bradstreet also have database. Number of Active Corporations on File: 73,000

Pennsylvania

Corporation Bureau, 206 N. Office Building, Harrisburg, PA 17120, 717-787-1057, Fax: 717-783-2244; {www.dos.state.pa.us}. Selected Publications: Corporate Guide. Phone Information: 717-787-1057. Copies of Documents on File: Available for $2 per page, $12 search fee, $28 for certified copies. Mailing Labels: No. Magnetic Tape: Copy of master file available for $3,500 startup fee. Monthly, you will be charged $48.12 for each tape received. This is the only way to receive the master file. It is not currently on disk or CD-Rom. Microfiche: No. New Corporate Listings: County or area listing available, four cents per name. Custom Searches: Yes. Categories: Nonprofit, Domestic, Foreign county location, Limited partnerships, Fictitious name, Trademarks, Foreign Nonprofits, Cooperatives, Professional Corporations cents per name. Online Access: Online Searches will be available in the future. Number of Corporations on File: 616,000

Rhode Island

Corporations Division, Secretary of State, 100 North Main Street, Providence, RI 02903, 401-222-3040, Fax: 401-222-1309; {www.state.ri.us}. Selected Publications: Instruction sheet, The Rhode Island Law Manual (Free). Phone Information: 401-222-3040. Staff will look up two corporations per call. Copies of Documents on File: Available for 50 cents per page, $5 for certified sheet. Mailing Labels: No. Magnetic Tape: Yes, master file is available. Microfiche: No. New Corporate Listings: Not usually provided. New corporate listings are published weekly in The Providence Journal, Sunday Business Section. Send a letter requesting weekly printouts. Custom Searches: No. Online Access: Yes. Number of Active Corporations on File: 90,000

South Carolina

Division of Corporation, Secretary of State, PO Box 11350, Columbia, SC 29211, 803-734-2158, Fax: 803-734-1614; {www.scsos.com}. Selected Publication: None. Phone Information: 803-734-2158. Copies of Documents on File: Available for $1 for first page, 50 cents thereafter. $3 for certified copies. Mailing Labels: No. Magnetic Tape: No. Microfiche: No. New Corporate Listing: Yes. Custom Searches: No. Online Access: Yes. Number of Active Corporations on File: 250,000

South Dakota

Corporate Division, Secretary of State, 500 East Capitol, Pierre, SD 57501, 605-773-4845; Fax: 605-773-4550; {www.sdos.gov}. Selected Publications: None. Phone Information: 605-773-4845. Copies of Documents on File: Available for 50 cents per page plus $5 for certification. Mailing Labels: No. Magnetic Tape: No. Microfiche: No. New Corporate Listings: No. Custom Searches: No. Online Access: No. Number of Active Corporations on File: 30,000

Tennessee

Office of Secretary of State, Services Division, 312 Eighth Ave. N. William R. Snodgrass Tower, Nashville, TN 37243, 615-741-2286, Fax: 615-741-7310; {www.state.tn.us/sos/}. Selected Publications: None. Phone Information: 615-741-2286. Copies of Documents on File: All available information on a corporation is available for $20. Mailing Labels: No. Magnetic Tape: Yes. Categories: All Corporations on file, Foreign, Domestic Profit, Nonprofit, Banks, Credit Unions, Cooperative Associations. Cost, done on a cost recovery basis, is determined at time of request. Contact 615-741-0584. Microfiche: No. New Corporate Listings: Monthly New Corporation Listing on a cost recovery basis of 25 cents per page, 8 names per page. Custom Searches: Yes. Online Access: Yes. Number of Active Corporations on File: 100,000

Texas

Corporation Section, Statute Filing Division, Secretary of State, James E. Rudder Bldg., 1019 Brazos St., Austin, TX 78701, 512-463-5586, Fax: 512-463-5709; {www.sos. state.tx.us}. Selected

Publications: Filing Guide to Corporations. Phone Information: 512-463-5555. Copies of Documents on File: Available for $35; for names and all filings of corporations. Certification is $10 plus $1 for each additional page. $5 for express services. Business entity information, excluding individual names is $3 per call, 10 cents for each page after 20 pages. Mailing Labels: No. Magnetic Tape: No. Microfiche: Names of officers and directors available. Cost determined at time of request. New Corporate Listings: Weekly Charter Update costs $27.50 per week. Custom Searches: No. Online Access: Number of Active Corporations on File: Not Available.

Utah

Corporations and UCC, Division of Business Regulations, P.O. Box 146705, 160 East 300 South, Second Floor, Salt Lake City, UT 84114-6705, 801-530-4849, Fax: 801-530-6438; {www.commerce.utah.gov}. Selected Publications: Doing Business in Utah; A Guide to Business Information (available online). Phone Information: 801-530-4849. Copies of Documents on File: Available for 30 cents a page plus $12 for certified copies. Mailing Labels: No. Magnetic Tape: No. Microfiche: No. New Corporate Listing: Updated every ten days. You can obtain by calling their information line. Custom Searches: Yes. Cost includes printing charge of 30 cents per page. Online Access: Number of Active Corporations on File: 40,000

Vermont

Corporate Division, Secretary of State, 81 River St., Drawer 09, Montpelier, VT 05609, 802-828-2386, Fax: 802-828-2853; {www.sec.state.vt.us}. Selected Publications: None. Phone Information: 802-828-2386. Copies of Documents on File: Available for $1 per page, $5 for certified copies. Send the $5 certification fee in advance. They will bill you for the copies. Mailing Labels: No. Magnetic Tape: No. Microfiche: No. Corporate Listings: Yes. Monthly New Corporations and Trade names on diskette cost $6 plus 1 cent per name. Total cost is never more than $15. Out-of-State Corporations, $50 for complete list. Custom Searches: Yes. Categories: Foreign, Domestic, Nonprofits, by date of registration. Cost is 1 cent per name plus $6 to run list. Online Access: Yes. Number of Active Corporation on File: 24,000

Virginia

Clerk of Commission, State Corporation Commission, Secretary of State, 1300 East Main

Street 23219, 804-371-9733, Fax: 804-371-9836; {www.state.va.us/scc}. Selected Publications: Business Registration Guide. Phone Information: 804-371-9733. Copies of Documents on File. Available for $1 per page, $3 for certified copies. Mailing Labels: No. Magnetic Tape: Yes. They provide you tapes for $1,000 a month and you do not have to provide blank tapes. Microfiche: No. New Corporate Listings: No. Custom Searches: Yes. Online Access: Available through Direct Access. You will dial into their database for free to obtain the information you need. Call 804-371-9733 to ask for a password. Number of Active Corporations on File: 160,000

Washington

Corporate Division, Secretary of State, 801 Capitol Way S. Olympia, WA 98504, 360-753-7115, Fax: 360-586-5629; {www.secstate.wa.gov}. Selected Publications: None. Phone Information: 360-753-7115. Copies of Documents on File: Fees are $1 for the first page and 20 cents thereafter. Certification is $10. Mailing Labels: No. Magnetic Tape: No. Microfiche: Cost is $10 a month. New Corporate Listings: No. Custom Searches: No. Online Access: Yes. Number of Active Corporations on File: 145,000

West Virginia

Corporate Division, Secretary of State, Room 139 West, State Capitol, Charleston, WV 25305, 304-558-8000, Fax: 304-558-9000; {www.wvsos.com}. Selected Publications: None. Phone Information: 304-558-8000. Copies of Documents on File: Available for 50 cents per page, $10 for certified copies. Mailing Labels: No. Magnetic Tape: No. Microfiche: No. New Corporate Listing: Monthly Report costs $5 a month or $50 per year. Custom Searches: Yes. Cost is $1 for first hour and $5 for every hour thereafter, prorated. Online Access: No. Number of Active Corporations on File: 39,000

Wisconsin

Corporate Division, Secretary of State, PO Box 7846, Madison, WI 53707; Street address: 345 West Washington Avenue, 3rd Floor, Madison, WI 53703, 608-261-7577, Fax: 608-267-6813; {www.wdfi.org}. Selected Publications: Chapter 180 Statutes Book ($4). Phone Information: 608-261-7577. Copies of Documents on File: Simple copy request must be in writing. Fee is $2. Requests for certified copies may be phoned in. Fee is $5. Mailing Labels: No. Magnetic Tape: No. Microfiche: Yes. Monthly New Corporations costs $12 per month. New Corporate Listing: Yes (see Microfiche entry). Minimum cost is $10 per week. Custom Searches: Yes. Online Access: Yes. Number of Active Corporations on File: 130,708

Wyoming

Corporate Division, Secretary of State, State of Wyoming, Capitol Building, Cheyenne, WY 82002, 307-777-7311; Fax: 307-777-5339; {http://soswy.state.wy.us}. Selected Publications: Wyoming Business Corporation Act (available free on website). Phone Information: 307-777-7311. Copies of Documents on File: Available for 50 cents for first 10 pages then 15 cents per page, $3 for certified copies. Mailing Labels: No. Magnetic Tape: No. Microfiche: No. New corporate Listings: yes: $300/yr for monthly listing of both foreign and domestic corporations, or $150 each. Custom Searches: Yes: Categories: Foreign, Domestic, Statutory trust, Nonprofit and Profit, Limited Partnership, Limited Liability, Trade Names and Trademarks. Listing of all active profit corporations can be purchased for $25 on diskette. They can email it to you at no cost. Online Access: Yes. Number of Active Corporations on File: 33,000

MORE HELP IN FINDING A GRANT

No one source can be a complete guide to finding a grant, including ours, so we wanted to include other resources you can use in your search. There are publications, experts, and even classes you can take to assist you in making your dreams come true.

As we stated earlier, The Foundation Center is a nonprofit organization which gathers and disseminates factual information on foundations. The Center's libraries in New York City, Atlanta, San Francisco, Cleveland, and Washington, DC, contain copies of foundations' tax returns, extensive collections of books, documents, and reports about the foundation field, and current files on the activities and programs of about 50,000 U.S. foundations, plus knowledgeable staff to assist users in locating appropriate information.

The Foundation Center also publishes funding directories specific to certain fields, such as: aging; arts and culture; children, youth, and families; health; higher education; international programs; libraries and information services; religion; women and girls; and elementary and secondary education.

In addition, the Center has established cooperating reference collections in each state, where Center publications and information on foundations in the immediate state or region can be consulted. A list of cooperating libraries housing these regional collections appears below. The Center also offers classes and seminars on a variety of topics, including proposal writing, basics of seeking a grant, and "how to" classes on the use of the resources and website. For further information, contact the Foundation Center, 79 Fifth Avenue, New York, NY 10003; 800-424-9836; 212-620-4230; {www.fdncenter.org}.

Foundation Center Reference Collections

The Foundation Center
2nd Floor, 79 Fifth Ave.
New York, NY 10003
212-620-4230

The Foundation Center
312 Sutter St., Room 606
San Francisco, CA 94108
415-397-0902

The Foundation Center
1627 K St., NW
Washington, DC 20006
202-331-1400

The Foundation Center
1422 Euclid Ave., Suite 1600
Cleveland, OH 44115
216-861-1934

The Foundation Center
50 Hurt Plaza, Suite 150
Atlanta, GA 30303
404-880-0094

Cooperating Collections

Alabama

Birmingham Public Library
Government Documents
2100 Park Place
Birmingham, AL 35203
205-226-3620

Huntsville Public Library
915 Monroe St.
Huntsville, AL 35801
256-532-5940

University of South Alabama
Library Building
Mobile, AL 36688
251-460-7025

Auburn University at Montgomery Library
7440 E. Drive
Montgomery, AL 36117
334-244-3200

Alaska

University of Alaska at Anchorage
Library
3211 Providence Dr.
Anchorage, AK 99508
907-786-1869

Juneau Public Library
Reference
292 Marine Way
Juneau, AK 99801
907-586-5267

Arizona

Phoenix Public Library
Information Services Department
1221 N. Central Ave.
Phoenix, AZ 85004
602-262-4636

Tucson Pima Library
101 N. Stone Ave.
Tucson, AZ 85701
520-791-4393

Arkansas

UA Fort Smith
Boreham Library
5210 Grand Ave.

Ft. Smith, AR 72913
479-788-7204

Central Arkansas Library System
100 Rock St.
Little Rock, AR 72201
501-918-3000

Pine Bluff-Jefferson County Library System
200 E. 8th Ave.
Pine Bluff, AR 71601
870-534-4802

California

Humboldt Area Foundation
373 Indianola Rd.
Bayside, CA 95524
707-442-2993

Ventura County Community Foundation
Resource Center for Nonprofit Organizations
1317 Del Norte Rd., Suite 150
Camarillo, CA 93010
805-988-0196

Fresno Regional Foundation
Nonprofit Advancement Center
3425 N. First St., Suite 101
Fresno, CA 93726
559-226-0216

Center for Nonprofit Management in Southern California
Nonprofit Resource Library
606 S. Olive St., Suite 2450
Los Angeles, CA 90014
213-623-7080

Flintridge Foundation
Philanthropy Resource Library
1040 Lincoln Ave., Suite 100
Pasadena, CA 91103
626-449-0839

Grant and Resource Center of Northern California
Building C, Suite A
2280 Benton Dr.
Redding, CA 96003
530-244-1219

Los Angeles Public Library
West Valley Regional Branch Library
19036 Vanowen St.
Reseda, CA 91335
818-345-9806

Riverside Public Library
3581 Mission Inn Ave.
Riverside, CA 92501
909-826-5201

Nonprofit Resource Center
Sacramento Public Library
828 I St., 2nd Floor
Sacramento, CA 95814
916-264-2772

San Diego Foundation
Funding Information Center
1420 Kettner Blvd.
Suite 500
San Diego, CA 92101
619-235-2300

CompassPoint Nonprofit Services
1922 The Alameda
Suite 212
San Jose, CA 95126
408-248-9505

Peninsula Community Foundation
Peninsula Nonprofit Center
1700 S. El Camino Real, #300
San Mateo, CA 94402
650-358-9369

Los Angeles Public Library
San Pedro Regional Branch
931 S. Gaffey St.
San Pedro, CA 90731
310-548-7779

Volunteer Center of Greater Orange County
Nonprofit Management Assistance Center
1901 E. 4th St., Suite 100
Santa Ana, CA 92705
714-953-5757

Santa Barbara Public Library
40 E. Anapamu St.
Santa Barbara, CA 93101
805-962-7653

Santa Monica Public Library
1324 5th St.
Santa Monica, CA 90401
310-458-8600

Seaside Branch Library
550 Harcourt Ave.
Seaside, CA 93955
831-899-2055

Sonora Area Foundation
20100 Cedar Rd., N, Suite E
P.O. Box 577
Sonora, CA 95370
209-533-2596

Colorado
El Pomar Nonprofit Resource Center
P.O. Box 1579
20 N. Cascade Ave.
Colorado Springs, CO 80903
719-531-6333 ext. 2335

Denver Public Library
General Reference
10 West 14th Ave. Parkway
Denver, CO 80204
720-865-1111

Connecticut
Danbury Public Library
170 Main St.
Danbury, CT 06810
203-797-4505

Greenwich Library
101 West Putnam Ave.
Greenwich, CT 06830
203-622-7900

Hartford Public Library
500 Main St.
Hartford, CT 06103
860-695-6300

New Haven Free Public Library
Reference Department
133 Elm St.
New Haven, CT 06510
203-946-8130

Delaware
University of Delaware
Morris Library
181 South College Ave.
Newark, DE 19717
302-831-2432

Florida
Volusia County Library
City Island
105 E. Magnolia Ave.
Daytona Beach, FL 32114
386-257-6036

Nova Southeastern University
Alvin Sherman Library, Research & Information
Technology Center
3100 Ray Ferrero Jr. Blvd.
Fort Lauderdale, FL 33314
954-262-4613

Indian River Community College
Learning Resources Division
3209 Virginia Ave.
Fort Pierce, FL 34981
772-462-4348

Jacksonville Public Library
Grants Resource Center
122 N. Ocean St.
Jacksonville, FL 32202
904-630-2665

Miami-Dade Public Library
Humanities/Social Science
101 W. Flagler St.
Miami, FL 33130
305-375-5575

Orange County Library System
Social Sciences Department
101 E. Central Blvd.
Orlando, FL 32801
407-835-7323

Selby Public Library
Reference
1331 First St.
Sarasota, FL 34236
941-861-1120

Tampa-Hillsborough County Public Library
John F. Germany Public Library
900 N. Ashley Dr.
Tampa, FL 33602
813-273-3652

Community Foundation for Palm Beach and Martin
Counties
700 South Dixie Highway, Suite 200
West Palm Beach, FL 33401
561-659-6800

Georgia
Atlanta-Fulton Public Library System
Foundation Collection- Ivan Allen Department
One Margaret Mitchell Square
Atlanta, GA 30303
404-730-1700

United Way of Georgia
Community Resource Center
277 Martin Luther King Jr. Blvd. W., Suite 301
Macon, GA 31201
478-745-4732

Savannah State University
Asa H. Gordon Library
P.O. Box 20394
Tompkins Rd.
Savannah, GA 31404
912-356-2183

Thomas County Public Library
201 N. Madison St.
Thomasville, GA 31792
229-225-5252

Hawaii
University of Hawaii
Hamilton Library
2550 McCarthy Mall
Honolulu, HI 96822
808-956-7214

Hawaii Community Foundation Funding Resource
Library
1164 Bishop St., Suite 800
Honolulu, HI 96813
808-537-6333

Idaho
Boise Public Library
715 S. Capitol Blvd.
Boise, ID 83702
208-384-4024

Caldwell Public Library
1010 Dearborn St.
Caldwell, ID 83605
208-459-3242

Illinois
Donors Forum of Chicago
208 South LaSalle St., Suite 735
Chicago, IL 60604
312-578-0175

Evanston Public Library
1703 Orrington Ave.
Evanston, IL 60201
847-866-0305

Rock Island Public Library
401 19th St.
Rock Island, IL 61201
309-732-READ (7323)

University of Illinois at Springfield
Brookens Library
One University Plaza, MS BRK 140
Springfield, IL 62703
217-206-6633

Indiana
Evansville-Vanderburgh County Public Library
22 Southeast Fifth St.
Evansville, IN 47708
812-428-8200

Allen County Public Library
200 E. Berry St.
Ft. Wayne, IN 46802
260-421-1200

Indianapolis-Marion County Public Library
Social Sciences
40 E. St. Clair St.
Indianapolis, IN 46206
317-269-1733

Vigo County Public Library
One Library Square
Terre Haute, IN 47807
812-232-1113

Iowa
Cedar Rapids Public Library
Foundation Center Collection
500 First St., SE
Cedar Rapids, IA 52401
319-398-5123

Southwestern Community College
Learning Resource Center
1501 W. Townline St.
Creston, IA 50801
641-782-7081

Public Library of Des Moines
100 Locust St.
Des Moines, IA 50309
515-283-4152

Sioux City Public Library
529 Pierce St.
Sioux City, IA 51101
712-255-2933

Kansas
Dodge City Public Library
1001 2nd Ave.
Dodge City, KS 67801
620-225-0248

Topeka and Shawnee County Public Library
1515 SW 10th Ave.
Topeka, KS 66604
785-580-4400

Wichita Public Library
223 S. Main St.
Wichita, KS 67202
316-261-8500

Kentucky
Western Kentucky University
Helm-Cravens Library
1 Big Red Way
Bowling Green, KY 42101
270-745-6125

Lexington Public Library
140 E. Main St.
Lexington, KY 40507
859-231-5530

Louisiana
East Baton Rouge Parish Library
Centroplex Branch Grants Collection
120 St. Louis St.
Baton Rouge, LA 70802
225-389-4967

Beauregard Parish Library
205 S. Washington Ave.
DeRidder, LA 70634
337-463-6217

Ouachita Parish Public Library
1800 Stubbs Ave.
Monroe, LA 71201
318-327-1490

New Orleans Public Library
Business and Sciences Division
219 Loyola Ave.
New Orleans, LA 70112
504-529-READ

Shreve Memorial Library
424 Texas St.
Shreveport, LA 71101
318-226-5897

Maine
Maine Grants Information Center
University of Southern Maine Library
314 Forest Ave.
Portland, ME 04104
207-780-5039

Maryland
Enoch Pratt Free Library
Social Science and History
400 Cathedral St.
Baltimore, MD 21201
410-396-5430

Massachusetts
Associated Grantmakers of Massachusetts
55 Court St., Ste. 520
Boston, MA 02108
617-426-2606

Boston Public Library
Social Science Reference
700 Boylston St.
Boston, MA 02116
617-536-5400

Western Massachusetts Funding Resource Center
65 Elliott St.
Springfield, MA 01101
413-452-0615

Worcester Public Library
Grants Resource Center
3 Salem Square
Worcester, MA 01608
508-799-1668

Michigan
Alpena County George N. Fletcher Library
211 N. First St.
Alpena, MI 49707
989-356-6188

University of Michigan-Ann Arbor
Harlan Hatcher Graduate Library
Reference and Research Services Department
920 N. University
Ann Arbor, MI 48109
734-764-9373

Willard Public Library
Nonprofit and Funding Resource Collections
7 W. Van Buren St.
Battle Creek, MI 49017
269-968-8166

Henry Ford Centennial Library
Adult Services
16301 Michigan Ave.
Dearborn, MI 48126
313-943-2330

Wayne State University
Purdy/Kresge Library
5265 Cass Ave.
Detroit, MI 48202
313-577-6424

Michigan State University Libraries
Social Sciences/ Humanities
Main Library
100 Library
East Lansing, MI 48824
517-353-8818

Farmington Community Library
32737 West 12 Mile Rd.
Farmington Hills, MI 48334
248-553-0300

University of Michigan-Flint Library
303 E. Kearsley St.
Flint, MI 48502
810-762-3400

Grand Rapids Public Library
111 Library St. NE
Grand Rapids, MI 49503
616-988-5400

Michigan Technological University
J. Robert Van Pelt Library
1400 Townsend Dr.
Houghton, MI 49931
906-487-2507

Maud Preston Palenske Memorial Library
500 Market St.
St. Joseph, MI 49085
269-983-7167

Northwestern Michigan College
Mark & Helen Osterlin Library
1701 E. Front St.
Traverse City, MI 49686
231-995-1540

Minnesota
Duluth Public Library
520 W. Superior St.
Duluth, MN 55802
218-723-3802

Southwest State University
University Library
1501 State St., North Highway 23
Marshall, MN 56258
507-537-6176

Minneapolis Public Library
Sociology Department
250 Marquette Ave.
Minneapolis, MN 55401
612-630-6200

Rochester Public Library
101 2nd St., SE
Rochester, MN 55904
507-285-8002

St. Paul Public Library
90 W. Fourth St.
St. Paul, MN 55102
651-266-7000

Mississippi
Jackson-Hinds Library System
The Eudora Welty Library
300 N. State St.
Jackson, MS 39201
601-968-5811

Missouri
Clearinghouse for Midcontinent Foundations
University of Missouri
5110 Cherry, Suite 310
Kansas City, MO 64110
816-235-1176

Kansas City Public Library
14 West 10th St.
Kansas City, MO 64105
816-701-3541

Metropolitan Association for Philanthropy, Inc.
1415 Olive St., Suite 100

St. Louis, MO 63103
314-621-6220

Springfield-Greene County Library
397 E. Central St.
Springfield, MO 65802
417-874-8150

Montana
Montana State University- Billings
Library- Special Collections
1500 University Drive
Billings, MT 59101
406-657-1662

Bozeman Public Library
220 E. Lamme
Bozeman, MT 59715
406-582-2410

Montana State Library
Library Services
1515 E. 6th Ave.
Helena, MT 59620
406-444-3115

University of Montana
Maureen and Mike Mansfield Library
Missoula, MT 59812
406-243-6800

Nebraska
University of Nebraska- Lincoln
Love Library
13th and R Sts.
Lincoln, NE 68588
402-472-2848

W. Dale Clark
Omaha Public Library
Social Sciences Department
215 S. 15th St.
Omaha, NE 68102
402-444-4826

Nevada
Clark County Library
1401 E. Flamingo Rd.
Las Vegas, NV 89119
702-507-3400

Washoe County Library
301 S. Center St.
Reno, NV 89501
775-327-8312

New Hampshire
Concord Public Library
45 Green St.
Concord, NH 03301
603-225-8590

Plymouth State University
Herbert H. Lamson Library
Highland St., MSC #47
Plymouth, NH 03264
603-535-2258

New Jersey
Cumberland County College Library
P.O. Box 1500
3322 College Dr.
Vineland, NJ 08362-1500
856-691-8600 ext. 236

Free Public Library of Elizabeth
11 S. Broad St.
Elizabeth, NJ 07202
908-354-6060

County College of Morris
Learning Resource Center
214 Center Grove Rd.
Randolph, NJ 07869
973-328-5296

New Jersey State Library
Governmental Reference Services
185 W. State St.
Trenton, NJ 08625
609-292-6220

New Mexico
Albuquerque Community Foundation
3301 Menaul, Suite 2
Albuquerque, NM 87176
505-883-6240

New Mexico State Library
Information Services
1209 Camino Carlos Rey
Santa Fe, NM 87507
505-476-9714

New York
New York State Library
Humanities Reference
Cultural Education Center, 6th Floor
Empire State Plaza
Albany, NY 12230
518-474-5355

Suffolk Cooperative Library System
627 N. Sunrise Service Rd.
Bellport, NY 11713
631-286-1600

New York Public Library
Bronx Reference Center
2556 Bainbridge Ave.
Bronx, NY 10458
718-579-4257

The Nonprofit Connection, Inc.
One Hanson Place, Suite 2504
Brooklyn, NY 11243
718-230-3200

Brooklyn Public Library
Social Sciences/Philosophy Division
Grand Army Plaza
Brooklyn, NY 11238
718-230-2122

Buffalo and Erie County Public Library
Business, Science and Technology Department
One Lafayette Square
Buffalo, NY 14203
716-858-8900

Huntington Public Library
338 Main St.
Huntington, NY 11743
631-427-5165

Queens Borough Public Library
Social Sciences Division
89-11 Merrick Blvd.
Jamaica, NY 11432
718-990-0700

Levittown Public Library
1 Bluegrass Lane
Levittown, NY 11756
516-731-5728

New York Public Library
Countee Cullen Regional Branch Library
104 W. 136th St.
New York, NY 10030
212-491-2070

Adriance Memorial Library
Special Services Department
93 Market St.

Poughkeepsie, NY 12601
845-485-3445

Rochester Public Library
Social Sciences
115 South Ave.
Rochester, NY 14604
585-428-8120

Onondaga County Public Library
447 S. Salina St.
Syracuse, NY 13202
315-435-1900

Utica Public Library
303 Genesee St.
Utica, NY 13501
315-735-2279

White Plains Public Library
100 Martine Ave.
White Plains, NY 10601
914-422-1480

North Carolina
Community Foundation of Western
  North Carolina
Nonprofit Resource Center
Pack Memorial Library
One West Pack Square, Ste. 1600
Asheville, NC 28801
828-254-4960

The Duke Endowment
100 N. Tryon St., Suite 3500
Charlotte, NC 28202
704-376-0291

Durham County Public Library
300 North Roxboro St.
Durham, NC 27701
919-560-0100

State Library of North Carolina
Government and Business Services
Archives Bldg.
109 E. Jones St.
Raleigh, NC 27601
919-807-7450

Forsyth County Public Library
660 W. 5th St.
Winston-Salem, NC 27101
336-727-2264

North Dakota
Bismarck Veterans Memorial Public Library
515 N. Fifth St.
Bismarck, ND 58501
701-222-6410

Fargo Public Library
102 N. 3rd St.
Fargo, ND 58102
701-241-1492

Ohio
Stark County District Library
Humanities
715 Market Ave. N
Canton, OH 44702
330-452-0665

Public Library of Cincinnati and
Hamilton County
Grants Resource Center
800 Vine St.
Cincinnati, OH 45202
513-369-6900

Columbus Metropolitan Library
Business and Technology
96 S. Grant Ave.
Columbus, OH 43215
614-645-2275

Dayton Metro Library
Grants Resource Center
215 E. Third St.
Dayton, OH 45402
937-227-9500 ext. 211

Mansfield/Richland County Public Library
43 W. 3rd St.
Mansfield, OH 44902
419-521-3110

Toledo-Lucas County Public Library
Social Sciences Department
325 N. Michigan St.
Toledo, OH 43624
419-259-5209

Public Library of Youngstown and
Mahoning County
305 Wick Ave.
Youngstown, OH 44503
330-744-8636

Muskingum County Library System
John McIntire Library
220 N. 5th St.
Zanesville, OH 43701
740-453-0391

Oklahoma
Oklahoma City University
Dulaney-Browne Library
2501 N. Blackwelder
Oklahoma City, OK 73106
405-521-5956

Tulsa City- County Library
400 Civic Center
Tulsa, OK 74103
918-596-7977

Oregon
Oregon Institute of Technology Library
3201 Campus Dr.
Klamath Falls, OR 97601
541-885-1772

Pacific Non-Profit Network
Grantsmanship Resource Library
1600 N. Riverside, Suite 1001
Medford, OR 97501
541-779-6044

Multnomah County Library
Government Documents
801 SW Tenth Ave.
Portland, OR 97205
503-988-5123

Oregon State Library
250 Winter St. NE
Salem, OR 97301
503-378-4277

Pennsylvania
Northampton Community College
Learning Resources Center
3835 Green Pond Rd.
Bethlehem, PA 18020
610-861-5359

Erie County Library System
160 East Front St.
Erie, PA 16507
814-451-6927

Dauphin County Library System
Central Library

101 Walnut St.
Harrisburg, PA 17101
717-234-4976

Lancaster County Public Library
125 N. Duke St.
Lancaster, PA 17602
717-394-2651

Free Library of Philadelphia
Regional Foundation Center
1901 Vine St.
Philadelphia, PA 19103
215-686-5423

Carnegie Library of Pittsburgh
Foundation Center
414 Wood St.
Pittsburgh, PA 15222
412-281-7143

Pocono Northeast Development Fund
James Pettinger Memorial Library
1151 Oak St.
Pittston, PA 18640
570-655-5581

Reading Public Library
100 South Fifth St.
Reading, PA 19602
610-655-6355

Martin Library
159 E. Market St.
York, PA 17401
717-846-5300

Rhode Island
Providence Public Library
225 Washington St.
Providence, RI 02903
401-455-8005

South Carolina
Anderson County Library
300 N. McDuffie St.
Anderson, SC 29622
864-260-4500

Charleston County Library
68 Calhoun St.
Charleston, SC 29401
843-805-6930

South Carolina State Library
1500 Senate St.
Columbia, SC 29211
803-734-8666

Community Foundation of Greater Greenville
27 Cleveland St., Suite 101
Greenville, SC 29601
864-233-5925

South Dakota
South Dakota State Library
Mercedes MacKay Building
800 Governors Dr.
Pierre, SD 57501
605-773-3131
800-423-6665 (SD only)

Dakota State University
Nonprofit Grants Assistance
132 S. Dakota Ave.
Sioux Falls, SD 57104
605-367-5380

Siouxland Libraries
Sioux Falls Library
201 N. Main Ave.
Sioux Falls, SD 57104
605-367-7081

Tennessee
Knox County Public Library
Lawson McGhee Library
500 W. Church Ave.
Knoxville, TN 37902
865-215-8750

Memphis Shelby County Public Library
3030 Poplar Ave.
Memphis, TN 38111
901-415-2700

Nashville Public Library
Business Information Division
615 Church St.
Nashville, TN 37219
615-862-5800

Texas
Amarillo Area Foundation
801 S. Fillmore St.
Amarillo, TX 79101
806-376-4521

Hogg Foundation for Mental Health
Lake Austin Centre, 4th Floor
3001 Lake Austin Blvd.
Austin, TX 78703
512-471-5041

Beaumont Public Library
801 Pearl St.
Beaumont, TX 77704
409-838-6606

Corpus Christi Public Library
Funding Information Center
805 Comanche St.
Reference Department
Corpus Christi, TX 78401
361-880-7000

Dallas Public Library
Urban Information
1515 Young St.
Dallas, TX 75201
214-670-1487

Center for Volunteerism and Nonprofit Management
1918 Texas Ave.
El Paso, TX 79901
915-532-5377

Southwest Border Nonprofit Resource Center
Nonprofit Resource Center
1201 W. University Dr.
Edinburg, TX 78539
956-384-5920

Funding Information Center of Fort Worth
329 S. Henderson
Ft. Worth, TX 76104
817-334-0228

Houston Public Library
Bibliographic Information Center
500 McKinney
Houston, TX 77002
832-393-1313

Nonprofit Management and Volunteer Center
Laredo Public Library
1120 East Calton Rd.
Laredo, TX 78041
956-795-2400 Ext. 2226

Longview Public Library
222 W. Cotton St.
Longview, TX 75601
903-237-1352

Lubbock Area Foundation, Inc.
1655 Main St., Suite 209
Lubbock, TX 79408
806-762-8061

Nonprofit Resource Center of Texas
Davidson Building
7404 U.S. Highway 90W, Suite 120
San Antonio, TX 78227
210-227-4333

Waco-McLennan County Library
1717 Austin Ave.
Waco, TX 76701
254-750-5975

NonProfit Management Center of Wichita Falls
2301 Kell Blvd., Suite 218
Wichita Falls, TX 76308
940-322-4961

Utah
Salt Lake City Public Library
210 East 400 South
Salt Lake City, UT 84111
801-524-8200

Vermont
Vermont Department of Libraries
Reference and Law Information Services
109 State St.
Montpelier, VT 05609
802-828-3261

Virginia
Hampton Public Library
4207 Victoria Blvd.
Hampton, VA 23669
757-727-1312

Richmond Public Library
Business, Science and Technology
101 East Franklin St.
Richmond, VA 23219
804-646-7223

Roanoke City Public Library System
706 S. Jefferson St.
Roanoke, VA 24016
540-853-2477

Washington
Mid-Columbia Library
405 South Dayton
Kennewick, WA 99336
509-586-3156

Seattle Public Library
Fundraising Resource Center
800 Pike St.
Seattle, WA 98101
206-386-4636

Spokane Public Library
Funding Information Center
906 West Main Ave.
Spokane, WA 99201
509-444-5300

United Way of Pierce County
Center for Nonprofit Development
1501 Pacific Ave., 4th Floor
P.O. Box 2215
Tacoma, WA 98401-2215
253-272-4263

Greater Wenatchee Community Foundation at the
Wenatchee Public Library
311 Douglas St.
Wenatchee, WA 98807
509-662-5021

West Virginia
Kanawha County Public Library
123 Capitol St.
Charleston, WV 25301
304-343-4646

Wisconsin
University of Wisconsin- Madison
Memorial Library
Grants Information Center
728 State St., Room 360
Madison, WI 53706
608-262-3242

Marquette University Memorial Library
Funding Information Center
1355 W. Wisconsin Ave.
Milwaukee, WI 53201
414-288-1515

University of Wisconsin- Stevens Point
Library- Foundation Collection
900 Reserve St.
Stevens Point, WI 54481
715-346-4204

Wyoming
Natrona County Public Library
307 E. 2nd St.
Casper, WY 82601
307-237-4935

Laramie County Community College
Instructional Resource Center
1400 E. College Dr.
Cheyenne, WY 82007
307-778-1206

Campbell County Public Library
2101 S4 J Rd.
Gillette, WY 82718
307-682-3223

Teton County Library
125 Virginian Lane
Jackson, WY 83001
307-733-2164

Rock Springs Library
400 C St.
Rock Springs, WY 82901
307-352-6667

(Library list courtesy of The Foundation Center)

Foundation Center Publications

(Remember that many of these publications are located in your library or in the state foundation libraries listed above. For further information, contact The Foundation Center, 79 Fifth Avenue, New York, NY 10003; 800-424-9836; 212-620-4230; {http://fdncenter.org}.)

✱ *Foundation Directory* ($215): Provides a description of over 10,000 large American foundations having at least $3 million in assets or $200,000 in annual giving. Each entry includes factual and financial data, statement of purpose and activities, and grant application procedures; indexed by fields of interest, names of donors, trustees, and administrators, and by state and city.

✱ *The Foundation Directory, Part 2* ($185): provides information on 8,700 private and community foundations making grants of $50,000-$200,000 annually and holding assets of less than $3,000,000. This is a guide to smaller but significant grantmakers whose giving often supports local organizations. Over 83% of the entries include geographic limitation statements showing preferences for giving within specific cities or states. The directory provides lists of sample grants whenever available, to provide concrete indications of the foundation's fields of interest, geographic preferences, and range of giving.

✱ *Foundation Grants Index* on CD-ROM ($165): Describes over 97,000 grants awarded by approximately 1,000 foundations within the previous year or two. This is a selective listing, useful for identifying potential funding sources based on previously awarded foundation grants. The main listing of grants is arranged by major subject fields with the grants listed alphabetically by state. A typical grant record includes the name and location of the recipient, the amount awarded, the date authorized and a description of the grant. Grant descriptions are succinct but descriptive, for example: "To promote community involvement in ground water protection in Ohio." Includes a detailed subject index.

✱ *Foundation Grants to Individuals* ($65): While the majority of foundations in the United States limit their grants to nonprofit organizations, this publication gives information on funds available to individuals from approximately 5,500 foundations. Emphasis is placed on educational and scholarship awards. Six indexes help users target prospective grants by subject area, types of support, geographic area, sponsoring company (for employee restricted awards), educational institutions, and foundation name. Bibliography included.

✱ *Guide to U.S. Foundations, Their Trustees, Officers, and Donors* ($325): Lists over 70,000 private, corporate, operating, and community foundations, including thousands of smaller ones not described in other sources. These smaller foundations are especially important as local sources of funding. Overall arrangement is by state, with foundations listed from largest to smallest in terms of grants awarded. For each foundation, the Guide gives the foundation's address, telephone number (when available), financial summary, list of officers, trustees and donors, geographic limitation, and (when available) contact person.

✱ *The Foundation 1000* ($295): Provides data on the 1,000 largest U.S. foundations, including names of officers and staff to contact, current program interests, and names of nonprofit organizations which have already received grants for similar projects. Indexed by subject field, foundation name, type of support, and geographic location.

✱ *National Directory of Corporate Giving* ($195): Comprehensive descriptions close to 2,300 corporate foundations plus 1,300 direct giving programs. Alphabetically arranged by company name with a general description of the company and its activities and a description of the company's direct giving program and/or foundation for each entry. Indexed by corporation, officers, donors, trustees, geographic areas, types of support, subject, and types of business.

Other Interesting Publications:

National Directory Of Corporate Public Affairs. New York, Columbia Books, 2004. 1277 p. ($189): This directory identifies the key people in the corporate public affairs profession. The first section is arranged by companies, an alphabetical list of almost 2,000 companies of varied sizes with public affairs programs. It includes corporate headquarters, and (where they exist) Washington, DC, area offices; political action committees; foundation or corporate giving programs; and corporate publications. Key facts and figures on corporate philanthropic activity and political action committee involvement are also summarized. Also included is a list of each company's public affairs personnel, and the office in which they are located. The second section of the book is an alphabetical list of approximately 16,000 individuals in the public affairs field.

Annual Register of Grant Support 2004: A Directory of Funding Sources. New Providence, NJ, Information Today Annual. ($239): Descriptions of over 3,000 government and private programs, arranged by broad fields of interest, which give purpose, types of awards, eligibility requirements, financial data, application, and deadline information. Access is provided by subject, organization, geographic, and personnel indexes.

Directory of Research Grants 2004. Phoenix, Oryx Press. Annual. ($135.00): Concise descriptions of nearly 6,000 research programs that offer nonrepayable funding for projects in medicine, the physical and social sciences, education, the arts, and humanities. Grant programs are listed in alphabetical order, followed by three indexes: subject, sponsoring organization, and program type.

Internet Resources

The dynamic nature of the Internet means that information resources appear and disappear without warning. The sources listed below were chosen because the organizations which provide the home pages are stable, committed to the sharing of grant information on the Internet.

It is possible to find additional Internet resources by using different World Wide Web search engines, such as AltaVista (www.altavista.com), Google (www.google.com), Yahoo (www.yahoo.com), Lycos (www.lycos.com), Hotbot (www.hotbot.com), Excite (www.excite.com), Metacrawler (www.metacrawler.com), and others. When searching for grants or funding resources, combine a subject of interest (e.g., education or small business) with terms such as:

- grants
- financial aid or financial assistance
- charities or charity
- foundations
- fund raising or fundraising

National Technical Information Service (NTIS) {www.ntis.gov}: An official resource for U.S. scientific, technical, engineering, and business-related information. Whether you are a research scientist, corporate librarian, or government engineer, NTIS can help you through its mission as the central source for U.S. government scientific, technical, and business information. You can conduct detailed subject searches through the NTIS Government Research Center's online databases or lookup any of the 600,000 documents in their collection.

GRANTSNet: {www.hhs.gov/grantsnet}: GrantsNet is a tool for finding and exchanging information about the U.S. Department of Health and Human Services (HHS) and selected other Federal grant programs. It is part of the much-publicized national movement toward providing government resources to the general public in a more accessible and meaningful manner. HHS has approximately 300 grant programs, most of which are administered in a decentralized manner by several agencies, and they do not have a single publication that describes all the grant programs. This site provides links to grant resources and other assistance for grantseekers.

FEDIX (Federal Information Exchange): {www.sciencewise.com}: FEDIX is a free outreach tool that provides grant information to educational and research organizations, as well as others, from participating federal agencies.

Council on Foundations: {www.cof.org}: The Council on Foundations is a nonprofit association of grantmaking foundations and corporations. For those interested in starting a foundation, the COF is a great resource. It explains what a foundation is, the different types of foundations, as well as the steps you need to take in establishing one. There are also helpful links, resources, workshops, and conferences.

The Internet Nonprofit Center: {www.nonprofits.org}: The Internet Nonprofit Center provides a wealth of information about nonprofits. An extensive topic list is posted in their Library section, and they have links and other resources as well.

FirstGov for Nonprofits: {www.firstgov.gov}: This incredible website is the federal government's attempt to help nonprofits access programs. There are links to departments and agencies that have programs of interest to nonprofits. You can learn about services and resources for nonprofits, general governmental information, and much more. Past grant recipients are often listed in the links. You can search the *Catalog of Federal Domestic Assistance*, and learn more about the various rules and regulations.

OVER 150 GOVERNMENT GRANTS FOR YOUR BUSINESS

One of the biggest frustrations we hear is from people looking for FREE MONEY from the government for their business. By free money, they usually mean grants or other programs where they don't have to pay back the money they receive. Many people will contact the Small Business Administration asking about free money programs and will be told that there is no such thing. Well, they are right and wrong. They are right, because the Small Business Administration does not offer grants. They specialize in loans and loan guarantees. But, they are wrong because there are dozens of other government organizations that do offer grants to businesses.

The real good stuff in life is never the most plentiful and always takes extra effort and sometimes ingenuity to uncover it.

A recent survey showed that approximately 33% of the top 500 fastest growing small businesses in the U.S. started with less than $10,000. It doesn't take much money to start a business in today's information age and service economy. We're no longer in the manufacturing age, when you needed a lot of money to start a business because you needed to buy an expensive plant and costly equipment. Today, many businesses are started with nothing more than a phone, a desk and business cards.

When people are looking for money to start a business, the first place that comes to mind is the Small Business Administration (SBA). Although they do not give out grants, they do offer a wide array of low-interest loans and loan guarantees. The SBA also has a variety of programs to provide technical assistance to entrepreneurs starting or expanding their businesses.

Just because the SBA does not give out grants, doesn't mean that grants do not exist. The Federal and state governments give out thousands of grants each year, but you have to do a little digging to uncover them. Here are some starting places to help you on your search.

As described earlier (see Government Grants), the Catalog of Federal Domestic Assistance is the best single resource for leads on federal funding programs. This manual of more than 1,000 pages provides the most comprehensive information on federal funds, cross-indexed by agency, program type, applicant eligibility, and subject. The Catalog is available in many libraries or online at {www.cfda.gov}, and describes federal government programs that provide funds or non-financial assistance to state and local governments, public agencies, organizations, institutions, and individuals. Included are the program's legislative authority, explanations of each program, types of assistance provided, restrictions, eligibility requirements, financial information, application and award procedures, information contacts, and related programs. The number and program title in parentheses refer to the Catalog.

$1 Billion To Work On Ideas

The Small Business Innovation Research (SBIR) Program is a highly competitive program that encourages small businesses to explore their technological potential and provides the incentive to profit from its commercialization. Each year, ten federal departments and agencies are required to reserve a portion of their research and development funds to award to small businesses. SBIR funds the critical start-up and development stages and it encourages the commercialization of the technology, product, or service. There are three phases to the program: start-up, development, and marketplace.

To learn more about how to apply and about the various agencies involved, contact Office of Technology, U.S. Small Business Administration, 409 Third St., SW, Washington, DC 20416; 202-205-6450; {www.sba.gov/sbir/indexsbir-sttr.html}.

Technology Assistance

The Small Business Technology Transfer (STTR) Program is a highly competitive program that reserves a specific percentage of federal research and development funding for awarding to small business and nonprofit research institution partners. Small business has long been where innovation and innovators thrive, and nonprofit research laboratories are instrumental in developing high-tech innovations. STTR combines the strengths of both entities by introducing entrepreneurial skills to hi-tech research efforts. There are specific requirements that must be met.

To learn more about how to apply and the various agencies involved, contact Office of Technology, U.S. Small Business Administration, 409 Third St., SW, Washington, DC 20416; 202-205-6450; {www.sba.gov/sbir/indexsbir-sttr.html}.

Invention Assistance

Do you have a plan to develop a company based on your energy-saving invention or innovation? Have you been searching for financial and technical support to bring your idea to market? The U.S. Department of Energy's Inventions and Innovation Program can help.

This program provides financial assistance for establishing technical performance and conducting early development of innovative ideas and inventions. Ideas that have a significant energy savings impact and future commercial market potential are chosen for financial support through a competitive solicitation process. In addition to financial assistance, this program offers technical guidance and commercialization support to successful applicants.

For more information, contact U.S. Department of Energy, Inventions and Innovation Program, 1000 Independence Ave., SW, Washington, DC 20585-0121; 202-586-2212; {www.eere.energy.gov/inventions}.

Hurt By Imports?

The Economic Development Administration of the U.S. Department of Commerce funds the Trade Adjustment Assistance Program. If your company is affected by import competition, you may file a petition for certification of impact. If your firm is certified, you may then apply for technical assistance in diagnosing your problems, and assessing your opportunities. Once approved, your firm can apply for technical assistance to implement the recovery strategy. The average grant is for over $869,312.50. For more information, contact Economic Development Administration, U.S. Department of Commerce, 14th and Constitution Ave., NW, Washington, DC 20230; 202-482-5081; {www.eda/gov}.

$1,000,000 For Air Service

The Airline Deregulation Act gave airlines almost total freedom to determine which markets to serve domestically and what fares to charge for that service. The Essential Air Service Program was put into place to guarantee that small communities that were served by certificated air carriers before deregulation maintain a minimal level of scheduled air service.

The Department of Transportation currently subsidizes commuter airlines to serve approximately 100 rural communities across the country that otherwise would not receive any scheduled air service. For more information, contact Office of Aviation and International Affairs, X-50, Room 6401, U.S. Department of Transportation, 400 7th St., SW, Washington, DC 20590; 202-366-1053; {http://ostpxweb.dot.gov/aviation/rural/ruralair.htm}.

Sell Overseas

The Foreign Market Development (FMD) Program is designed to develop, maintain, and expand long-term export markets for U.S. agricultural products. The program has fostered a trade promotion partnership between the U.S. Department of Agriculture (USDA) and U.S. agricultural producers and processors who are represented by nonprofit commodity or trade associations called cooperators.

The USDA and the cooperators pool their technical and financial resources to conduct market development activities outside the United States. Trade organizations compete for funds on the basis of the following allocation criteria: past export performance, past demand expansion performance, future demand expansion goals, and contribution levels. Projects include market research, trade servicing and more.

For more information, contact the USDA Foreign Agriculture Service Marketing Operations Staff, Stop 1042, 1400 Independence Ave. SW, Washington, DC 20250-1000; 202-720-4327; {www.fas.usda.gov/mos/programs/fmd.html}.

Advanced Technology Money

Not-yet-possible technologies are the domain of the National Institute of Standards and Technology's Advanced Technology Program (ATP).

The ATP is a unique partnership between government and private industry to accelerate the development of high-risk technologies that promise significant commercial payoffs and widespread benefits for the economy. ATP projects focus on the technology needs of the U.S. industry. The ATP does not fund product development. It supports enabling technologies that are essential to the development of new products, processes, and services across diverse application areas. There are strict cost-sharing rules and peer-review competitions.

For more information on how to apply for funding, contact Advanced Technology Program, National Institute of Standards and Technology, 100 Bureau Dr., Stop 4701, Gaithersburg, MD 20899-4701; 800-ATP-FUND (287-3863); {www.atp.nist.gov}.

$525,000 To Save Energy

The U.S. Department of Energy sponsors an innovative, cost-sharing program to promote energy efficiency, clean production, and economic competitiveness in industry. The grant program, known as NICE[3] (National Industrial Competitiveness through Energy, Environment, and Economics), provides funding to state and industry partnerships for projects that develop and demonstrate advances in energy efficiency and clean production technologies. The overall goal of NICE[3] is to improve industry energy efficiency, reduce industry's costs, and promote clean production.

Grants support innovative technology deployment that can significantly conserve energy and energy-intensive feedstocks, reduce industrial wastes, prevent pollution, and improve industrial cost competitiveness. For more information, contact U.S. Department of Energy, Office of Industrial Technologies, Denver Regional Office, 1617 Cole Blvd., Golden, CO 80401; 303-275-4824; {www.oit.doe.gov/nice3}.

Venture Capital

The Small Business Investment Company (SBIC) programs are privately organized and privately managed investment firms that are licensed by the Small Business Administration. With their own capital and with funds borrowed at favorable rates through the federal government, SBICs provide venture capital to small independent businesses, both new and already established.

A major incentive for the SBICs to invest in small businesses is the chance to share in the success of the small business if it grows and prospers. Small businesses qualifying for assistance from the SBIC program are able to receive equity capital, long-term loans, and expert management assistance. For more information on SBICs or for a Directory of Small Business Investment Companies, contact Investment Division, U.S. Small Business Administration, 409 Third St., SW, Washington, DC 20416; 202-205-6510; {www.sba.gov/INV}.

$500,000 Venture Capital from New York

High tech entrepreneurs, companies with technologies ready for market, and leading-edge enterprises each have different needs for investment capital. New York State has the seed and growth capital that will enable your high tech business to grow. The Small Business Technology Investment Fund Program (SBTIF) is a source of early-stage debt and equity funding for high tech companies. Initial investments can come to as much as $350,000 and later stage investments can go up to $500,000. New York State is banking on a strong high tech future.

For more information, contact Empire State Development/Small Business Technology Investment Fund, 30 S. Pearl St., 6th Floor, Albany, NY 12245; 518-292-5100; 800-STATE-NY; {www.nylovesbiz.com/High_Tech_Research_and_Development/Investment_fund.asp}.

Grants To Train Employees

The Job Creation Grant Fund is designed to provide matching job training funds to companies that are either relocating to Rhode Island or expanding present operations in the state. The funds are used for the training of new employees through either customized training programs or on the job training. The Fund may also be used to upgrade and/or retrain existing employees in order to develop increased business and long term employment.

For more information, contact Rhode Island Economic Development Corporation, One West Exchange St., Providence, RI 02903; 401-222-2601; {www.riedc.com/growth/jobs/job_programs.htm}.

$30,000 To Upgrade Employees Skills

The Excellence Through Training Grant Program allows an employer to upgrade the skills of existing employees, thus improving the productivity of the business. The program awards matching grants of up to $30,000 per company through a competitive proposal process. Businesses are urged to work through trade associations and local colleges and universities to increase the effectiveness of the training programs.

For more information, contact Rhode Island Economic Development Corporation, One West Exchange St., Providence, RI 02903; 401-222-2601, ext. 149; {www.riedc.com/growth/jobs/job_programs.htm}.

$5,000 To Learn New Technology

Rapid changes require rapid and effective responses. To meet your organizational needs, the Rhode Island Economic Development Corporation can afford you the opportunity to increase your overall productivity. The intent of the Project Upgrade funds is to upgrade skills of currently employed workers who are being impacted by technological or organizational changes in the workplace. Any small for-profit business can apply. A maximum $5,000 Project Upgrade grant can be obligated to each eligible company.

For more information, contact Rhode Island Economic Development Corporation, One West Exchange St., Providence, RI 02903; 401-222-2601; {www.riedc.com/growth/jobs/job_programs.htm}.

Money For Job Training

Pennsylvanian companies can take advantage of the Opportunity Grant Program. This Program provides grant funds to create or preserve jobs within the Commonwealth. Funds may be used for job training, infrastructure improvements, land and building improvements, machinery and equipment, working capital and environmental assessment and redemption. A 4 to 1 private to public match is required.

For more information, contact Department of Community and Economic Development, 400 North St., 4th Floor, Commonwealth Keystone Building, Harrisburg, PA 17120-0225; 717-787-5327; 800-379-7448; {www.inventpa.com}.

Convert Gas Vehicles to Alternative Fuels

In an effort to improve Pennsylvania air quality and reduce the consumption of imported oil, the Office of Pollution Prevention and Compliance Assistance developed the Alternative Fuels Incentive Grant Fund. Money can be used to increase the use of alternative fuel vehicles and develop a refueling infrastructure in Pennsylvania. Applicants may request a grant to cover a percentage of their costs to convert an existing gasoline vehicle that meets certain age and mileage restrictions to operate on alternative fuel, as well as, purchase and install a refueling or recharging facility.

For more information, contact Department of Environment Protection, Bureau of Air Quality, Rachel Carson State Office Building, 12th Floor, P.O. Box 8468, Harrisburg, PA 17105-8468; 717-787-9702; {www.dep.state.pa.us/dep/deputate/airwaste/aq/default.htm}.

Keep Jobs In Pennsylvania

The Customized Job Training Program provides grants to businesses in need of training assistance for new hires, retraining efforts, and upgrading employees in an effort to retain and create jobs in Pennsylvania. Grants are available of up to 75% of the eligible costs for new job creations, job retention, and upgrade training. Money can be used for instructional costs, supplies, consumable materials, contracted services, and relevant travel costs for instructors. For more information, contact Department of Community and Economic Development, Center for Financing, 400 North St., 4th Floor, Commonwealth Keystone Building, Harrisburg, PA 17120-0225; 717-787-3405; 800-379-7448; {www.inventpa.com}.

Clean Up Assistance

Pennsylvania companies involved in the reuse of former industrial land may be eligible for the Industrial Sites Reuse Program. Grants and low interest loan financing are provided to perform environmental site assessment and remediation work at former industrial sites. This program provides grants and loans of up to $200,000 for environmental assessment and up to $1 million for remediation. A 25% match is required for grant and loan projects. The interest rate for loans is 2%. For more information, contact Department of Community and Economic Development, Center for Business Financing, Grants Division, 400 North St., 4th Floor, Commonwealth Keystone Building, Harrisburg, PA 17120-0225; 717-787-7120; 800-379-7448; {www.inventpa.com}.

Pollution Control Grants From Virginia

The Virginia Department of Environmental Quality has partnered with others to offer $60,000-$100,000 pollution prevention grants. The Pollution Prevention Grants Program is designed to encourage the implementation of pollution prevention techniques in businesses and governments throughout Virginia. It is an effort to support industrially significant pollution prevention programs that reduce the production waste and to help contribute to the bottom line of Virginia's manufacturers and businesses.

For more information, contact Virginia Department of Environmental Quality, 629 E. Main St., Richmond, VA 23219; 804-698-4000; 800-592-5482; {www.deq.state.va.us/}.

Agriculture Marketing Grants

North Dakota agricultural products or by-products can get a helping hand from the Agricultural Products Utilization Commission. Funds are available for the development or implementation of a sound marketing plan for the promotion of these products. The products should be new to the area or should be an expansion of a use or uses of existing products.

For more information on requirements, contact North Dakota Agricultural Products Utilization Commission, 1600 East Century Ave., Suite 2, P.O. Box 2057, Bismarck, ND 58503-2057; 701-328-5350; {www.marketplaceofideas. com/directory/beginning/apuc.htm}.

$150,000 to $2 Million
in Delaware Venture Capital

Venture capital is needed for both technology-based and non-technology oriented companies to get them up and running. In order to help these companies grow, the State of Delaware has joined as a partner in three venture capital funds. Each one funds businesses at various stages of development, but their investment focus varies.

For more information on the funds, contact the fund managers directly:
- Blue Rock Capital: Terry Collison, 5700 Kennett Pike, Wilmington, DE 19807-1312; 302-426-0981; www.bluerockcapital.com.

Money For Development And
Marketing In Delaware

Companies based in Delaware may be eligible for the Delaware Innovation Fund that "provides financial and technical assistance to businesses which have the potential to launch innovative products and processes into national markets, to create new jobs, and to make a significant contribution to the economic diversity and the technology base of Delaware's communities." Money can be used to establish patents, develop business plans, and begin the commercialization process. A match is required for investments, but sweat equity is considered.

For more information, contact Delaware Innovation Fund, 3 Mill Road, Suite 201, Wilmington, DE 19806; 302-777-1616; {www.difonline.org}.

$50,000 For
Delaware Inventors

The Small Business Innovation Research (SBIR) grant program is a federal government program designed to encourage small business to explore their technological potential and provides the incentive to profit from its commercialization. SBIR funds the critical start-up and development stages. Phase I provides awards up to $100,000 for six months support for the exploration of technical merit or feasibility of an idea or technology. Delaware businesses that receive Phase I support are eligible for a bridge grant of up to $50,000 if they submit a Phase II proposal.

For more information, contact Delaware Economic Development Office, 99 Kings Highway, Dover, DE 19901; 302-739-4271; {www.state.de.us/dedo/new_web_site/}.

Money To Train
Kentucky Employees

The Bluegrass State Skills Corporation (BSSC) works with business and industry and Kentucky's educational institutions to establish a program of skills training. The BSSC provides funding support for the training of workers of Kentucky's new and expanding industries, and for skills upgrade and occupational upgrade training of workers of existing industries. There is a matching funds requirement.

For more grant information, contact Bluegrass State Skills Corporation, Capital Plaza Tower, 500 Mero St., Frankfort, KY 40601; 502-564-7670; {www.thinkkentucky.com/bssc}.

12.2 MILLION DOLLARS TO TRAIN OHIO EMPLOYEES

The Ohio Investment Training Program is designed to provide financial assistance and resources for customized training involving employees of new and expanding Ohio manufacturing businesses. Financial assistance is on a reimbursement basis for a portion of training expenses incurred, including instructor costs, materials, special needs, and more. For more information, contact Office of Investment Training, Ohio Department of Development, Economic Development Division, 77 South High St., Columbus, OH 43215-6130; 614-466-4551; 800-848-1300; {www.odod.state.oh.us/OITP.htm}.

$30,000 to Reduce Wood Waste

The North Carolina Division of Pollution Prevention and Environmental Assistance set a goal to reduce solid waste by 40 percent. They have created the Organic Waste Recycling Grant which funds projects up to $30,000, with a 25% match from the business, to help in meeting that goal. Projects that reduce the flow of organic wastes to landfills or incinerators, or that stimulate market demand for recycled organic wastes are eligible for this project.

For more information, contact North Carolina Division of Pollution Prevention and Environmental Assistance, 1639 Mail Service Center, Raleigh, NC 27699-1639; 919-715-6500; {www.p2pays.org/localgov/assistance/financial.asp}.

Money To Recycle Tires

The Ohio Department of Natural Resources administers the Scrap Tire Market Development Grant. Grants and loans are available to scrap tire recyclers who locate or expand in Ohio and who demonstrate that they will create new/reuse scrap tire products. Grants up to $350,000 are available for projects involving more than 1 million scrap tires yearly.

For more information, contact Ohio Department of Natural Resources, Division of Recycling & Litter Prevention, 2045 Morse Road, Columbus, OH 43229-6693; 614-265-6333; {www.dnr.state.oh.us/recycling/grants/rmdg/default.htm#stmdg}.

$30,000 For Alternative Fuel In Indiana

Indiana's Energy Policy Division has two grant programs for businesses that deal with alternative energy and transportation. The Alternative Power and Energy Grant Program has grants of up to $30,000 available to businesses, institutions, and units of local government that install and study renewable energy systems for producing electricity, heating or cooling. The Alternative Fuel Transportation Grant Program offers grants of up to $30,000 for businesses to acquire alternative fuel vehicles and to make use of alternative transportation fuels.

Contact Indiana Department of Commerce, Energy Policy Division, Alternative Energy and Transportation Programs, One North Capital, Suite 700, Indianapolis, IN 46204; 317-234-2082; {www.IN.gov/doc/businesses/EP_transportation.html}

Grants and Help For Ohio Business

The Business Development Account 412 helps Ohio businesses prosper through technical assistance programs and customized assistance resources. It provides assistance with up-to-date information on sites, buildings, labor, markets, taxes, and financing. It helps companies seek state, local, or private financing and coordinates tax incentive programs and assists companies' infrastructure needs.

For more information, contact Office of Business Development, Ohio Department of Development, 77 South High St., 28th Floor, Columbus, OH 43215; 614-466-4551; 800-848-1300; {www.odod.state.oh.us/obd.htm}.

$5,000 To Go Overseas

The Trade Show Assistance Program (TSAP) provides financial assistance to Indiana manufacturers by reimbursing a portion of the costs incurred while exhibiting their products at overseas trade shows. Reimbursement includes 100% of exhibit space rental or $5,000 whichever is less. Eligible companies may use this program one time per fiscal year and may not use the grant for the same show in two consecutive years. Applicants must be ready to export, have available manufacturing capacity for export and have basic export knowledge. For more information, contact Indiana Department of Commerce, International Trade Division, One North Capitol Ave., Suite 700, Indianapolis, IN 46204; 317-232-8845; {www.state.in.us/doc/businesses/IT_TSAP.html}.

$14 Million For Illinois Job Training

Employer Training Investment Program assists companies in meeting their employee training needs. There are two ways employers can access state training funds available through ETIP. One way is for individual employers to apply for grant funds to assist with training the employees. The second way is through the Multi-Company Industrial Training Program that allows companies with common employee training needs to join together. For more information, contact Office of Industrial Training, 620 East Adams, Springfield, IL 62701; 217-785-6284; {www.illinoisbiz.biz/bus/gri/grants_bus_large.html}.

Use Recycled Materials

The Recycling Market Development Program provides funding assistance in the form of loans and grants for the purchase or conversion of equipment to manufacture products from recycled products, and procurement and end-use testing of recycled content products. For more information, contact Resource Development Section, Bureau of Energy and Recycling, Illinois Department of Commerce and Community Affairs, 100 W. Randolph, Ste 3-400, Chicago 60601; 312-814-8429; {www.illinoisbiz.biz/com/recycling/bus_program_market.html}.

Used Tire Grants

The Used Tire Recovery Program's mission is to develop self-sustaining markets for used and waste tires. The program offers funding in the form of grants and loans for projects which reuse, recycle, or recover energy from used tires. For more information, contact Used Tire Recovery Program, Recycling Division, Illinois Department of Commerce and Community Affairs, 620 East Adams, Springfield, IL 62701; 217-785-3984; {www.illinoisbiz.biz/com/recycling/bus_program_used.html}.

Grants to Recycle Solid Waste

The mission of the Recycling Industry Modernization (RIM) Program is to divert materials from the solid waste stream and improve the competitiveness of Illinois manufacturing firms, through modernization. RIM projects increase the use of recycled materials and/or promote solid waste source reduction. Grants are available to fund modernization assessments and implementation projects.

For more information, contact Bureau of Energy and Recycling, Illinois Department of Commerce and Community Affairs, 620 East Adams, Springfield, IL 62701; 217-785-2638; {www.illinoisbiz.biz/com/recycling/grants_guidelines.html}.

$1,000 Job Training Grants

The Economic Development Job Training program is a major feature of Michigan's economic development incentive package. While the employer matches 30% of the state assistance, under this program employers customize training programs to meet their needs; training funds are channeled through Michigan's expansive educational network; and grants average $500- $1,000 per employee. For more information, contact Michigan Economic Development Corporation, 300 N. Washington Square, Lansing, MI 48913; 517-373-9808; 517-373-8281; {http://medc.michigan.org}.

Grants For Environmental Cleanup In Wisconsin

Brownfields are potential business sites, but currently pose a danger due to environmental problems. The Brownfields Grant Initiative provides grants to persons or businesses for environmental remediation activities where the owner is unknown, cannot be located, or cannot meet the cleanup costs. For more information, contact the Department of Commerce, 201 W. Washington Ave., Madison, WI 53703-7970; 608-261-7714; 800-HELP-BUS; {www.commerce.state.wi.us/mt/mt-fax-0965.html}.

Get 50% off Training Costs

The Customized Labor Training Fund provides training grants to businesses that are implementing new technology or production processes. The goal is to help Wisconsin manufacturers maintain a workforce that is on the cutting edge of technological innovation. The program can provide up to 50% of the cost of customized training that is not available from the Wisconsin Technical College System. For more information, contact the Department of Commerce, 201 W. Washington Ave., Madison, WI 53703; 608-266-1018; 800-HELP-BUS; {www.commerce.state.wi.us}.

RECYCLE MISSOURI

The Missouri Market Development Program assists recycling throughout Missouri by focusing economic development efforts on businesses and projects that use materials recovered from solid waste in manufacturing operations and other end-uses. They can help identify what financial and business development assistance is available to you through a variety of resources and connect you with collection systems, processors, and manufacturers using recovered materials. Maximum amount of financial assistance is $50,000.

For more information, contact Missouri Market Development Program, Environmental Improvement and Energy Resources Authority, P.O. Box 744, 235 Jefferson Street, Jefferson City, MO 65102; 573-751-4919; {www.dnr.state.mo.us/eiera/Missouri%20Market%20development%20program.htm}

Grants To Train Arkansas Employees

The primary purpose of the Existing Workforce Training Program (EWTP) is to provide financial assistance to Arkansas manufacturing industries for upgrading the skills of their existing workforce and to increase the capacity of state supported educational institutions. There are two ways in which to get financial assistance. Businesses that use a state-supported educational institution can receive direct funding or income tax credits up to 50% of the cost of training or up to $60 per instructional hour, whichever is less. Businesses that use their own employees or company-paid consultants as trainers can receive an income tax credit of $15 per instructional hour. A combination of the direct funding and income tax credit cannot exceed $50,000 in each calendar year for any one company site.

To learn more, contact the Arkansas Department of Economic Development, One Capitol Mall, Little Rock, AR 72201; 501-682-1121; 800-ARKANSAS; {www.1800arkansas.com}.

Quality Oklahoma Jobs

The innovative Oklahoma Quality Jobs Program allows qualifying businesses that are creating new quality jobs to receive a special incentive to locate or expand in Oklahoma. The program provides quarterly cash payments of up to 5% of new taxable payroll directly to a qualifying company, for up to ten years. There are requirements such as payroll amount, health insurance coverage, workweek, and more. For more information, contact Office of Business Development, Oklahoma Department of Commerce, P.O. Box 26980, Oklahoma City, OK 73126-0980; 800-879-6552; 405-815-5178; {www.odoc.state.ok.us}.

Money For Small Businesses

The Oklahoma Small Employer Quality Jobs Program allows qualifying small businesses that are creating a minimum of ten new direct jobs within one year of the date of application to receive a special incentive to locate or expand in Oklahoma. The program provides annual cash payments of 5% of taxable payroll for new employees to a qualifying company for up to five years. There are requirements that must be met including health insurance coverage, hours worked, and more. For more information, contact Office of Business Development, Oklahoma Department of Commerce, P.O. Box 26980, Oklahoma City, OK 73126-0980; 800-879-6552; 405-815-5178; {www.odoc.state.ok.us}.

Iowa Job Training

The Iowa Industrial New Jobs Training Program provides funds to train new employees of eligible Iowa businesses. Eligible businesses may be new to Iowa, expanding their Iowa workforce, or relocating to the state. Employees qualifying for training services must be in a newly created position and pay Iowa withholding tax. Job training services are defined as any training needed to enhance the performance of a business' new employees. Services

Forgivable Loans For Training

The Community Economic Betterment Account (CEBA) program provides financial assistance to businesses creating new job opportunities or retaining existing jobs. Assistance may be provided to encourage new business start-ups, expansion or retention of existing businesses, or recruitment of out-of-state businesses into Iowa. Assistance may be in the form of loans and/or forgivable loans.

For more information, contact Iowa Department of Economic Development, Workforce Development, 200 East Grand Ave., Des Moines, IA 50309; 515-242-4700; {www.iowasmart.com/services/new_business/ceba.html}.

include vocational and skill assessment testing, adult basic education, job-related training, cost of company, college, or contracted trainer or training services, and more.

The program is administered and operated by Iowa's 15 community colleges. Each college works with eligible businesses to assess training needs, determine funds availability, and provide training. For more information, contact Iowa Department of Economic Development, Workforce Development, 200 East Grand Ave., Des Moines, IA 50309; 515-242-4867; {www.iowasmart.com/services/workforce/iinjtp.html}.

BUSINESS NETWORK

The Iowa Community College Business Network Training Project consists of five or more businesses located in two or more community college districts with at least two community colleges sponsoring the training project. A community college business network training project is eligible for up to $50,000 in program assistance per participating community college. A 25% cash match from the participating businesses is required for consortia projects costing $5,000 or more. Projects costing less than $5,000 do not require a cash match.

For more information, contact Iowa Department of Economic Development, Workforce Development, 200 East Grand Ave., Des Moines, IA 50309; 515-242-4867; {www.iowasmart.com/services/workforce/ccbnt.html}.

Entrepreneurs With Disabilities

The Entrepreneurs With Disabilities Program provides technical and/or financial assistance to qualified individuals with disabilities seeking self-sufficiency by establishing, maintaining, expanding, or acquiring a small business. Program services include technical assistance such as business plan development, accounting, legal services, and financial assistance for the purpose of purchasing business equipment, supplies, inventory, rent and more. Financial assistance shall not exceed $10,000. For more information, contact Iowa Department of Economic Development, Workforce Development, 200 East Grand Ave., Des Moines, IA 50309; 515-242-4819; 888-472-6055; {www.iowasmart.com/services/small_business/ewd.html}.

Kansas Job Training Grants

The High Performance Incentive Program promotes the establishment and expansion of high performance industry in the state. The program provides incentives to qualified firms to provide training to employees to upgrade existing employee job skills and offers a sales tax exemption and substantial tax credits in connection with capital investment.

For more information, contact Business Development, Kansas Department of Commerce, 1000 SW Jackson St., Suite 100, Topeka, KS 66612; 785-296-7174; {http://kdoch.state.ks.us}.

Venture Capital For Kansas Businesses

The Innovation and Commercialization Corporations (ICCs) seek entrepreneurs and scientists who are in need of help, to aid in commercializing high-tech products in the development stage. The ICCs aid clients in preparing quality business plans to attract venture capital as well as assistance in preparing competitive ARMF proposals. ICCs help client corporations find affordable business incubator space nearby, so that they can take clients "on-board" and provide constant support. The ICCs also each operate a pre-seed capital fund, which empowers start-up businesses to commercialize new technology. The type of aid available differs slightly between the three corporations. For more information, contact one of the following:

- Lawrence Regional Technology Center, 1617 St. Andrews Dr., Suite 210, Lawrence, KS 66047; 785-832-2110; {www.lrtc.biz}.

- Mid-America Commercialization Corp., 1500 Hayes Dr., Manhattan, KS 66502, 785-532-3900; {www.ksu.edu/tech.transfer/macc/macc.htm}.

- Wichita Technology Corporation, 7829 E. Rockhill Road, Suite 307, Wichita, KS 67206; 316-651-5900; {www.wichitatechnology.com}.

- Alliance for Technology Commercialization, BTI-Shirk Hall, 1501 S. Joplin, Pittsburg, KS 66762; 620-235-4927; {www.atckansas.com}.

Grants For Businesses In Rural Kansas

The Rural Economic Development Loan and Grant Program provides zero-interest loans and grants to projects with the purpose of promoting rural economic development and job creation. For more information, contact Kansas Electric Power Cooperative, Inc., P.O. Box 4877, Topeka, KS 66604; 785-273-7010; {www.kepco.org}.

- Enterprise Center of Johnson County, 8527 Bluejacket, Lenexa, KS 66214; 913-438-2282. {www.ecjc.com}.

- Quest Center for Entrepreneurs, Quest Center, One East Ninth, Hutchinson, KS 67501; 620-665-8468; {www.hutchquest.com}.

- KU Medical Center Research Institute, KUMC-Research Institute, 6003 Wescoe Pavilion, Mail Stop 1039, 3901 Rainbow Blvd., Kansas City, KS 66160; 913-588-1261; {www2.kumc.edu/researchinstitute}.

- Western Kansas Technology Corporation, 1922 Main, Great Bend, KS 67530; 620-793-7964; {www.ktec.com}.

New Mexico Job Training

The New Mexico Industrial Development Training Program provides funds for classroom or on-the-job training to prepare New Mexico residents for employment. Training may be tailored to the needs of the business and is usually provided in one of three ways: classroom in nature and provided by a public education institution facility; training conducted at the business facility; and on-the-job and/or classroom training. Trainees must be guaranteed full-time employment upon successful completion of training. Trainees wages are reimbursed to the company at 60%-65% during hours of training, depending on the location of the business.

For more information, contact New Mexico Economic Development Department, Development Division, 1100 St. Francis Dr., Santa Fe, NM 87505; 505-827-0323; 800-374-3061; {www.edd.state.nm.us}.

Washington Job Skills

The Job Skills Program brings together employers or industries who have specific training needs with educational institutions that can provide customized employee training. Through matching grants and JSP funds, the Job Skills Program funds industry-education partnerships in which customized training materials are developed and short-term, job-specific training is delivered.

For more information, contact Washington State Board for Community and Technical Colleges, P.O. Box 42495, Olympia, WA 98504-2495; 360-704-4335; {www.sbctc.ctc.edu/workforce/jobskills.asp}.

Child Care Money

Alaska offers the Child Care Grant program that provides funds for child care centers and licensed homes. Grantees must use the money for the long-term benefit of the child care facility and the children in care. Most child care facilities use these funds for staff salaries and benefits, goods relating to health, safety and nutrition, and age appropriate equipment, supplies and activities for the children.

For more information, contact Child Care Programs Office, Division of Community and Rural Development, Department of Education and Early Development, 619 E. Ship Creek, Suite 230, Anchorage, AK 99501; 907-269-4671; {www.eed.state.ak.us}.

$1,500-$3,500 For Trade Shows

The Kansas International Trade Show Assistance Program provides Kansas companies with financial assistance to target new markets. Companies who receive approval can be reimbursed for up to 50% of the show related expenses to attend trade shows.

To apply, contact Trade Development Division, Kansas Department of Commerce, 1000 SW Jackson St., Suite 100, Topeka, KS 66612; 785-296-3481; {www.kansascommerce.com}.

$25,000 To Develop Business Plans And Patents

The Delaware Innovation Fund provides financial and technical assistance to Delaware-based businesses that have the potential to launch innovative products and processes into national markets, to create new jobs, and to make a contribution to the economic diversity of Delaware. Demonstration Funding provides $10,000 to $25,000 to aid in establishing patents, business plans, and proof of concept issues. Commercialization Funding goes up to $250,000 to be used to begin the commercialization process of early-stage businesses.

For more information, contact Delaware Innovation Fund, Three Mill Road, Suite 201, Wilmington, DE 19806; 302-777-1616; {www.difonline.com}.

TRAIN COLORADO EMPLOYEES

The Colorado FIRST Program is to encourage quality economic development by providing training assistance as an incentive for the location of new or expanding firms in Colorado. Companies can utilize innovative approaches to training. Training programs are not designed to assist companies with normal, on-going training requirements. Companies should provide a health plan for their employees.

To learn more, contact Colorado Office of Economic Development and International Trade, 1625 Broadway, Suite 1710, Denver, CO 80202; 303-892-3840; {www.state.co.us/oed/index.cfm}.

Utah's Short Term Intensive Training Grants Cover New Employees

Utah's Short Term Intensive Training (STIT) Grant programs are customized and designed to meet full-time job openings. Programs are usually less than one year in length and are designed to meet the specific training needs of a company. Although employees must pay tuition to participate, STIT can provide qualified employees from which a company can hire. STIT gives the option of training at 50%-70% discount of normal training costs. For more information, contact Department of Community and Economic Development, 324 South State St., Suite 500, Salt Lake City, UT 84111; 801-538-8700; {http://dced.utah.gov/national/incentiv.htm}.

Money To Move Your Business To Utah

The State of Utah has an Industrial Assistance Fund that can be used for relocation costs. This incentive loan can be repaid as Utah jobs are created. For more information about eligibility and requirements, contact Department of Community and Economic Development, 324 South State St., Suite 500, Salt Lake City, UT 84111; 801-538-8700; {http://dced.utah.gov/incentives/iaf.html}.

Vermont Grants for Women

The Women's Small Business Program is for women that are looking to start or expand a small business. The program includes a workshop, a 15-week business plan and skill course, skills training, and networking. This program is available statewide. Grants and scholarships are available to income eligible women. For more information, contact Women's Small Business Program, Trinity College, 208 Colchester Ave., Burlington, VT 05401; 802-846-7160; {www.thinkvermont.com/workforce/wsbp.cfm}.

$25,000 to Reduce Wood Waste

North Carolina is offering funding that will help reduce the flow of wood byproducts to disposal facilities. Examples of eligible projects include: equipment purchase to establish or expand wood waste processing, marketing, or end use; establishing cooperative processing between several facilities using stationary or mobile equipment; using wood for reuse or as manufacturing feedstock; and developing or encouraging other end-use applications of wood byproducts. For more information, contact North Carolina Division of Pollution Prevention and Environmental Assistance, 1639 Mail Service Center, Raleigh, NC 27699-1639; 919-715-6500; 800-763-0136; {www.p2pays.org}.

GRANTS TO START A BUSINESS

The Early Planning Grant Program offers individual grants for planning and managerial assistance to entrepreneurs and business owners. Grants are to be used to hire professional consultants for feasibility studies, business and management planning, marketing assistance and planning, and/or financial statements and loan packaging. Grants are up to $3,000 with a 25% match required.

For more information, contact the Department of Commerce, 201 W. Washington Ave., P.O. Box 7970, Madison, WI 53717-7970; 608-266-1018; 800-HELP-BUS; {www.commerce.state.wi.us}.

Money for Rural Business

Wisconsin's Rural Economic Development (RED) Program offers money for businesses that have fewer than 50 employees and are located in a rural area. The funds can be used for working capital, construction and expansion, and acquisition and existing businesses, land, buildings and equipment. The Department of Commerce provides up to 50% of allowable costs with a $100,000 maximum. For more information, contact the Department of Commerce, 201 W. Washington Ave., P.O. Box 7970, Madison, WI 53717-7970; 608-266-1018; {www.commerce.state.wi.us}.

Washington Job Skills

The Job Skills Program brings together employers or industries who have specific training needs with educational institutions that can provide customized employee training. Through matching grants, the Job Skills Program funds industry-education partnerships in which customized training materials are developed and short-term, job-specific training is delivered.

For more information, contact Washington State Board for Community and Technical Colleges, P.O. Box 42495, Olympia, WA 98504-2495; 360-704-4333 or 360-704-4335; {www.sbctc.ctc.edu/workforce/jobskills.asp}.

50% Off a Marketing Consultant

Have you planned for electronic markets? Are you an agile manufacturer? The Maine Development Center will pick up 50% of the cost of hiring an experienced marketing consultant for qualified Maine small businesses.

To see if you are eligible for the Alternative Marketing Program, contact Market Development Center, 233 Oxford St., Portland, ME 04101; 207-780-8894; or One Cumberland Place, Suite 300, P.O. Box 2579, Bangor, ME 04402-2579; 207-942-6389; or 95 Park Street, Suite 411, Lewiston, ME 04240; 207-777-5067; {www.mdcme.org}.

$100,000 from Valley Management in Tennessee

The Minority Business Development Loan Fund (MBDLF) is a $9 million fund designed to invest in equity or debt to finance the growth and development of minority-owned socially and financially disadvantaged businesses in the

Tennessee Valley. MBDLF will consider investments in start-up, growth or established companies and finance their working capital, building, or plant equipment needs. For more information, contact TVA Economic Development, Highland Ridge Tower, 535 Marriott Dr., Nashville, TN 37214; 615-232-6068; {www.tva.gov/econdev/smallbiz.htm}.

Workforce Training Grants

The Workforce Development Training Fund in Wyoming offers training grants to businesses in the state, or businesses relocating in the state. To receive funds, a job either must exist now or will exist at the end of training. Eligible costs are those that are directly related to training; materials, instructor fees, etc. The maximum grant amount is $2,000 per trainee.

For more information, contact the Wyoming Business Council, 214 West 15th Street, Cheyenne, WY 82002; 307-777-2800; 800-262-3425; {www.wyomingbusiness.org/workforce/index.cfm}.

Iowa Venture Capital

The Community Economic Betterment Account has a "Venture Project" component for early-stage and start-up businesses. This program makes equity-like investments up to $250,000.

For more information, contact Iowa Department of Economic Development, Workforce Development, 200 East Grand Ave., Des Moines, IA 50309; 515-242-4878; {www.iowasmart.com/services/entrepreneurial/ceba.html}.

$125,000 in Kansas Venture Capital

The Kansas Applied Research Matching Fund awards grants to academic/business partnerships to offset the cost of financing research that leads to new or enhanced projects. Matching funds are required to develop products that can be commercialized.

For more information, contact Kansas Technology Enterprise Corporation, 214 SW 6th St., First Floor, Topeka, KS 66603; 785-296-5272; {www.ktec.com}.

Capital Funds for Colorado Business

Colorado has established companies to serve as Certified Capital Companies (CAPCO). With this program, each CAPCO receives funds to invest in businesses in the state. Eligible businesses can then go to one of the CAPCOs for funding. The type and amount of the investment is determined differently.

For a list of CAPCOs and more information, contact the Colorado Office of Economic Development and International Trade, 1625 Broadway, Suite 1710, Denver, CO 80202; 303-892-3840; {www.oed.state.co.us/oed}.

Grants to Dairy Farmers Whose Milk Is Contaminated Because of Pesticides
(10.053 Dairy Indemnity Program)

The Dairy Indemnity Program is designed to protect dairy farmers and manufacturers of dairy products who through no fault of their own, are directed to remove their milk or dairy products from commercial markets because of contamination from pesticides which have been approved for use by the federal government. Dairy farmers can also be indemnified because of contamination with chemicals or toxic substances, nuclear radiation or fallout. Types of assistance: direct payments with unrestricted use. Estimate of annual funds available: Direct payments: $450,000.

Contact: U.S. Department of Agriculture, Farm Service Agency, 1400 Independence Ave., SW, STOP 0506, Washington, DC 20250-0506; 202-720-7809; {www.fsa.usda.gov/pas/default.asp}.

Grants to Sell Food Related Products Overseas
(10.601 Market Access Program)

The Market Access Program was created to encourage the development, maintenance, and expansion of commercial export markets for U.S. agricultural commodities through cost-share assistance to eligible trade organizations that implement a foreign market development program. Assistance also helps agricultural commodities or products in the case of an unfair trade practice. Funding of the program is accomplished through the issuance by the Commodity Credit Corporation (CCC) of a dollar check to reimburse participants for activities authorized by a specific project agreement. Types of assistance: direct payments. Estimate of annual funds available: Direct payments: $90,000,000. Contact: Deputy Administrator, Commodity and Marketing Programs, Foreign Agricultural Service, U.S. Department of Agriculture, AG Box 1042, USDA Washington DC 20250-1042; 202-720-4327; {www.fas.usda.gov/mos/programs/mapprog.html}.

Money to Local Communities Near National Forests to Help Businesses Grow or Expand
(10.670 National Forest-Dependent Rural Communities)

This program provides accelerated assistance to communities faced with acute economic problems associated with state, federal or private sector resource management decisions and policies or that are located in or near a national forest and are economically dependent upon forest resources. Aid is extended to these communities to help them to diversify their economic base and to improve the economic, social, and environmental well-being of rural areas. Types of assistance: project grants; direct loans; use of property, facilities, and equipment; training. Estimate of annual funds available: $9,000,000. Contact: Deputy Chief, State and Private Forestry, USDA Forest Service, U.S. Department of Agriculture, P.O. Box 96090, Washington, DC 20090-6090; 202-205-1657; {www.fs.fed.us/spf.html}.

Grants to Nonprofits to Lend Money to New Businesses
(10.769 Rural Business Enterprise Grants)

Rural Business Enterprise Grants facilitate the development of small and emerging private business, industry, and related employment for improving the economy in rural communities. Types of assistance: project grants. Estimate of annual funds available: Grants: $47,060,000. Contact: Director, Specialty Lenders Division, Rural Business-Cooperative Service, U.S. Department of Agriculture, Washington, DC 20250-3222; 202-720-1400; {www.rurdev.usda.gov/rbs/busp/rbeg.htm}.

Grants and Loans to Telephone Companies That Then Provide Financing to Small Businesses
(10.854 Rural Economic Development Loans and Grants)

These loans and grants are designed to promote rural economic development and job creation projects, including funding for project feasibility studies, start-up costs, incubator projects, and other reasonable expenses for the purpose of fostering rural development. Types of assistance: direct loans; project grants. Estimate of annual funds available: Loans: $15,000,000; Grants: $3,000,000. (Note: Grants to establish Revolving Loan Fund Programs.)

Contact: Director, Specialty Lenders Division, Rural Business-Cooperative Service, U.S. Department of Agriculture, Washington, DC 20250; 202-720-1400; 856-787-7780; {www.rurdev.usda.gov/rbs/busp/bprogs.htm}.

Free Plants to Nurseries
(10.905 Plant Materials for Conservation)

The Plant Materials for Conservation Program is designed to assemble, evaluate, select, release, and introduce into commerce, and promote the use of new and improved plant materials for soil, water, and related resource conservation and environmental improvement programs. To develop technology for land management and restoration with plant materials. To transfer technology on plant materials. Types of assistance: provision of specialized services. Estimate of annual funds available: Salaries and expenses: $10,701,000.

Contact: Deputy Chief For Science and Technology, Natural Resources Conservation Service, U.S. Department of Agriculture, P.O. Box 2890, Washington, DC 20013; 202-720-4630; {www.nrcs.usda.gov}.

GRANTS TO COMMUNITIES THAT PROVIDE MONEY AND HELP TO SMALL BUSINESS INCUBATORS
(11.300 Grants for Public Works and Economic Development Facilities)

Grants for Public Works and Economic Development Facilities promote long-term economic development and assist in the construction of public works infrastructure and economic development facilities needed to initiate and encourage the creation or retention of high-skill, high wage jobs in the private sector in areas experiencing substantial economic distress. Types of assistance: project grants. Estimate of annual funds available: Grants: $288,115,000. Contact: Public Works Division, Economic Development Administration, Room H7326, Herbert C. Hoover Building, U.S. Department of Commerce, Washington, DC 20230; 202-482-5265; {www.eda.gov}.

GRANTS TO COMMUNITIES FACING A THREAT TO THEIR ECONOMY
(11.307 Economic Adjustment Assistance)

This program assists state and local interests design and implement strategies to adjust or bring about change to an economy. The focus is on areas that have experienced or are under threat of serious structural damage to the underlying economic base. The economic change can occur suddenly or over time, and generally results from industrial or corporate restructuring, new federal laws or requirements, reduction in defense expenditures, depletion of natural resources or natural disaster. It aids the long-range economic development of areas with severe unemployment and low family income problems; aids in the development of public facilities and private enterprises to help create new permanent jobs. Types of assistance: project grants. Estimate of annual funds available: $40,900,000 (includes funds for economic adjustments.)

Contact: Economic Adjustment Division, Economic Development Administration, Room H 7327, Herbert C. Hoover Building, Department of Commerce, Washington, DC 20230; 202-482-2659; {www.eda.gov}.

Grants to Producers of Corn, Sorghum, Barley, Oats, and Rye
(10.055 Production Flexibility Payments for Contract Commodities)

The objective of this grant program is to support farming certainty and flexibility while ensuring continued compliance with farm conservation and wetland protection requirements. Estimate of annual funds available: Contract Payments: $3,951,656,000. Contact: U.S. Department of Agriculture, Farm Service Agency, Economic and Policy Analysis Staff, Stop 0506, 1400 Independence Ave. SW, Washington, DC 20250-0506; 202-720-2711; {www.fsa.usda.gov/}.

Grants to Fishermen Hurt by Oil and Gas Drilling on the Outer Continental Shelf
(11.408 Fishermen's Contingency Fund)

The Fishermen's Contingency Fund compensates U.S. commercial fishermen for damage/loss of fishing gear and 50 percent of resulting economic loss due to oil and gas related activities in any area of the Outer Continental Shelf. Types of assistance: direct payments with unrestricted use. Estimate of annual funds available: Direct payments: $1,000,000. Contact: National Marine Fisheries Service, 1315 East-West Highway, Silver Spring, MD 20910; 301-713-2396; {www.nmfs.noaa.gov/sfweb/financial_services/fcf.htm}.

GRANTS FOR MARINE RESEARCH
(11.417 Sea Grant Support)

Grants for Marine Research support the establishment and operation of major university centers for marine resources research, education, and training and to support marine advisory services. Some individual efforts in these same areas also receive funding. Types of assistance: Project grants. Estimate of annual funds available: $61,100,000.

Contact: National Sea Grant College Program, National Oceanic and Atmospheric Administration, 1315 East-West Highway, Silver Spring, MD 20910; 301-713-2431; {www.nsgo.seagrant.org}.

Grants to Organizations That Help Minorities
Start Their Own Businesses
(11.800 Minority Business Development Centers)

Minority Business Development Centers provide business development services for a minimal fee to minority firms and individuals interested in entering, expanding, or improving their efforts in the marketplace. Minority business development center operators provide a wide range of services to clients, from initial consultations to the identification and resolution of specific business problems. Types of assistance: project grants. Estimate of annual funds available: Grants: $10,129,370. Contact: Business Development Specialist, Field Coordination Division, Room 5071, Minority Business Development Agency, U.S. Department of Commerce, 1401 Constitution Avenue, NW, Washington, DC 20230; 202-482-1940; 888-324-1551; {www.mbda.gov}.

Grants to Organizations That Help American Indians
Start Their Own Businesses
(11.801 Native American Program)

The Native American program was created to provide business development service to American Indians interested in entering, expanding, or improving their efforts in the marketplace. To help American Indian business development centers and American Indian business consultants to provide a wide range of services to American Indian clients, from initial consultation to the identification and resolution of specific business problems. Types of assistance: project grants. Estimate of annual funds available: Grants: $1,583,500. Contact: Business Development Specialist, Field Coordination Division, Room 5079, Minority Business Development Agency, U.S. Department of Commerce, 1401 Constitution Ave., NW, Washington, DC 20230; 202-482-6022; 888-324-1551; {www.mbda.gov}.

Grants to Help Minority Businesses
Enter New Markets
(11.802 Minority Business Development)

The resource development activity provides for the indirect business assistance programs conducted by MBDA. These programs encourage minority business development by identifying and developing private markets and

Grants to Develop New Technologies
For Your Business
(11.612 Advanced Technology Program)

The Advanced Technology Program works in partnership with industry to foster the development and broad dissemination of challenging, high-risk technologies that offer the potential for significant, broad-based economic benefits for the nation. Types of assistance: project grants (cooperative agreements). Estimate of annual funds available: Cooperative Agreements: $13,626,000. Contact: Advanced Technology Program, NIST, 100 Bureau Drive, Stop 4701, Gaithersburg, MD 20899-4701; 301-975-4447; {www.atp.nist.gov/}. To receive application kits, call ATP customer service staff 1-800-ATP-FUND.

capital sources; expanding business information and business services through trade associations; promoting and supporting the mobilization of resources of federal agencies and state and local governments at the local level; and assisting minorities in entering new and growing markets. Types of assistance: project grants (cooperative agreements). Estimate of annual funds available: Cooperative Agreements/Contracts: $1,721,730. The range of average assistance is $300,000. Contact: Minority Business Development Agency, U.S. Department of Commerce, 1401 Constitution Avenue, NW, Washington, DC 20230; 202-482-3238; 888-324-1551; {www.mbda.gov}.

EMERGENCY HOUSING GRANTS
(14.231 Emergency Shelter Grants Program)

The program is designed to help improve the quality of emergency shelters and transitional housing for the homeless, to make available additional shelters, to meet the costs of operating shelters, to provide essential social services to homeless individuals, and to help prevent homelessness. Types of assistance: Formula grants. Estimate of annual funds available: $150,000,000.

Contact: Office of Special Needs Assistance Programs, Department of Housing and Urban Development, 451 7th Street, SW, Washington, DC 20410; 202-708-1112; {www.hud.gov/offices/cpd/homeless/programs/esg/index.cfm}.

Grants to Organizations That Will Help You Sell to the Department of Defense
(12.002 Procurement Technical Assistance For Business Firms)

Procurement Technical Assistance grants increase assistance by the DoD for eligible entities furnishing Procurement Technical Assistance (PTA) to business entities, and to assist eligible entities in the payment of the costs of establishing and carrying out new PTA Programs and maintaining existing PTA Programs. Types of assistance: Project grants (cooperative agreements). Estimate of annual funds available: Cooperative Agreements: $12,000,000.

Contact: Defense Logistics Agency, Office of Small and Disadvantaged Business Utilization (DDAS), 8725 John J. Kingman Rd., Suite 2533, Ft. Belvoir, VA 22060-6221; 703-767-9400; 800-523-2601; {www.dla.mil/}.

GRANTS FOR HOUSING RESEARCH
(14.506 General Research and Technology Activity)

General Research and Technology Activity grants carry out research, demonstration and program evaluation and monitoring projects of high priority and pre-selected by the Department of improve the operations of the Department's programs. Types of assistance: Project grants. Estimate of annual funds available: $49,750,000.

Contact: Assistant Secretary for Policy Development and Research, Department of Housing and Urban Development, P.O. Box 23268, Washington, DC 20026-3268; 202-708-3178; 800-245-2691; {www.huduser.org}.

Grants to Small Coal Mine Operators to Clean Up Their Mess

(15.250 Regulation of Surface Coal Mining and Surface Effects of Underground Coal Mining)

The objective of this program is to protect society and the environment from the adverse effects of surface coal mining operations consistent with assuring the coal supply essential to the Nation's energy requirements. Types of assistance: project grants; direct payments for specified use. Estimate of annual funds available: Administration and Enforcement grants: $57,575,000. Small Operator Assistance: $1,500,000. Contact: Chief, Division of Regulatory Support, Office of Surface Mining Reclamation and Enforcement, U.S. Department of the Interior, 1951 Constitution Ave., NW, Washington, DC 20240; 202-208-2719; {www.osmre.gov/grantsindex.htm}.

GRANTS TO ASIAN ELEPHANTS

(15.621 Asian Elephant Conservation)

The Asian Elephant Conservation grant is to provide financial assistance to any organization or individual responsible for Asian elephant conservation, and any organization or individual with experience in Asian elephant conservation, for approved elephant conservation projects to support research, conservation, management and protection of Asian elephants. Types of assistance: Project grants. Estimate of annual funds available: $1,030,000. Contact: U.S. Fish and Wildlife Service, U.S. Department of Interior, Chief, Division of International Conservation, 4401 N. Fairfax Dr., Room 700, Arlington, VA 22203; 703-358-1754; {www.international.fws.gov/grants/grants.html}.

GRANTS FOR PROTECTION OF IMMIGRATION RIGHTS

(16.110 Education and Enforcement of the Antidiscrimination Provision of the Immigration and Nationality Act)

This program was created to educate employers and workers about their rights and responsibilities under the Immigration and Nationality Act in order to prevent employment discrimination based on citizenship status or national origin. Types of assistance: project grants; provision of specialized services; investigation of complaints. Estimate of annual funds available: (Grants) $700,000; (Salaries and Expenses) $7,172,000. Contact: U.S. Department of Justice, Civil Rights Division, Office of Special Counsel for Immigration-Related Unfair Employment Practices, 950 Pennsylvania Ave., NW, Washington, DC 20530; 202-616-5594; 800-255-7688; {www.usdoj.gov/crt/osc/index.html}.

Money to Fishermen Who Have Their Boats Seized by a Foreign Government

(19.204 Fishermen's Guaranty Fund)

The Fishermen's Guaranty Fund provides for reimbursement of losses incurred as a result of the seizure of a U.S. commercial fishing vessel by a foreign country on the basis of rights or claims in territorial waters or on the high seas which are not recognized by the United States. Effective November 28, 1990, the United States acknowledges the authority of coastal states to manage highly migratory species, thus reducing the basis for valid claims under the

Fishermen's Protective Act. Types of assistance: insurance. Estimate of annual funds available: Reimbursement of Losses: $500,000. Contact: Office of Marine Conservation, Bureau of Oceans and International Environmental and Scientific Affairs, Room 5806, U.S. Department of State, 2201 C St., NW, Washington, DC 20520; 202-647-3941, Fax: 202-736-7350; {www.state.gov/g/oes}.

GRANTS TO BUILD AN AIRPORT
(20.106 Airport Improvement Program)

The Airport Improvement Program assists sponsors, owners, or operators of public-use airports in the development of a nationwide system of airports adequate to meet the needs of civil aeronautics. Types of assistance: project grants; advisory services and counseling. Estimate of annual funds available: Grants: $3,400,000,000. Contact: Federal Aviation Administration Airports, Office of Airport Planning and Programming, Airports Financial Assistance Division, APP-500, 800 Independence Avenue, SW, Washington, DC 20591; 202-267-3831; {www.faa.gov/arp/financial/aip/index.cfm?ARPnav=aip}.

GRANTS TO BUS COMPANIES
(20.509 Formula Grants for Other Than Urbanized Areas)

Formula Grants for Other Than Urbanized Areas improve, initiate, or continue public service in nonurbanized areas by providing financial assistance for the operating and administrative expenses and for the acquisition, construction, and improvement of facilities and equipment. Also to provide technical assistance for rural transportation providers. Types of assistance: formula grants. Estimate of annual funds available: Grants: $351,634,000. Contact: Federal Transit Administration, Office of Management, Office of Capital and Program Formula Assistance, 400 Seventh Street, SW, Washington, DC 20590; 202-366-2053; {www.fta.dot.gov}.

GRANTS TO BECOME A WOMEN-OWNED TRANSPORTATION RELATED COMPANY
(20.511 Human Resource Programs)

Human Resource Programs provide financial assistance for national, regional and local initiatives that address human resource needs as they apply to public transportation activities. Such programs may include but are not limited to employment training programs; outreach programs to increase minority and female employment in public transportation activities; research on public transportation manpower and training needs; and training and assistance for minority business opportunities. This description is applicable only to projects awarded directly by the Federal Transit Administration (FTA) under the authority of Section 5314(a), the National component of the Transit Planning and Research Program. Types of assistance: project grants (grants, cooperative agreements, and direct procurement contracts) funded under National Planning and Research programs. Estimate of annual funds available: $31,700,000. Contact: Director, Office of Civil Rights, Federal Transit Administration, U.S. Department of Transportation, 400 Seventh Street, SW, Room 9102, Washington, DC 20590; 202-366-4018; {www.fta.dot.gov}.

Grants to U.S. Shipping Companies That Have to Pay Their Employees Higher Salaries Than Foreign Shipping Companies
(20.804 Operating Differential Subsidies)

Operating Differential Subsidies promote development and maintenance of the U.S. Merchant Marine by granting financial aid to equalize cost of operating a U.S. flag ship with cost of operating a competitive foreign flag ship. Types of assistance: direct payments for specified use. Range of financial assistance: $5,000 to $10,000 (depending on the type of service vessel and trade) per day subsidy payments per ship.

Contact: Office of Insurance and Shipping Analysis, Maritime Administration, U.S. Department of Transportation, 400 Seventh Street, SW, Washington, DC 20590; 202-366-2279; 800-99-MARAD; {www.marad.dot.gov}.

Money for Airlines to Fly to Small Towns and Make a Profit
(20.901 Payments for Essential Air Services)

The Payments for Essential Air Services Program is designed to assure that air transportation is provided to eligible communities by subsidizing air carriers when necessary to provide service. Types of assistance: direct payments for specified use. Estimate of annual funds available: Direct payments to air carriers: $50,000,000.

Contact: Director, Office of Aviation Analysis, X-50, U.S. Department of Transportation, 400 Seventh Street, SW, Room 6401, Washington, DC 20590; 202-366-1030; {www.faa.gov}.

GRANTS TO WOMEN-OWNED BUSINESSES TO HELP GET CONTRACTS FROM THE DEPARTMENT OF TRANSPORTATION
(20.903 Support Mechanisms for Disadvantaged Businesses)

The objective of this program is to develop support mechanisms, including liaison and assistance programs, that will provide outreach and technical assistance to small disadvantaged business enterprises (DBEs) to successfully compete on transportation-related contracts. Recipients will provide a communications link between the Department of Transportation; its grantees, recipients, contractors, subcontractors; and minority, women-owned and disadvantaged business enterprises (DBEs) in order to increase their participation in existing DOT programs and DOT funded projects. Types of assistance: project grants (cooperative agreements). Estimate of annual funds available: Cooperative Agreements: $1,100,000.

Contact: Office of Small and Disadvantaged Business Utilization, S-40, Office of the Secretary, 400 Seventh Street, SW, Washington, DC 20590; 800-532-1169; 202-366-1930; {www.dot.gov}.

Grants to Help Learn About Computers
(47.070 Computer and Information Science and Engineering)

Computer and Information Science and Engineering grants support research improving the fundamental understanding of computer and information processing, to enhance the training and education of scientists and engineers who contribute to and exploit that understanding, to enhance the personnel pool for these fields, to provide access to very advanced computing and networking capabilities, and to provide the information intensive knowledge underlying selected national initiatives. Types of assistance: Project Grants. Estimate of annual funds available: $526, 940,000. Contact: Directorate for Computer and Information Science and Engineering, National Science Foundation, 4201 Wilson Blvd., Room 1105, Arlington, VA 22230; 703-292-8900; {www.cise.nsf.gov}.

Grants to Provide Technical Assistance to Businesses
(59.007 Management and Technical Assistance)

This grant program was created to provide business development assistance for socially and economically disadvantaged businesses. SBA performs this task by entering into grants, cooperative agreements, and contracts with qualified service providers that have the capacity to provide this assistance to eligible businesses and individuals under sections 7(i), 7(j), and 8(a) of the Small Business Act. Types of assistance: Project grants. Estimate of annual funds available: $10,000,000. Contact: Assistant Administrator for Management and Technical Assistance, Office of Business Development, 409 Third St., SW, Washington, DC 20416; 202-205-7343; {www.sba.gov}.

Help for Contractors and Others to Get Bonded to Obtain Contracts
(59.016 Bond Guarantees for Surety Companies)

This program guarantees surety bonds issued by commercial surety companies for small contractors unable to obtain a bond without a guarantee. Guarantees are for up to 90 percent of the total amount of bond. Types of assistance: insurance (guaranteed surety bonds). Estimate of annual funds available: Guaranteed Surety Bonds: $1,672,000,000.

Contact: Associate Administrator, Office of Surety Guarantees, Small Business Administration, 409 Third Street, SW, Washington, DC 20416; 202-205-6540; {www.sba.gov/osg}.

Grants to Local Organizations That Help Women Start Their Own Businesses
(59.043 Women's Business Ownership Assistance)

The Women's Business Ownership Assistance program funds non-profit economic development organizations to assist, through training and counseling, small business concerns owned and controlled by women, and to remove, in so far as possible, the discriminatory barriers that are encountered by women in accessing capital and promoting their businesses. Types of assistance: project grants (cooperative agreements). Estimate of annual funds available: $12,000,000.

Contact: Office of Women's Business Ownership, Small Business Administration, 409 Third Street, SW, Washington, DC 20416; 202-205-6673; {www.sba.gov/financing/special/women.html}.

Grants to Local Organizations That Help Veterans Start Their Own Businesses

(59.044 Veterans Entrepreneurial Training and Counseling)

This program looks to provide long term training, counseling and mentoring to benefit small business concerns and potential small business concerns owned and controlled by eligible veterans. An eligible veteran is one that (A) is entitled to compensation (or who but for the receipt of military retirement pay would be entitled to compensation) under laws administered by the Secretary, or (B) was discharged or released from active duty because of a service-connected disability. Types of Assistance: grants. Estimate of annual funds available: Grants: $350–$1,500 per client. Contact: Office of Veteran Affairs, Small Business Administration, 5th Floor, 409 Third Street, SW, Washington, DC 20416; 202-205-6773; {www.sba.gov/VETS}.

GRANTS TO VA HOMELESS PROVIDERS

(64.024 VA Homeless Providers Grant and Per Diem Program)

These grants assist public and nonprofit private entities in establishing new programs and service centers to furnish supportive services and supportive housing for homeless veterans through grants that may be used to acquire, renovate or alter facilities, and to provide per diem payments, or in-kind assistance in lieu of per diem payments, to eligible entities which established programs after November 10, 1992 that provide supportive services and supportive housing for homeless veterans. Types of assistance: project grants. Estimate of annual funds available: $31,653,000. Contact: VA Homeless Providers Grant and Per Diem Program, Mental Health Strategic Healthcare Group (116E), Department of Veterans Affairs, 810 Vermont Ave., NW, Washington, DC 20420; 202-273-8966; 202-273-8443; {www1.va.gov/homeless/index.cfm}.

Money for Disabled Veterans to Start New Businesses

(64.116 Vocational Rehabilitation for Disabled Veterans)

The Vocational Rehabilitation for Disabled Veterans grant program provides all services and assistance necessary to enable service-disabled veterans and service persons hospitalized or receiving outpatient medical care services or treatment for a service-connected disability pending discharge to get and keep a suitable job. When employment is not reasonably feasible, the program can provide the needed services and assistance to help the individual learn

Help for Retired Military to Start a Business

(64.123 Vocational Training for Certain Veterans Receiving VA Pension)

These vocational training grants assist new pension recipients to resume and maintain gainful employment by providing vocational training and other services. Types of assistance: direct payments for specified use; advisory services and counseling. Estimate of annual funds available: Direct Payments: $15,000. Contact: Veterans Benefits Administration, Vocational Rehabilitation and Employment Service (28), U.S. Department of Veterans Affairs, Washington, DC 20420; 202-273-7419; {www.vba.va.gov/bln/vre/index.htm}.

skills to achieve maximum independence in daily living. Types of assistance: direct payments with unrestricted use; direct payments for specified use; direct loans; advisory services and counseling. Estimate of annual funds available: Direct payments: $449,192,000; Loan advances: $3,415,000.

Contact: Veterans Benefits Administration, Vocational Rehabilitation and Employment Service (28), U.S. Department of Veterans Affairs, Washington, DC 20420; 202-273-7419; {www.vba.va.gov/bln/vre/index.htm}.

INSURANCE AGAINST YOUR BUSINESS IN ANOTHER COUNTRY BEING HURT BY FOREIGN POLITICS
(70.003 Foreign Investment Insurance)

Political Risk Insurance is used to insure investments of eligible U.S. investors in developing countries and emerging markets, against the political risks of inconvertibility, expropriation, and political violence. Special programs include insuring contractors and exporters against arbitrary drawings of letters of credit posted as bid, performance or advance payment guaranties, energy exploration and development, and leasing operations. Types of assistance: insurance. Estimate of annual funds available: Insurance Issued. $1,800,000,000.

Contact: Information Officer, Overseas Private Investment Corporation, 1100 New York Ave., NW, Washington, DC 20527; 202-336-8799; Email: {info@opic.gov}; {www.opic.gov}.

Money to Work on an Energy-Related Invention
(81.036 Inventions and Innovations)

The Inventions and Innovations program is designed to encourage innovation in developing non-nuclear energy technology by providing assistance to individual and small business companies in the development of promising energy-related inventions. Types of assistance: project grants; use of property, facilities, and equipment; advisory services and counseling; dissemination of technical information. Estimate of annual funds available: Grants: $1,200,000.

Contact: Lisa Barnett, Office of Industrial Technologies (EE-23), U.S. Department of Energy, 1000 Independence Ave., SW, Washington, DC 20585; 202-586-2212; {www.eere.energy.gov/inventions}.

Grants for Science Research
(81.049 Office of Science Financial Assistance Program)

The Office of Science Financial Assistance Program provides financial support for fundamental research, training and related activities in the basic sciences and advanced technology concepts and assessments in fields related to energy. Types of assistance: Project grants. Estimate of annual funds available: $515,000,000.

Contact: Grants and Contracts Division, Office of Science, SC-64/Germantown Building, Department of Energy, 19901 Germantown Rd., Germantown, MD 20874 (Federal Express Only); 1000 Independence Ave., SW, Washington, DC 20585-1290; 202-586-5430 (Regular Mail Only); 301-903-5212; {www.science.doe.gov/grants}.

Grants for Biomass Energy Technologies

(81.079 Regional Biomass Energy Programs)

Regional Biomass Energy Programs build State and municipal capacity for accelerating biomass technology deployment, in partnership with industry; and provide assistance in outreach, public education, and behavior modification activities. To conduct a balanced, long-term demonstration of biomass technologies tailored to specific regions of the country for feedstock production, conversion technologies, and feasibility studies. Grants will be offered to develop and transfer technology to various regions of the continental United States. Types of assistance: Project Grants. Estimate of annual funds available: $4,000,000. Contact: Office of Fuels Development, Regional Biomass Energy Program, EE-31, Department of Energy, Washington, DC 20585; 202-586-8594; {www.eere.energy.gov/biomass.html}.

Grants to Local Organizations That Help Women and Minorities Get Department of Energy Contracts

(81.082 Management and Technical Assistance for Minority Business Enterprises)

The objectives of this grant program are: (1) To support increased participation of minority, and women-owned and operated business enterprises (MBE's); (2) to develop energy-related minority small business assistance programs; (3) encourage public/private partnerships to provide technical assistance to MBE's; (4) to transfer applicable technology from national federal laboratories to MBE's; and (5) to increase the Department of Energy's (DOE) high technology research and development contracting activities. Types of assistance: advisory services and counseling. Estimate of annual funds available: Contracts and Grants: $500,000. Contact: Office of Minority Economic Impact and Diversity, U.S. Department of Energy, ED-1, Forrestal Building, Room 5B-110, 1000 Independence Ave., SW, Washington, DC 20585; 202-586-8383; {www.energy.gov/}.

Grants to Develop Energy Saving Products

(81.086 Conservation Research and Development)

This grant program was created to conduct a balanced long-term research effort in the areas of buildings, industry, and transportation. Grants will be offered to develop and transfer to the non-federal sector various energy conservation technologies. Types of assistance: project grants. Estimate of annual funds available: Grants: not separately identified. (Note: Discretionary funds for grants are not specifically contained in the President's request for Energy Conservation Programs. However, the Department does issue grants if found to be appropriate as a result of competitive solicitations and unsolicited proposals that clearly are consistent with program objectives and are appropriate as grants in lieu of other contractual methods. Financial assistance ranges from $50,000 to $500,000.) {www.eere.energy.gov}.

Contact: Energy Efficiency and Renewable Energy Programmatic Offices:

- Office of Building Technology, State and Community Programs, 202-586-2300
- Office of Freedom Car and Vehicle Technologies Program, 202-586-3835
- Office of Industrial Technologies, 202-586-7285
- Residential, Commercial and Institutional Buildings, 202-586-1214

Grants to Work on Solar Energy Products
(81.087 Renewable Energy Research and Development)

Renewable Energy Research and Development grants are used to conduct balanced research and development efforts in the following energy technologies; solar buildings, photovoltaics, solar thermal, biomass, alcohol fuels, hydropower, hydrogen and wind. Grants will be offered to develop and transfer to the nonfederal sector various renewable energy technologies. Types of assistance: project grants. Estimate of annual funds available: Grants: not separately identified. (Note: Discretionary funds for grants are not specifically contained in the President's request for Renewable Energy Research and Development Programs. However, the Department does issue grants if found to be appropriate as a result of competitive solicitations and unsolicited proposals that clearly are consistent with program objectives and are appropriate as grants in lieu of other contractual methods. Financial assistance ranges from $10,000 to $100,000.) {www.eere.energy.gov}.

Contact: Energy Efficiency and Renewable Energy Programmatic Offices:
- Office of Building Technology, State and Community Programs, 202-586-2300
- Residential, Commercial and Institutional Buildings, 202-586-1214
- Office of Industrial Technologies, 202-586-7285
- Office of Freedom Car and Vehicle Technologies Program, 202-586-3835
- Office of Power Technologies, 202-586-9244

Grants to Develop Uses of Fossil Fuels
(81.089 Fossil Energy Research and Development)

The mission of the Fossil Energy (FE) Research and Development program is to promote the development and use of environmentally and economically superior technologies for supply, conversion, delivery and utilization of fossil fuels. These activities will involve cooperation with industry, DOE laboratories, universities, and states. Success in this mission will benefit the Nation through lower energy costs, reduced environmental impact, increased technology exports, and reduced dependence on insecure energy sources. Types of assistance: project grants; project grants (cooperative agreements). Estimate of annual funds available: Grants and cooperative agreements: $150,500,000.

Contact: Fossil Energy Program, 19901 Germantown Road, Mail Stop FE-3, U.S. Department of Energy, Germantown, MD 20545 (Federal Express Only); 1000 Independence Ave., SW, Washington, DC 20585 (Regular Mail Only); 301-903-3514; 202-586-6503; {www.fe.doe.gov}.

grants for health research
(81.108 Epidemiology and Other Health Studies Financial Assistance Program)

This financial assistance program provides financial support for research, education, conferences, communication and other activities relating to the health of Department of Energy workers, as well as other populations potentially exposed to health hazards associated with energy production, transmission, and use. Types of assistance: Project grants. Estimate of annual funds available: $1,400,000.

Contact: Office of Health Programs, U.S. Department of Energy, Mail Stop EH-6/270CC, 1000 Independence Ave., SW, Washington, DC 20585 (Regular Mail Only); 20300 Century Blvd., 4th Floor, Germantown, MD 20874; 301-903-7030; {http://www.energy.gov}.

Grants to Businesses That Employ People with Disabilities
(84.234 Projects with Industry)

Projects with Industry grants create and expand job and career opportunities for individuals with disabilities in the competitive labor market, to provide appropriate placement resources by engaging private industry in training, career advancement services and placement. Types of assistance: project grants; project grants (cooperative agreements). Estimate of annual funds available: Grants: $21,928,000. Contact: Rehabilitation Services Administration, U.S. Department of Education, Room 3332-MES, 400 Maryland Ave., SW, Washington, DC 20202-2740; 202-205-8922; {www.ed.gov/about/offices/list/users/rsq/index.html?src=mr}.

Grants for International Peace
(91.001 Unsolicited Grant Program)

Grants for International Peace provide support for education and training, research, and public information on international peace and conflict resolution. Types of assistance: project grants. Estimate of annual funds available: $2,149,000. Contact: United States Institute of Peace, 1200 17th St., NW, Suite 200, Washington, DC 20036-3006; 202-429-3842; {www.usip.org/grants/unsolicited.html}.

Grants for Family Violence Prevention
(93.592 Family Violence Prevention and Services/ Grants for Battered Women's Shelters-Discretionary Grants)

This grant program was created to fund a wide range of discretionary activities for the purpose of preventing family violence; protecting victims and their dependents; improving the design, delivery, and coordination of services to address family violence; gathering information on the incidence of family violence; and increasing knowledge and understanding of the issue through research, demonstration, and evaluation projects. Types of assistance: Project grants. Estimate of annual funds available: $15,445,900. Contact: Office of Community Services, Administration for Children and Families, 370 L'Enfant Promenade, SW, Washington, DC 20447; 202-401-5529; {www.acf.hhs.gov}.

Grants for Agricultural Safety Research
(935.956 Agricultural Health and Safety Programs)

Agricultural Health and Safety Programs address the research, education, and intervention activities that are unique to agriculture by establishing centers for agricultural research, education, and disease and injury prevention. Types of assistance: Project grants. Estimate of annual funds available: Centers for Agricultural Disease and Injury Research, Education and Prevention: $8,000,000. Community Partners for Healthy Living: $1,000,000. Contact: Grants Management Branch, Procurement and Grants Office, Centers for Disease Control and Prevention, 1600 Clifton Rd., Mail Stop E74, Atlanta, GA 30333; 770-488-2800. Program Management, National Institute for Occupational Safety and Health, Centers for Disease Control and Prevention, 1600 Clifton Rd., Mail Stop F05, Atlanta, GA 30333; 404-639-2453; {www.cdc.gov}.

GOVERNMENT CONTRACTS
How to Sell Your Goods and Services To The World's Largest Buyer

If you produce a product or service, you've probably always wondered how you could offer what you produce to the biggest client in the world — the Federal government. Have you thought of the government as being a "closed shop" and too difficult to penetrate? Well, I'm happy to say that you're entirely wrong on that score. The Federal government spends over $200 billion each year on products ranging from toilet paper to paper clips and writes millions of dollars in contracts for services like advertising, consulting, and printing. Most Americans believe that a majority of those federal purchasing contracts have been eliminated over the last few years, but that's simply not true — they've just been replaced with new contracts that are looking for the same kinds of goods and services. Last year the government took action (either initiating or modifying) on over 500,000 different contracts. They buy these goods and services from someone, so why shouldn't that someone be you? To be successful doing business with the government, you need to learn to speak "governmenteze" to get your company into the purchasing loop, and I can show you how to accomplish that in just a few easy steps.

Step 1

Each department within the Federal government has a procurement office that buys whatever the department requires. Most of these offices have put together their own *Doing Business With the Department of _____* publication, which usually explains procurement policies, procedures, and programs. This booklet also contains a list of procurement offices, contact people, subcontracting opportunities, and a solicitation mailing list. Within each department there is also an Office of Small and Disadvantaged Business Utilization, whose sole purpose is to push the interests of the small business, and to make sure these companies get their fair share of government contracts. Another good resource is your local Small Business Administration Office which should have a listing of U.S. Government Procurement Offices in your state. Check their website at {www.sba.gov/GC}.

Step 2

Once you have familiarized yourself with the process, you need to find out who is buying what from whom and for how much. There are three ways to get this important information.

A.   Federal Business Opportunities (FedBizOpps)
FedBizOpps lists products and services (costing more than $25,000) needed by Government buyers directly on the Internet. Businesses wanting to sell to the Federal Government can search, monitor and retrieve opportunities solicited by the entire Federal contracting community. Department, then office within that agency, and then each specific office location lists opportunities. For instance, the General Services Administration has recently posted 4,125 solicitations for each of their offices throughout the states. Within that, the Public Building Services has posted 167 business possibilities. Synopses and solicitations are listed by posted date, class code, award and set aside. They can also be searched by the same criteria as well as zip code, agency, and office.

Sellers can sign up for the Vendor Notification Service. This sends emails containing announcements, presolicitations and their modification, notices of solicitation and amendment releases, and general procurement announcements. Notices can be received based on solicitation number, specific organizations, and product service classification, or all procurement notices. Other items of interest to sellers are the FBO Datafeed, which lists daily postings in html format daily, and Interested Vendors Module that promotes teaming opportunities for businesses wanting to sell to the government.

The General Services Administration Federal Supply Service publishes the FBO Vendors Guide that explains the system in detail. To begin viewing the vast amounts of potential opportunities, go to {www.fedbizopps.gov}. For information, call 877-472-3779; {fbo.support@gsa.gov}.

B. Federal Procurement Data System (FPDC)

This Center distributes consolidated information about federal purchases, including research and development. FPDC can tell you how much the Federal government spent last quarter on products and services, which agencies made those purchases, and what contractors did business with the government. FPDC summarizes this information through two types of reports: The FPDC standard report and the FPDC special report. The standard report compilation containing statistical procurement information in "snapshot" form for over 60 federal agencies, as well as several charts, graphs, and tables which compare procurement activities by state, major product and service codes, method of procurement, and contractors can be printed out, in whole or in part, at the website below. The report also includes quarterly and year-to-year breakdowns of amounts and percentages spent on small, women owned, and minority businesses. Special reports are prepared upon request for a fee, based on computer and labor costs. They are tailored to the specific categories, which can be cross-tabulated in numerous ways. A special report can help you analyze government procurement and data trends, identify competitors, and locate federal markets for individual products or services. Your Congressman may have access to the Federal Procurement Database from his/her office in Washington, which you may be able to use for free. For more information, contact: General Services Administration, Government Wide Information Systems Division, Federal Procurement Data System, U.S General Services Administration, 1800 F Street, NW, Room 4020, Washington, DC 20405; 202-219-3416; {www.fpdc.gov/fpdc/fpdc_home.htm}.

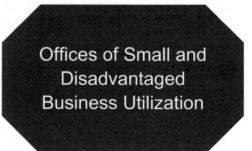

Offices of Small and Disadvantaged Business Utilization

C. Other Contracts

For contracts under $25,000, you must be placed on a department's list for solicitation bids on those contracts. The mailing list forms are available through the Procurement Office, the Office of Small and Disadvantaged Business Utilization, or your local Small Business Association office. Last year 18.7 billion dollars was spent on these "small" purchases, so these contracts should not be overlooked. Smaller contracts, completed over the course of a fiscal year, can mean lots of revenue for your business bottom line.

Step 3: Subcontracting Opportunities

All of the federal procurement offices or Offices of Small and Disadvantaged Business Utilization (SDBU) can provide you with information regarding subcontracting. Many of the departments' prime contracts require that the prime contractor maximize small business subcontracting opportunities. Many prime contractors produce special publications which can be helpful to those interested in subcontracting. The SDBU Office can provide you with more information on the subcontracting process, along with a directory of prime contractors. Another good source for subcontract assistance is your local Small Business Administration (SBA) office, 1-800-827-5722. SBA develops subcontracting opportunities for small business by maintaining close contact with large business prime contractors and by referring qualified small firms to them. The SBA has developed agreements and close working relationships with hundreds of prime contractors who cooperate by offering small firms the opportunity to compete for their subcontracts. In addition, to complete SBA's compliance responsibilities, commercial market representatives monitor prime contractors in order to assess their compliance with laws governing subcontracting opportunities for small businesses. Check the website at {www.sba.gov}. For a list of major federal OSDBU offices, check the following website: {www.osec.doc.gov/osdbu}.

Step 4: Small Business Administration's 8(a) Program

Are you a socially or economically disadvantaged person who has a business? This group includes, but is not limited to, Black Americans, Hispanic Americans, Native Americans, Asian Pacific Americans, and Subcontinent Asian Americans. Socially and economically disadvantaged individuals represent a significant percentage of U.S. citizens, yet account for a disproportionately small percentage of total U.S. business revenues. The 8(a) program assists firms in participating in the business sector and to become independently competitive in the marketplace. SBA may provide participating firms with procurement, marketing, financial, management, or other technical assistance. A Business Opportunity Specialist will be assigned to each firm that participates, and is responsible for providing the firm with access to assistance that can help the firm fulfill its business goals. SBA undertakes an extensive effort to provide government contracting opportunities to participating businesses. The SBA has the Procurement Automated Source System (PASS) which places your company's capabilities online so that they may be available to government agencies and major corporations when they request potential bidders for contracts and subcontracts. To apply for the 8(a) program, you must attend an interview session with an official in the SBA field office in your area. For more information, contact your local Small Business Administration Office, or call 1-800-827-5722 or {www.sba.gov} for the SBA office nearest you. Check their website at {www.sba.gov/8abd}.

Step 5: Bond

A Surety bond is often a prerequisite for government and private sector contracts. This is particularly true when the contract involves construction. In order for the company to qualify for an SBA Guarantee Bond, they must make the bonding company aware of their capabilities based on past contract performance and meeting of financial obligations. SBA can assist firms in obtaining surety bonding for contracts that do not exceed $2,000,000. SBA is authorized, when appropriate circumstances occur, to guarantee as much as 90 percent of losses suffered by a surety resulting from a breach of terms of a bond. Check their website at {www.sba.gov/osg}.

Step 6: Publications

The Government Printing Office has several publications for sale which explain the world of government contracts. For ordering information, contact: Superintendent of Documents, U.S. Government Printing Office, Washington, DC 20401; 202-512-1800; {www.gpoaccess.gov}.

* *Guidebook for Performance-Based Services Acquisition in the Department of Defense.* This publication highlights the key elements of performance-based services acquisition and encourages innovative business practices within the Department of Defense acquisition process. S/N 008-020-01501-6 $7.50

* *Code of Federal Regulations, Title 41, Public Contracts and Property Management.* Chapter 1-100. S/N 869-048-00162-0 $23.00

* *Best Practices: How to Avoid Surprises in the World's Most Complicated Technical Process, The Transition From Development to Production.* This is a guide for defense contractors that shows common mistakes that were made at all stages of the procurement process, form proposal submission to research, test and development. S/N 008-050-00234-4 $35.00

Step 7: What is GSA?

General Services Administration (GSA) is the Government's business agent. On an annual budget of 25 billion dollars, it directs and coordinates nearly $8 billion a year worth of purchases, sales, and services. Its source of supply is private enterprise, and its clients include all branches of the Federal government. GSA plans and manages leasing, purchase, or construction of office buildings, laboratories, and warehouses; buys and delivers nearly $9 billion worth of goods and services; negotiates the prices and terms for an additional $2.3 billion worth of direct business between federal groups and private industry; sets and interprets the rules for federal travel and negotiates reduced fares and lodging rates for federal travelers; and manages a 185,000 vehicle fleet with a cumulative yearly mileage of over 1 billion. For a copy of *Doing Business With GSA, GSA's Annual Report*, visit www.gsa.gov/smallbusiness. For information on GSA's architect and engineer services, such as who is eligible for GSA professional services contracts, how to find out about potential GSA projects, what types of contracts are available, and where and how to apply, contact: Public Buildings Service, GSA, 1800 F Street, NW, Washington, DC 20405; 202-501-1888. Information on specifications and standards of the Federal government is contained in a booklet, *Guide to Index of Federal Specifications*, which is available free from Federal Supply Service, General Services Administration, 1941 Jefferson Davis Hwy., Suite 1121, Crystal Mall 4, Arlington, VA 22202; 703-605-5400; {www.gsa.gov}.

Step 8: Bid and Contract Protests

The General Accounting Office (GAO) resolves disputes between agencies and bidders of government contracts, including grantee award actions. The free publication, *Bid Protests at GAO; A Descriptive Guide*, contains information on GAO's procedures for determining legal questions arising from the awarding of government contracts. Contact General Accounting Office, 441 G Street, NW, Washington, DC 20548; 202-512-6000. For Contract Appeals, the GSA Board of Contract Appeals works to resolve disputes arising out of contracts with GSA, the Departments of Treasury, Education, Commerce, and other independent government agencies. The Board also hears and decides bid protests arising out of government-wide automated data processing (ADP) procurements. A contractor may elect to use either the GSA Board or the General Accounting Office for resolution of an ADP bid protest. Contractors may elect to have their appeals processed under the Board's accelerated procedures if the claim is $50,000 or less, or under the small claims procedure if the claim is $10,000 or less. Contractors may also request that a hearing be held at a location convenient to them. With the exception of small claims decisions, contractors can appeal adverse Board decisions to the U.S. Court of Appeals for the Federal Circuit. For more information, contact: Board of Contract Appeals, General Services Administration, 1800 F Street, NW, Washington, DC 20405; 202-501-0116; {www.gsbca.gsa.gov}. There are other Contract Appeals Boards for other departments. One of the last paragraphs in your government contract should specify which Board you are to go to if a problem with your particular contract should arise.

Free Local Help:
The Best Place To Start To Sell To The Government

Within each state there are offices that can help you get started in the federal procurement process. As stated previously, your local Small Business Administration (SBA) office is a good resource. In addition to their other services, the SBA can provide you with a list of Federal Procurement Offices based in your state, so you can visit them in person to gather valuable information. Another place to turn is your local Small Business Development Center (look under Economic Development in your phone book). These offices are funded jointly by federal and state governments, and are usually associated with the state university system in your area. They are aware of the federal procurement process, and can help you draw up a sensible business plan that will be successful.

Some states have established programs to assist businesses in the federal procurement process for all departments in the government. These programs are designed to help businesses learn about the bidding process, the resources available, and provide information on how the procurement system operates. They can match the product or service you are selling with the appropriate agency, and then help you market your product. Several programs have online bid matching services, whereby if a solicitation appears in on FedBizOpps that matches what your company markets, then the program will automatically contact you to start the bid process. The program office can then request the appropriate documents, and assist you in achieving your goal. These Procurement Assistance Offices (PAOs) are partially funded by the Department of Defense to assist businesses with Defense Procurement. For a current listing of PAOs contact:

Defense Logistics Agency
Office of Small and Disadvantaged Utilization
4031 University Dr., Suite 200
Fairfax, VA 22030   703-277-7750
{www.gmu.edu/gmu/PTAP}, then go to the small business site

Let Your Congressman Help You

Are you trying to market a new product to a department of the Federal government? Need to know where to try to sell your wares? Is there some problem with your bid? Your Congressman can be of assistance. Because they want business in their state to boom, most Congressmen will make an effort to assist companies in obtaining federal contracts. Frequently they will write a letter to accompany your bid, or if you are trying to market a new product, they will write a letter to the procurement office requesting that they review your product. Your Congressman can also be your personal troubleshooter. If there is some problem with your bid, your Congressman can assist you in determining and resolving the problem, and can provide you with information on the status of your bid. Look in the blue pages of your phone book for your Senators' or Representatives' phone numbers, or call them in Washington at 202-224-3121.

Small Business Set-Asides

The Small Business Administration (SBA) encourages government purchasing agencies to set aside suitable government purchases for exclusive small business competition. A purchase which is restricted to small business bidders is identified by a set aside clause in the invitation for bids or request for proposals. There is no overall listing of procurements which are, or have been, set aside for small business. A small business learns which purchases are reserved for small business by getting listed on bidders' lists. It also can help keep itself informed of set aside opportunities by referring to the FedBizOpps. Your local SBA office can provide you with more information on set asides, and so can the Procurement Assistance Offices listed at the end of this section. To locate your nearest SBA office, call 1-800-827-5722 or {www.sba.gov}.

Veterans Assistance

Each Small Business Administration District Office has a Veterans Affairs Officer which can assist veteran-owned businesses in obtaining government contracts. Although there is no such thing as veterans set aside contracts, the Veterans Administration does make an effort to fill its contracts using veteran-owned businesses whenever possible. Contact your local SBA office for more information, or check the following websites: {www.sba.gov/VETS}; {www.va.gov}.

Women-Owned Business Assistance

There are 9.1 million women-owned businesses in the United States, and the number is growing each year. Current government policy requires federal contracting officers to increase their purchases from women-owned businesses. Although the women-owned firms will receive more opportunities to bid, they still must be the lowest responsive and responsible bidder to win the contract. To assist these businesses, each SBA district office has a Women's Business Ownership Representative, who can provide you with information regarding government programs. There is a helpful publication, *Selling to the Federal Government: Forward* which provides information on procurement opportunities

Procurement Assistance Offices

available. Contact your local SBA office or your Procurement Assistance Office (listed below) for more information; or check the website at {www.sba.gov/financing/special/women.html}.

Minority and Labor Surplus Area Assistance

Are you a socially or economically disadvantaged person who has a business? This group includes, but is not limited to, Black Americans, Hispanic Americans, Native Americans, Asian Pacific Americans, and Subcontinent Asian Americans. Socially and economically disadvantaged individuals represent a significant percentage of U.S. citizens yet account for a disproportionately small percentage of total U.S. business revenues. The 8(a) program assists firms to participate in the business sector and to become independently competitive in the marketplace. SBA may provide participating firms with procurement, marketing, financial, management, or other technical assistance. A Business Opportunity Specialist will be assigned to each firm that participates, and is responsible for providing that company with access to assistance that can help it fulfill its business goals. Check the website at {www.sba.gov/8abd}.

Some areas of the country have been determined to be labor surplus areas, which means there is a high rate of unemployment. Your local SBA office can tell you if you live in such an area, as some contracts are set aside for labor surplus areas. For more information, contact your local Small Business Administration office (call 1-800-827-5722 for the SBA office nearest you; or online at {www.sba.gov}), or call the Procurement Assistance Office in your state (listed on the following pages).

Federal Procurement Assistance Offices

Alabama
Information unavailable at time of printing. Check your state *Yellow Pages* directory under the Federal Government section. Look for "Small Business Assistance" or "Procurement Assistance."

Alaska
University of Alaska Anchorage
Small Business Development Center
430 W. 7th Ave., Suite 110
Anchorage, AK 99501
907-274-7232
800-478-7232
Fax: 907-274-9524
www.ptacalaska.org

Arizona
The National Center for AIED
National Center Headquarters
953 E. Juanita Ave.
Mesa, AZ 85204
480-545-1298
Fax: 480-545-4208
www.ncaied.org/mpsp

Bid Match USA
P.O. Box 3739
Gilbert, AZ 85299-3739
480-361-8721
Fax: 480-361-8723

Email: bidmatch@bidmatchusa.com
www.bidmatchusa.com

Arkansas
Board of Trustees
University of Arkansas
Cooperative Extension Service
2301 South University Ave.,
Little Rock, AR 72204
501-670-2000
Fax: 501-671-2209
Email: apac@uaex.edu
www.arcommunities.org/apac/default.asp

California
Riverside Community College District
4745 Riverside Dr.,
Riverside, CA 92518-909-571-6441,
Fax: 909-653-1051
www.rcchelpsbusiness.com

Action Business Center
California Central Valley PTAC
2000 "M" St.
Merced, CA 95340
209-385-7686
Fax: 209-383-4959
Email: ptac1@pacbell.net
www.abc.merced.ca.us/sbdc.html

Southwestern Community College
Contracting Opportunities Center
3443 Camino Del Rio South, Suite 116
San Diego, CA 92108-3913
619-285-7020
Fax: 619-285-7030
Email: sdcoc@pxac-sandiego.org
www.ptac-sandiego.org

Los Angeles County Office of Small
Business and Procurement Technical Assistance
4800 Cesar E. Chavez Avenue
Los Angeles, CA 90022
323-260-2311
Fax: 323-881-1871
www.laosb.org

Federal Technology Center PTAC
4700 Roseville Road, Suite 105
North Highlands, CA 95660
916-334-9388
Fax: 916-334-9078
www.theftc.org/ptac

Colorado
Denver Metro Chamber of Commerce
1445 Market St.
Denver, CO 80202-1729
303-534-8500
Fax: 303-534-3200

Connecticut
Southeastern Connecticut Enterprise Region (seCTer)
190 Governor Winthrop Blvd., Suite 300
New London, CT 06320
860-437-4659, ext. 208
1-888-6-SECTER
Fax: 860-437-4662
Email: secter@secter.org
www.secter.org/

Delaware
Procurement Technical Assistance Center of Delaware
1318 North Market Street
Wilmington, DE 19801
302-571-1555
Fax: 302-571-5222
Email: info@delawarecontracts.com
www.delawarecontracts.com

District of Columbia
1110 Vermont Ave. NW
Washington, DC 20005
202-606-4000

Florida
University of West Florida
Florida PTA Program
401 E. Chase St., Suite 100
Pensacola, FL 32501
850-473-7806
Fax: 850-473-7813
www.dla.mil/db/procurem.htm

Georgia
GA Institute of Technology
760 Spring St., Ste 330
Atlanta, GA 30332-0640
478-953-3155
Fax: 478-953-3169
www.edi.gatech.edu/gtpac

United Indian Development Association Consulting
Group, Inc.
86 South Cobb Drive, MZ:0510
Marietta, GA 30063-0510
770-494-0431
Fax: 770-494-1236
Email: uida1@uida.org
www.uida.org/ptac.html

Hawaii
State Procurement Office
1151 Punchbowl St.,
Honolulu, Hawaii 96813
808-586-0554
Fax: 808-586-0570
www.2.state.hi.us/spo

Idaho
Idaho Department of Commerce
State of Idaho
700 West State St.
Boise, ID 83720-0093
208-334-2470
800-842-5858
Fax: 208-334-2631
www.idoc.state.id.us

Illinois
Latin American Chamber of Commerce
The Chicago Pac
3512 W. Fullerton
Chicago, IL 60647
773-252-5211
Fax: 773-252-7065
www.lacc1.com

State of Illinois
Dept. of Commerce and Economic Opportunity
620 E. Adams St., Third Floor
Springfield, IL 62701
217-782-7500
Fax: 217-782-0038
www.commerce.state.il.us

Indiana

Partners in Contracting Corporation
PTA Center
6100 Southport Rd.
Portage, IN 46368
219-762-8644
Fax: 219-763-1513
Email: picc@piccorp.org
www.piccorp.org

Indiana Small Business Development Corporation
Government Marketing Assistance Group
One N. Capitol Ave., Suite 900
Indianapolis, IN 46204
317-234-2082
Fax: 317-232-8872
www.isbdc.org

Iowa

Iowa State University
Iowa Procurement Center
2272 Howe Hall
Ames, IA 50011-2270
515-294-4473
800-458-4465
Fax: 515-294-4483
www.ciras.iastate.edu/ipoc

Kansas

Heartland Procurement
Technical Assistance Ctr.
4747 Trout Bldg.
Room 227-5100
Rockhill Rd.,
Kansas City,
MO 64110
816-235-2891
Fax: 816-235-2947

Kentucky

Kentucky Cabinet For Economic Development
Department of Community Development
500 Mero St.
Capital Plaza Tower
Frankfort, KY 40601

800-838-3266
502-564-7670
Fax: 502-564-5932
Email: econdev@ky.gov
www.thinkkentucky.com/kyedc/proassist.asp

Louisiana

Louisiana Procurement Center
University of Southwest Louisiana
P.O. Box 44172
241 E. Lewis St.
Lafayette, LA 70504-4172
337-482-6422
Fax: 337-482-5837

Greater Shreveport Chamber of Commerce
Northwest Louisiana Government Procurement
Center
400 Edwards St. 71101
P.O. Box 20074
Shreveport, LA 71120-0074
318-677-2500
Fax: 318-677-2541
Email: info@shreveportchamber.org
www.shreveportchamber.org/shreveport/bus-eco/bus-assist/govproc.html

Maine

Eastern Maine Development Corp.
Market Development Center
One Cumberland Pl., Suite 300
Bangor, ME 04401
207-942-6389
800-339-6389
Fax: 207-942-3548
Email: info@emdc.org
www.emdc.org

Maryland

Maryland PTAP
Small Business Development Center
7100 Baltimore Avenue, Suite 303
College Park, MD 20740
301-403-2739
866-228-0432
Fax: 301-403-8303
www.mdptap.umd.edu

Massachusetts

Massachusetts Small Business Development Center
Network
Office of Grants and Contracts
227 Isenberg School of Management
121 Presidents Drive

University of Massachusetts
Amherst, MA 01003-9310
413-545-6301
Fax: 413-545-1273
http://msbdc.som.umass.edu

Michigan
Schoolcraft College Business Development Center
18600 Haggerty Rd.
Livonia, MI 48152-2696
734-462-4438
Fax: 734-462-4439
Email: inforeq@schoolcraft.edu
www.schoolcraft.cc.mi.us/bdc/default.htm

Office of Business Development
SW Michigan Technical Assistance Center
4717 Campus Dr., Box 100
Kalamazoo, MI 49008
269-372-3941
Fax: 269-353-5569
www.michigantac.org

Downriver Community Conference
Economic Development
15100 Northline Rd.
Southgate, MI 48195
734-362-3477
Fax: 734-281-6661
www.dccwf.org

Warren, Center Line
Sterling Heights Chamber of Commerce
30500 Van Dyke Ave., Suite 118
Warren, MI 48093
586-751-3939
Fax: 586-751-3995
www.michigantac.org

Michigan Works! West Central
PTA Center
110 Elm St.
Big Rapids, MI 49307
231-796-4891, ext. 15
Fax: 231-796-8316
www.michigantac.org

Northwestern Michigan Council of Governments
PTA Center
1209 S. Garfield
Traverse City, MI 48685
231-929-5036
Fax: 231-929-5042
www.michigantac.org

Technical Assistance Center of South Central
Michigan
The Enterprise Group of Jackson, Inc.
One Jackson Sq.
Jackson, MI 49204
517-788-4455
Fax: 517-782-0061
www.enterprisegroup.org

Michigan Works! West Central
900 Third Street, Suite 113
Muskegon, MI 49440
231-722-7700
Fax: 231-722-6182
www.michigantac.org

Flint-Genesee Economic Growth Alliance
519 South Saginaw Street, Suite 210
Flint, MI 48502
810-238-7803
Fax: 810-238-7866
www.growthalliance.com/gamain.html

Economic Development Alliance of St. Clair County
735 Erie St. Suite 250
Port Huron, MI 48060
810-982-9511
Fax: 810-982-9531
www.edaofstclaircounty.com

Saginaw Future, Inc.
515 N. Washington Ave.
Saginaw, MI 48607
989-754-8222
Fax: 989-754-1715
Email: info@saginawfuture.com
www.saginawfuture.com

Michigan Works!
1498 O'Dovero Dr.
Marquette, MI 49855
906-228-3075
Fax: 906-228-4372
www.jobforce.org

NE Michigan Consortium
P.O. Box 711
Onaway, MI 49765
989-733-8548
Fax: 989-733-8069
www.michigantac.org

Wayne State University
Room 240 Rands
Detroit, MI 48202
313-577-2241
Fax: 313-577-4354
www.michigantac.org

Minnesota
Minnesota Project Innovation, Inc.
Procurement Technical Assistance Center
100 Mill Place
111 Third Ave. South
Minneapolis, MN 55401
612-338-3280
Fax: 612-349-2603
www.mpi.org/ptac/index.htm

Mississippi
Mississippi Contract Procurement Center, Inc.
1636 Poppsferry Rd., Suite 229
Biloxi, MS 39532
228-396-1288
Fax: 228-396-2520
www.mscpc.com

Missouri
Missouri Procurement Technical Assistance Centers
300 University Pl.
Columbia, MO 65211
573-882-8058
Fax: 573-884-4297
www.missouribusiness.net/ptac/index.asp

Heartland Procurement Technical Assistance Center
Missouri Southern State College MH-107
3950 E. Newman Rd.
Joplin, MO 64801-1595
417-625-9538
Fax: 417-625-9782
Email: heartlandptac@mssc.edu
www.mssc.edu/heartlandptac/ptac

Montana
Big Sky Economic Development Authority
222 North 32nd Street
Billings, MT 59101
406-256-6871
Fax: 406-256-6877
www.bigskyeda.org

Nebraska
Economic Business Development Center
PTA Omaha Business Technology Center

2505 North 24th Street, Suite 103
Omaha, NE 68182-0072
402-595-3511
Fax: 402-595-3832
www.ohioptac.org/natiptac3.htm

Nevada
Nevada Commission on Economic Development
555 East Washington, Suite 5400
Las Vegas, NV 89101
702-486-2700
800-336-1600
Fax: 702-486-2701
www.expand2nevada.com

New Hampshire
State of New Hampshire
Office of Business and Economic Development
172 Pembroke Rd.
Concord, NH 03302
603-271-2591
Fax: 603-271-6784
www.nheconomy.com/ptac.html

New Jersey
Union County Economic Development Corp.
PTA Program
1085 Morris Ave.
Liberty Hall Center
Union, NJ 07083
908-527-1166
Fax: 908-527-1207
Email: info@ucedc.com
www.ucedc.com/services/contracts.shtml

New Jersey Institute of Technology (NJIT)
PTA Center
University Heights
Newark, NJ 07102-9895
973-596-3000
Fax: 973-596-5806
www.njit.edu

New Mexico
State of New Mexico General Services Department
Procurement Assistance Program
P.O. Drawer 26110
Santa Fe, NM 87502-0110
1100 St. Francis Dr., Room 2006
Santa Fe, NM 87503
505-827-0425
Fax: 505-827-0499
www.state.nm.us/spd/pap/index.html

New York

South Bronx Overall Economic Development
Corporation
555 Bergen Ave., Third Floor
Bronx, NY 10455
718-292-3113
Fax: 718-292-3115
Email: info@sobro.org
www.sobro.org

Cattaraugus County
Economic Development, Planning & Tourism
303 Court St.
Little Valley, NY 14755
716-938-9111, ext. 2331
Fax: 716-938-9431
www.co.cattaraugus.ny.us/economic-
development/gma/index.asp

Long Island Development Corporation
PTA Program
45 Seaman Ave.
Bethpage, NY 11714
516-433-5000
Fax: 516-433-5046
Email: gov-contracts@LIDC.org
www.lidc.org

New York City Dept. of Business Services
Procurement Outreach Program
110 William St., 9th Floor
New York, NY 10038
212-513-6472
Fax: 212-618-8899
www.nyc.gov/html/dbs/html/procure.html

PTAC
Rockland Economic Development Corporation
One Blue Hill Plaza, P.O. Box 1575
Pearl River, NY 10965-1575
845-735-7040
Fax: 845-735-5736
Email: info@redc.org
www.redc.org/business/sell_to_gov/
index_sell_to_gov.html

Laguardia Community College
Urban Center for Economic Development
31-10 Thomson Ave.
Long Island City, NY 11101
718-482-5330
Fax: 718-482-5176
Email: IMRP@lagcc.cuny.edu
www.lagcc.cuny.edu/ace

The Rochester Business Alliance
150 State St.,
Rochester, NY 14614
585-244-1800
Fax: 585-263-3679
www.rochesterbusinessalliance.com

North Carolina
University of North Carolina at Chapel Hill
Small Business and Tech Development Center
5 West Hargett St., Suite 600
Raleigh, NC 27601-1348
919-715-7272
Fax: 919-715-7777
Email: info@sbtdc.org
www.sbtdc.org

North Dakota
No PTA awarded

Ohio
Northeast Ohio Procurement Technical Assistance
Center
Lake Erie College
391 W. Washington St.
Painesville, OH 44077
440-357-2290
Fax: 440-357-2296
Email: lcedc@lcedc.org
www.lcedc.org

Lawrence Economic Development Corporation
Procurement Outreach Center
216 Collins Ave.
P.O. Box 488
South Point, OH 45680
740-377-4550
800-408-1334
Fax: 740-377-2091
www.lawrencecountyohio.org/5.htm

Ohio Department of Development
Procurement Technical Assistance Centers of Ohio
77 South High Street
Columbus, OH 43215-6130
614-466-5700
800-848-1300
Fax: 614-466-4172
www.odod.state.oh.us

Mahoning Valley Economic Development
4319 Belmont Ave.

Youngstown, OH 44505
330-759-3668
Fax: 330-759-3686
www.mvedc.com/development.htm

Oklahoma

Oklahoma Department of Career and Technology
Education
Oklahoma Bid Assistance Network (OBAN)
1500 W. Seventh Ave.
Stillwater, OK 74074
405-743-5571
Fax: 405-743-6821
www.okcareertech.org/business/oban/oban.htm

Tribal Government Institute
421 E. Comanche, Suite B
Norman, OK 73071
405-329-5542
Fax: 405-329-5543

Oregon

The Organization for Economic Initiatives
Government Contract Assistance Program
1144 Gateway Loop, Suite 203
Springfield, OR 97477
541-736-1088
800-497-7551
Fax: 541-736-1090
Email: info@gcap.org
www.gcap.org

Pennsylvania

Mon-Valley Renaissance
CA University of Pennsylvania
250 University Ave.
California, PA 15419
724-938-5881
Fax: 724-938-4575
www.cup.edu/Advancement/MVR

Private Industry Council of Westmoreland/Fayette,
Inc.
Procurement Assistance Center
531 S. Main St.
Greensburg, PA 15601
724-836-2600
Fax: 724-836-8058
www.privateindustrycouncil.com

Johnstown Area Regional Industries
Defense PAC
111 Market St.
Johnstown, PA 15901

814-535-8675
Fax: 814-535-8677
www.jari.org

SEDA Council of Governments
201 Furnace Rd.
Lewisburg, PA 17837
570-524-4491
Fax: 570-524-9190
Email: Admin@seda-cog.org
www.seda-cog.org/seda_cog/site/default.asp

University of Pennsylvania-Wharton
SBDC
3733 Spruce St.
Vance Hall, 4th Floor
Philadelphia, PA 19104-6374
215-898-4861
Fax: 215-898-1063
www.pasbdc.org/consulting

The Northeastern Pennsylvania Alliance
1151 Oak St.
Pittston Township, PA 18640-3795
570-655-5581
Fax: 570-654-5137
Email: info@nepa-alliance.org
www.nepa-alliance.org

Northern Tier Regional Planning and Development
Commission
Economic/Community Development
312 Main St.
Towanda, PA 18848
570-265-9103
Fax: 570-265-7585
http://northerntier.org

Puerto Rico

Commonwealth of Puerto Rico
Economic Development Administration
P.O. Box 362350
San Juan, PR 00936-2350
787-753-6861
Fax: 787-751-6239

Rhode Island

Rhode Island Economic Development Corporation
Business Expansion Division
One W. Exchange St.
Providence, RI 02903
401-222-2601
Fax: 401-222-2102
Email: riedc@riedc.com
www.riedc.com/growth/procure/procurementframe.html

South Carolina
University of South Carolina
Frank L. Roddey SBDC of South Carolina
1200 Woodruff Rd., Suite C-38
Greenville, SC 29607
864-297-1016
Fax: 864-329-0453
http://business.clemson.edu/sbdc/

South Dakota
No PTA awarded

Tennessee
University of Tennessee
Center for Industrial Services
193 Polk Ave., Ste C
Nashville, TN 37210
615-532-8657
888-763-7439
Fax: 615-532-4937
www.cis.utk.edu

Texas
Panhandle Regional Planning Commission
Economic Development Unit
P.O. Box 9257
Amarillo, TX 79105-9257
806-372-3381
Fax: 806-373-3268
www.prpc.cog.tx.us/programs/econ/econ_contract.htm

University of Texas at Arlington
Automation and Robotics Research Institute
Cross Timbers Procurement Center
7300 Jack Newell Blvd. S.
Fort Worth, TX 76118
817-272-5900
Fax: 817-272-5952
www.uta.edu

University of Texas at Brownsville/ITSC
Center for Business and Economic Development
1600 E. Elizabeth St.
Brownsville, TX 78520
956-548-8713
Fax: 956-548-8711
www.utb.edu

University of Houston, TIPS
2302 Fannin, Suite 200
Houston, TX 77002
713-752-8444
Fax: 713-756-1515
www.sbdc.uh.edu

Texas Technical University
Northwest Texas Small Business Development Center
2579 S. Loop 289, Suite 210
Lubbock, TX 79423
806-745-3973
800-992-7232
Fax: 806-745-6207
www.nwtsbdc.org

Angelina College
Procurement Assistance Center
P.O. Box 1768
3500 South First Street
Lufkin, TX 75902
936-639-1301
888-326-5223
Fax: 936-639-4299
www.angelina.cc.tx.us/comserv/cs%20procur.htm

San Antonio Procurement Outreach Program
Economic Development Department
P.O. Box 839966
215 S. San Saba, Room 102
San Antonio, TX 78283-3966
210-207-8080
Fax: 210-207-8151
www.sanantonio.gov/edd/small_bus/contracting/ptac.asp

El Paso Community College
Center for Business Services
P.O. Box 20500
El Paso, TX 79998
915-831-7748
Fax: 915-831-7755
www.epcc.edu

Del Mar College
Procurement Technical Assistance Center Services
Small Business Development Center
101 Bladwin, VB 351
Corpus Christi, TX 78404
361-698-1021
Fax: 361-698-1024
www.delmar.edu/sbdc/ptac.html

Utah
Utah Department of Community and Economic Development
Utah Procurement Technical Assistance Center (UPTAC)
324 South State St., Suite 500
Salt Lake City, UT 84111
801-538-8652
Fax: 801-538-8611
http://dced.utah.gov/procure

Vermont
State of Vermont
Department of Economic Development
National Life Building
Drawer 20
Montpelier, VT 05620-0501
802-828-5237
Fax: 802-828-3258
www.vermontbidsystem.com/gmac.asp

Virginia
George Mason University
Procurement Technical Assistance Program (PTAP)
Mason Enterprise Center
4031 University Dr., Suite 200
Fairfax, VA 22030
703-277-7757
Fax: 703-352-8195
Email: ptap@gmu.edu
www.gmu.edu/gmu/PTAP

Crater Planning District Commission
Crater Procurement Assistance Center
1964 Wakefield St.
P.O. Box 1808
Petersburg, VA 23805
804-861-1666
Fax: 804-732-8972
Email: craterpd@cpd.state.va.us
www.craterpdc.state.va.us/

Southwestern Virginia Community College
Economic Development Division
P.O. Box SVCC
Richlands, VA 24641
276-964-7334
Fax: 276-964-7575
www.sw.edu/ptac2/pacnew.htm

Washington
Economic Development Council of
Snohomish County
728 134th St., SW
Suite 128
Everett, WA 98204
425-743-4567
Fax: 425-745-5563
Email: ptac@snoedc.org
www.snoedc.org/securing_government_contracts.shtml

West Virginia
Regional Contracting Assistance Center, Inc.
1116 Smith St., Suite 202
Charleston, WV 25301
304-344-2546
Fax: 304-344-2574
www.rcacwv.com

Mid-Ohio Valley Regional Council
PTA Center
#2 Rosemar Circle, Suite B
Parkersburg, WV 26101
304-428-6889
Fax: 304-428-6891
www.wvptac.org

Wisconsin
Madison Area Technical College
Business Procurement Assistance Center
3591 Anderson St., Suite 100
Madison, WI 53704
608-243-4490
Fax: 608-243-4486
Email: bpac@matcmadison.edu
http://matcmadison.edu/bpac/home.htm

Wisconsin Procurement Institute, Inc.
756 N. Milwaukee St.
Milwaukee, WI 53202
414-270-3600
Fax: 414-270-3610
Email: info@wispro.org
www.wispro.org

Wyoming
University of Wyoming
Government Resources and Opportunities for
Business (GRO-BIZ)
LCCC, Room 209
1400 E. College Dr.
Cheyenne, WY 82007
307-637-4990
Fax: 307-632-6061
www.gro-biz.com

How To Become a Consultant With The Government

If you are between jobs or just thinking about quitting the one you have and want something to tide you over until you get your next one, you should seriously think about freelancing for the Federal government.

The Interior Department hires ecologists and geologists. The Justice Department hires business consultants. The Department of Energy hires conservation consultants. Here's a sample listing of the kinds of projects freelance consultants do for the Federal government:

Types of Government Freelancing

Landscaping
Carpentry Work
Painting and Paper Hanging
Security Guards
Computer Services
Data Processing
Detective Services
Electrical Work
Plumbing
Accounting Services
Chaplain Services (Priest)
Management Consulting
Engineering Services
Information Retrieval
  Services
Real Estate Agents
Secretarial Services
Court Reporting
Legal Services
Business Consulting
Photography
Insurance Agents
Computer Programming
Research
Drafting
Interior Decorating
Library Services
Word Processing

Translation Services
Courier and Messenger Services
Cleaning Services
Food Service
Auditing Services
Advertising Services
Nursing Services
Housekeeping Services
Administrative Support
  Services
Education and Training
Medical Services
Social Services
Special Study and Analysis
Wildlife Management
Salvage Services
Travel Agent
Personnel Testing Services
Photography
Animal Care
Mathematics and Computer
  Science
Environmental Research
Historians
Recreation Research
Economic Studies
More, More, More...

Practically every major government agency hires freelance consultants to work on both small and large projects which might be exactly what you need until you land a full time job down the road.

The feds hire all kinds of professionals to perform consulting work, from accountants and business specialists, to computer experts, social scientists, and security and surveillance consultants. The offices listed on the following pages, called Offices of Small and Disadvantaged Business Utilization, specialize in helping individuals and small businesses get involved in contracting with their agency.

Subcontracting

Not only do the feds themselves hire consultants, so do the large prime contractors who sell their products and services to the government. By law, any large company that receives contracts worth $500,000 or more from the Federal government must make an effort to subcontract some of that work to small businesses. So, for example, if a company gets a large computer consulting contract with the Defense Department, they have to make an effort to hire some freelance computer consultants to work on that contract. And that could be you.

How to Find Subcontracting Work

All of the federal procurement offices or Offices of Small and Disadvantaged Business Utilization (SADBU) (see list below) can provide you with information regarding subcontracting. Many of the departments' prime contracts require that the prime contractor maximize small business subcontracting opportunities. The SADBU offices can show you the way to get this work.

Each of the large federal agencies listed below, except the Department of Education, maintain directories of large contractors who are looking to do work with the feds in your area of expertise. And since the companies listed in these directories, for the most part, have just landed big government contracts, they might very well be looking to take on more full-time employees to help fulfill those contracts. A great lead on new job openings that probably won't be listed in the Sunday newspaper!

Offices of Small and Disadvantaged Business Utilization

Note: Offices designated as Offices of Small and Disadvantaged Business Utilization (OSDBUs) provide procurement assistance to small, minority, 8(a) and women-owned businesses. Their primary function is to ensure that small and disadvantaged businesses receive their fair share of U.S. Government contracts. "OSDBUs" are the contacts for their respective agencies and are excellent sources of information.

Agency for International Development
Ronald Reagan Building
Washington, DC 20523-1000
202-712-4810
Fax: 202-216-3524
www.usaid.gov

Air Force Department
The Pentagon
SAFSB 1060 Air Force
Washington, DC 20330-1060
703-696-1103
Fax: 703-696-1170
www.selltoairforce.org/sell2airforce/toc.htm

Army Department
106 The Pentagon
Washington, DC 20310-0106
703-697-2868

Fax: 703-693-3898
www.sellingtoarmy.info

Corporation for National and Community Service
1201 New York Ave., NW
Washington, DC 20525
202-606-5000
Fax: 202-565-2777
www.nationalservice.org

Defense Contract Management Agency
6350 Walker Lane
Alexandria, VA 22310
703-428-0786
Fax: 703-428-3578
www.dcma.mil

Defense Information Systems Agency
701 S. Courthouse Road

D04 Room 1108B
Arlington, VA 22204-2199
703-607-6436
Fax: 703-607-4173
www.disa.mil/main/sadbu.html

Defense Logistics Agency
8725 John J. Kingman Road
DB Room 1127
Ft. Belvoir, VA 22060-6221
703-767-1662
Fax: 703-767-1670
www.dla.mil

Department of Agriculture
1400 Independence Ave., SW
AG Stop 9501
Room 1566, South Bldg.
Washington, DC 20250-9400
202-720-7117
Fax: 202-720-3001
www.usda.gov/da/smallbus

Department of Commerce
Office of Small and Disadvantaged Business Utilization
14th and Constitution Ave, NW
Herbert C. Hoover Building
Room 6411
Washington, DC 20230
202-482-1472
Fax: 202-482-0501
www.osec.doc.gov/osdbu

Department of Defense
1777 North Kent Street, Suite 9100
Arlington, VA 22209
703-588-8631
Fax: 703-588-7561
www.acq.osd.mil/sadbu

Department of Education
400 Maryland Ave., SW
Room 3082-ROB-3
Washington, DC 20202
202-708-9820
800-USA-LEARN
Fax: 202-401-0689
www.ed.gov/about/offices/list/ods/index.html?src-mr

Department of Energy
1000 Independence Ave., SW
Room 5B148
Washington, DC 20585
202-586-7377
Fax: 202-586-5488
www.energy.gov/

Department of Health and Human Services
200 Independence Ave., SW
Room 517D
Washington, DC 20201
202-690-7300
Fax: 202-260-4872
www.hhs.gov/osdbu

Department of Housing and Urban Development
451 7th St., SW, Room 3130
Washington, DC 20410
202-708-1428
Fax: 202-708-7642
www.hud.gov/offices/osdbu/index.cfm

Department of the Interior
1849 C St., NW, MS-2252
Washington, DC 20240
202-208-3493
Fax: 202-219-2131
www.doi.gov/

Department of Justice
Director, OSDBU
U.S. Department of Justice
1331 Pennsylvania Ave., NW
National Place Building, Rm. 1010
Washington, DC 20530
202-616-0521
800-345-3712
Fax: 202-616-1717
www.usdoj.gov/jmd/osdbu/index.html

Department of Labor
Frances Perkins Building
200 Constitution Ave., NW
Washington, DC 20210
202-693-6460
866-4-USA-DOL
Fax: 202-693-6485
www.dol.gov/osbp/programs/osdbu.htm

Department of State
A/SDBU-Department of State
SA-6, Room L500
Washington, DC 20522-0602
703-875-6822
Fax: 703-875-6825
www.state.gov/m/a/sdbu

Department of Transportation
400 7th St., SW, Room 9414
Washington, DC 20590
202-366-1930
800-532-1169

Fax: 202-366-7538
http://osdbuweb.dot.gov

Department of the Treasury
1500 Pennsylvania Ave., NW
Room 1310 G, 400 West
Washington, DC 20220
202-622-0530
Fax: 202-622-4963
www.ustreas.gov/offices/management/dcfo/osdbu

Department of Veterans Affairs
810 Vermont Ave., NW
Washington, DC 20420
202-565-8124
800-949-8387
Fax: 202-565-8156
www.va.gov/osdbu

Environmental Protection Agency
1200 Pennsylvania Ave., NW
Mail Code 1230 A
Washington, DC 20460
202-564-4142
Fax: 202-501-0756
www.epa.gov/osdbu

Export-Import Bank of the U.S.
811 Vermont Ave., NW
Washington, DC 20571
202-565-3338
Fax: 202-565-3528
www.exim.gov

Federal Emergency Management Agency
Financial and Acquisition Management
500 C St., SW
Washington, DC 20472
202-646-4006
Fax: 202-646-3846
www.fema.gov/ofm

Federal Trade Commission
Acquisition Branch, Rm. 701
600 Pennsylvania Ave., NW
Washington, DC 20580
202-326-2258
Fax: 202-326-3529
www.ftc.gov/ftc/oed/fmo/procure/procure.htm

General Services Administration
Office of Enterprise Development
1800 F Street, NW
Washington, DC 20405
202-501-1021

Fax: 202-208-5938
www.gsa.gov/smallbusiness

National Aeronautics and Space Administration
Headquarters
300 E St., SW
Washington, DC 20546
202-358-2088
Fax: 202-358-3261
www.hq.nasa.gov/office/codek

National Institute of Health
6100 Executive Blvd., Room 6D05
Bethesda, MD 20892-7540
301-496-9639
Fax: 301-480-2506
http://sbo.od.nih.gov/sbomain.htm

National Science Foundation
4201 Wilson Blvd.
Arlington, VA 22230
703-292-8242
Fax: 703-292-9140
www.nsf.gov/bfa/dacs/contracts/start.htm

Department of the Navy
Small and Disadvantaged Business Utilization
720 Kennon St., SE, Room 207
Washington, DC 20374-5015
202-685-6485
Fax: 202-685-6865
www.hq.navy.mil/sadbu

Nuclear Regulatory Commission
Small Business Program
Washington, DC 20555
301-415-7380
Fax: 301-415-5953
www.nrc.gov/who-we-are/small-business.html

Office of Personnel Management
Contracting Division
1900 E St., NW, Room 7520
Washington, DC 20415
202-606-2180
Fax: 202-606-1464
www.opm.gov/procure/index.asp

Small Business Administration
Director
Office of Government Contracting
409 Third St., SW, 8th Floor
Washington, DC 20416
202-205-6460
www.sba.gov/GC/osdbu.html

Smithsonian Institution
Small and Disadvantaged Business Utilization
Program
750 9th St. NW, Ste. 8100
Washington, DC 20013
202-275-0145
Fax: 202-275-2055
www.si.edu/oeema

Tennessee Valley Authority
26 One Century Blvd., Ste. 100
Nashville, TN 37214
615-232-6169
www.tva.gov

Transportation Security Administration
Office of Civil Rights
601 S 12th St.
Arlington, VA 22202
571-227-2800
www.tsa.dot.gov/public/theme_home3.jsp

U.S. Postal Service
Supply Diversity Development
475 L'Enfant Plaza, SW
Room 4506
Washington, DC 20260-6200

202-268-6578
Fax: 202-268-4633
www.usps.com/purchasing

Office of Federal Procurement Policy
725 17th St., NW
Room 9013
Washington, DC 20503
202-395-3080
www.arnet.gov

Railroad Retirement Board
844 N. Rush St., 9th Flr.
Chicago, IL 60611-2092
312-751-4500
Fax: 312-751-7136
www.rrb.gov

Minority Business Development Agency
Department of Commerce
Herbert C. Hoover Bldg.
14th & Constitution Ave., NW
Room 6411
Washington, DC 20230
202-482-1472
Fax: 202-482-0501
www.osec.doc.gov/osdbu/

State Procurement Assistance

Have you ever wondered where the government buys all of the products that it works with each day? You might be surprised to learn that they buy from small businesses just like yours that produce products such as:

- ◆ work clothing
- ◆ office supplies
- ◆ cleaning equipment
- ◆ miscellaneous vehicles
- ◆ medical supplies and equipment

Imagine what your bottom line could look like each year if you won just ONE lucrative government contract that would provide your business with a secure income! It might even buy you the freedom to pursue other clients that you wouldn't have the time or money to go after otherwise. If your business performs well and completes a government contract satisfactorily, chances are you'll have a shot at more and maybe even bigger contracts.

The offices listed below are starting places for finding out who in the state government will purchase your products or services.

State Procurement Offices

Alabama
Finance Department
Purchasing Division
RSA Union Building
100 N. Union, Suite 192
Montgomery, AL 36104
334-242-7250
Fax: 334-242-4419
www.purchasing.state.al.us

Alaska
State of Alaska
Department of Administration
Division of General Services
P.O. Box 110210
Juneau, AK 99811-0210
907-465-2250
Fax: 907-465-2189
www.state.ak.us/local/akpages/ADMIN/dgs/
purchasing/home.htm

Arizona
State Procurement Office
100 North 15th Ave.
Suite 104
Phoenix, AZ 85007
602-542-5511
Fax: 602-542-5508
http://sporas.ad.state.az.us

Arkansas
Office of State Procurement
P.O. Box 2940
Little Rock, AR 72203
501-324-9316
Fax: 501-324-9311
www.accessarkansas.org/dfa/purchasing/index.html

California
Department of General Services
Procurement Division
707 Third Street, 2nd Floor
West Sacramento, CA 95605
916-375-4400
800-559-5529
Fax: 916-375-4613
www.pd.dgs.ca.gov/default.htm

Colorado
State Purchasing Office
225 E. 16th Ave., Suite 802
Denver, CO 80203
303 866-6100
Fax: 303-894-7445
www.gssa.state.co.us

Connecticut
State of Connecticut
Department of Administrative Services
Bureau of Procurement/Purchasing
165 Capitol Ave.

Hartford, CT 06106
860-713-5086
Fax: 860-622-2915
www.das.state.ct.us/busopp.asp

Delaware
Division of Support Services
Contracting Unit
820 Silver Lake Blvd., Suite 100
Dover, DE 19904
302-739-5371
Fax: 302-739-3779
www.state.de.us/purchase

District of Columbia
Office of Contracts and Procurement
441 4th St. NW, Suite 700 South
Washington, DC 20001
202-727-0252
Fax: 202-727-9385
http://ocp.dc.gov/

Florida
Department of Management Services
State Purchasing Office
4050 Esplanade Way
Tallahassee, FL 32399
850-488-8440
Fax: 850-488-5498
www.myflorida.com/myflorida/business/purchasing.
html

Georgia
Administrative Services Department
State Purchasing Office
200 Piedmont Ave., Ste. 1804, West Tower
Atlanta, GA 30334-9010
404-656-5514
Fax: 404-657-8444
www.doas.state.ga.us

Hawaii
State Procurement Office
Dept. of Accounting and General Services
1151 Punchbowl St.
Honolulu, HI 96813
808-586-0554
Fax: 808-586-0570
www2.state.hi.us/spo

Idaho
Division of Purchasing and Bids
Department of Administration
5569 Kendall St.
P.O. Box 83720

Boise, ID 83720-0075
208-327-7465
Fax: 208-327-7320
www2.state.id.us/adm/purchasing

Illinois
Department of Central Management Services
Procurement Services Division
401 South Spring
801 Stratton Office Bldg.
Springfield, IL 62706-4100
217-782-2301
Fax: 217-782-5187
www.state.il.us/cms/purchase/default.htm

Indiana
Department of Administration
Procurement Division
402 W. Washington St., Room W 468
Indianapolis, IN 46204
317-232-3053
Fax: 317-232-7312
www.in.gov/idoa/proc/

Iowa
State of Iowa
Department of General Services
Operations/Purchasing Division
Hoover State Office Building
Des Moines, IA 50319-0101
515-242-5120
Fax: 515-242-5974
www.state.ia.us/government/dgs/Purchase/business.
htm

Kansas
Division of Purchasing
900 Jackson, Room 102N
Landon State Office Bldg.
Topeka, KS 66612-1286
785-296-2376
Fax: 785-296-7240
http://da.state.ks.us/purch

Kentucky
Purchases, Department of Finance
Room 373, Capital Annex Building
Frankfort, KY 40601
502-564-4510
Fax: 502-564-7209
http://eprocurement.ky.gov

Louisiana
Office of State Purchasing & Travel
Division of Administration

1201 N. 3rd Street, Suite 2-160
P.O. Box 94095
Baton Rouge, LA 70804-9095
225-342-8010
Fax: 225-342-8688
www.doa.state.la.us/osp/osp.htm

Maine
Division of Purchases
Burton Cross Building, 4th Floor
9 State House Station
Augusta, ME 04333
207-624-7340
Fax: 207-287-6578
www.state.me.us/purchase

Maryland
Office of Procurement and Contracting
301 W. Preston St.
Mezzanine, Room M3
Baltimore, MD 21201
410-767-4083
Fax: 410-333-5482
www.dgs.state.md.us

Massachusetts
Operational Services Division
One Ashburton Place
Room 1017
Boston, MA 02108-1552
617-720-3300
Fax: 617-727-4527
www.mass.gov

Michigan
Office of Purchasing
Mason Bldg., 2nd Floor
P.O. Box 30026
Lansing, MI 48909
or 530 W. Allegan, 48933
517-335-0230
Fax: 517-335-0046
www.michigan.gov/doingbusiness

Minnesota
State of Minnesota
Department of Administration
Administration Bldg., Rm. 112
50 Sherburne Ave.
St. Paul, MN 55155
651-296-1424
Fax: 651-297-3996
www.mmd.admin.state.mn.us

Mississippi
Office of Purchasing and Travel
1401 Woolfolk Building, Ste. A
501 North West St.
Jackson, MS 39201
601-359-3409
Fax: 601-359-3910
www.dfa.state.ms.us

Missouri
State of Missouri
Division of Purchasing and Materials Management
301 W. High St., Room 630
P.O. Box 809
Jefferson City, MO 65102-0809
573-751-2387
Fax: 573-522-8726
www.oa.state.mo.us/purch/purch.htm

Montana
Department of Administration
State Procurement Bureau
Rm. 165 Mitchell Bldg.
125 North Roberts St.
P.O. Box 200135
Helena, MT 59620-0135
406-444-2575
Fax: 406-444-2529
www.discoveringmontana.com/doa/gsd/css/default.asp

Nebraska
State Purchasing Bureau
DAS Materiel Division
301 Centennial Mall S., Mall Level
P.O. Box 94847
Lincoln, NE 68509-4847
402-471-2401
Fax: 402-471-2089
www.das.state.ne.us/materiel/

Nevada
Nevada State Purchasing Division
Blasdel Bldg., Room 304
209 E. Musser St.
Carson City, NV 89701
775-684-0170
Fax: 775-684-0188
http://purchasing.state.nv.us

New Hampshire
Department of Administrative Services
Division of Plant and Property Management
Bureau of Purchase and Property
State House Annex, Room 102

25 Capitol St.
Concord, NH 03301-6312
603-271-2201
Fax: 603-271-2700
http://admin.state.nh.us/

New Jersey
Division of Purchase and Property
P.O. Box 230
Trenton, NJ 08625-0230
609-292-4700
Fax: 609-292-0490
www.state.nj.us/treasury/purchase

New Mexico
State Purchasing Division
Joseph Montoya Bldg., Room 2016
1100 St. Francis Dr.
Santa Fe, NM 87505
505-827-0472
Fax: 505-827-2484
www.state.nm.us/spd

New York
Procurement Services Group
Corning Tower, Room 3711
Empire State Plaza
Albany, NY 12242
518-474-6717
Fax: 518-474-2437
www.ogs.state.ny.us/purchase/default.asp

North Carolina
Department of Administration
Division of Purchase and Contract
116 W. Jones St.
Raleigh, NC 27603-8002
919-733-3581
Fax: 919-733-4782
www.state.nc.us/PandC

North Dakota
Central Services Division
State Procurement Office
14th Floor, Capitol Tower
600 E Blvd. Ave., Dept. 012
Bismarck, ND 58505-0310
701-328-4912
Fax: 701-328-1615
http://discovernd.com

Ohio
State Procurement
4200 Surface Rd.
Columbus, OH 43228

614-466-8218
Fax: 614-644-1785
http://procure.ohio.gov/proc/index.asp

Oklahoma
Office of Public Affairs
Central Purchasing Division
Will Rogers Office Building
2401 N. Lincoln, Ste. 116
P.O. Box 528803
Oklahoma City, OK 73152-8803
405-522-0955
Fax: 405-521-4475
www.dcs.state.ok.us/okdcs.nsf/htmlmedia/central_
purchasing.html

Oregon
General Services
State Procurement Office
1225 Ferry St., SE
Salem, OR 97310
503-378-4642
Fax: 503-373-1626
http://tpps.das.state.or.us/purchasing

Pennsylvania
Bureau of Purchases
414 North Office Bldg.
Harrisburg, PA 17125
717-787-5733
Fax: 717-783-6241
www.dgs.state.pa.us

Rhode Island
Department of Administration
Purchases Office
One Capital Hill
Providence, RI 02908-5855
401-222-2317
Fax: 401-222-6387
www.purchasing.state.ri.us

South Carolina
Materials Management Office
General Service Budget and Control Board
1201 Main St., Suite 600
Columbia, SC 29201
803-737-0600
Fax: 803-737-0639
www.state.sc.us/mmo

South Dakota
Bureau of Administration
Office of Procurement Management

PMB 01236
523 E. Capitol Ave.
Pierre, SD 57501-3128
605-773-3405
Fax: 605-773-4840
www.state.sd.us/boa/opm

Tennessee
Department of General Services
Division of Purchasing
Third Floor, William R. Snodgrass Tennessee Tower
312 8th Ave. North
Nashville, TN 37243-0530
615-741-1035
Fax: 615-741-0684
www.state.tn.us/generalserv/purchasing

Texas
Procurement Division
1711 San Jacinto Blvd.
Austin, TX 78701
512-936-3000
Fax: 512-463-7994
www.tbpc.state.tx.us/stpurch

Utah
Utah State Division of Purchasing and General Services
Department of Administrative Services
3150 State Office Bldg.
Capitol Hill
Salt Lake City, UT 84114
801-538-3026
Fax: 801-538-3882
www.purchasing.state.ut.us

Vermont
Purchasing and Contract Administration Division
1078 US Route 2 Drawer 33
Montpelier, VT 05633-7601
802-828-2211
Fax: 802-828-2222
www.bgs.state.vt.us/pca

Virginia
Department of General Services
Division of Purchasing and Supply

P.O. Box 1199
805 E. Broad St.
Richmond, VA 23218
804-786-3842
Fax: 804-225-3707
http://159.169.222.200/dps

Washington
Office of State Procurement
Department of General Services
210 11th Ave. SW, Room 201
P.O. Box 41000
Olympia, WA 98504-1000
360-902-7400
Fax: 360-586-2426
www.ga.wa.gov/purchase

West Virginia
Department of Administration
Purchasing Division
2019 Washington St. East
P.O. Box 50130
Charleston, WV 25305-0130
304-558-2538
Fax: 304-558-6026
www.state.wv.us/admin/purchase

Wisconsin
Division of State Agency Services
Bureau of Procurement
101 E. Wilson, 6th Floor
P.O. Box 7867
Madison, WI 53707-7867
608-266-2605
Fax: 608-267-0600
http://vendornet.state.wi.us/

Wyoming
Department of Administration
General Services Division
Herschler Building, 2nd Flr. E
122 W. 25th
Cheyenne, WY 82002
307-777-7253
Fax: 307-777-5852
http://ai.state.wy.us/generalservices/procurement.asp

GRANTS FOR LIVING EXPENSES

Sometimes you just need a little help getting through to the end of the month. Whether you need help with your heating or phone bill, or help with transportation and medical issues, resources are available. The trick is knowing who to call. What we have done is pulled together information on programs and services across the country. Some are available to anyone, whereas others are only for a specific target group or residents of a particular town. This may give you ideas of who in your area may offer grants or other forms of assistance to those in need. Many of these groups and organizations are small and have limited funds, so they asked not to be included in a major publication for fear of being inundated with requests for funds. But they do exist and they do provide help, so call around and ASK. You will be surprised by what you hear. There are also organizations to help with issues such as:

* Free child care
* Money to fix your car
* Money for adoptions
* Private school tuition for your kids
* Child support help
* Money for heating, phone or food bills
* Free hospitalization and medications
* Discounts for seniors
* Dental and vision care assistance
* Free mammograms and immunizations

We have touched the tip of the iceberg. Read on and see what else is out there waiting for you.

STATES OFFER MONEY FOR: CARS, BUS FARE, AUTO REPAIRS, INSURANCE AND DRIVERS ED

The following are examples of what just some of the states are offering in transportation assistance for those who have serious transportation needs. Transportation is a growing concern in the workforce and programs are being added and changed every day. Be sure to contact your state transportation agency for the latest benefits your state has to offer. For a listing of the websites of all state departments of transportation, see {http://www.fhwa.dot.gov/webstate.htm}

* Alaska: $85 a month towards transportation
* Arizona: $5 a day towards transportation
* Delaware: Free 3-week pass with a new job
* Illinois: $60 a month for gas or $88 a month to take the bus
* Kansas: $30 a month for gas and money for car repairs
* Kentucky: $60 a month for gas and $300 to get a drivers license, pay for auto registration, taxes or repairs, and $900 to move to another city to get a job
* Louisiana: $100 a year for auto repairs
* Massachusetts: $150 a month towards transportation

* Michigan: Money for auto repairs and insurance
* Mississippi Provides Door to Door Service
* Nebraska: Money for insurance, auto repairs; $2,000 to buy you a car; 3 months of auto insurance, $500 for taxes, licensing, etc.
* New Hampshire: $130 a month for transportation; $240 a year for auto repairs; and money to take drivers education
* New Jersey: $500 for car repairs
* New York: $500 for car repairs
* Oklahoma: Money for auto repairs and insurance
* Pennsylvania: $200 for auto repairs
* South Dakota: Money for auto repairs
* Vermont: $200 for auto repairs
* Washington: $546 a month for transportation
* Wisconsin: $1600 interest free to buy a car or repay with community service

FREE TAXI SERVICE
To Work, School, or Day Care

One county in Oregon has a program that picks up you and your child, taking your child to day care and you to work. It doesn't charge you anything, and doesn't even ask your income. North Carolina has programs where counties are given vans to transport people back and forth to work, with lower fees charged to those in welfare-to-work programs. Mississippi has a program that will pick you up at your house, almost anywhere in the state and take you back and forth to work if you are working to get off welfare.

Some communities, like Fairfax County in Virginia, maintain a database that helps locate the necessary transportation for work and day care needs. And Kentucky operates an 800 hotline that tries to solve any work-related transportation need, and soon they will have a separate hotline for each county. Do these people want you to get to work, or what?

To start looking for programs like this in your area, contact your local congressman's office or your local social service agency. They won't know about all the programs but can probably give you some starting places. You should also find out about local vanpool and rideshare programs. Your local chamber of commerce or library should have this kind of information for you.

Get up to $100 a Month Free From Your Boss For Commuting To Work

Your employer can give you up to $100 a month to help pay for bus, train, ferry, or vanpool commuting expense and neither you nor the employer has to pay taxes on this money.

Contact your local transit authority for more details on the program called *Tax Free Qualified Transportation Fringe Benefits*, or contact: Commuter Check Services Corporation, 401 S. Van Brunt Street, Suite 403, Englewood, NJ 07631; 201-833-9700; Fax: 201-833-8704; {www.commutercheck.com}.

Money For Auto Repairs, Car Insurance, Driver's Ed, Or Just A Tank Of Gas

Whatever it takes to keep you on the road! There are federal programs as well as state programs to help people with limited incomes keep their vehicles on the road so that they can get back and forth to work, focusing on those trying to get off welfare. Some states will even give you money for driver's education or to pay for a driver's license. The issue, like the programs for free cars, is to **help people make it to work**. Illinois and Kentucky offer $60 a month for gas money. New York and New Jersey give people up to $500 for car repairs. Pennsylvania and Vermont only give $200 for car repairs. But Washington State provides people up to $546 a month for their transportation.

Limousines anyone? These programs are organized like a patchwork quilt in most areas involving federal, state, county and non-profit organizations.

To start looking for programs like this in your area, contact your local congressman's office or your local Social Services. They won't know about all the programs but can probably give you some starting places. Most branches of the Goodwill Industries have a Wheels to Work program. Other programs can be found by typing in the keywords "Wheels to Work" in an Internet search engine.

Here is just a *SAMPLING* of the Wheels to Work programs that we found:

Wabash Valley Goodwill
Industries, Inc.
2702 South 3rd Street
P.O. Box 2720
Terre Haute, IN 47802
812-235-1827
Fax: 812-235-1397
Email: office@wvgoodwill.org
http://wvgoodwill.org/wtw1.htm

Goodwill Industries of Central
North Carolina
1235 S. Eugene St.
Greensboro, NC 27406-2393
336-275-9801
Fax: 336-274-1352
Email: cgorham@goodwill-cnc.org
www.triadgoodwill.org/

Wheels to Work
Forsyth County Department of
Social Services
741 North Highland Ave.
Winston Salem, NC 27101
336-703-3400
Fax: 336-727-2850
www.co.forsyth.nc.us/dss

The Cooperative Ministry
Helping People in Crisis
The C.A.R. Program
1928 Taylor St.
P.O. Box 1705
Columbia, SC 29202
803-799-3853
Fax: 803-252-8621
www.midnet.sc.edu/tcm/tcm.htm

Wheels to Work
Resource Conservation &
Development Council
750 S. Perry, Ste. 212
Lawrenceville, GA 30045
678-442-1392

One Month of Free Bus Passes

Detroit's **Suburban Mobility Authority for Regional Transportation (SMART)** has a program called "Get a Job/Get a Ride" that gives a month's worth of free rides to anyone in the Detroit area who gets a job.

The only requirement is that you started a new job within the last 30 days. You can be making $100,000 a year and they'll still give you the free passes. New Jersey will give a free one-month pass to those on low income that get a job or are going to training.

Check with your local Chamber of Commerce, Transit Authority, or your state Department of Transportation.

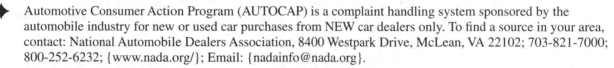

Free Legal Help To Fight A Car Dealer Or Repair Shop

When you can't get satisfaction from the manager or owner, then it is time to bring in the big guns:

◆ Your state attorney general's office is set up to handle automobile complaints. Sometimes all you have to do is send a letter to the attorney general with a copy to the business owner.

◆ Automotive Consumer Action Program (AUTOCAP) is a complaint handling system sponsored by the automobile industry for new or used car purchases from NEW car dealers only. To find a source in your area, contact: National Automobile Dealers Association, 8400 Westpark Drive, McLean, VA 22102; 703-821-7000; 800-252-6232; {www.nada.org/}; Email: {nadainfo@nada.org}.

◆ Better Business Bureau (BBB) Auto Line is a FREE, out-of-court arbitration program, paid for by the business community to handle automobile complaints between consumers and most auto manufacturers. Contact your local Better Business Bureau or BBB Auto Line, Dispute Resolution Division, Council of Better Business Bureaus, Inc., 4200 Wilson Blvd, Suite 800, Arlington, VA 22203; 703-276-0100; 800-955-5100; {www.bbb.org}.

Free and Low Cost Seminars on How To Buy a Car

You can't just go on color alone! You need to become savvy as to what options to look for and how to negotiate with the dealer. Do you really need rust proofing? What is the difference between the invoice and the sticker price? How can I find out what the dealer paid for the car?

Don't be intimidated by salesmanship. The dealer wants your money, so they don't want you to leave without signing on the bottom line. Many different organizations and groups offer classes on how to buy a car. Contact your county cooperative extension service, your local adult education department, or women's organizations in your area to see what they may have to offer.

GET YOUR CAR REPAIRED FOR FREE

June Rapp of Massachusetts took her family van into a dealer to have it fixed and they wanted to charge her more than $1000 to make the repairs. She called the U.S. Department of Transportation and found out that her problem was part of a manufacturer recall. Recalls have to be fixed for free and the repair shop didn't know that. To find out about recalls for any car, contact:

❑ **Auto Safety Hotline**, US Dept. of Transportation, NEF-11.2HL, 400 7th St. SW, Washington, DC 20590; 888-327-4236; {www.nhtsa.dot.gov/}

❑ The **Consumer Reports** people have a searchable database for car recall information; {www.consumerreports.org}. Click on "Autos" and then go to "Safety & Recalls."

FREE AND LOW COST SEMINARS ON HOW TO FIX UP A CAR

What do you do if you are driving on a freeway and you get a flat tire? How often should you change the oil and can you do it yourself? How do you jump start a car? It is better to plan ahead for emergencies, but where do you go for help?

Many different organizations and groups offer classes on how to fix a car. Begin by contacting your local car insurance company, automobile road service company, or department of motor vehicles. I have even seen classes being offered by automobile dealerships. Once you are there, maybe they can sell you a new car as well.

Other places to check include your county Cooperative Extension Service, your local adult education department, or women's organizations in your area. You can save yourself worry, stress, and money if you are prepared and knowledgeable regarding your car.

GRANDMA NEEDS A RIDE TO THE DOCTOR

Many seniors have to give up driving their cars, perhaps because of the cost or illness. But then how do they get to the doctor or the bank or the store? Many rely upon their friends and children to solve their transportation needs, but there are times when you need to come up with another alternative.

The Eldercare Locator provides access to an extensive network of organizations serving older people at state and local community levels. This service can connect you to information sources for a variety of services including transportation.

For more information, contact Eldercare Locator, National Association of Area Agencies on Aging, 1730 Rhode Island Ave., NW, Ste. 1200, Washington, DC 20036; 202-872-0888; 800-677-1116; {www.aoa.gov}.

I Don't Have A Car &
My Child Is Sick At School

Suppose your child is sick at school and needs you in the middle of the day, but you don't have a way to get there because you go to work most days by some other way than using your car. Don't panic. You can probably get a free ride, taxi, or free rental car from the local *"Guaranteed Ride Home Program"*. You can also use the service for most family emergencies if your normal ride falls through, or if you have to work late unexpectedly. Call your local carpool or vanpool service to see if they have a similar program. Most of these programs require that you pre-register, but it is always best to plan ahead for emergencies anyway.

If you do a computer search using the terms (including the quotes) "guaranteed ride home program," you will find a listing of many of the programs offered. You can also contact your state Department of Transportation for starting places.

DISCOUNTS on
Buses, Trains and Subways

If you are a senior citizen, you can usually ride most forms of transportation for about half-price. Amtrak and Greyhound offer discounts of 5%-15% for the senior set. Children even get to take advantage of discount programs, with the youngest group often getting a free ride. Check out these websites: {www.amtrak.com}; {www.greyhound.com}.

Don't forget to ask about a variety of reduced fare programs, including student and military discounts. Often job training programs will compensate you for your travel, so before you begin training, inquire about support services such as transportation and child care.

Free & Discounted Child Safety Seats

It's easy to spend $100 on a child's car seat, so look for the deals. There are hospitals that give out free child safety seats as you leave with your new baby, with no questions asked and no income requirements. Local police and fire departments inspect child safety seats to see that they are in proper order and properly installed, and sometimes provide free seats to those whose current equipment is not considered safe. Local organizations, like the Easter Seals Society were part of a federal program that gives out millions of dollars worth of free seats because of a settlement the U.S. Department of Transportation made with General Motors. Other groups will lend you a seat for as little as $5. The state of Minnesota alone has over 225 such programs.

To find a program near you, contact your local police or fire department. Or contact your state information operator listed in the Appendix and ask them for your state office for Highway Safety or Traffic Safety. These national organizations may also be able to give you a local source:

- *National SAFE KIDS Campaign*, 1301 Pennsylvania Ave., NW, Suite 1000, Washington, DC 20004; 202-662-0600; Fax 202-393-2072; {www.safekids.org}
- *National Highway Traffic Safety Administration*, U.S. Department of Transportation, 400 Seventh St., SW, Washington, DC 20590; 888-327-4236; {www.nhtsa.dot.gov}

Cheap Air Fare To See a Sick Relative

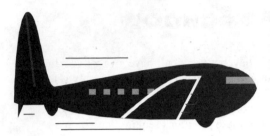

Not free, but at least you don't have to pay full price. When a family member is very ill or has died, families have to make last minute airline reservations. Obviously you lose out on the 21-day advance purchase rates, but almost all airlines offer *bereavement* or *compassion* fares for domestic travel.

Generally the fares are available to close family members, and the discount on the full-fare rate varies from airline to airline. Many require that you provide the name of the deceased and the name, address and phone number of the funeral home handling arrangements. In the case of a medical emergency, the name and address of the affected family member and the name, address and phone number of the attending physician or hospital are required. Contact the airline of your choice to learn more about the "Bereavement/Compassion Fares." Full fare rate and discounts vary from airline to airline.

Free Cars To Go On Vacation

Not quite as easy as it sounds, but there are programs out there to help people move their cars. Most of the cars need to be driven across the country and in exchange, many car moving companies offer free gas and airline travel home.

This is not to say that you can take your family on a minivan vacation across the country. Certain rules and restrictions apply. But I have known many a college kid that has gotten to drive across the U.S. for free.

Obviously, you do not get to pick your make and model, and you need to be flexible as to the departure time and destination, but this is one way to see America. Contact local moving companies to see what they have to offer. There is even a website for those interested in having their cars moved at {www.movecars.com}, and they may be able to provide you with information.

Discounts on Car Rentals

You never should pay full-price for car rentals and there are deals aplenty if you keep your eyes opened. AAA and AARP membership will save you a few bucks, as will many other membership programs. Car rental agencies also often offer discounts to senior citizens (check what age they consider "senior"). Many times, if you book your flight and car rental at the same time, you can get a discount rate, plus get miles added to your frequent flyer program. All you have to do is ask!

The free brochure, *Renting a Car*, outlines some points to consider and questions to ask when you reserve a rental car. You can learn how to choose a rental car company and understand the terms they use for insurance and charges. For your copy, contact Consumer Response Center, Federal Trade Commission, 600 Pennsylvania Ave., NW, Rm. H-130, Washington, DC 20580-0001; 877-FTC-HELP; or online at {www.ftc.gov}.

Bus Money or Parking Money From Your Boss

Your employer can give you $100 a month to pay for going to work in a bus, van or metro, or give you $195 a month for parking. You get the money tax free, and the employer gets to take a tax deduction. Everybody wins! It's called the *Qualified Transportation Fringe Benefit* or *Transit Benefit Program*. Get a copy of IRS Publication 15B, *Employer's Tax Guide to Fringe Benefits* and show your boss the section entitled "Fringe Benefit Exclusion Rules". The publication is available from your local IRS office or from 800-TAX-FORM or from their web site at {www.irs.gov}.

Tax Deductions For Your Car

You can deduct:
- 37.5 cents per mile if you use your car for business (IRS Publication 463, Travel Entertainment, Gift, and Car Expenses)
- 14 cents per mile if you use your car during charity work (IRS Instructions for Schedule A, Itemized Deductions)
- 14 cents per mile if you use your car for medical care (IRS Instructions for Schedule A, Itemized Deductions)
- 14 cents per mile if you use your car to move to a new job (IRS Publication 521, Moving Expenses)

These publications are free from your local IRS office, by calling 1-800-829-3676 or download from {www.irs.gov}

Your Child Has A Doctor's Appointment and Your Car Won't Work

The Federal Transit Administration provides over $84 million a year to over 1,000 local organizations to provide free non-emergency transportation for people who are elderly or have a disability. But the groups who get this federal money can also provide free transportation services to moms who are in a jam.

The regulations state that the vehicles can also be used to "serve the transportation needs of the general public on an incidental basis." You may have to do some educating to get a local group to give you a ride. Tell them to see Circular FTA C9070, 1D, for Section 5310 Program, Chapter V, Program Management, paragraph 3b. It's available from the U.S. Federal Transit Administration or on the web at {www.fta.dot.gov/library/policy/circ9070/chapter5.html}.

To find groups in your area who receive these FTA Section 5310 grants for Elderly and Persons With Disabilities, contact your state department of transportation or the U.S. Federal Transit Administration, Office of Program Management, Office of Resource Management and State Programs, 400 7th St., SW, Rm. 9315, Washington, DC 20590; 202-366-2053; {www.fta.dot.gov}.

MAKE $39,000 AND GET FREE CHILD CARE

In Connecticut your income can be $39,168 and you can get $680 a month for child care. Make $26,484 in Indiana and get $1,116 a month for infant care. Earn $38,244 in Alaska and receive $880 a month for child care.

The Child Care and Development Block Grant gives money to states to help families meet their child care needs. Parents may choose from a variety of child care providers, including center-based, family child care and in-home care, care provided by relatives, and even sectarian child care providers. You can even get money to start a day care center! Income qualifications vary from state to state, and each state operates their programs slightly differently.

To find out how to take advantage of this program in your state and to learn the eligibility requirements, contact National Child Care Information Center, 243 Church St., NW, 2nd Flr., Vienna, VA 22180; 800-616-2242; {http://nccic.org}.

Free Child Care
When Training Or Looking For A Job

Welfare reform, called *Temporary Assistance for Needy Families (TANF),* does more to help people not wind up on welfare. The program includes free training, education, child care, and transportation assistance necessary to help you obtain employment.

Child care is an important part of the program. Eligibility requirements vary from state to state, so contact your TANF office nearest you to learn what options are available to you. For more information, contact U.S. Department of Health and Human Services, Administration for Children and Families, Office of Family Assistance, 370 L'Enfant Promenade, SW Washington, DC 20201; 202-401-9215; {www.acf.hhs.gov/programs/opa/facts/tanf.htm}.

$9 a Week Child Care at Local Nonprofits

Local non-profits around the country get grants from the United Way or other institutions and offer free and sliding scale day care services. The United Way spends about a third of its funds, about $1 billion a year, on programs for children and families.

For example, the Community Partnerships for Children Program in Brockton, MA provides child care for a family of 2 with weekly income of $210 for only $9 a week, and families of 4 with income of $1,000 a week can get care for $114 a week per child. There are about 500 local United Way Information and Referral Services around the country that can point you to local groups that can help you solve your child care problems.

Look in the phone book for your local United Way agency, or contact United Way of America, 701 N. Fairfax Street, Alexandria, VA 22314-2045; 703-836-7112; {http://national.unitedway.org}.

Free Child Care For AmeriCorp
and VISTA Workers

Over $10,000,000 a year is paid out to cover child care services for people working with AmeriCorps or VISTA. These programs allow you to tackle community problems on everything from disaster relief to tutoring. National Service jobs also provide a stipend, housing, and even college money; child care is a bonus.

Contact Corporation for National and Community Service, 1201 New York Ave., NW, Washington, DC 20525; 202-606-5000; {www.nationalservice.org}.

YOUR CHILD MAY BE ELIGIBLE FOR A HEAD START

Head Start is one of those government programs that has proven to actually work. It's preschool that has a great student teacher ratio and all teachers are certified in early childhood development. It prepares the children with school readiness, and research shows that these children enter kindergarten with the skills necessary to succeed. Some Head Start programs are even home-based. There are income requirements for acceptance into the program, but the program does allow 10% of the students to have higher incomes. And 10% of the program needs to be offered to kids who have a disability.

To learn more about Head Start programs near you, contact your local board of education, the state Department of Social Services, or Administration for Children and Families, U.S. Department of Health and Human Services, Head Start Bureau, 330 C Street, SW, Washington, DC 20447; 202-205-8572; {www.acf.hhs.gov/programs/hsb}.

WORK FOR COMPANIES THAT OFFER FREE/DISCOUNT CHILD CARE

You may be surprised at the number of daycare centers offering services right inside company office buildings. In fact the federal government may be in the lead as they have over 1,000 child care centers that are sponsored by various governmental agencies. Talk to other moms and dads on the playground, call human resources departments, and even check with your local chamber of commerce. All may be able to direct you to companies providing this benefit.

Free Child Care For Teens With Disabilities

48 states provide a subsidy to parents who qualify for childcare for children ages 14 to 19 who are physically and/or mentally incapable of self-care. Each state sets their eligibility requirement and the amount of funds they have available for this type of care. To learn what your state has to offer, contact your state Child Care and Development Block Grant lead agency.

A directory of sites is available for $25 from the Work and Family Connection, 5197 Beachside Dr., Minnetonka, MN 55343; 800-487-7898; {www.workfamily.com}. Another resource is your local Child Care Resource and Referral Agency, who should be aware of programs in their area. To locate your local referral agency, contact Child Care Aware, 1319 F Street, NW, Suite 500, Washington, DC 20004; 800-424-2246, {www.childcareaware.org}.

Besides child care centers, some employers offer a dependent care assistance plan that allows you to pay for child care out of pre-tax dollars. You get more care for your buck. Other employers offer direct subsidies to offset child care costs. Talk to your company human resources office to learn more.

GET MONEY FOR YOUR OWN CHILD CARE CENTER

Child Care Works is a partnership between the District of Columbia, eight area banks and three community organizations that make training, grants and loans available to licensed neighborhood day care providers to provide slots for 1,000 children. Maryland and Ohio provide special low-interest loans through their Department of Economic Development to fund child care centers. Even the Child Care and Development Block Grant provides money to develop child care centers and before and after school programs. For more information, contact your state Department of Economic Development or your Child Care and Development Block Grant lead agency.

Get $4,800 From The IRS To Pay For Child Care

Remember that the Internal Revenue Service (IRS) offers some benefits for child care costs. IRS Publication 503, *Child and Dependent Care Expenses*, outlines the rules covering this benefit and describes how to figure the benefit if your employer covers some of the cost. You may take a credit of dependent care expenses of between 20%–35% (based on your income) of up to $3,000 for the care of one child (or $6,000 for two or more).

For more information, contact the IRS Information Line at 800-829-1040; or {www.irs.gov}. In addition, 25 states and the District of Columbia offer some type of child care income tax benefit either in the form of credits or deductions. Contact your state Tax Revenue office to see what your state offers.

GRANTS AND LOANS FOR ADOPTIONS

The National Adoption Foundation (NAF) is a national non-profit organization dedicated to providing financial support, information, and services for adoptive and prospective adoptive families. They recently announced the expansion of its programs to include home equity loans, as well as unsecured loans and grants for adoption expenses. A grant program to cover adoption expenses is also available on a limited basis for prospective adoptive parents.

Other sources of money for adoption include:

- Ask your employer for employee adoption assistance benefits. Approximately 65 percent of Fortune 500 companies now offer some kind of adoption benefit.

- Take advantage of the new adoption expense tax credit in advance by modifying your income tax withholding to reflect your tax savings when you file your return. This frees up cash for adoption expenses due now.

Contact: National Adoption Foundation, 100 Mill Plain Road, Danbury, CT 06811; 203-791-3811; Fax: 203-791-3801; {Email: info@nafadopt.org}; {www.nafadopt.org/default.asp}.

Free Credit Repair

It always seemed strange to me that if you're in debt enough to need help with credit repair, why in the world would you spend more money on a credit repair service? You can do it for free, yourself!

Spending money needlessly is what got you there in the first place. And more importantly, federal and state regulators have been warning consumers against using credit counseling companies. Companies, lawyers and others will charge you $300 to $1000 for something you can do for free.

Here are some of the free reports you can get from the Federal Trade Commission:

- ❑ *Credit Repair: Self-Help May Be Best*
- ❑ *Knee Deep in Debt*
- ❑ *How To Dispute Credit Report Errors*
- ❑ *Credit Repair: Getting Back in the Black Campaign*
- ❑ *Take Charge of Your Credit*

For your copies, contact Consumer Response Center, Federal Trade Commission, 600 Pennsylvania Ave., NW, Room H-130, Washington, DC 20580; 877-FTC-HELP; {www.ftc.gov}.

If you don't want to do it ALL yourself, you can ask for **FREE HELP**. The following non-profit and government organizations provide free, or low-fee credit counseling services. You can contact them to find the office nearest you. Some of these offices are financed by the bank and credit card industry, who are biased toward having you pay all your bills without using the bankruptcy option. So be sure that they explain your bankruptcy options.

> ❑ *National Foundation for Credit Counseling*, 801 Roeder Rd., Ste. 900, Silver Spring, MD 20910; 800-388-2227; 301-589-5600; {www.nfcc.org}.
> ❑ Free internet credit counseling services from the non-profit organization, *Credit Counseling Centers of America*, P.O. Box 830489, Richardson, TX 75083-0488; 800-493-2222; {www.cccamerica.org}.
> ❑ *County Cooperative Extension Service*: to find your local office, see the blue pages of your phone book.

GET FREE COPIES OF YOUR CREDIT REPORT

You can get a free copy of your credit report if:

- ★ you have been denied credit, insurance, or employment within the last 60 days
- ★ you're unemployed and plan to look for a job within 60 days
- ★ you're on welfare, or
- ★ your report is inaccurate because of fraud.

Otherwise they can charge you up to $15 for a copy of your report. For copies of your report, contact the credit reporting agencies listed in the *Yellow Pages* of your telephone book, or contact the three major national credit bureaus:

Equifax
PO Box 740241, Atlanta, GA 30374; 800-685-1111; {www.equifax.com}

Experian
PO Box 949, Allen, TX 75013; 888-EXPERIAN; {www.experian.com}

TransUnion
P.O. Box 2000, Chester, PA 19022; 800-888-4213; {www.transunion.com}

If you have trouble getting satisfaction from a credit reporting agency contact: Consumer Response Center, Federal Trade Commission, CRC-240, Washington, DC 20580; 877-FTC-HELP; {www.ftc.gov}.

EMERGENCY Aid AvailAble TO MusiC TeAchERS

Emergency aid for medical needs is available to U.S. music teachers through the Presser Foundation. Assistance is primarily given to retired teachers. Contact Presser Foundation, 385 Lancaster Ave., #205, Haverford, PA 19041; 610-658-9030.

Free Help Fighting a High ELECTRIC BILL Or Stopping A TURN-OFF

The state utility commissions can help you fight high gas or electric bills. Some will even come out and make sure that your meter is not over charging you. They don't have money to pay for your bills, but they can negotiate payment arrangements with the company for you or suggest non-profit organizations that may have emergency funds to help. For example Maryland suggests the Fuel Fund for Central Maryland or the Maryland Energy Assistance program. The office can also force the utility not to cut off your service because of medical emergencies or cold weather. Contact your state utility commission listed in the blue pages of your phone book for further assistance.

Check For A $100 Or More Heating Bill Tax Credit

The state of Michigan offers a home heating bill tax credit (that means you pay less in taxes) for people who are low income, receiving public assistance or unemployment. Call your state department of taxation to learn about tax credits available to you. Michigan Department of Treasury, Lansing, MI 48922; 800-487-7000; {www.michigan.gov/treasury}.

Free Voice Mail

If you are unemployed and the phone company cut off your phone, how does a potential employer get in touch with you? Free voice mail. You can get set up with your own personalized greeting, as well as get a security code and instructions on how you can retrieve your messages 24 hours a day. The program is available in over 39 cities and is growing.

See if you're eligible for your area by contacting Community Voice Mail, a program of the Community Technology Institute, P.O. Box 61385, Seattle, WA 98121; 206-441-7872; Fax: 206-443-3755; {www.cvm.org}.

GET AN $84 REDUCTION ON YOUR TELEPHONE BILL

Link-Up America and *Lifeline Assistance Program Outreach Campaign* are two government programs that offer up to $84 a year in discounts on your monthly bill and up to a 50% reduction for your hook-up service, or up to $30 whichever is less. These programs have income requirements that vary from state to state.

Ask your phone company about them or contact your state Utility Commissioner listed in the blue pages of your phone book or Federal Communications Commission, 445 12th St., SW, Washington, DC 20554; 888-CALL-FCC; {www.fcc.gov}.

Dress For Success For Free

Looking for work and can't afford the right wardrobe? There are about 50 non-profit organizations around the country that provide women with two separate outfits for free. One can be used to go to an interview and the other can be used once you get the job. The following organization acts as a clearinghouse for similar opportunities around the country. Bottomless Closet, 445 North Wells St., Chicago, IL 60610; 312-527-9664; Fax: 312-527-4307; {www.bottomlesscloset.org}.

Career Gear, 120 Broadway New York, NY 10271; 212-577-6190; Email: {info@careergear.org}; {www.careergear.org/}. This organization has locations in New York, Michigan, Ohio, Florida, and Washington, DC.

Dress for Success, 32 East 31st Street, Ste. 602, New York, NY 10016; 212-545-DSNY; Email: {newyork@dressforsuccess.org}; {www.dressforsuccess.org/}. This organization has locations in almost every state and internationally.

StyleWorks, 328 Flatbush Ave., # 350, Brooklyn, NY 11238; 718-398-1264; {www.styleworks.org}.

Suited For Change, 1712 I Street, NW, Suite B100, Washington, DC 20006-3750; 202-293-0351; {www.suitedforchange.org}.

FOOD MONEY

You don't get the cash, but you do get it in the form of Food Stamps. The Food Stamp Program was designed to help low-income families buy the food they need to stay healthy and productive. The amount of Food Stamps you get each month is determined by the number of people in your family and by the household income. The average benefit is about $149 dollars a month, but a 4-person household could get up to $499 a month. There are obviously income requirements you must meet.

To apply for the Program, look in the blue pages of your telephone book under "Food Stamps," "Social Services," or "Public Assistance." You can also find more information by contacting U.S. Department of Agriculture, Food and Nutrition Service, 3101 Park Ctr. Dr., Park Office Center Bldg., Alexandria, VA 22302; 703-305-2062; {www.fns.usda.gov/fsp}.

$500 For Seniors and Disabled

The state of Pennsylvania offers up to $500 for seniors and people with disabilities who pay property taxes or rent. If you live in Pennsylvania, contact Department of Aging, 555 Walnut St., 5th Floor, Harrisburg, PA 17101-1919; 717-783-1550; Email: {aging@state.pa.us}; {www.aging.state.pa.us/}. If you live elsewhere, contact your state Office on Aging listed in the blue pages of your phone book, or your state Department of Revenue.

Money When You're Out Of Work

In Massachusetts, you can receive up to $402 a week for 30 weeks, and in special circumstances they will extend the benefits another 18 weeks. Mass lay-offs, base closings, trade agreements, and high unemployment in your state, all affect your ability to find and keep a job. If you are out of work, take advantage of unemployment insurance. This is the government's first line of defense against the ripple effects of unemployment.

All states are required to provide benefits up to 26 weeks and some extend them further. If your state has very high unemployment, you may be eligible for 13 additional weeks of compensation. If you lost your job because of an increase in imports, you may qualify to have your benefits extended up to an extra 52 weeks if you are in a job-retraining program.

Your weekly benefit amount depends upon your past wages within certain minimum and maximum limits that vary from state to state. Many states also will add additional funds depending upon the number of dependents. If you are denied benefits, learn about the appeal process, as your chances of winning are good. For more information, contact your state Unemployment Insurance office listed in the blue pages of your phone book.

Free Help In Writing A Will

Estate planning is not something that people often relish doing, but it is extremely important. It is difficult enough when a loved one dies, but then to have to search through papers trying to find information about insurance, or investments is often too much. When children are involved, estate planning is essential. Who will take care of the children and how can you secure their financial future?

Your local Cooperative Extension Service often offers classes or publications on estate planning. The time to plan ahead is now. Look in the blue pages of your phone book for the nearest Cooperative Extension office, as they are in almost every county across the country.

$700 Discount On Your Utility Bills

The legislature in Massachusetts passed a law giving discounts up to $700 on heating bills for families making up to $30,000, along with up to 40% discount on electric bills, $108 off telephone bills, and $100 off oil bills. It's in the Massachusetts Budget for FY 04 (Line Item 4403-2110). Also:

✿ **Mason County** in the state of Washington offers a utility bill discount of $12–$15 a month for seniors making less than $18,000, and disabled people at 125% of poverty. Contact Public Utility District #3, 307 W. Cota St., Shelton, WA 98584; 360-426-8255; {www.masonpud3.org}.

✿ **Phoenix, Arizona** offers discounts on utility bills, discounts on phone bills and even help paying utility deposits and heating repairs for low-income residents through the Arizona Public Service Energy Support Program, P.O. Box 53999, Phoenix, AZ 85072; 602-371-7171; {www.aps.com}.

✿ **SBC in Illinois** gives a 60% discount on connection charges and $6.25 off the monthly bill to low-income residents. To sign up, call SBC at 800-244-4444; {www.sbc.com}.

☼ **Ohio** offers reduced or free phone hook up service and possibly $12.39 a month off your phone bill for low-income residents. Contact Public Utilities Commission, 180 E. Broad St., Columbus, OH 43215; 800-686-7826; {www.puco.ohio.gov}.

☼ **Pennsylvania Bell Atlantic** offers free telephone hook up and $11.60 monthly discount to low-income residents through Lifeline and Universal Telephone Assistance Programs. To sign up, call 800-621-9900.

Contact your state's utilities office in the blue pages of your phone book to find out about special discounts on your gas, electric, cable or telephone in your state.

Free Tax Help for Seniors

It is nice to get special treatment every now and then, and tax time is no exception. The Tax Counseling for the Elderly program was designed to provide free taxpayer assistance to those ages 60 and above. The staff usually consists of retired individuals associated with nonprofit organizations that receive grants from the IRS to perform this service. Often they provide counseling in retirement homes, neighborhood sites or private houses of the homebound.

For information on the Tax Counseling for the Elderly program near you, contact your local IRS office, call the hotline at 800-829-1040; {www.irs.gov}.

Government Supported Agencies Offer Free Money And Help When You Don't Know Where To Turn

If you need emergency money to pay a bill, or for housing, training, health care, or just additional support, these organizations can be of service and they are likely to have an office near you. Although these are private organizations, they do receive a portion of their funds from your favorite Uncle Sam.

1) *Community Action Agencies*
Nearly 1,000 agencies around the country received funds from the U.S. Government's Community Services Block Grants to offer education, counseling, employment, training, food packages, vouchers, weatherization and utility assistance, life skills, affordable housing, transportation, furnishings, recreation, emergency services, information and referral services. To locate an agency serving your area, contact: Community Action Partnership, 1100 17th St., NW, Suite 500, Washington, DC 20036; 202-265-7546; Fax: 202-265-8850; Email: {info@communityaction partnership.com}; {www.communityactionpartnership.com}.

2) *Catholic Charities*
Over 14,000 local organizations offer a variety of services for many different communities including: child care, elderly services, emergency financial services, emergency shelter, food pantries, housing assistance, job training, out-of-home care, parenting education, youth services, rental assistance, utility assistance, and health care. For an office near you, contact Catholic Charities USA, 1731 King Street #200, Alexandria, VA 22314; 703-549-1390; Fax: 703-549-1656; {www.catholiccharitiesusa.org}.

3) *Salvation Army*

Families in need can receive a wide range of services including: utility assistance, transitional housing, emergency food, furnishings, Section 8 tenant counseling, counseling, rent or mortgage assistance, and even clothing. Most services are for households who are below 150% of the poverty level (about $24,000 for a family of 4). For an office near you, contact Salvation Army National Headquarters, 615 Slaters Lane, P.O. Box 269, Alexandria, VA 22313; 703-684-5500; Fax: 703-519-5889; {www1.salvationarmy.org}.

FREE DIRECTORY/OPERATOR ASSISTANCE IF YOU HAVE A DISABILITY

Directory assistance can cost up to 95 cents per request and an additional 50 cents for the connection. To assist persons with visual, hearing, or other disabilities, local telephone companies offer directory and operator assistance exemptions. Simply request and complete a form from the local telephone company and have your physician complete the appropriate section. When you return the form to the phone company, you'll be eligible for the exemptions. Contact the business office of your local telephone company.

GET EXTRA CASH FINDING LOST MONEY AND SURPLUS PROPERTY

Make $2,000 in 45 minutes. That's what the author, Mary Ann Martello, did when she searched state databases looking for old forgotten utility deposits and bank accounts set up by grandparents. Every state has an office that collects money in that state that has been abandoned, forgotten, or left unclaimed, including:

- Savings and checking accounts
- Uncashed payroll or cashiers checks
- Money orders and travelers checks
- Certificates of deposit
- Customer deposits or overpayment
- Paid up life insurance policies
- Health and accident insurance payments
- Uncashed death benefit checks
- Gift certificates and Christmas club accounts
- Stock and dividends
- Utility deposits
- Oil and gas royalty payments

The money could be a savings account that grandma set up for you when you were born. Or it could be a Christmas fund Great Aunt Rose contributed to before she passed away. Your father may have even had a safe deposit box he never told you existed.

According to reports, state agencies across the U.S. may be holding over $8 billion dollars in abandoned money. Although the rules vary from state to state, generally after two or more years without activity on an account (no deposits or withdrawals), the bank will try to contact you. If their efforts fail, the property is considered abandoned and transferred to the state of your last known address.

To locate funds, contact the unclaimed property office in the state (usually part of the state treasurer's department) where you or your benefactors have lived or conducted business. Most state agencies have websites, and many have searchable databases. You can contact the National Association of Unclaimed Property Administrators, NAUPA c/o

NAST, P.O. Box 11910, Lexington, KY 40578-1910; 859-244-8150; Fax: 859-244-8053; {www.unclaimed.org}; {www.missingmoney.com}. Not only does the website give you a listing of state offices, it also links you to those that have existing websites.

Checking Into Your Retirement Check

Did you work some place twenty years ago that is no longer in business? What about an old pension fund that was in financial trouble? Don't give up. The Pension Benefit Guaranty Corporation (PBGC) monitors and sometimes takes over private sector-defined benefit plans. These are traditional pensions that promise a specified monthly benefit at retirement.

The PBGC operates a Pension Search Directory to find people who are owed pensions from the plans PBGC now controls. You can search by name, company worked for, or by state where the company is/was headquartered. The directory found 16,598 people owed more that $4 million with the average benefit being $4,100. There is still $13 million just waiting to be claimed.

For more information, contact Pension Benefit Guaranty Corporation, Pension Search Program, 1200 K St., NW, Washington, DC 20005-4026; 800-326-LOST; {www.pbgc.gov}.

165,000 Unclaimed Social Security Checks

Social Security checks go out to 92% of those over the age of 65, so once in awhile a check may go astray. If you think you are missing some checks, or if you find un-negotiated checks, contact your local Social Security Administration office. They can reissue the checks to the person or to the estate.

Social Security assures me that this occurs rarely, as they send out 612 million payments with only 165,000 checks that were not endorsed. Contact Social Security Hotline at 800-772-1213.

The IRS Has "GOOD NEWS" For 100,000 Taxpayers

Seems impossible, doesn't it? Close to 100,000 taxpayers are due a refund, yet their checks have been returned to the tune of over $62.6 million. The average check is $627. What do you do if you think you or someone you love is missing a check? Contact the IRS toll-free hotline at 800-829-1040 and talk to a customer service representative. They can plug your name in the computer and see if your name pops up on their screen.

The same deal holds true with the Veterans Affairs Administration. If you feel you are missing checks or find checks that have not been endorsed, contact your local Veterans Affairs office so that checks can be reissued to you or to the estate of a loved one. Contact Veterans Affairs at 800-827-1000.

Free Private Eye and Mediation For Missing Children

Besides location and investigative services, as well as mediation services for families estranged by parental abduction, you can also get free kidnapping prevention programs and referral and support services. Contact Child Find of America, Inc., P.O. Box 277, New Paltz, NY 12561; 800-I-AM-LOST; 845-255-1848; 800-A-WAY-OUT (for mediation and support); {www.childfindofamerica.org}.

AN EXTRA $6,000 A YEAR IF YOU CAN'T WORK

Is your check too small to live on? If so, don't be discouraged. If you don't qualify for Social Security, or if your benefits are very low, you may qualify for Supplemental Security Income (SSI). This program was established to help poor seniors over 65, as well as the blind and disabled, meet basic living needs. To qualify, you must meet a maximum monthly income test. Some of the income and services you receive are excluded when they calculate your monthly income in relation to your personal expenses.

Those who meet SSI's eligibility usually automatically qualify for Medicaid coverage and food stamp benefits. Studies have found that only between 40 and 60 percent of those who qualify for SSI actually receive benefits under the program. To find out if you qualify, contact your local Social Security office or call the Social Security Hotline at 800-772-1213.

Law Gives Kids With ADD Free Special Classes

The nonprofit organization, *Children and Adults with Attention-Deficit/Hyperactivity Disorder (CHADD),* identifies a number of federal laws that require the government to provide children with this disorder special educational services. It is only recently that these children became eligible for such services, so many eligible children may not be receiving what they deserve.

To learn more about these free educational services, or to find out more and how to treat a child with ADD, or what's good and bad about available treatments, contact: CHADD, 8181 Professional Place, Suite 150, Landover, MD 20785; 800-233-4050; Fax: 301-306-7090; {www.chadd.org}.

Get Money While You're Waiting For Government Money

General Public Assistance or just Public Assistance (it is known by many different names) is a welfare program offered in 42 states. This is a program of last resort for people either waiting to qualify for other government programs such as disability benefits, or who do not qualify for any programs, yet need money to live. The program eligibility and benefit levels vary within and across state lines. In some states, this benefit is only available in certain areas. There are strict income and asset levels that you must meet to qualify.

In Kansas, General Assistance pays families $278 per month while they are waiting for other government money. In California, the benefit is $225. Contact your local welfare office, your state Department of Social Service, or your state Temporary Assistance to Needy Families office to see what your state offers and the eligibility requirements.

10% Off Your Airline Tickets

Some airlines offer discounts to seniors amounting to usually 10%. What happens, though, is that some of the airlines' special offers may be exempt from the discount. It is best to see what the lowest available rate is and then inquire about the discount.

Some airlines periodically offer coupon books for seniors that are four round-trip tickets good for wherever the airline flies. In many instances, the airline only requires that one person meet the age requirement for a discount, so your companion can receive the lower rate as well.

50% Off Camping

Almost all states offer discounts to seniors at state parks. Entrance fees are usually waived for seniors, or states like Illinois offer 50% off camping fees. Eighteen states have no residency requirements to receive the discount, so if you are planning a cross country camping trip, contact the state Parks Department to find out about eligibility criteria.

For those wanting to camp in the National Forest, the Golden Age Passport is available to those 62 and over. For $10 you receive free lifetime admission to the parks, plus 50% off on camping and many other services. The Passport is available at all National Forests.

10%-50% OFF HOTEL ROOMS

Almost all major hotel chains offer discounts from 10%-50% off the cost of rooms. Some require that you belong to AARP or AAA, so it is best to call ahead and ask.

Two hotel chains, Ramada Inn {www.ramada.com}, and Hilton {www.hilton.com}, offer special deals to seniors who frequent their hotels. You are entitled to 10%–25% off regular two double bed room rates, plus you receive points redeemable for travel and prizes (800-FOR-TRIP; available at most Ramadas). Hilton Senior HHonors program charges $55 ($40 annual renewal fee), and seniors receive up to 50% off rooms and 20% off hotel restaurants (800-492-3232).

10%-15% OFF
WHEN YOU TRAVEL

All car rental chains offer senior discounts, but again AARP or AAA membership may be required. The amount of discount varies from location to location, but usually is 10%. You should call ahead to see if a discount is available. Some chains also require reservations 24 hours in advance.

For those that prefer to leave the driving to others, two other discount programs include AMTRAK and Greyhound. Amtrak offers 15% off any fare available to those 62 and older (800-USA-RAIL). Greyhound has an 10% discount for people 62 and over (800-231-2222).

50% Discount On Telephone Service

Under the Federal Communication Commission's LinkUp America and Lifeline programs, low-income households seeking telephone service are given a 50% discount on local connection charges, and may be able to pay installment payments on the remaining charge. These programs are available in most states.

To sign up for this service, contact the customer service representative at your local telephone company.

10% OFF AT RESTAURANTS

The Early Bird specials can happen all day once you hit a certain age. Many restaurant chains offer special deals for seniors. Most restaurant chains are independently owned and operated, but they usually follow the recommendations from the headquarters.

Places like Denny's, Bob Evan's, and International House of Pancakes frequently offer seniors a reduced price menu. Other chains, such as Applebee's, Kentucky Fried Chicken, and Wendy's, often give seniors a 10% discount on their meals. It never hurts to ask if a discount is offered.

5%-10% Off When You Shop

Banana Republic offers seniors age 62 and older 10% off every day, while Ross, Stone & Thomas, and Glik's offer 10% off to seniors on specific days during the week. Other stores like Wal-mart and May Co. frequently offer advertised senior specials. Ask at the main offices of stores where you shop to see what may be available to you. Even grocery stores are getting into the act!

Free (Or Cheap) Hunting and Fishing Licenses

Practically every state has a special license rate for seniors. States such as Alabama, Alaska, Delaware, Georgia, Kansas, and others do not require that people age 65 and over to carry a fishing and hunting license. Other states offer seniors, on average, half off the cost of licenses.

Inquire where you usually purchase these licenses to learn what age you need to be to receive the discount and the specific details.

Save Money When You Bank

First Citizens Bank has **Charter Quest Accounts** where customers 60 and over receive unlimited check writing, no per check charge, interest bearing checking, no monthly service charge, free safe deposit box, no ATM fees, free cashier's checks, travelers' checks, and money orders. They even offer special rates on 6 and 12 month CD's, no annual fee credit card, free direct deposit and discount brokerage fees, with some of these services requiring a minimum balance. Not a bad deal. Other banks offer similar services, with most offering free checks, no minimum balance, and unlimited check writing.

Grants Aid Needy Professional Musicians and Singers

Assistance is available to financially needy New York residents once prominent in opera and classical music through the Bagby Foundation for the Musical Arts, Inc. The Foundation also provides monetary support for coaching assistance to students desiring to make their professional opera debut. Contact The Bagby Foundation for the Musical Arts, Inc., 501 5th Ave., Suite 801, New York, NY 10017; 212-986-6094.

Christian Scientists Assisted by Two Agencies

The New Horizons Foundation provides financial assistance to residents of Los Angeles County, CA, who are over 65 years of age and active Christian Scientists. Contact: New Horizons Foundation, c/o Gifford & Dearing, 700 S. Flower St., Suite 1222, Los Angeles, CA 90017-4114; 213-626-4481.

Grants and camperships are available through the Sunnyside Foundation, Inc. to underprivileged Christian Science children under the age of 20 who regularly attend Sunday School and are Texas residents. Contact Sunnyside Foundation, Inc., 8222 Douglas Ave., Suite 501, Dallas, TX 75225-5936; 214-692-5686.

General Welfare Grants Support Utah Residents

The Marion D. and Maxine C. Hanks Foundation, Inc. offers general welfare grants and support for medical expenses to needy Utah residents. Contact The Marion D. and Maxine C. Hanks Foundation, Inc., 8 E. Broadway, Suite 520, Salt Lake City, UT 84111; 801-364-7705.

Pittsburgh-Area Jewish
Families In Need
Receive Aid

Financial assistance is offered to needy Jewish families residing in the Pittsburgh area through the Jewish Family Assistance Fund for living, personal, food and medical expenses. Contact Jewish Family Assistance Fund, 5743 Bartlett St., Pittsburgh, PA 15217-1515; 412-521-3237.

Oregon Masons Assisted

The Portland Area Acacia Fund provides relief assistance to distressed Masons and their widows and orphans living in Oregon. Contact Portland Valley Acacia Fund, 709 SW 15th Ave., Portland, OR 97205; 503-228-9405.

Vet Services Hotline

The Department of Veterans Affairs hotline can provide you with information on such programs as life insurance, comprehensive dental and medical care, nursing homes, home loan programs, burial services, and more. Contact Department of Veterans Affairs, 810 Vermont Ave., NW, Washington, DC 20420; 800-827-1000; {www.va.gov}.

Health Care Grants

3 Million Seniors & Disabled
Don't Apply for Their Free $1,000 For Health Care

Each year over 3 million eligible seniors and people with disabilities fail to apply for a little-known program that will give them up to an extra $1,051 in their Social Security check. That's how much the government deducts from their Social Security to pay for their Medicare premiums. It amounts to $108 a month for couples and $54 for individuals. There are three basic programs:

1) *Pays for Medicare premiums, deductibles and co-payments under the Qualified Medicare Beneficiaries (QMBs) plan.*
2) *Pays for Medicare Part B premiums under the Specified Low-Income Medicare Beneficiaries (SLMBs) plan.*
3) *Pays for Medicare Part B premiums under the Qualified Individuals Plan for people with incomes up to $14,892.*

Studies show that only 5,000 of the 500,000 eligible apply for this program. With so few eligible people applying, it's understandable that many people don't know about this program.

Here's where to go. Contact your local Social Security Office. If they don't know, contact your state Office of Social Services. You can also contact the Medicare Hotline and request the publication, *Guide to Health Insurance for People With Medicare*. This publication is also available online at {www.medicare.gov/Publications}. Contact Medicare Hotline at 800-MEDICARE (800-633-4227); {www.medicare.gov}.

Discounts On Dental And Vision Care

If you live near a university that has a dental or optometry school, then you may be in luck. Many of these schools offer reduced fee services for dental care or vision screening. You will receive treatment from students, but they will be supervised by some of the best people in the field.

Grants Assist with Low Vision Equipment

The Pearle Vision Foundation offers grants to U.S. residents for low vision equipment. Funding is also available to non-profit organizations for vision-care assistance. Contact Pearle Vision Foundation, 2465 Joe Field Rd., Dallas, TX 75229, 972-277-6191; Fax: 972-277-6422.

These schools also often conduct research studies, so if you qualify, you may be able to receive treatment for free. My eleven-year-old daughter gets glasses, contacts, plus free contact solution for three years, because she is part of a study on nearsightedness in children. Not a bad deal! To locate schools near you, you can contact American Dental Education Association, 1400 K Street, NW, Suite 1100, Washington, DC 20005; 202-289-7201; Fax: 202-289-7204; {www.adea.org}. You can also contact American Optometric Association, 243 N. Lindbergh Blvd., St. Louis, MO 63141; 314-991-4100; {www.aoanet.org}.

Free Plastic Surgery For Children

Austin Smiles provides free reconstructive plastic surgery, mainly to repair cleft lip and palate, to the children around Austin, Texas. They do about 75 surgeries a year. Austin Smiles, P.O. Box 26694, Austin, TX 78755-0694; 512-451-9300; Fax: 512-451-9312; {www.austinsmiles.org}.To see if similar services are available anywhere near you contact Cleft Palate Foundation, 1504 East Franklin St. Suite 102, Chapel Hill, NC 27514; 800-24-CLEFT; 919-933-9044; {www.cleftline.org}.

Grants Up To $2,500 and Loans To Finance Adoptions

The National Adoption Foundation helps arrange loans and provides limited grants for parents to cover expenses before and after adoption. They award grants in the amounts ranging from $500–$2,500 and the Foundation has developed exclusive partnerships to provide assistance. Contact: National Adoption Foundation, 100 Mill Plain Rd., Danbury, CT 06811; 203-791-3811; {www.nafadopt.org}.

The following organizations also provide free publications, referral services and advice on adoption and searching for birth relatives:

★ **National Adoption Information Clearinghouse**, 370 L'Enfant Promenade SW, Washington, DC 20201; 888-251-0075; 703-352-3488; Fax: 703-385-3206; {http://naic.acf.hhs.gov/index.cfm}.
★ **National Adoption Center**, 1500 Walnut St, Suite 701, Philadelphia, PA, 19102; Answer Line: 215-735-9988; 800-TO-ADOPT; {www.adopt.org}.
★ **National Council For Adoption**, 225 N. Washington St., Alexandria, VA 22314-2561; 703-299-6633; Fax: 703-299-6004; {www.adoptioncouncil.org}.

Camp Wheeze-Away Is Free For Kids With Asthma

Every year, about 100 kids with asthma, between 8 and 12 years of age, can go to summer camp for free in Jackson's Gap, Alabama. For information on how to apply, contact American Lung Association of Alabama, 3125 Independence Dr., Suite 325, Birmingham, AL 35209; 205-933-8821; Fax: 205-930-1717; {www.alabamalung.org}.

For more information on other camps for children with asthma, or other questions concerning asthma, contact The American Lung Association, 61 Broadway, 6th Flr., New York, NY 10006; 212-315-8700; 800-LUNG-USA; {www.lungusa.org}.

Free Speech Therapy For Toddlers

It doesn't matter how much money you earn. You can have your child tested to see if any speech problems are developing and even get free speech therapy. It's part of the U.S. Individuals with Disabilities Education Act (IDEA) to make sure that children in need receive special education beginning on their third birthday, and in some states, like Virginia, it starts at age 2.

The program is run through your local school district, so check with them first, or your state Department of Education. You can also contact Office of Special Education Programs, Office of Special Education and Rehabilitative Services, U.S. Department of Education, 400 Maryland Ave., SW, Washington, DC 20202; 202-205-5507; {www.ed.gov/about/offices/list/osers/osep/index.html?src=mr}.

Free Flu Shots

Who should get flu shots? The U.S. Center for Disease Control recommends it for

- adults at or over 50 years
- residents of nursing homes
- persons at or over 6 months of age with chronic cardiovascular or pulmonary disorders, including asthma
- persons at or over 6 months of age with chronic metabolic diseases (including diabetes), renal dysfunction, hemoglobinopathies, immunosuppressive or immunodeficiency disorders
- women in their 2nd or 3rd trimester of pregnancy during flu season
- persons 6 months to 18 years receiving aspirin therapy
- groups, including household members and care givers who can infect high risk persons

Almost anyone can get free or low cost ($10-$15) flu shots from their county health office or other community sources. Some doctors, like Dr. Donald McGee in New Hampshire {www.drmcgee.com}, offer free shots in their office. Medicare Part B also pays for flu shots.

Contact your county office of public health listed in your telephone book or your state Department of Health. If you have trouble finding a local low cost source, or would like more information on the flu vaccine contact the National Immunization Information Hotline at 800-232-2522 (English); 800-232-0233 (Spanish); {www.cdc.gov/nip}.

Free Help ○ At Your Home ○ Every Day ○ After Childbirth

The Healthy Families America Project operates 440 programs in the US and Canada. It helps new mothers cope with the pressures of being a new parent by offering volunteer home visitors who come to your home for the first three weeks after birth. They are trained to show you how to deal with the physical, emotional and financial strains of a new baby. First time mothers and older mothers are among those considered for the program.

To see if there is a program in your area and if you qualify, contact Prevent Child Abuse America, 200 S. Michigan Ave., 17th Floor, Chicago, IL 60604-2404; 312-663-3520; Fax: 312-939-8962; {www.preventchildabuse.org}.

Kids Get Free Expert Care At 22 Hospitals

Children suffering from orthopedic injuries, diseases of the bones, joint and muscles, or burns can get free treatment from one of the 22 Shriners Hospitals. The requirements for admission are that the child is under the age of 18, and there is a reasonable possibility the condition can be helped. For more information, contact Shrine and Shriners Hospitals, 2900 Rocky Point Dr., Tampa, FL 33607-1460; 813-281-0300; 800-237-5055 (in Canada 800-361-7256); {www.shrinershq.org}.

$2,000 Worth Of Dental Care For Seniors and Disabled

The National Foundation of Dentistry for the Handicapped started the Donated Dental Services program to help disabled and elderly persons who are low-income by matching them with volunteer dentists. Homeless and mentally ill people are also helped.

Volunteer dentists agree to treat one or two people each year with dental problems, and dental laboratories that make dentures, crowns, and bridges also donate services. The program has served almost 50,000 people in 34 states with patients receiving over $60 million worth of free services. In some areas of the country, Dental House Call projects have been started where dentists will come to homes or centers to provide dental care.

To learn where services are located in your area, contact National Foundation of Dentistry for the Handicapped, 1800 15th St., Suite 100, Denver, CO 80202; 303-534-5360, Fax: 303-534-5290; {www.nfdh.org}.

Sightless Get Free Seeing Eye Dogs, Training, Travel and Air Fare

Pilot Dogs gives its trained animals to the blind at absolutely no charge. They also include four weeks of training in using the dog and will pay for room and board, all equipment, and round trip transportation. Other groups provide similar services:

* ***Pilot Dogs, Inc.,*** 625 West Town Street, Columbus, OH 43215; 614-221-6367; Fax: 614-221-1577; {www.pilotdogs.org}.
* ***Guide Dog Foundation for the Blind, Inc***, 371 East Jericho Tpke., Smithtown, NY 11787-2976; 800-548-4337; 631-265-2121; Fax: 631-361-5192; {www.guidedog.org}.

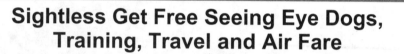

Alcohol and Drug Abuse Counseling & Treatment

Georgia provides outpatient counseling services, short-term residential programs, and even school student assistance programs. Florida provides substance abuse treatment programs through a partnership with 102 public and private not-for-profit community providers. Delaware contracts with private organizations around the state to provide screening, outpatient counseling, and detoxification, as well as short term and long term treatment. Contact your state Department of Health to see what your state has to offer.

There are also nonprofit organizations who, by themselves, offer free treatment to people, like the Center for Drug-Free Living in Orlando, Florida (P.O. Box 538350, Orlando, FL 32853-8350; 407-245-0012; Fax: 407-245-0011; {www.cfdfl.com}). If your state can't help you get the information or treatment you need, one or both of the following hotlines should be able to help:

■ ***National Drug and Treatment Routing Service***, Center for Substance Abuse Treatment, National Institute on Alcohol Abuse and Alcoholism (NIAAA), 5635 Fishers Lane, MSC-9304., Bethesda, MD 20892-9304; 800-662-HELP; {www.niaaa.nih.gov}.

■ *The National Clearinghouse for Alcohol and Drug Information*, 11420 Rockville Pike, Rockville, MD 20852; 800-729-6686 24 hours a day; 800-487-4889 TDD; {www.health.org}.

Free Wheelchairs

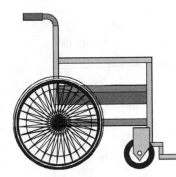

Easter Seals, the American Cancer Society and other helpful organizations provide free wheelchairs and other medical related equipment, like walkers, commodes, bathtub rails, bathtub chairs, crutches, transfer benches, electric wheelchairs and scooters, on a short- or long-term basis. Some programs require deposits that are completely refundable.

Check with your local office of Easter Seals and the American Cancer Society. You can also contact your state Department of Health.

• *American Cancer Society, Inc.*, 1599 Clifton Road, NE, Atlanta, GA 30329; 800-ACS-2345; {www.cancer.org}.

• *Easter Seals*, 230 West Monroe Street, Suite 1800, Chicago, IL 60606; 800-221-6827; 312-726-6200; fax: 312-726-1494; {www.easterseals.org}.

MAKE $40,000 & GET FREE PRESCRIPTION DRUGS — EVERYTHING BUT VIAGRA

Valium, Prozac, Dilantin are just a few of the medications you can get FREE directly from the drug companies themselves. That's right: drug companies don't want everybody to know this, but they will give certain people who can't afford their medications their drugs free of charge.

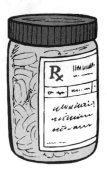

So what's the catch? It sounds too easy. The drug companies require that you participate in their "patient assistance programs." Your doctor needs to write them a note stating that you cannot afford the drugs that you need. Your doctor is the one that needs to call the drug manufacturer. Once the forms are filled out, you will be able to pick up your drugs directly from your doctor's office.

Call the Pharmaceutical Research and Manufacturers of America hotline to receive a listing of the drug companies and their programs. Contact Pharmaceutical Research and Manufacturers of America, 1100 15th St., NW, Washington, DC 20005; 800-PMA-INFO; {www.phrma.org}.

Make Under $34,041 And Get Free Health Care For Your Kids

Over 4.7 million children are eligible for this program and are not enrolled. Almost every state now has a Children's Health Insurance Program (CHIP) which extends medical coverage to many children who may not be covered.

A family of four living in Connecticut can make under $34,041 and get free health care for their children under 19 years of age. For a family of three, it's under $28,232. And a family of four making $43,240 will pay only $30 a month for insurance. Contact Department of Social Services, State of Connecticut, 25 Sigourney St., Hartford, CT 06106;

Healthcare for UninSured Kids and Youth (HUSKY Program), 877-CT-HUSKY, P.O. Box 280747, East Hartford, CT 06108; {www.huskyhealth.com/qualify.htm}. A family of four living in Virginia and making under $34,041 can get free coverage. Contact FAMIS (Family Access to Medical Insurance Security Plan), P.O. Box 1820, Richmond, VA 23218; 866-873-2647; {www.famis.org}.

Maryland's program covers pregnant women of any age and children under 19 if the family of four has an income below $34,040. Their program includes dental and vision care. Contact Health Choice, Maryland Department of Health and Mental Hygiene, W. Preston St., Room L, Baltimore, MD 21201; 800-456-8900; 410-767-6860; {http://dhmh.state.md.us/mma/mchp/}.

Contact your state Department of Health to see what version of the CHIP program is offered in your area. It is usually part of the state's Medicaid program. A new government hotline can also help you locate free health care for kids. Call toll-free 877-KIDS-NOW (877-543-7669); {www.insurekidsnow.gov}.

Free Care
Even If You Don't Qualify

You or your child may still be able to get free health care from local government programs even if you don't qualify. Many local health offices have the authority to stretch the rules if they see fit. Others have set up special arrangements with the local medical society for people who don't qualify for their programs. These offices can direct you to local nonprofit organizations or groups that can give you the care you need at the price you can afford.

Contact your county office of public health listed in your telephone book or your state Department of Health. If you cannot get satisfaction from these offices, contact your local office of your state or federal elected official.

Free Mammograms /
Free Tests For Breast and Cervical Cancer

An estimated 3 million American women will be diagnosed with breast or cervical cancer in the next decade, and half a million will lose their lives from these diseases. Screening could prevent up to 30% of these deaths for women over 40.

The government's Centers for Disease Control will spend about $210 million a year to maintain a state-by-state program to establish greater access to screening and follow-up services. Each state runs their program a little differently. Most states have the following requirements:

→ women starting at 40 or 50 years old
→ are underinsured or have no insurance
→ have income below a certain level (usually $35,000 for a family of 4)

Some states can adjust eligibility requirements for special cases. States vary in the array of services covered but they normally include:

→ breast and cervical cancer screening
→ mammograms
→ treatment if diagnosed with cancer
→ breast reconstruction or prosthesis

Cancer Patients Receive Help with Expenses

Limited financial assistance is available through Cancer Care, Inc. to cancer patients and their families who are residents of NY, NJ and CT for home care, child care and transportation expenses. Contact Cancer Care, Inc., 275 7th Ave., New York, NY 10001; 800-813-HOPE; 212-712-8080; Fax: 212-712-8495; {www.cancercare.org}.

States that don't have direct funds for treatment often make arrangements with other facilities to provide treatment for free. If your screening has been done elsewhere, you can still receive free treatment under this program. Men diagnosed with breast cancer can also receive free treatment.

Contact your county office of public health listed in your telephone book or your state Department of Health. You can also contact the main office of this program at Division of Cancer Prevention and Control, National Center for Chronic Disease Prevention and Health Promotion, Center for Disease Control and Prevention, 4770 Buford Highway, NE, MS K-64, Atlanta, GA 30341, 770-488-4751; 888-842-6355; Fax: 770-488-4760; {www.cdc.gov/cancer/nbccedp/index.htm}.

More Free Mammograms

Not all insurance companies pay for mammograms, and not every woman is eligible for the government's program described earlier. The following organizations can help you identify free and low cost mammograms in your area.

1) *The American Cancer Society*: contact your local office or the national office at 800-ACS-2345.
2) *YMCA's Encore Plus Program*: contact your local office or the national office at 800-95-EPLUS.
3) *National Cancer Institute*: 800-4-CANCER.
4) *State Office of Breast and Cervical Cancer*: contact your state Department of Health.
5) *October is National Breast Cancer Awareness Month*: many mammogram facilities offer their services at special fees during this period. Call and see what kind of deal you can get.
6) *Medicare coverage of mammograms*: call 800-MEDICARE.

For a free copy of *How To Get A Low Cost Mammogram*, contact National Alliance of Breast Cancer Organizations, (NABCO) 9 East 37th Street, 10th Floor, New York, NY 10016; (888) 80-NABCO; {www.nabco.org}. This publication is also available online at {www.nabco.org/index.php/13/index.php/214.}

Free Hospital Care

Don't have money for your gall bladder surgery? What about that hospital visit you had two months ago? You might not have to pay a cent. Call the Hill-Burton Hotline.

Under this program, certain hospitals and other health care facilities provide free or low-cost medical care to patients who cannot afford to pay. You may qualify even if your income is up to double the Poverty Income Guidelines. That's $37,700 for a family of four! You can apply before or after you receive care, and even after the bill has been sent to a collection agency.

Call the Hotline to find out if you meet the eligibility requirements and to request a list of local hospitals who are participating. For more information, contact Hill-Burton Hotline, Health Resources and Services Administration, U.S. Department of Health and Human Services, Parklawn Building, 5600 Fishers Lane, Rockville, MD 20857; 800-638-0742; 800-492-0359 (in MD); 301-443-3376; {www.hrsa.gov/osp/dfcr/about/aboutdiv.htm}.

Free Food At School For Your Kids

A 1998 Tufts University study states: "Children who participate in the U.S. Department of Agriculture's School Breakfast Program were shown to have significantly higher standardized achievement test scores than eligible non-participants. Children getting school breakfasts also had significantly reduced absence and tardiness rates."

Your child can get a free breakfast at one of the 72,000 participating schools at one income level ($23,530 for a family of four) and at a reduced fee at another level ($33,485 for a family of four). Families who pay full price still get a bargain. Over 7.7 million kids participate and 6.4 million get it for free or at a reduced rate. Lunch is also available under the U.S. Department of Agriculture's National School Lunch program at 97,700 schools serving 27 million children. The same general requirements apply to both programs.

Ask your school if they participate, or contact your local School Food Service Authority in your school system. If all this fails, contact your state Department of Education. Check out the Food and Nutrition Services web page at {www.fns.usda.gov/fns}.

Free Milk

Milk at this price is available to students, no matter what the family income, at over 8,000 schools, 1,400 summer camps, and 562 non-residential child care institutions. The program is called the U.S. Department of Agriculture's **Special Milk Program** and is available to institutions that do not use the School Breakfast Program or the National School Lunch program.

Ask your school if they participate, or contact your local School Food Service Authority in your school system. If all this fails, contact your state Department of Education. If you cannot get satisfaction from these offices, contact your local office of your state or federal elected official.

Free Immunizations For Your Kids

Only 78% of children receive their full recommended vaccinations that protect them against polio, diphtheria, mumps, whooping cough, German measles, tetanus, spinal meningitis, chicken pox, and hepatitis B. An increasing number of children are exposed to diseases in day-care settings and elsewhere.

Almost any child, no matter what their income, can receive free or very low cost immunizations in their local area. Contact your county office of health listed in your telephone book, or your state Department of Health. If you have trouble, call the National Immunization Information Hotline at 800-232-2522 (English); 800-232-0233 (Spanish); {www.cdc.gov/nip}.

Low Cost Immunizations for Travelers

In order to prevent contracting diseases like yellow fever, cholera or Japanese encephalitis when traveling in other countries, the government's Center for Disease Control recommends that certain vaccines would eliminate your risk of infection. Some local Public Health offices offer these vaccines at a fraction of what you would pay at a doctor's office.

To find your local county office of health, look in your telephone book or contact your state Department of Health. For more information about disease and vaccines for travel, contact: Center for Disease Control and Prevention, National Center for Infectious Diseases, Division of Global Migration and Quarantine, 1600 Clifton Road, MS E-03, Atlanta, GA 30333; 877-394-8747; 404-639-3534; {www.cdc.gov/travel/index.htm}.

Fund Helps Foster Independence of Physically Disabled

Individuals with physical disabilities residing in Oregon may be eligible to receive financial assistance through the Blanche Fisher Foundation. The fund assists with the expense of hearing aids, eyeglasses, wheelchairs, ramps, tuition and skills training. Contact Blanche Fischer Foundation, 1509 SW Sunset Blvd., Suite 1-B, Portland, OR 97239-2676; 503-819-8205; Fax: 503-246-4941; {www.bff.org}.

How To Fight Your Doctor, Hospital, Or Insurance Company – Call The Marines

Well, not the actual Marines from the Department of Defense, dressed in fatigues and armed with high tech weapons. But you can call other government offices and advocacy groups that will do your fighting for you or give you the needed weapons to do your own fighting. Before you call a lawyer, call these free offices first:

- *State Insurance Commissioner*: will help you learn your legal rights regarding insurance.
- *State Medical Boards*: will review your complaint (including billing issues) and help resolve disputes.
    - *State HMO boards*: will review your complaint (including billing issues) and help resolve disputes.
    - *Center for Medicare Advocacy, Inc*, P.O. Box 350, Willimantic, CT 06226; 800-262-4414 (toll free in Connecticut); 860-456-7790; 202-216-0028 (Washington, DC office); {www.medicareadvocacy.org}. Attorneys, paralegals, and technical assistants provide free legal help for elderly and disabled who are unfairly denied Medicare coverage in the state of Connecticut. Legal help and other services are also available to residents outside of Connecticut for a fee.
    - *American Self-Help Group Clearinghouse*, Mental Help Net, 570 Metro Place, Dublin, OH 43017; {www.mentalhelp.net/selfhelp}: makes referrals to self-help organizations world wide and helps people interested in starting their own self help group.
    - *National Self-Help Clearinghouse*, Graduate School and University Center of the City University of New York, 365 5th Ave., Suite 3300, New York, NY 10016; 212-817-1822; {www.selfhelpweb.org}: makes referrals to self-help groups nationwide.

Free Hepatitis B Shots To Children

Oswego County Health Department offers free shots for children 18 and younger. The same with Buena-Vista County in Iowa, but people 19 and over are charged $31.75 for the shot. However, you won't be turned away if you cannot pay.

Hepatitis can cause serious liver disease, cancer and even death. About 1 in 20 people in U.S. have been infected, and over 5,000 a year die. To find out about services in your area, contact the county office of health listed in your telephone book or your state Department of Health.

Medical, Dental and Educational Expense Assistance to Children of Emergency Medical Technicians

Medical and dental assistance is available to children under the age of 18 through the Eagles Memorial Foundation, Inc. Assistance is provided for doctor, dentist and hospital bills, eyeglasses, drugs, and medical and dental devices. Educational Assistance not to exceed $6000/yr. or $30,000/4 yrs. is available through the Eagles Memorial Foundation, Inc. to individuals over the age of 18. These benefits are offered to children of members of the Fraternal Order of Eagles and the Ladies Auxiliary who die from injuries or diseases incurred while in military service; while serving as a volunteer law enforcement officer, volunteer firefighter, or volunteer emergency medical service (EMS) officer; or in the commission of their daily employment. Contact Eagles Memorial Foundation, Inc., 4710 14th St. W., Bradenton, FL 34207; 941-775-1976; Fax: 941-758-4042; {www.foe.com/memorial}.

30% of All Families Eligible For Free Health Services — Others Pay Sliding Scale

Many services provided by county governments are free and persons who don't qualify for free services are charged on a sliding scale based on income. A typical fee chart is the one below from Denton, Texas. The data is based on 1996 Federal Poverty Rates from the Bureau of the Census. Denton also states that *NO ONE WILL BE REFUSED SERVICES FOR INABILITY TO PAY*, which is typical for most counties. **REMEMBER**, if you don't qualify for free services, everyone qualifies for services on a sliding scale.

Estimated Income Limits For Free Service			
Service	Single Person	Family of 2	Family of 4
Food Vouchers and Nutritional Info (185% of poverty AND a medical or nutritional need)	$16,391	$22,089	$33,485
Prenatal Care During Pregnancy (200% of poverty)	$17,720	$23,880	$36,200
Child Medical Care (200% of poverty)	$17,720	$23,880	$36,200
Adult Health Care (150% of poverty)	$13,290	$17,910	$27,150
Dental Care (150% of poverty)	$13,290	$17,910	$27,150
HIV Counseling & Testing	No limits, $10.00 donation requested		
Sexually Transmitted Disease Clinic	No limits, $10.00 donation requested		
Tuberculosis	No limits, $4.00 for testing		
Overseas Vaccinations	No limits, $5.00 to $105.00		
Immunizations	No limits, up to $30 per family, no one refused		
Substance Abuse Screening & Referral	No limits, some fees vary based on patient income according to poverty guidelines or program requirements		

Estimate of Families Living At Poverty Levels		
% of Poverty Level	Number of Families	% of Total Families
Below 100%	7,229,000	9.6%
Below 150%	13,148,000	17.4%
Below 185%	17,629,000	23.3%
Below 200%	19,547,000	25.8%
(Poverty Data from Census Report POV04 2002 — One Person = $9,183, Two Persons = $11,756, Four Persons = $18,392, Household Income Data from Census Current Population Reports, POV 35)		

Grants and Fundraising Help For Transplant Patients

Organizations like The National Foundation for Transplants and National Transplant Assistance Fund assist patients, their families, and friends in raising significant amounts of money for the patient's transplant care when there is no public or private insurance that will cover all the costs. They also provide grants to help pay for medications required after a transplant, or money for transplant-related emergencies.

Other transplant related non-profits, like the Liver Foundation's Liver Transplant Fund, provide services and help for patients and families to raise money for an organ transplant.

- *National Foundation for Transplants*, 1102 Brookfield Rd., Suite 200, Memphis, TN 38119; 800-489-3863, 901-684-1697, Fax: 901-684-1128; {www.transplants.org}.

- *National Transplant Assistance Fund*, 3475 West Chester Pike, Suite 230, Newtown Square, PA 19073; 800-642-8399; 610-353-9684; Fax: 610-353-1616; {www.transplantfund.org}.

- *American Liver Foundation*, 75 Maiden Lane, Suite 603, New York, NY 10038; 800-GO LIVER; 212-668-1000; Fax: 212-483-8179; {www.liverfoundation.org}.

Working People With Disabilities Can Get Cheap Health Insurance

A change to the Balanced Budget Act of 1997 passed by Congress allows states to offer Medicaid to individuals who are working and who have a disability. Prior to this, states could only offer Medicaid to people with disabilities who were NOT working. The income limit goes up to $45,250 (for a family of four), and the state can charge premiums on an income-related sliding scale.

Contact your state Department of Health to identify your Medicaid office. You can contact the local office of your congressman or senator for more information on the law. You can also check out the website of The Judge David L. Bazelon Center for Mental Health Law at {www.bazelon.org}.

Free Transportation To Medical Appointments For Your Mom

Mom has to get to a doctor's visit in the middle of the day and you can't take her. Or you have a disability that may cause you to miss an appointment if someone else doesn't drive. You may be able to get free transportation and escort services provided by either your local health office or local office on aging. Some communities even provide very low cost door-to-door services for seniors to go anywhere.

If you can't find your local area agency on aging or public health office in your telephone book, contact your state Department of Aging or Health. If that fails, contact the Eldercare Locator Hotline at 1-800-677-1116. They are available to help anyone identify services for seniors.

Free Health Insurance Counseling

Free one-on-one counseling is available to seniors and, in most areas, people with disabilities, to answer questions like:

- ◆ How much insurance is too much?
- ◆ If something sounds like fraud, where can I go for help?
- ◆ What's the best Medigap insurance plan?
- ◆ Do I qualify for government health benefits?
- ◆ Should I buy long-term care insurance?

The program is called **Health Insurance Counseling and Advocacy Program (HICAP)** and is sponsored by the Centers for Medicare & Medicaid Services (formerly U.S. Health Care Financing Administration). In most states, it is usually run by the state Department on Aging or the State Insurance Commissioner's office. If that fails, contact the Eldercare Locator hotline at 1-800-677-1116. They can give you the local number.

Free Take Out Taxi For Seniors

People 60 and over who are homebound because of illness, incapacity, or disability, or who are otherwise isolated can receive hot meals delivered to their home. The program is funded in every state by the Older Americans Act. Contact your local area agency on aging or your state Department on Aging. If that fails, contact the Eldercare Locator hotline at 1-800-677-1116. They are available to help anyone identify services for seniors.

Low Cost Home Health Care

Montgomery County in Maryland provides home health care free or on a sliding scale, depending on income, through the local public health office. You don't have to be a senior to qualify. A survey by the Center for Disease Control reports that about half of all local public health agencies provide similar services. To see what is available in your area, contact your county office of health listed in your telephone book or your state Department of Health. If you cannot get satisfaction from these offices, contact your local office of your state or federal elected official.

For similar services for seniors, contact your local area agency on aging or your state Department on Aging. If that fails, contact the Eldercare Locator hotline at 1-800-677-1116. They are available to help anyone identify services for seniors.

$$$$$ Money To Buy A Van, A Talking Computer Or Rubber Door Knob Grips

People with disabilities now have a place to turn to learn everything they need to know about how the latest in technology can improve their lives. It can be a specially equipped van, a talking computer, a special kitchen or eating aid, or adaptive toys for children. Or it may be a student with learning disabilities who needs special help getting through school.

A project funded by the U.S. Department of Education, called Technical Assistance Project has established an office in each state that can provide:

▲ *Information Services*: will help you identify the special products that are available to help you cope with your disability.

▲ *Equipment Loan Program*: allows people to borrow new technology devices for a number of weeks before they purchase them.

▲ *Recycling Program*: matches up people with needs for products with people who want to sell or donate products.

▲ *Funding Information*: collects information on the various sources of funding for this equipment from public and private sources.

▲ *Loans*: many states are offering special loans to help people purchase the necessary equipment; Ohio offers low-interest loans up to $10,000, North Carolina has loans up to $15,000, and California offers loan guarantees up to $35,000.

Contact your state information operator listed in the Appendix and ask for your state Office of Social Services or Vocational Rehabilitation. They should be aware of your state Assistance Technology Office. If you have trouble locating your state office, you can contact the office that coordinates all state activities: Rehabilitation Engineering & Assistive Technology Society of North America, (RESNA), 1700 North Moore Street, Suite 1540, Arlington, VA 22209-1903; 703-524-6686; Fax: 703-524-6630; TTY: 703-524-6639; {www.resna.org}.

Easter Seals in Arizona Offers Free Computers to People With Disabilities

Washington State chapter has a free loan program, and the chapters in Missouri offer computer classes. Contact your local Easter Seals Society to see what they may offer in the way of computers and computer skills for people with disabilities. If you can't find your local office, contact: Easter Seals, 230 West Monroe Street, Suite 1800, Chicago, IL 60606; 800-221-6827; 312-726-6200; Fax: 312-726-1494; {www.easterseals.com}.

Service Organizations

Need help with child care, elderly services, substance abuse treatment? What about youth programs or disaster assistance? Many large service organizations have local offices that provide all this and more. Services vary depending upon the needs of the community, but before you fight your battles alone, contact these main offices to find out about local programs:

✦ *Catholic Charities USA*, 1731 King St., #200, Alexandria, VA 23314; 703-549-1390; Fax: 703-549-1656; {www.catholiccharitiesusa.org}.

✦ *Salvation Army*, 615 Slaters Lane, P.O. Box 269, Alexandria, VA 22313; 703-684-5500; 800-SAL-ARMY; Fax: 703-684-3478; {www.salvationarmyusa.org}.

✦ *United Way of America*, 701 N. Fairfax St., Alexandria, VA 22314; 800-UWA-2757; 703-836-7112; {http://national.unitedway.org}.

Free & Low Cost Dental Care for Kids, Seniors, and Certain Incomes

Many of the local health offices provide dental services to children and to income-eligible adults on a sliding fee scale. Contact your county office of health listed in your telephone book or your state Department of Health.

Many states have special free or discount services just for seniors. Contact your local Area Agency on Aging or your state Department on Aging. If that fails, contact the Eldercare Locator Hotline at 1-800-677-1116.

Free Care By the Best Doctors In The World

Bob Dole knew where to go when he had his cancer surgery — The National Institutes of Health (NIH). Each year, over 80,000 patients receive free medical care by some of the best doctors in the world. Medical research professionals receive millions of dollars each year to study the latest causes, cures, and treatments to various diseases or illnesses. If your health condition is being studied somewhere, you may qualify for what is called a "clinical trial" and get the treatment for free.

There are several ways to find out about ongoing clinical trials across the nation. Your first call should be to the National Institutes of Health Clinical Center. NIH is the federal government's focal point for health research. The Clinical Center is a 242-bed hospital that has facilities and services to support research at NIH. Your doctor can call the Patient Referral Line to find out if your diagnosis is being studied and to be put in contact with the primary investigator who can then tell if you meet the requirements for the study.

You can also search their website for your diagnosis and qualifying information, or search the newly established website {clinicaltrials.gov}, which contains information on approximately 12,000 clinical studies sponsored by NIH, other federal agencies, and the pharmaceutical industry. In addition, each Institute at NIH also funds research that is conducted by universities, research institutions, and others. To learn about those studies, contact the Institute that handles your diagnosis. Or conduct a CRISP (Computer Retrieval of Information on Scientific Projects) search, which is a database of research projects and programs supported by the U.S. Department of Health and Human Services.

✦ **Patient Recruitment and Public Liaison Office**, Warren Grant Magnuson Clinical Center, National Institutes of Health, Bethesda, Maryland 20892-2655; 800-411-1222; {www.cc.nih.gov}.

✦ **National Institutes of Health**, 9000 Rockville Pike, Bethesda, MD 20892-2655; 301-496-4000; {www.nih.gov}.

Free Eye Care

If you or someone you love needs eye care, but cannot afford it, the following organizations can help:

♥   For those 65 and older: *EyeCare Program*, American Academy of Ophthalmology (AAO), P.O Box 7424, San Francisco, CA 94120-7424; 415-561-8500; 800-222-3937; Fax: 415-561-8533; {www.aao.org}.

♥ For low-income families and children, applications are accepted in January with treatment following later in the year: *VISION USA*, American Optometric Association, 243 North Lindbergh Blvd., St. Louis, MO 63141; 314-991-4100; 800-766-4466; Fax: 314-991-4101; {www.aoanet.org}.

♥ *Lions Clubs International Foundation*, 300 W. 22nd St., Oak Brook, IL 60523-8842; 630-571-5466; {www.lcif.org}.

ARE YOU ELIGIBLE?

Health insurance can be quite confusing. What exactly do you qualify for?

Medicare is a health insurance program, generally for people age 65 or older who are receiving *Social Security* retirement benefits. You can also receive Medicare if you are under 65 and receive Social Security or Railroad Retirement Board disability benefits for 24 months, or if you are a kidney dialysis or kidney transplant patient.

Medicaid is a federal program administered by each state, so eligibility and benefits vary from state to state. The program is administered by a state welfare agency, and it provides health insurance to people with low income and limited assets.

To determine your eligibility, contact your state Office of Social Services. For Medicare eligibility, contact Medicare Hotline, Centers for Medicare & Medicaid Services, John F. Kennedy Federal Building, Rm. 2375, Center Station, Boston, MA 02203; 617-565-1232; 800-MEDICARE; {www.medicare.gov}.

EYE CARE HELPLINE

The *National Eye Care Project Helpline* puts callers in touch with local ophthalmologists who have volunteered to provide medical eye care at no out-of-pocket expense. Individuals must be 65 or older and not have had access to an ophthalmologist within the past three years. The emphasis of this program is to help disadvantaged people.

For more information, contact National Eye Care Project Helpline, American Academy of Ophthalmology, P.O. Box 7424, San Francisco, CA 94120-7424; 800-222-3937; Fax: 415-561-8533; {www.aao.org}.

Free Help For Cancer Families

Local chapters of the American Cancer Society sponsor a wide range of services for cancer patients and their families, including self-help groups, transportation programs, and lodging assistance for those who must travel far for treatment. To find your local chapter or for more information on cancer detection, prevention and treatment, contact American Cancer Society, 1599 Clifton Rd., NE, Atlanta, GA 30329; 800-ACS-2345; {www.cancer.org}.

Financial Assistance for Ill and Indigent Registered Nurses

Nurses House, Inc. offers short-term financial assistance to ill and indigent U.S. Registered Nurses to help meet basic living expenses. Costs of medical and educational expenses are not funded. Contact Nurses House, Inc., VMD Center for Nursing, 2113 Western Ave., Suite 2, Guilderland, NY 12084; 518-456-7858; Fax: 518-452-3760; {www.nurseshouse.org}.

Money For New Hearing Aids

You can get information on different types of hearing loss, lists of hearing professionals, and information on locating financial assistance for assistive hearing devices by calling The Better Hearing Institute, 515 King St., Suite 420, Alexandria, VA 22314; 800-EAR-WELL; 888-432-7435; 703-684-3391; Fax: 703-684-6048; {www.betterhearing.org}.

Grants Assist with Low Vision Equipment

The Pearle Vision Foundation offers grants to U.S. residents for low vision equipment. Funding is also available to non-profit organizations for vision-care assistance. Contact Pearle Vision Foundation, 2465 Joe Field Rd., Dallas, TX 75229; 972-277-6191; Fax: 972-277-6422.

Foundation Assists Individuals with Spinal Cord Injuries

The William Heiser Foundation for the Cure of Spinal Cord Injuries, Inc. provides general welfare assistance to individuals with spinal cord injuries residing in the Wantagh, New York area. Contact: The Heiser Foundation for the Cure of Spinal Cord Injuries, 3280 Sunrise Highway, Suite 65, Wantagh, NY 11793; 516-826-9747; {http://hometown.aol.com/cure4sci/index.htm}.

Discounts On Bicycle Helmets

The Department of Health in Mesa County Colorado offers discounts on bicycle helmets for children in the county. Check with your local office of health to see if there are any programs like this in your area. If not, you can start one with a free *Toolkit for Helmet Promotion Programs* from Bicycle Helmet Safety Institute, 4611 Seventh Street South, Arlington, VA 22204-1419; 703-486-0100; Fax 703-486-0100; {www.helmets.org}. This organization will also send you a free copy of *A Consumer's Guide to Bicycle Helmets*.

Free Legal Help For Living Expenses

Legal Help For Millionaires

No matter what your income, you can get the most powerful organization in the world, *your government*, to fight for you to:

1) Establish paternity;
2) Set up a court order for child support;
3) Track down a missing parent and collect your child support; and even
4) Get the courts to adjust child support orders when circumstances change.

Actually I lied. There are a few states that may charge you up to $25. So the maximum you will pay is $25. So, why hire an attorney, who may or may not know the law, and will charge you up to $200 an hour, when you can call someone who wrote the law, whose duty is to enforce it for you, and who is free?

Contact your state Child Support Enforcement Office, or contact Office of Child Support Enforcement, U.S. Department of Health and Human Services, 370 L'Enfant Promenade, SW, Washington, DC 20447; 202-401-9373; {www.acf.dhhs.gov/programs/cse/}. A state by state office locator map is available at {www.acf.dhhs.gov/programs/cse/extinf.htm}.

More Free Legal Services

You don't have to go to your neighbor's brother's cousin's kid who is an attorney, unless you want to pay for his legal advice. Uncle Sam has set up law offices all across the country to help those who cannot afford standard legal fees. It is the Legal Services Corporation's job to give legal help to low-income individuals in civil matters. These offices are staffed by over 6,400 attorneys and paralegals. Each program follows certain guidelines as to what cases it accepts and specific financial eligibility that possible clients must meet.

To learn about the program nearest you, look in the blue pages of your phone book, or contact Legal Services Corporation, 3333 K St. NW, 3rd Fl., Washington, DC 20007-3522; 202-295-1500; Fax: 202-337-6797; {www.lsc.gov}; Email: {info@lsc.gov}. A state by state program map is available at {www.lsc.gov/fundprog.htm}.

Get Rid of Neighborhood Troublemakers Without the Police, For FREE

Some states allow local community groups to get tenants or property owners thrown out of the neighborhood — under civil laws, not criminal laws — if they are involved with drugs or are a nuisance to the community. It's easier to enforce a civil law than a criminal law.

The Community Law Center in Maryland provides free legal assistance to communities in Maryland to enforce these laws. Their services are free to non-profit community groups who seek to rid their neighborhood of troublemakers.

To find out if your community has similar services, contact your state Attorney General's office. The Community Law Center can be reached at 2500 Maryland Ave., Baltimore, MD 21218; 410-366-0922; Fax: 410-366-7763; {mail@communitylaw.org}; {www.communitylaw.org/}.

10,000 Lawyers That Work For Free

If your income is less than $32,000 (for a family of 4), it's worth checking out the pro bono legal services that are available in your state. And even if your income is more, it's worth checking because some of these services have flexible requirements depending upon your situation and the problem involved. Every year tens of thousands of lawyers volunteer their services to people who need help with almost any kind of problem.

For a listing of pro bono organizations in your state, contact your state bar association listed in your state capitol. The state information operator listed in the Appendix can provide you with a number, or you can contact: American Bar Association, 321 North Clark Street, Chicago, IL 60610; 312-988-5000; Email: {service@abanet.org}. A list of services is available at their website. A state by state listing of programs is available at {www.abanet.org/legalservices/probono/directory.html}.

Help For Families Fighting For Veterans Benefits

Through low cost publications, training courses and other services, for 25 years the **National Veterans Legal Services Program (NVLSP)** has been helping veterans get their due. Current publications include: *VA Claims*, *Agent Orange*, and *Veterans Family Benefits*. NVLSP is not, except in unusual cases, available to represent individual VA claimants before a VA Regional Office or the Board of Veterans' Appeals. Contact: National Veterans Legal Services Program, 2001 S Street NW, Suite 610, Washington DC 20009; 202-265-8305, ext. 105; Fax 202-328-0063; {nvlsp@nvlsp.org}; {www.nvlsp.org}.

Free Legal Help With Family, Consumer, Housing, Income, Work, Children and Senior Citizen Issues

Legal Services Corporation is a collection of over 269 government supported local offices that provide free legal services in their area. Over 5000 attorneys and paralegals are available to individuals and families that are under certain income limits. The maximum income can be up to $26,000 for a family of four, or even more depending on certain financial obligations.

To find an office near you, contact your state information operator listed in the Appendix and ask for the Legal Services Office or contact: Legal Services Corporation, 3333 K Street NW, 3rd Floor, Washington, DC 20007-3522; 202-295-1500; Fax: 202-337-6797; {www.lsc.gov}. A state by state program map is available at {www.lsc.gov/fundprog.htm}.

FREE LAWYERS WILL FIGHT FOR YOUR RIGHTS

We've all heard of the ***American Civil Liberties Union (ACLU)***. They have over 300 offices around the country and handle close to 6,000 cases a year. The ACLU has more than 60 staff attorneys who collaborate with at least 2,000 volunteer attorneys in handling cases. They have appeared before the Supreme Court more than any other

Free Legal Assistance For Domestic Violence Problems

Seven days a week, 24 hours a day, you can call the hotline and not only get access to sources that will solve your immediate problem, but also get information and sources in your area that can explain your legal options and get you through the legal process. Contact: National Domestic Violence Hotline, P.O. Box 161810, Austin, TX 78716; 800-799-SAFE; TTY: 800-787-3224; {ndvh@ndvh.org}; {www.ndvh.org}.

organization except the U.S. Department of Justice. If you feel that your civil liberties have been violated, they may take your case. The kinds of issues they are most currently active in include: women's rights, reproductive freedom, workplace rights, AIDS, arts censorship, capital punishment, children's rights, education reform, lesbian and gay rights, immigrants' rights, national security, privacy and technology, prisoners' rights, and voting rights.

Contact the local ACLU office listed in your telephone directory or the main office website can provide you with a local contact: ACLU - American Civil Liberties Union, 125 Broad Street, 18th Floor, New York, NY 10004-2400; 212-549-2500 (NY Office); Email: {aclu@aclu.org}; {www.aclu.org/}. An online map of state affiliated offices is available online.

FREE LEGAL HELP WITH SEXUAL HARASSMENT AT WORK OR SCHOOL

Free assistance is available to women and girls who are facing sex or race discrimination, sexual harassment at work or at school, pregnancy, discrimination, or problems with family medical leave and other employment issues related specifically to women. The staff offers information and answers questions, and occasionally can draft "demand" letters, demanding that an employer or other person or organization stop doing something. In some circumstances, they can help you pursue internal grievance or administrative procedures, and in some precedent-setting cases, they will provide legal representation.

Contact: Equal Rights Advocates, 1663 Mission Street, Suite 250, San Francisco, CA 94103; 415-621-0672; Fax: 415-621-6744; Advice and Counseling Line: 800-839-4ERA; {info@equalrights.org}; {www.equalrights.org}.

Help For You Or Your Child With A Learning Or Physical Disability

The disability laws not only cover people with disabilities that everyone can see. It's also for children who aren't getting the education they need from the local school, or for the cancer patient who feels discriminated against at work. Disability Rights Education and Defense Fund, Inc. (DREDF) is a national law and policy center dedicated to protecting and advancing the civil rights of people with disabilities through legislation, litigation, advocacy, technical assistance, and education and training of attorneys, advocates, persons with disabilities, and parents of children with disabilities.

A free hotline will help you learn about your rights, help you enforce them, and will even handle some high impact legal cases. Contact: Disability Rights Education and Defense Fund, Inc., 2212 Sixth Street, Berkeley, CA 94710; 510-644-2555 V/TTY; Fax: 510-841-8645; Email: {dredf@dredf.org}; {www.dredf.org}. Washington, DC Office: 1629 K Street NW, Suite 802, Washington, D.C. 20006; 202-986-0375.

Publications on Family Income, Welfare, and Poverty

These publications help families with children gather information and find assistance to help them in their lives. Contact: Children's Defense Fund, CDF Publications, 25 E Street NW, Washington, DC 20001; 202-628-8787; Fax: 202-662-3510; Email: {cdfinfo@childrensdefense.org}; {www.childrensdefense.org}.

FREE LEGAL HELP FOR BREAST CANCER PATIENTS

If you are a breast cancer patient living in California, you maybe eligible to receive free legal assistance on issues such as:

★ Debt collection problems with hospital and doctor bills.
★ Barriers to access to diagnosis and treatment.
★ Negotiations with insurance carriers for coverage and payment options.
★ Housing discrimination.
★ Employment discrimination.
★ Temporary guardianships or modification of custody arrangements.

If you don't live in California, ask them if they are aware of similar services in your area. Contact: Breast Cancer Legal Project, California Women's Law Center, 3460 Wilshire Blvd., Suite 1102, Los Angeles, CA 90010; 213-637-9900; Fax: 213-637-9909; {cwlc@cwlc.org}; {www.cwlc.org/}.

FREE WOMEN'S LAW CENTERS

Rich or poor, women in **Maryland** can get free telephone help in filling out the forms to represent themselves in family court matters that are simple and uncontested. The hotline number is *800-845-8550*. Or women can call the hotline for information on family law issues, such as, how to obtain a separation, child custody, child support, and how to escape domestic violence. Contact: The Women's Law Center of Maryland, Inc., 305 West Chesapeake Ave., Suite 201, Towson, MD 21204; 410-321-8761; Fax: 410-321-0462; {admin@wlcmd.org}; {www.wlcmd.org}.

Women in the state of **Washington** can call a free legal *Information and Referral line* that is staffed with attorneys and paralegals to respond to questions about family law or employment. They also can receive legal rights publications including *Sexual Harassment in Employment and Education*; *Family Law in Washington State: Your Rights and Responsibilities*; and *Grandparents Raising Grandchildren; A Legal Guide for Washington State*. You can also attend free legal workshops, or receive help in filling out legal forms, and free legal consultations in domestic violence cases. Contact: Northwest Women's Law Center, 3161 Elliott Ave., Suite 101, Seattle, WA 98121; 206-682-9552; Fax: 206-682-9556; Legal Information and Referral: 206-621-7691; {nwwlc@nwwlc.org}; {www.nwwlc.org}.

Free Legal Help To Fight Your Union At Work

If you feel your rights have been violated by compulsory unionism or you simply have a question about your Right to Work, legal experts are available for free to help answer your questions. Contact: The National Right to Work Legal Defense Foundation, 8001 Braddock Rd., Springfield, VA 22160; 800-336-3600; {www.nrtw.org}.

Free Help With Welfare Rights

Over 157 local organizations around the country fight for the rights of low-income people on welfare. These organizations can be a good place to turn to ensure that you are getting the proper benefits, and for knowing your rights in dealing with the bureaucracy.

You can contact your local social services agency to locate an office near you or the website for the Welfare Law Center that contains a directory of all the organizations. Contact: Welfare Law Center, 275 Seventh Ave., Suite 1205, New York, NY 10001; 212-633-6967; {dirk@welfarelaw.org}; {www.lincproject.org/}.

Free Legal Help To Fight For Your Home Schooling Rights

The Home School Legal Defense Association (HSLDA) provides legal help for members on home schooling issues. Families receive legal consultation by letter and phone, and representation for negotiations with local officials, and court proceedings.

HSLDA also takes the offensive, filing actions to protect members against government intrusion and to establish legal precedent. On occasion, HSLDA will handle precedent-setting cases for non-members, as well. Contact: HSLDA, P.O. Box 3000, Purcellville, VA 20134-9000; 540-338-5600; Fax: 540-338-2733; {info@hslda.org}; {www.hslda.org}. A state by state info map is available at {www.hslda.org/hs/state/default.asp}.

Free Legal Rights For Women's Issues

The National Organization for Women Legal Defense and Education Fund (NOW LDEF, www.nowldef.org) has a hotline that provides free information and referrals on women's issues including reproductive rights, violence against women, economic justice, and gender equity in education. They also provide low-cost legal guides, some of which are available free on the Internet, on the following topics:

➡ *A Guide to Court Watching in Domestic Violence and Sexual Assault Cases*
➡ *Divorce: A Guide for Women*
➡ *Domestic Violence and Child Custody*
➡ *Employment Sexual Harassment & Discrimination*
➡ *Incest and Child Sexual Abuse*
➡ *Pregnancy & Parental Leave*
➡ *Sexual Harassment in Housing*
➡ *Sexual Harassment in the Schools*
➡ *Sexual Harassment in the Schools: A Blueprint for Action* (Spanish)
➡ *Stalking*
➡ *Violence Against Women*
➡ *How to Find a Lawyer*

Contact: NOW LDEF, 395 Hudson Street, New York, NY 10014; 212-925-6635; Fax: 212-226-1066; email your question to {policy@nowldef.org}; {www.nowldef.org}.

Free Consulting Services In Sex Discrimination Law Suits

If, as a woman, you feel discriminated against in higher education, the Legal Advocacy Fund (LAF) of the American Association of University Women (AAUW) may be able to help by providing financial support for sex discrimination lawsuits. LAF organizes a network of volunteer attorneys and social scientists who consult with women on legal strategy, informational resources, and the strength of current or potential lawsuits.

To find out if you're eligible, please contact: AAUW Legal Advocacy Fund, Dept. LAF.INT., American Association of University Women, 1111 16th St., NW, Washington, DC 20036; 800-326-AAUW; Fax: 202-872-1425; TDD: 202-785-7777; {info@aauw.org}; {www.aauw.org}.

Legal Assistance for Overseas Teachers

Free legal aid is available for teachers employed in U.S. Department of Defense schools overseas and are members of the *Federal Education Association (FEA)*. The FEA legal staff conducts arbitration and other legal actions to ensure the rights and benefits of teachers. Contact: Federal Education Association, 1201 16th St. NW, Suite 117, Washington, DC 20036; 202-822-7850; Fax: 202-822-7867; (fea@feaonline.org); {www.feaonline.org}.

Free Legal Help For Pregnant Teens Discriminated In Honors Society

Feminists for Life of America, along with the ACLU, got a federal court to rule that two high school seniors, whose school denied them National Honor Society membership because they became pregnant and chose to give birth, must be admitted into the society. For free legal information on these kinds of issues, contact Feminists for Life of America, 733 15th St. NW, Suite 1100, Washington, DC 20005; 202-737-FFLA; {info@feministsforlife.org}; {www.feministsforlife.org}.

Free Legal Help On Civil Liberties and Rights

The Rutherford Institute defends people who have been denied civil and human rights without charging them for such services. The issues they cover include civil liberties, religious freedom, parental rights, and sexual harassment. You may remember them from their involvement in the Paula Jones case. If you need legal help, contact The Rutherford Institute, Legal Department, P.O. Box 7482, Charlottesville, VA 22906; 434-978-3888; Fax: 434-978-1789; {staff@rutherford.org}; {www.rutherford.org}. A help request form is available at {www.rutherford.org/help_now/online_help_request_form.asp}.

Free Legal Help for Lesbians, Gay Men and People With HIV/AIDS

Lambda carries out legal work on issues such as discrimination in employment, housing, public accommodations, and the military; HIV/AIDS-related discrimination and public policy issues; parenting and relationship issues; equal marriage rights; equal employment and domestic partnership benefits; "sodomy" law challenges; immigration issues; anti-gay initiatives; and free speech and equal protection rights. If you are seeking assistance with a legal matter, contact one of the offices listed below. They can guide you to a solution or help you directly:

National Headquarters Lambda
120 Wall Street, Suite 1500
New York, NY 10005-3904
212-809-8585
Fax: 212-809-0055

Western Regional Office
3325 Wilshire Boulevard, Suite 1300
Los Angeles, CA 90010-1729
213-382-7600
Fax: 213-351-6050

Midwest Regional Office
11 East Adams, Suite 1008
Chicago, IL 60603-6303

312-663-4413
Fax: 312-663-4307

South Central Regional Office
3500 Oak Lawn Avenue, Suite 500
Dallas, TX 75219-6722
214-219-8585
Fax: 214-219-4455

Southern Regional Office
1447 Peachtree Street, NE, Suite 1004
Atlanta, GA 30309-3027
404-897-1880
Fax: 404-897-1884

Lambda's website is {www.lambdalegal.org}.

Paralegals Offer Legal Work at 75% Discount

The only things a paralegal can't do that a lawyer can, is give legal advice and represent you in court. That means they can file uncontested divorce papers, family court petitions, wills and probate, power of attorney, bankruptcy, incorporation, etc.

There are states where paralegals can represent clients in cases like those involving evictions or government agencies. And if you are seeking a legal opinion from an attorney, you may want to get a paralegal to research the law for you, so that you can make your own decisions.

Remember 50% of all lawyers lose their cases in court. So why pay $200 an hour for a lawyer, when you can get a lot of the same services done for less than $50 an hour. Paralegals are in the yellow pages and you can contact your state or local paralegal association by contacting the national association that can give you a local contact. The National Federation of Paralegal Associations maintains an online research database with links to information about federal, state and local laws and updates on legal issues at {www.paralegals.org/LegalResources/home.html}. For more information, contact National Federation of Paralegal Associations, 2517 Eastlake Ave. E, Ste. 200, Seattle, Washington 98102; 206-652-4120; Fax: 206-652-4122; {info@paralegals.org}; {www.paralegals.org}.

FREE HELP COLLECTING CHILD SUPPORT

An association of concerned parents helps others learn about their rights and the remedies available for collecting what is due to them. They can show you that you don't need to use a professional collection agency, and they will even contact officials on your behalf. Association for Children for Enforcement and Support (ACES) membership is based on your income: $5 for income of $10,000 a year; $15 for income of $10,000- $20,000; $25 for income over $20,000. ACES waives dues upon request for special circumstances. They can also track down absent and non-paying parents using a name and address, property and business, or social security number search. The fee is $5 per search.

Contact: Association for Children for Enforcement of Support (ACES), PO Box 7842, Fredericksburg, VA 22404-7842; 800-738-ACES; Fax: 800-739-2237; {ACES@Childsupport-ACES.org}; {www.childsupport-aces.org}.

FREE LEGAL LATINO HELP

The Mexican American Legal Defense and Educational Fund (MALDEF) is a national nonprofit organization whose mission is to protect and promote the civil rights of the more than 29 million Latinos living in the United States in the areas of education, employment, political access, and more. They take cases to court and provide other legal help for the Latino community. Contact: MALDEF, 634 South Spring St., Los Angeles, CA 90014; 213-629-2512; Fax: 213-629-0266; {www.maldef.org}.

Fight Your Bank, Credit Card Company, Etc.

Finding the right bank, savings and loan, or credit union means figuring out your own needs first. How much money can you keep on deposit and how many checks will you write? Examine your future loans and savings needs, as well as look at the convenience of the financial institution, its service charges, fees, and deposit and loan interest rates. You can contact one of the following offices to learn more. These offices will also help you if you think the bank is messing with your money.

National Banks (banks that have the word "National" in their names or the intitals "N.A." after their names)
   Comptroller of the Currency
   U. S. Department of the Treasury
   Customer Assistance Group
   1301 McKinney St., Suite 3450
   Houston, TX 77010-9050
   800-613-6743
   {www.occ.treas.gov}

FDIC-Insured Banks
   Office of Consumer Affairs
   Federal Deposit Insurance Corporation
   550 17th St., NW, Room F-130
   Washington, DC 20429-9990
   202-736-0000
   877-275-3342
   {www.fdic.gov}

Savings and Loans
   Office of Thrift Supervision
   U.S. Department of Treasury
   1700 G St., NW
   Washington, DC 20552
   202-906-6000
   800-842-6929
   {www.ots.treas.gov}

State Banks
   Contact your State Government Banking
   Commissioner located in your state capital (look
   in the blue pages of your phone book or contact
   your state capitol operator).

Housing Discrimination

Buying your first home is a very exciting time. But for many, house shopping is more than an eye opening experience. Some people are not shown houses in particular neighborhoods or are denied a home because of their sex, race, or living arrangement. If you feel you have been treated unfairly, contact Office of Fair Housing and Equal Opportunity, U.S. Department of Housing and Urban Development, 451 7th St., SW, Room 5204, Washington, DC 20410; 202-708-1112; 800-669-9777; {www.hud.gov}. A complaint and/or assistance request can be registered online at: {www.hud.gov/complaints/housediscrim.cfm}.

Discrimination Because You're A Woman, Pregnant, Person of Color, etc.

There's no need to take harassment or bullying on the job. Here is your chance to fight back. If you believe you have been discriminated against by an employer, labor union, or employment agency when applying for a job or while on the job because of race, color, sex, religion, national origin, age, or disability, you may file a charge with the Equal Employment Opportunity Commission (EEOC). For more information, contact U.S. Equal Employment Opportunity Commission, 1400 L St., NW, Washington, DC 20005; 202-275-6365; 800-669-4000; {www.eeoc.gov}. A state by state list of EEOC field offices is available online at {www.eeoc.gov/offices.html}.

Lawyers, Accountants, Pharmacists, Doctors, Real Estate Agents, and Other Professionals

Lawyer over-charging you? Do you feel you have been mistreated by your doctor?

These issues and more are handled by the agency or board that licenses that particular profession. Whether it is your accountant, real estate agent, doctor, dentist, or other professional, you can contact the licensing board directly to file a grievance. These boards will then help you to resolve the problem. To locate the correct board usually located in your state capital, contact your state operator.

Retailers, Mail Order Companies, Auto Dealers, Contractors, Etc.

You go to a store to get the best price on the gift for Uncle George, only to learn that the store is out of stock despite the product being advertised in the paper. Did the salesman try to get you to buy a higher priced item? You could be the victim of the old bait and switch scam. Is the paint peeling off of the new toy doll you bought your daughter? Problems dealing with your car dealership or car repair shop? (This is the number one complaint heard.) What about the contractor that has yet to finish the job?

There are ways to deal with all these problems and get them resolved to your satisfaction. You just need to pull in the big guns. Attorney General's Offices have Consumer Protection Offices, and many also have separate offices that handle only car complaints. They will take your complaint and try to help you get the satisfaction you deserve. For other problems contact:

- *Defective Products* — contact US Consumer Product Safety Commission, 4330 East-West Highway, Bethesda, MD 20814-4408; 800-638-2772; Fax: 301-504-0124; {www.cpsc.gov}. There is an online complaint/report form available at: {www.cpsc.gov/incident.html}.
- *Contractor or Licensed Professional Problems* — contact the state Licensing Board for the profession located in your state capitol. You can contact the state operator for assistance in finding the office.
- *Mail Order Problems* — contact the U.S. Postal Service, Public Affairs Branch, 475 L'Enfant Plaza, SW, Room 3140, Washington, DC 20260; 202-268-5400; {www.usps.com}.
- *Fraud Issues* — contact Federal Trade Commission, 600 Pennsylvania Avenue, NW CRC-240, Washington, DC 20580; 202-326-2222, 877-FTC-HELP; {www.ftc.gov}.

Where to Get Help to Stop Sexual Harassment

Call **"9 to 5"** if you experience any of the following at work:

- ➡ Suggestive comments about your appearance
- ➡ Unwanted touching or other physical contact
- ➡ Unwanted sexual jokes or comments
- ➡ Sexual advances

Sexual harassment is not only offensive, it's against the law. It is illegal even if the harasser is not your boss, even if he is not threatening that you will lose your job if you don't go along. 9to5's **toll free job problem hotline** and trained job counselors give information and support to thousands of working women.

If you decide to pursue a legal remedy, contact your state discrimination agency or the federal Equal Employment Opportunity Commission (look in your phone book for the field office closest to you). The federal agency covers workplaces of 15 or more. State law covers workplaces with fewer employees.

Contact: 9to5, National Association of Working Women, 152 W. Wisconsin Ave., Suite 408, Milwaukee, WI 53203 800-522-0925; 414-274-0925; {hotline9to5@igc.org}; {www.9to5.org}. A list of local chapters is available at: {www.9to5.org/locals}.

HOW AN ABUSER CAN DISCOVER YOUR INTERNET ACTIVITIES
(And what you can do about it)

The *American Bar Association's (ABA) Commission on Domestic Violence* has issued a warning concerning possible threats to you if an abuser has access to your e-mail account and thus may be able to read your incoming and outgoing mail. If you believe your account is secure, make sure you choose a password he or she will not be able to guess. If an abuser sends you threatening or harassing e-mail messages, they may be printed and saved as evidence of this abuse. Additionally, the messages may constitute a federal offense.

For more information on this issue, contact your local United States Attorney's Office. For more information about what you can do, and the efforts of the ABA's Commission on Domestic Violence, please contact American Bar Association Commission on Domestic Violence, 740 15th Street, NW, 9th Floor, Washington, DC 20005-1019; 202-662-1737; Fax: 202-662-1594, {cdv@staff.abanet.org}; {www.abanet.org}.

Free Legal Help If Your Child Is Suspended or Expelled From School

"Zero Tolerance" and other school system disciplinary practices can place your child's education in jeopardy if you are not aware of your rights. Your first meeting with the principal on such matters can actually serve as a trial for your child's future.

The School House Legal Services of Baltimore, Maryland provides free attorneys and paralegals to represent Maryland families in these matters. Maryland has an income limit for representation that is about $30,000 for a family of four, but information about the process is free.

If you don't live in Maryland, contact your local Legal Services Office or your State Department of Education for more information and help. School House Legal Services can be reached at Maryland Disability Law Center, The Walbert Building, 4th Floor, 1800 N. Charles St., Baltimore, MD 21201; 410-727-6352; 800-233-7201; Fax: 410-727-6389; {www.mdlcbalto.org/}.

Emergency Shelter, Housing & Counseling For Violence Victims

If violence is ripping your life apart, you have nowhere to go, and you do not know how to reclaim your life, the YWCA, the nation's leading provider of shelter and services to women and their families can help you! In the United States, more than 650,000 people come to the YWCA each year for services and support to overcome violence. For more information about the services offered in your state, contact your local YWCA.

The YWCA takes a holistic approach to helping women escape, recover from and prevent violence in their lives and the lives of their families. Many local YWCAs offer programs and services including emergency shelter for women and children, transitional housing, support to victims of rape and sexual assault, individual and group counseling, peer support, self-defense training, programs for batterers and legal advocacy.

Contact: YWCA of the U.S.A., 1015 18th St., NW, Ste. 1100, Washington, DC 20036, 202-467-0801; Fax: 202-467-0802; 800-YWCA-US1 {webdiva@ywca.org}; {www.ywca.org}. National Domestic Violence Hotline 800-799-SAFE; hearing impaired 800-787-3224. A locator for local YWCA's is available at {www.ywca.org/html/B6.asp}.

LAWYER'S REFERRAL SERVICE

The *American Bar Association's* lawyer referral service is designed to assist you in finding the appropriate service-provider to help you solve your legal problem. There are two steps to this process: first, helping you determine whether you need to see a lawyer, and second, referring you to a lawyer who handles your type of case or to an appropriate community or governmental agency if that will be of more help to you. Lawyer referral can also provide you with information on procedures in the courts and legal system in your community.

When you contact lawyer referral, be prepared to briefly describe your situation so that the consultant can determine what kind of help you need. Lawyer Referral does not offer legal advice or free legal services. If you are referred to an attorney, you are entitled to a half-hour initial consultation at no charge, or for a nominal fee that goes to fund the lawyer referral service's operation. If additional legal services are required, you may choose to hire the lawyer. It is important to discuss legal fees and costs with the lawyer. We strongly recommend that you and the lawyer sign a written fee agreement, so that there is no question about what services the lawyer will perform, and what those services will cost you.

Contact your state Bar Association listed in your state capital or The American Bar Association, 750 N. Lake Shore Dr., Chicago, IL 60611; 312-988-5000; {askaba@abanet.org}; {www.abanet.org}.

WHEN ALL ELSE FAILS

People forget that they can turn to their representative or senators for help resolving a complaint. You vote these people into office, and most of them want to stay there. They know that if they can help you, then you and your family will vote for them in each and every election.

Their offices have case managers whose job is to cut the red-tape and push your case through quickly. Look in your phone book for their local office or you can call U.S. House of Representatives, Washington, DC 20515; 202-224-3121; TTY: 202-225-1904; {www.house.gov}; or U.S. Senate, Washington, DC 20510; 202-224-3121; {www.senate.gov}. Representatives can be located online by zip code and contacted via email at {www.house.gov/writerep/}. US Senate: Senators can be located by state online and contacted via email at {www.senate.gov/contacting/index.cfm}.

HELP FOR INVENTORS
Patents, Trademarks, and Copyrights

Most inventors realize that it's vitally important to protect their idea by copyrighting it and obtaining the necessary patents and copyrights, but did you know that it's also important to look around for loans and other grants to support your business while working on your invention? If you want an idea to become an actual product, you have to invest an awful lot of your time into its research, and not just on a part time basis. Loans and grants programs for inventors help you do just that. For example, Hawaii offers low cost loans to inventors, as do other states around the country. First, let's talk about getting the necessary information concerning trademark and patent procedures.

Patent and Trademark Office

United States patent and trademark laws are administered by the Patent and Trademark Office (PTO). States also have trade secret statutes, which generally state that if you guard your trade secret with a reasonable amount of care, you will protect your rights associated with that secret. The PTO examines patent and trademark applications, grants protection for qualified inventions, and registers trademarks. It also collects, assembles, and disseminates the technological information patent grants. The PTO maintains a collection of almost 6 million United States patents issued to date, several million foreign patents, and more than 2.2 million trademarks, together with supporting documentation. Here's how to find out what you need to do to patent your idea.

What a Great Idea

To help you get started with patenting your invention, the Patent and Trademark Offices will send you a free booklet upon request called General Information Concerning Patents. There are three legal elements involved in the process of invention: the conception of the idea, diligence in working it out, and reducing it to practice - i.e., getting a finished product that actually works. If you have a great idea you think might work, but you need time to develop it further before it is ready to be patented, what should you do? For answers to general questions on patent examining policies and procedures, contact the Patent Assistance Center at 800-PTO-9199 or 703-308-HELP; TTY: 703-305-7785; Email: usptoinfo@uspto.gov. They will not answer legal questions or opinions. Applications, forms, and part or all of pamphlets are at their website; {www.uspto.gov}. To order them through the mail write to:

Superintendent of Documents
U.S. Government Printing Office   Toll-Free 866-512-1800
P.O. Box 371954   202-512-1800
Pittsburgh, PA 15250-7954   Fax: 202-512-2250
www.gpoaccess.gov/index.html

You can also order them online from {http://bookstore.gpo.gov}.

What is a Patent

A patent is a grant of a property right to the inventor for an invention. It lasts for 20 years from the date that the application is filed. United States patent grants are effective within the US, its territories and its possessions. By the language of the grant it is "the right to exclude others from making, using, offering for sale, or selling" the invention in the US or "importing" the invention into the US. It is not the right of the inventor to do so himself that is granted. It is personal property and can be sold or mortgaged, bequeathed or transferred and that person then has the same rights as the original grantee.

What Can Be Patented

A patent can be received for an invention or discovery of any new and useful process, machine, manufacture, or composition of matter, or any new and useful improvement to the original. A design patent is the invention of any new and non-obvious ornamental design for an article of manufacture. Its appearance is protected, not its structural or functional features. A plant patent is the invention or discovery and asexual reproduction of any distinct and new variety of plant. This includes cultivated sports, mutants, hybrids, and newly found seedlings, other than a tuber-propagated plant or a plant found in an uncultivated state. Physical phenomena, abstract ideas, and laws of nature can not be patented. There must be a complete description and not just an idea or suggestion of a subject. It must also do what it claims to do; it must work.

> **A patent can be received for an invention or discovery of any new and useful process.**

If an invention has been described in a publication anywhere in the world, or has been used publicly, or put up for sale, a patent must be applied for before one year passes, or the right to a patent is lost.

Who May Apply

There are only a few situations where a person other than the inventor may apply for a patent application.
- a representative if the inventor has died
- a guardian if the inventor is insane
- a joint inventor or a person that has ownership interest if the inventor refuses to apply or can not be found

If two or more persons are the inventors, they may file jointly. However, someone who contributed only financially, is not a joint inventor and cannot be included on the application.

Non-Provisional Application

The application must include:
1) a written document consisting of the specifications of the invention, and an oath or declaration
2) a drawing where it is necessary
3) the filing fee.

It must be in English, legible and written on only one side of white paper with a typewriter or its equivalent. The applicant will be notified if all the requirements are not met. The date that the completed application is filed will then become the filing date. Specifications must include a written description of the invention and the method and process of how it was made and is to be used. It must be in clear, concise, and exact terms to allow any skilled person related to the area of the invention to make and use the same discovery. The oath or declaration is a statement made by the inventor that he/she is the original and first inventor of the subject matter, as well as various other statements, made in front of a notary. The filing fee, excluding design and plant inventions, is a basic fee and additional fees. The basic fee covers 20 claims, including not more than 3 in independent form. There is an additional fee for each claim over 20, whether independent or dependent. The filing fees are cut in half for applicants that file a verified statement claiming small entity status; independent inventor, small business or non-profit. The drawing must show every feature of the invention specified in the claim. Generally, photographs are not accepted. Applications have legal requirements and must be followed precisely.

Provisional Application

These applications create an early effective filing date and the term "Patent Pending" can be applied to the invention. There must be a written description of the invention, any necessary drawings and the name of the inventor(s). Claims and oath or declarations are not required. Also needed, is a cover sheet that states it is a provisional application and a filing fee. The filing date is the date that the PTO receives the application. This type of application can not be filed for design inventions. A non-provisional application must be filed within 12 months or else it will be discarded.

Protect Your Idea for $10

You can file a Disclosure Document with the Patent and Trademark Office, and they will keep it in confidence as evidence of the date of conception of the invention or idea.

Disclosure Document
Commissioner for Patents
Mail Stop DD
P.O. Box 1450
Alexandria, VA 22313-1450

800-786-9199
www.uspto.gov/web/offices/pac/disdo.html   703-308-HELP (4357)

Send an 8 1/2 x 11" drawing, a copy, signed disclosure, SASE, and a check or money order for $10 to file. Upon request, the above office will also send you a free brochure on Disclosure Documents.

This is the best way to keep the idea you are working on completely secret and yet document the date you conceived the idea. You can file the Disclosure Document at any time after the idea is conceived, but the value of it will depend on how much information you put into it - so put as much detail into this statement as you can.

The Purpose of Documenting The Date of Conception

If someone else should try to patent your idea, filing a Disclosure Document shows that you thought of it first, although filing this statement does not legally protect your invention. Documentation of the conception date gives you time to patent your invention, and is invaluable if you need to prove when you thought of your idea if a dispute should arise. (Note that filing a Disclosure Document gives you limited defensive legal protection only if you follow it up with a patent in two years. Unlike a patent, it cannot be used offensively, to stop someone else from patenting the same idea.) When you go to file for a patent, if you and a competitor get into a dispute as to who was the first to invent it, the Patent and Trademark Office (PTO) will hold an Interference Proceeding. If you thought of the idea first, your Disclosure Document will go a long way towards establishing that you were the first inventor and should therefore receive the patent for it.

Examining the Application

They look to see that the application follows the legal requirements and also that the invention is new, useful and non-obvious and meets all requirements. It is not unusual for some, or all, of the claims to be rejected on the first examination. Few are accepted as filed. The applicant will be notified in writing of any errors found. Then the inventor must request reconsideration, specifically pointing out and addressing any errors found and amend any claims that need to be revised. The second examination will generally be made final. Patents are granted in about every 2 out of 3 applications that are filed.

Patent Electronic Business Center

This is the center where you can do business electronically with the USPTO. In order to check the status of your patent application and also find general patent information, you can access the Patent Application Information Retrieval (PAIR). You will also be able to search for specific patents or applications by their number. The Electronic Filing System (EFS) accepts electronically filed applications, but you must have a digital certification and meet other requirements first. This program is only open to select number of people at this time because it is in the beginning stages of operation. Contact the office to see if you may participate!

Research Resources That Can Help You Turn Your Idea Into Reality

While diligently working out the details of your invention you can use the extensive resources of over 190,000 scientific and technical journals, articles, and books at the Scientific and Technical Information Center in Arlington, VA.

Facilitating public access to the more than 25 million cross-referenced United States patents is the job of PTO's Technology Assessment and Forecast Program (TAF); 703-306-2600. It has a master database which covers all United States patents, and searches are available free. A TAF search will not result in an in-depth patent search. (More on that, and how to find classifications in the Conducting Your Own Patent Search section below.) TAF extracts information from its database and makes it available in a variety of formats, including publications, custom patent reports, and statistical reports. The purpose of most of the reports generated by a TAF search is to reveal statistical information.

Copies of the specifications and drawings of all patents are available from PTO. Design patents and trademark copies are $3 each. Plant patents in color are $6 each. To make a request, you must have the patent number. For copies, contact:

Office of Public Records (OPR)   800-972-6382
1213 Jefferson Davis Hwy., Rm. 300   703-308-9726
Arlington, VA 22202   Fax: 703-308-7048
Email: dsd@uspto.gov

Mail Stop Patent Application
Commissioner for Patents
P.O. Box 1450
Alexandria, VA 22313-1450   703-308-4357

Conducting Your Own Patent Search

Before investing too much time and money on patenting your idea, you will want to see if anyone has already patented it. You may conduct the search yourself on the PTO website at {www.uspto.gov} or hire someone to do it for you. If you wish to hire a professional to do your patent search, consult the local yellow pages or again, search the PTO website for a roster of patent attorneys. Even if your search is not as in-depth as that of a patent attorney or a patent agent, you may still find the information that you need. You may also conduct your patent search at the Patent and Trademark Office Search Room.

Patent and Trademark Office (PTO)
Patent and Trademark Search Room
Crystal Plaza 3, Lobby Level
2021 S. Clark Pl.
Arlington, VA 22202   703-305-4463

For information about the Patent and Trademark Depository Library, contact the office listed below.

Patent and Trademark Depository Library (PTDL)
U.S. Patent and Trademark Office
Crystal Plaza 3, Suite 481   703-308-5558
Washington, DC 20231   Fax: 703-306-2662

You may also conduct your patent search at any of the 86 Patent Depository Libraries (PDLs) throughout the country as listed below.

Patent and Trademark Depository Libraries

Alabama
Ralph Brown Draughon Library, Auburn University, 231 Mell Street, Auburn, AL 36849; 334-844-1738; {www.lib.auburn.edu}.

Birmingham Public Library, 2100 Park Place, Birmingham, AL 35203; 205-226-3620; {www.bplonline.org}.

Alaska
Z.J. Loussac Public Library, 3600 Denali Street, Anchorage, AK 99503-6093; 907-343-2975; {www.muni.org/library1/index.cfm}.

Arkansas
Arkansas State Library, One Capitol Mall, Little Rock, AR 72201; 501-682-2053; Fax: 501-682-1529; {www.asl.lib.ar.us/patents/index.html}.

California
Los Angeles Public Library, 630 West Fifth Street, Los Angeles, CA 90071; 213-228-7200; Fax: 213-228-7209; {www.lapl.org/central/science.html}.

California State Library, Library & Courts Building I, 914 Capitol Mall, Rm. 220, Sacramento, CA 95814; 916-654-0174; {www.library.ca.gov/index.cfm}.

San Diego Public Library, 820 E Street, San Diego, CA 92101-6478; 619-236-5813; {www.sandiego.gov/public-library/index.shtml}.

San Francisco Public Library, 100 Larkin Street, San Francisco, CA 94102; 415-557-4400; {http://sfpl.lib.ca.us}.

Sunnyvale Center for Innovation, Invention & Ideas, 665 West Olive Avenue, Sunnyvale, CA 94086; 408-730-7300; Fax: 408-735-8762; {www.sci3.com}.

Colorado
Denver Public Library, 10 West 14th Avenue Parkway, Denver, CO 80204; 720-865-1111; {www.denver.lib.co.us/index.html}

Connecticut
Hartford Public Library, 500 Main Street, Hartford, CT 06103; 860-695-6300; {www.hartfordpl.lib.ct.us}.

Delaware
University of Delaware Library, 181 South College Avenue, Newark, DE 19717-5267; 302-831-2965; {www.lib.udel.edu}.

District of Columbia
Founders Library, Howard University, 500 Howard Place, NW, Washington, DC 20059; 202-806-7234; {www.howard.edu/library}.

Florida
Broward County Main Library, 100 South Andrews Avenue, Fort Lauderdale, FL 33301; 954-357-7444; {www.browardlibrary.org}.

Miami-Dade Public Library, 101 West Flagler Street, Miami, FL 33130; 305-375-2665; {www.mdpls.org}.

University of Central Florida Libraries, P.O. Box 162666, 4000 Central Florida Blvd., Orlando, FL 32816; 407-823-2562; {http://library.ucf.edu/GovDocs/PAT_TRAD.htm}.

Tampa Campus Library, 4202 East Fowler Avenue, Tampa, FL 33620-5400; 813-974-2729; {www.lib.usf.edu/tampa/govdocs}.

Georgia
Library and Information Center, Georgia Institute of Technology, 2nd Floor-East Building, Atlanta, GA 30332; 404-894-4530; {www.library.gatech.edu/patents}.

Hawaii
Hawaii State Library, 478 South King Street, 2nd Floor, Honolulu, HI 96813-2994; 808-586-3477; {www.state.hi.us/libraries/feddocs}

Idaho
University of Idaho Library, P.O. Box 442350, Moscow, ID 83844-2350; 208-885-6584; {www.lib.uidaho.edu}

Illinois
Chicago Public Library, 400 South State St. Chicago, IL 60605; 312-747-4450; {www.chipublib.org/008 subject/009scitech/patents.html}

Illinois State Library, 300 South 2nd Street, Springfield, IL 62701-1796; 217-785-5659; {www.cyberdriveillinois.com/departments/library/home.html}

Indiana
Indianapolis-Marion County Public Library, 202 N. Alabama, Indianapolis, IN 46204; 317-269-1741; {www.imcpl.lib.in.us/bst_patents.htm}.

Circulation Engineering Library, Purdue University, Potter Engineering Center, Engineering Library, 504 W. State St., W. Lafayette, IN 47907; 765-494-2869; {www.lib.purdue.edu/engr/index.html}.

Iowa
State Library of Iowa, 1112 East Grand Avenue, Des Moines, IA 50319; 515-281-4105; {www.silo.lib.ia.us}.

Kansas
Ablah Library, Wichita State University, 1845 Fairmount, Wichita, KS 67260-0068; 316-978-3622; 800-572-8368; {http://library.wichita.edu/govdoc/patents.html}.

Kentucky
Louisville Free Public Library, 301 York Street, Louisville, KY 40203; 502-574-1611; {http://lfpl.org/govdoc.htm}.

Louisiana
Troy H. Middleton Library, Louisiana State University, Baton Rouge, LA 70803; 225-578-5652; {www.lib.lsu.edu/index.html}.

Maine
University of Maine, 5729 Raymond H. Fogler Library, Orono, ME 04469-5729; 207-581-1678; {http://library.umaine.edu/patents/default.htm}.

Maryland
Engineering and Physical Sciences Library, University of Maryland, College Park, MD 20742-7011; 301-405-9152; {www.lib.umd.edu/ENGIN/Kworking/patents.html}.

Massachusetts
Physical Sciences and Engineering Library, Lederle Graduate Research Center, Room 273, University of Massachusetts, Amherst, 740 North Pleasant St., Amherst, MA 01003-4630; 413-545-1370; {www.library.umass.edu/subject/patents}.

Boston Public Library, 700 Boylston St., Copley Sq., Boston, MA 02116; 617-536-5400, ext. 2226; {www. bpl.org/research/govdocs/patent_trademark.htm}.

Michigan
Art, Architecture & Engineering Library, University of Michigan, 2281 Bonisteel Boulevard, Ann Arbor, MI 48109-2094; 734-647-5735; {www.lib.umich.edu/aael}.

Abigail S. Timme Library, Ferris State University, 1010 Campus Drive, Big Rapids, MI 49307-2279; 231-591-3500; {www.ferris.edu/library}.

Great Lakes Patent and Trademark Center, Detroit Public Library, 5201 Woodward Avenue, Detroit, MI 48202; 313-833-3379, 800-547-0619; {www.detroit.lib.mi.us/glptc}.

Minnesota
Minneapolis Public Library, 250 Marquette Ave., Minneapolis, MN 55401; 612-630-6000; {www.mplib.org}.

Mississippi
Mississippi Library Commission, 1221 Ellis Ave., Jackson, MS 39209-7328; 601-354-7007, 877-KWIK-REF; {www.mlc.lib.ms.us}.

Missouri
Linda Hall Library, Science, Engineering, & Technology, 5109 Cherry Street, Kansas City, MO 64110-2498; 816-363-4600, 800-662-1545; {www.lindahall.org}.

St. Louis Public Library, 1301 Olive Street, St. Louis, MO 63103; 314-241-2288, ext. 390; {www.slpl.lib.mo.us/library.htm}.

Montana
Montana Tech Library, 1300 West Park Street, Butte, MT 59701; 406-496-4281; {www.mtech.edu/library}.

Nebraska
Engineering Library, Nebraska Hall, Rm. W204, City Campus 0516, 900 N 16th St., Lincoln, NE 68588-0516; 402-472-3411; {iris.unl.edu}.

Nevada
Clark County Library, 1401 East Flamingo Road, Las Vegas, NV 89119; 702-507-3400; {www.lvccld.org/special_collections/patents/index.htm}.

Getchell Library, University of Nevada, 1664 N. Virginia St., Reno, NV 89557; 775-784-6500 {www.library.unr.edu/depts/bgic}.

New Hampshire
New Hampshire State Library, 20 Park Street, Concord, NH 03301; 603-271-2143; {www.state.nh.us/nhsl/patents/index.html}.

New Jersey
Newark Public Library, 3rd Floor, Main Library, 5 Washington St., Newark, NJ 07101; 973-733-7779; {www.npl.org/Pages/Collections/bst.html}.

Library of Science and Medicine, Rutgers, The State University of New Jersey, 165 Bevier Road, Piscataway, NJ 08854-8009; 732-445-3854; {www.rutgers.edu}.

New Mexico
Centennial Science and Engineering Library, The University of New Mexico, Albuquerque, NM 87131; 505-277-4412; {http://zoobert.unm.edu/newcsel}.

New York
New York State Library, Cultural Education Center, Empire State Plaza, Albany, NY 12230; 518-474-5355; {www.nysl.nysed.gov/patents.htm}.

Buffalo and Erie County Library, 1 Lafayette Square, Buffalo, NY 14203; 716-858-8900; {www.buffalolib.org}.

Science Industry and Business Library, New York Public Library, 188 Madison Avenue, New York, NY 10016; 212-592-7000; {www.nypl.org/research/sibl/index.html}.

Central Library of Rochester & Monroe County, 115 South Ave., Rochester, NY 14604-1896; 585-428-8110; {www.rochester.lib.ny.us/central}.

Science & Engineering Library, SUNY at Stony Brook, Stony Brook, NY 11794; 631-632-7148; {www.stonybrook.edu}.

North Carolina
D.H. Hill Library, North Carolina State University, 2205 Hillsborough Street, P.O. Box 7111, Raleigh, NC 27695-7111; 919-515-2935; {www.lib.ncsu.edu/risd/govdocs}.

North Dakota
Chester Fritz Library, University of North Dakota, University Ave. & Centennial Dr. Grand Forks, ND 58202; 701-777-4888; {www.und.nodak.edu/dept/library/resources/patents/ptdlp.new.jsp}.

Ohio
Akron Summit County Public Library, 1040 E Tallmadge Ave., Akron, OH 44310; 330-643-9000; {http://ascpl.lib.oh.us/pat-tm.html}.

Public Library of Cincinnati and Hamilton County, 800 Vine Street, 2nd Floor, North Building, Cincinnati, OH 45202-2071; 513-369-6971; {www.cincinnatilibrary.org/info/main/pd}.

Cleveland Public Library, 325 Superior Avenue, NE, Cleveland, OH 44114-1271; 216-623-2800; {www.cpl.org/}.

Paul Laurence Dunbar Library, Wright State University, 3640 Colonel Glenn Highway Dayton, OH 45435; 937-775-2525; {www.libraries.wright.edu}

Science and Engineering Library, Ohio State University, 175 West 18th Avenue, Columbus, OH 43210; 614-292-3022; {www.lib.ohio-state.edu/phyweb}.

Toledo-Lucas County Public Library, 325 N. Michigan Street, Toledo, OH 43624; 419-259-5209; {www.toledolibrary.org/discover/maintwo.htm}.

Oklahoma
Oklahoma State University, Patent & Trademark Depository Library, 5th Floor, Edmon Low Library, Stillwater, OK 74078; 405-744-7086; {www.library.okstate.edu/patents/index.htm}.

Oregon
Paul L. Boley Law Library, Lewis and Clark Law School, 10015 SW Terwilliger Blvd., Portland, OR 97219; 503-768-6786; {www.lclark.edu/~lawlib/ptointro.html}.

Pennsylvania
The Free Library of Philadelphia, 1901 Vine Street, Philadelphia, PA 19103; 215-686-5331; {www.library.phila.gov/}.

Carnegie Library of Pittsburgh, Science and Technology Department, 4400 Forbes Avenue, Pittsburgh, PA 15213; 412-622-3138; {www.clpgh.org/locations/scitech/ptdl/}.

Schreyer Business Library, 301 Paterno Library, 3rd Floor, University Park, PA 16802; 814-865-6369; {www.libraries.psu.edu}.

Puerto Rico
General Library, University of Puerto Rico at Mayaguez, P.O. Box 9022, Mayagüez, PR 00681-9022; 787-832-4040, ext. 2022; {www.uprm.edu/library/patents}.

Rhode Island
Providence Public Library, 225 Washington Street, Providence, RI 02903; 401-455-8005; {www.provlib.org}.

South Carolina
R.M. Cooper Library, Clemson University, Campus Box 343001, Clemson, SC 29634-3001; 864-656-3024; {www.lib.clemson.edu/govdocs/patents/newpat.htm}.

South Dakota
Devereaux Library, South Dakota School of Mines and Technology, 501 East Saint Joseph Street, 2nd Floor, Rapid City, SD 57701; 605-394-1264; {www.sdsmt.edu/services/library/library.html}.

Tennessee
Stevenson Science & Engineering Library, 3200 Stevenson Center, Nashville, TN 37240; Mailing Address: 419 21st Ave. S., Nashville, TN 37240; 615-322-2717; {www.library.vanderbilt.edu/science/patents.html}.

Texas
McKinney Engineering Library, University of Texas at Austin Engineering Library, ECJ 1.300, Austin, TX 78713; 512-495-4500; {www.lib.utexas.edu/engin/patent/uspat.html}.

Evans Library, Texas A&M University, College Station, TX 77843-5000; 979-845-5745; {http://library.tamu.edu/}.

Dallas Public Library, J. Erik Jonsson Central Library, 1515 Young Street, 6th Floor, Dallas, TX 75201; 214-670-1468; {http://dallaslibrary.org/central.htm}.

Fondren Library, Government Publications, MS225 Rice University, P.O. Box 1892, Houston, TX 77251-1892; 713-348-5483; {www.rice.edu/Fondren/ptdl}.

Texas Tech University Libraries, 18th and Boston, Lubbock, TX 79409-0002; 806-742-2282; {http://library.ttu.edu/ul/index.php}.

San Antonio Public Library, 600 Soledad, 2nd Floor, San Antonio, TX 78205; 210-207-2500; {www.sanantonio.gov/library/central/govdocs.asp}.

Utah
Marriott Library, University of Utah, 295 South 1500 E, Salt Lake City, UT 84112-0860; 801-581-8394; {www.lib.utah.edu/govdocs}.

Vermont
Bailey/Howe Library, University of Vermont, Burlington, VT 05405; 802-656-2542; {http://library.uvm.edu/reference/government/patent.html}.

Virginia
James Branch Cabell Library, Virginia Commonwealth University, 901 Park Avenue, 1st Floor, Richmond, VA 23284-2033; 804-828-1104; {www.library.vcu.edu/jbc/govdocs/govhome.html}.

Washington
Engineering Library, University of Washington, P.O. Box 352170, Seattle, WA 98195; 206-543-0740; {www.lib.washington.edu/engineering/ptdl}.

West Virginia

Evansdale Library, West Virginia University, P.O. Box 6105, Morganstown, WV 26506-6105; 304-293-4696; {www.libraries.wvu.edu/patents/index.htm}.

Wisconsin

Wendt Library, University of Wisconsin, 215 North Randall Ave., Madison, WI 53706-1688; 608-262-6845; {www.wisc.edu/wendt/patent/patent.html}.

Milwaukee Public Library, 814 West Wisconsin Avenue, Milwaukee, WI 53233; 414-286-3051; {www.mpl.org/}.

Wyoming

Wyoming State Library, 2301 Capitol Ave., Cheyenne, WY 82002-0060; 307-777-7281; {www-wsl.state.wy.us/sis/ptdl/index.html}.

The Patent and Trademark Library Program distributes the information to the 86 PDLs. The information is kept on CD-Rom discs, which are constantly updated, and you can use them to do a patent search. CD-Rom discs have been combined to incorporate CASSIS (Classification and Search Support Information System). CD-Rom discs do not give you online access to the PTO database. Online access is available through APS (Automated Patent Systems), and is presently available to public users of the PTO Search Room and to the 86 Patent Libraries. Each PDL with the online APS has its own rules regarding its use. To use the online APS at the PTO Search Room, it is recommended that you take a class at the Search Room. West, East, and X-Search classes are offered once per month for a cost of $25. Off Schedule 3-hour personal training sessions are available for a fee of $120. Online access costs $40 per connect hour, and the charge for paper used for printouts is an additional $.25 per sheet. Public user Ids are required to access all Public Search Facilities. They are available at the Search Room Reception Desk with a valid government issued photo ID.

If you do not live near a PDL, several CD-Rom discs are available through subscription. You may purchase the Classification disc, which dates back to 1790, for $450; the Bibliography disc, which dates back to 1969, for $450; and the ASIST disc, which contains a roster of patent attorneys, assignees, and other information for $300. You can also conduct your patent search and get a copy of it through commercial database services such as:

Lexis, Nexis: 800-543-6862; Fax: 937-865-1008; {www.lexisnexis.com/patentservices}. Printouts are billed per page plus shipping. Copies are available via email, mail, fax, or on a CD-Rom. If you intend on doing many searches over time, Lexis, Nexis will customize a package for you as a subscriber for approximately $400 per month.

Derwent, 1725 Duke St., Suite 250, Alexandria, VA 22314; 800-337-9368, Fax: 800-457-0850; {www.derwent.com}. Patent searches are free, but the printouts range from $3 and up per page.

If you are going to do your own patent search at your local Patent Depository Library, begin with the Manual and Index to U.S. Patent Classifications to identify the subject area where the patent is placed. Then use the CD-Rom discs to locate the patent. CD-Rom discs enable you to do a complete search of all registered patents but do not enable you to view the full patent, with all its specific details. Lastly, view the patent, which will be kept on microfilm, cartridge, or paper. What information there is to view varies by library, depending on what they have been able to purchase. If the library you are using does not have the patent you want, you may be able to obtain it through inter-library loan.

Copies of patents can be ordered from the PTO at 703-308-9726; 800-972-6382; Fax: 703-308-7048, for $3 per copy.

To obtain a certified copy of a patent, call 703-308-9726 (Patent Search Library at the PTO). The fee is $25 and you must have the patent number. For a certified copy of an abstract of titles, the fee is $25. For a certified copy of patent assignments, with a record of ownership from the beginning until present, call 703-308-9726. The cost is $25, and to request specific assignments you must have the reel and frame number.

Now You Have Got Your Patent

Once a Notice of Allowance stating that your application for patents has been approved, you have 3 months to pay another filing fee. If not, the application will be deemed abandoned. There are also maintenance fees due at 3 1/2, 7 1/2, and 11 1/2 years after the original grant. After it has expired, anyone may make, use, offer for sale, or sell or import the invention without the patentee's approval. A patent is personal property.

Tips

* Most importantly, do not reveal the details of your invention to anyone! If you need to do so, establish a confidential relationship with them by law or regulation, or a written agreement. Your plans and information you have gathered can be trade secrets and you must protect them.
* Record your discovery in detail as soon as possible and keep a record as you go. Have it witnessed by two reliable persons with a confidentiality agreement.
* Developing a new product is time consuming and expensive. Determine how much of your time, money, and effort you can invest. Know your personal limitations and when to get professional help.
* Twenty percent of patents issued each year are to private inventors. They must be effective business people to also research business concepts.
* Read articles by successful inventors for tips on what it took for them to market their product. Talk to potential customers to see what they would look for in the type of product that you are discovering.
* Remember, if a product similar to yours exists, you can still patent an improvement that is significant.
* Lastly, many times it is not the first try at inventing a product that is successful, it gets better as you go.

What Are Trademarks and Servicemarks?

A trademark is a word, name, symbol or device used in trade with goods to indicate the source of the goods and to set them apart from the goods of others. A servicemark is used to distinguish the source of a service instead of a product. Trademark or mark is generally the term used to refer to both trademarks and servicemarks. They are to keep others from using a confusingly similar mark, but not to keep others from making or selling the same goods or services under a clearly different mark. The Trademark Assistance Center will provide general information about the registration process and will respond to questions concerning the status of a specific trademark application and registration. They are available at 703-308-4357; 800-786-9199; {www.uspto.gov/main/trademarks.htm}.

Trademarks

Registering a trademark for your product or service is the way to protect the recognition quality of the name you are building. The PTO keeps records on more than 3 million trademarks and records. Over 500,000 active trademarks are kept on the floor of the library, while "dead" trademarks are kept on microfilm. Books contain every registered trademark ever issued, starting in 1870. You can visit the Patent and Trademark Office to research a trademark using the US Trademark Electronic Search System (TESS). You can access TESS at http://tess2.uspto.gov. You can then conduct your search manually for no charge or use their Trademark Search System (T-Search) for no charge.

Mail Stop Documentation Services
Director of the United States Patent and Trademark Office
P.O. Box 1450
Alexandria, VA 22313-1450   703-308-9800

If you can't do it yourself, you can hire someone to do the search for you. For an agent to do this, consult the local yellow pages under "Trademark Agents/Consultants" or "Trademark Attorneys". You can also locate an agent by calling your local bar association for a referral.

To conduct your own search at a Patent Depository Library, use the CD-Rom disc on trademarks. It is available for purchase. The CD-Rom discs deliver patent and trademark information including full-text facsimile images and searchable text records. Images can be found in the Official Gazette, which contains most current and pending trademarks. The price for an annual subscription to the Official Gazette for trademarks is $980. It is issued every Tuesday and can be ordered from the U.S. Government Printing Office. You can also purchase an image file which contains pending and registered trademarks and corresponding serial or registration numbers through Thomson & Thomson by calling 1-800-692-8833. The information contained in it dates back to April 1, 1987 and is updated by approximately 500 images weekly. However, the PDL you use is likely to have an image of the trademark on microfilm or cartridge, and also have copies of the Official Gazette. If not, and you have the registration number, you may obtain a copy of the trademark you want for $3 from the PTO. Contact:

2900 Crystal Dr.
Second Floor, Room 2B30
Arlington, VA 22202   703-308-9800

There are also several commercial services you can use to conduct trademark searches.

Trademark Scan produced by Thomson & Thomson. It can be purchased by calling 800-692-8833 (ask for online services), or accessed directly via Saegis. Trademark Scan is updated three times per week, and includes state and federal trademarks, foreign and domestic. To access Trademark Scan you must already have Dialog or Saegis. Many online options are free. The Internet address is {www.thomson-thomson.com}.

Thomson Derwent, 800-337-9368, is a commercial service that will conduct patent searches only. The cost ranges from $410 and up with a turnaround time of 2–10 days. The Internet address is {www.derwent.com}.

Online services and database discs for both patents and trademarks are constantly being expanded. For information on an extensive range of existing and projected products, call the PTO Office of Electronic Information at 703-306-2600 and ask for the U.S. Department of Commerce, PTO Office of Information Systems' Electronic Products Brochure. For example, there is a Weekly Text File, containing text data of pending and registered trademarks. Information can be called up by using almost any term. It can be purchased from AvantIQ and Thomson & Thomson. You can reach AvantIQ at online at {www.avantiq.lu/}.

How to Register a Trademark

The right of a trademark comes from either the actual use of the mark, or by filing the correct application. There are two types of rights in a mark, the right to register it and the right to use the mark. The right to register is given to the first party that uses a mark in commerce, or who files an application at the PTO. The right to use a mark can be a complicated matter. For example, in the case where two people who do not know each other, start to use the same or similar marks without a registration. A court will have to decide who has the right to use the mark. Trademark rights last indefinitely if the owner continues its use. The registration lasts 10 years with 10 year renewal periods. You can order a free copy of Basic Facts about Trademarks from the U.S. Government Printing Office, or by calling the Trademark Search Library at 703-308-9000.

Types of Applications

The "use" application is for an applicant that already has been using their mark in commerce. The "intent-to-use" application is for those who have a bona fide intention of using the mark in commerce. These offer protection only in the US and it territories. Applications must be filed in the name of the owner of the mark.

For automated information about the status of a trademark application and registration, call 703-305-8747.

The Trademark Electronic Center

The Trademark Electronic Application System (TEAS) has step-by-step instructions for filling out forms and also contains information about the USPTO's procedures and practices. It also allows you to fill out the trademark forms, check them to be sure they are complete, and using e-TEAS, submit it on-line. You must be able to attach either a black-and-white GIF or JPG file to apply for a stylized or design mark. If a sample of actual use in commerce is needed, a scanned image or digital photo in GIF or JPG format must be attached. The final requirement is payment with a credit card or from an account already set up with the PTO. One mark can be filed with each application for a fee of $335, except for Class 9 and Class 25, where there is a $650 fee. E-TEAS will not accept applications from 11pm Saturday to 6am Sunday. Also, if you prefer to send the forms by mail, you can use PrinTEAS to print out your completed forms. You can send check, money order, or make arrangements for payment through a USPTO account. This system can be accessed 24 hours a day, 7 days a week.

You can check the status of marks using TARR-Trademark Application and Registration Retrieval at {http://tarr.uspto.gov}.

Symbols

Anyone who claims rights in a mark can use the symbols, TM (trademark) or SM (servicemark) to show that right. However, the registration symbol, an r in a circle (®), cannot be used until the mark is registered.

The Right Way to Get a Copyright

Copyrights are filed on intellectual property. A copyright protects your right to control the sale, use of distribution, and royalties from a creation in thought, music, films, art, or books. It is an automatic form of protection for authors of published and unpublished "original works of authorship." The concrete form of expression as opposed to the subject matter is what is protected. Since a copyright is automatic when a work is created, registration is not required for protection. However, there are advantages to registration. If it is registered within 5 years of publication of the work, it establishes prima facie evidence of its validity and can be helpful in case of a court action. Generally the work is protected for the author's life plus 70 years after death.

For more information, contact:

Library of Congress
U.S. Copyright Office
101 Independence Avenue SE
Washington, DC 20559-6000
Public Information Office   202-707-3000
Email: copyinfo@loc.gov   TTY: 202-707-6737
www.loc.gov
www.copyright.gov

If you know which copyright application you require, you can call the Forms Hotline, at 202-707-9100. The fee is $30 for each registration. Information on all of the different types of copyrights and their applications can be found at their web site.

The Library of Congress provides information on copyright registration procedures and copyright card catalogs that cover several million works that have been registered since 1870. The Copyright Office will research federal copyrights only for varying fees. Requests must be made in writing and you must specify exactly what information you require. If a work does not show any elements of copyright notice, you can search the Copyright Office's catalogs and records. The records from January 1, 1978, to the present can be searched on the Internet through the Library of Congress Information System (LOCIS). That web site address is {www.copyright.gov/rb.html}.

Contact the Copyright Office, Reference and Bibliography, Library of Congress, 101 Independence Ave., SE, Washington, DC 20559-6000; 202-707-6850, Public Information 202-707-3000.

What is Not Protected by Copyright

Works that have not been notated, recorded, or written can not be protected by copyright. Here are some others:

★   titles, short phrases, and slogans; familiar symbols or designs; variations of ornamentation, lettering or coloring, listings of ingredients or contents
★   concepts, methods, systems, principles, or devices, as opposed to description, explanation, and illustration
★   works that are entirely made of information that is common property and do not contain any original authorship

Invention Scams: How They Work

Fake product development companies prey on amateur inventors who may not be as savvy about protecting their idea or invention as experienced inventors might be. Most of the bogus/fake companies use escalating fees.

The following is a description of how most of them operate:

1) The inventor is invited to call or write for free information.

2) The inventor is then offered a free evaluation of his idea.

3) Next comes the sales call. The inventor is told he has a very good potential idea and that the company is willing to share the cost of marketing, etc. Actual fact, there is no sharing with these companies. Most times the inventor has to come up with the money (usually several hundred dollars or more) for a patent search and a market analysis. Neither of these are worth anything.

4) Then the inventor receives a professional/ impressive looking portfolio which contains no real information at all. All the paper crammed into this portfolio looks topnotch, but it's all computer generated garbage.

5) Upon receiving this portfolio, the inventor is lured into signing a contract that commits him to giving the company thousands of dollars to promote/license the product. The company sends some promotional letters to fulfill their obligation, but large manufacturers simply toss them into the trash.

After all this, the inventor has spent thousands of dollars, wasted a lot of time, and gotten nowhere with his product.

How To Avoid Losing a Fortune

According to the experts, the inventor should:

- Beware of the come-ons offered by these unethical companies. Avoid using the invention brokers who advertise on TV late in the evening; in public magazines; those who offer 800 numbers; and those on public transit display signs.

- When upfront money is required, look out. There are very few legitimate consultants who insist on a retainer or hourly fee.

- Don't allow the enthusiasm of your idea to take over your inherent common sense. Talk to your patent attorney and see if he knows anything about this company. Plus, check with inventors associations in the state, and see what they have to say about this particular company.

- Demand to know what percentage of ideas the company accepts. Legitimate brokers might accept 2 ideas out of every 100. The fake companies tend to accept about 99 out of 100.

- Find out their actual success rate. Any corporation/ company that will not give you their success rate (not licensing agreements) is a company to stay away from.

- Get an objective evaluation of your invention from reputable professionals. This will save you plenty of money on a bad idea.

A number of highly recommended programs are listed in the next section.

Free Help for Inventors

If you have a great idea and want to turn it into reality, don't rush out and spend what could be thousands of dollars for a private invention company and a patent attorney. You can get a lot of this help for free or at a fraction of the cost. There is a lot of help out there; university-sponsored programs, not-for-profit groups, state affiliated programs, profit-making companies, etc. Depending on the assistance and the organization, some services are free, others have reasonable fees.

Many of the inventors' organizations hold regular meetings where speakers share their expertise on topics such as licensing, financing and marketing. These groups are a good place for inventors to meet other inventors, patent attorneys, manufacturers, and others with whom they can talk and from whom they can get help.

If the listings in the state-by-state section of this chapter do not prove to be useful, you can contact one of the following organizations for help.

1. Small Business Development Centers
   Washington State University
   Parkplace Building
   1200 6th Ave., Suite 1700
   Seattle, WA 98101
   206-553-7328
   Fax: 206-553-7044
   www.wsbdc.org
This service will evaluate your idea for a fee.

2. Wisconsin Innovation Service Center/Technology
   Small Business Development Center
   University of Wisconsin - Whitewater
   402 McCutchan Hall
   Whitewater, WI 53190
   262-472-1365
   Fax: 262-472-1600
   www.uww.edu/sbdc
The only service that is guaranteed is the evaluation. However, efforts are made to match inventors with exceptional high evaluation scores with manufacturers seeking new product ideas. (Do not offer direct invention development or marketing services). WISC charges a $495 flat fee for an evaluation. The goal is to keep research as affordable as possible to the average independent inventor. Most evaluations are completed within 30-45 days. Those inventions from specialized fields may require more time. WISC also provides preliminary patent searches via on-line databases to client.

3. Drake University
   Small Business Development Center
   Drake Business Center
   2507 University
   Des Moines, IA 50311-4505
   515-271-2655
   800-532-1216
   Fax: 515-271-1899
   www.iabusnet.org

INVENTURE is a program of the Drake University Business Development and Research Institute designed to encourage the development of valid ideas through the various steps to becoming marketable items. INVENTURE has no paid staff. The entire panel is made up of volunteers. The administration of the program is handled by existing staff from the Small Business Development Center and the College of Business and Public Administration. They will review items from any person regardless of their place of residence. They will review a product idea and check it for market feasibility. INVENTURE may link individuals with business and/or financial partners.

INVENTURE screens every product submitted, but will not consider toy/game or food items. Products are evaluated on 33 different criteria (factors related to legality, safety, business risk, and demand analysis, to market acceptance/ competition). It normally takes up to 6 weeks to receive results of the evaluation. Evaluators are experienced in manufacturing, marketing, accounting, production, finance and investments.

INVENTURE acts in a responsible manner to maintain confidence of an idea, but cannot guarantee confidentiality.

For assistance with business plans, financial projections, and marketing help, you're encouraged to contact your Small Business Development Center (SBDC).

4. Office of Weatherization & InterGovernmental Program
    Office of Industrial Technologies
    Mail Stop EE-24
    1000 Independence Ave., SW
    Washington, DC 20585-0121
    202-586-0984
    Fax: 360-956-2214
    www.eere.energy.gov/inventions/

Financial assistance is available in two categories: up to $50,000 and up to $250,000 by the Inventions and Innovations program as stated by the Office of Industrial Technologies (OIT) Department of Energy (DOE) for ideas that significantly impact energy savings and future commercial market potential. Successful applicants will find technical guidance and commercialization support in addition to financial assistance.

DOE has given financial support to more than 500 inventions with nearly 25% of these reaching the marketplace bringing in nearly $710 million in cumulative sales.

5. U.S. Environmental Protection Agency
    Center for Environmental Research Information
    26 Martin Luther King Drive
    Cincinnati, OH 45268
    513-569-7578
    www.epa.gov

Directory Description: Environmental Protection Agency, Office of Research and Development, 1200 Pennsylvania Ave., NW, Mail Code 8101R, Washington, DC 20460; 202-564-6620, Fax: 202-565-2910.

The Office of Research and Development conducts an Agency wide integrated program of research and development relevant to pollution sources and control, transport and fate processes, health/ecological effects, measurement/monitoring, and risk assessment. The office provides technical reviews, expert consultations, technical assistance, and advice to environmental decision-makers in federal, state, local, and foreign governments.

Center for Environmental Research Information
26 W. ML King Drive, Cincinnati, OH 45268, 513-569-7578; Fax: 513-569-7585.
A focal point for the exchange of scientific/technical information both within the federal government and to the public.

Office of Research and Development

Is responsible for working with laboratories, program offices, regions to produce information products that summarize research, technical, regulatory enforcement information that will assist non-technical audiences in understanding environmental issues. Contact Office of Research and Development, U.S. Environmental Protection Agency, 1200 Pennsylvania Ave., NW, Washington, DC 20460; 202-564-6620; Fax: 202-565-2910.

Office of Exploratory Research

1200 Pennsylvania Ave., NW, Washington, DC 20460; 202-564-6852.
The Office of Exploratory Research (OER) plans, administers, manages, and evaluates the Environmental Protection Agency's (EPA) extramural grant research. It supports research in developing a better understanding of the environment and its problems. Main goals are: to support the academic community in environmental research; maintain scientific/technical personnel in environmental science/ technology; to support research for the identification/solution of emerging environmental problems.

Goals are accomplished through four core programs:

1. The Research Grants Program:
    Supports research initiated by individual investigators in areas of interest to the agency.

2. The Environmental Research Centers Program:
    Has two components: The Academic Research Center Program (ARC) and the Hazardous Substance Research Centers Program (HSRC).

3. The Small Business Innovation Research (SBIR) Program:
    Program supports small businesses for the development of ideas relevant to EPA's mission. Focuses on projects in pollution control development. Also receives 1.5% of the Agency's resources devoted to extramural Superfund research.

4. The Visiting Scientists Program:
    Components are an Environmental Science and Engineering Fellows Program and a Resident Research Associateship Program. The Fellows Program supports ten mid-career post-doctoral scientists and engineers at EPA headquarters & regional offices. The Research Associateship Program attracts national and international scientists and engineers at EPA research laboratories for up to 3 years to collaborate with Agency researchers on important environmental issues.

Other programs available are:
A Minority Fellowship Program
A Minority Summer Intern Program
The Agency's Senior Environmental Employment Program (SEE)
The Federal Workforce Training Program
An Experimental Program to Stimulate Competitive Research (EPSCoR).

To learn more, contact Grants Administration, U.S. Environmental Protection Agency, 1200 Pennsylvania Ave., NW, Washington, DC 20460; 202-272-0167. The best way, though, is to search for the word "grant" at the EPA's website, {www.epa.gov}.

State Sources for Inventors

Free Money For Inventors

People pay good money for good ideas, especially, the government. There is even government grant money available to work on ideas, either your own or the ones that the government has. Here is how some state governments give money to inventors:

☺ North Dakota gives inventors up to $100,000 to work on new ideas through Technology Transfer, Inc.

☺ Rhode Island offers grant money to develop new products using the ocean, (how about seaweed cereal), through the Ocean Technology Center.

☺ Pennsylvania offers grants from $5,000 to $250,000 for entrepreneurs to work on new ideas through the Ben Franklin Challenge Grant Program.

☺ Delaware offers inventors up to $25,000 in venture capital to write business plans and get patents, and then up to $250,000 to do marketing, as part of the Delaware Innovation Fund.

☺ North Carolina grants up to $25,000 to develop ideas to eliminate wood waste through the Solid Waste Reduction Assistance Grant.

☺ Wisconsin gives out grants for new ways of recycling in their Recycling Early Planning Grant Program.

☺ Ohio and Indiana have grants for inventors who have new ideas on what to do with old tires.

Contact your local state Office of Economic Development listed in the Appendix to investigate what your state has to offer inventors.

Other Inventing Grants

Some states also offer grant money to inventors who are working on getting government grants for their ideas. The largest source of these grants is the Small Business Innovative Research Grants that offer over $1 billion from 11 different agencies. The Small Business Administration acts as a clearinghouse for this information.

Other federal grant programs for inventors include:

☞ The Inventions and Innovation Program, managed by the U.S. Department of Energy, provides grants for ideas that result in the more efficient use of energy.

☞ The Advanced Technology Program gives $1.8 million a year in grants for developing new technology from the U.S. Department of Commerce's National Institute of Standards and Technology.

☞ The U.S. Department of Energy's National Industrial Competitiveness through Energy, Environment and Economics (NICE3) offers grants up to $400,000 to develop ideas that save energy.

You can find these programs in a government book in your library called *The Catalog of Federal Domestic Assistance* or by contacting your local Federal Information Center at 800-FED-INFO; {http://fic.info.gov}.

Below is a listing of a variety of inventors groups, listed state by state. Some organizations listed under the state where they are located are regional or national in scope. In states where there is no specific program for inventors, the Small Business Development Centers (under the U.S. Small Business Administration) can often be of help. They are usually found at the colleges and universities. The Small Business Development Center office is located at 6302 Fairview Rd., Ste. 300, Charlotte, NC 28210; 800-UASK-SBA; {www.sba.gov}.

Alabama
Office for the Advancement of Developing Industries
University of Alabama - Birmingham
2800 Milan Ct.   205-943-6560
Birmingham, AL 35211   Fax: 205-943-6563
http://main.uab.edu/show.asp?durki=694
Inventors can receive help on the commercialization and patent processes and critical reviews of inventions in this office. Assessments can be made on an invention's potential marketability and assistance is available for patent searches. There is a charge for services.

Small Business Development Center
University of Alabama at Birmingham
901 S. 15th St.   205-934-6760
Birmingham, AL 35294   Fax: 205-934-0538
www.business.uab.edu/SBDC/Index.htm
The center offers counseling for a wide range of business issues and problems.

U.S. Small Business Administration
Business Development
801 Tom Martin Drive   205-290-7101
Birmingham, AL 35211   Fax: 205-290-7404
www.sba.gov
This office offers counseling for a wide range of business issues and problems.

Alaska
UA Small Business Development Center of Alaska
430 W. 7th Ave., Suite 110   907-274-7232
Anchorage, AK 99501-3550   Fax: 907-274-9524
www.aksbdc.org
The SBDC provides general assistance, including free counseling to inventors on commercialization and patent processes, and arranging meetings between inventors, investors, manufacturers, and others who can be of help.

Alaska Inventors and Entrepreneurs Association
P.O. Box 241801
Anchorage, AK 99524   907-276-4337
www.arctic.net/~inventor/inventor.htm
They provide access to the tools and resources needed in order to empower inventors to bring their product to market. The InventorNet Resource Directory lists professional service providers, agents, designers, and much more. There are also monthly meetings, magazine subscription discounts, free access to the Internet and other benefits. There is a membership fee.

Inventors Institute of Alaska
PO Box 876154
Wasilla, AK 99687   907-376-5114

Arizona

Arizona SBDC Network
2411 West 14th Street   480-731-8720
Tempe, AZ 85281   Fax: 480-731-8729
www.dist.maricopa.edu/sbdc
The center offers counseling for a wide range of business issues and problems.

Inventor's Association of Arizona   520-751-9966
2220 N. Camino Principal, Ste. C,   888-299-6787
Tucson, AZ 85715   Fax: 602-912-9455
www.azinventors.org/
Their goal is to guide the creativity of the members through experience, support and confidentiality so that they will be able to market their new invention or idea. Some of the areas they offer assistance in are patent, trademark, and copyrights, manufacture, finance, and obtaining a product license. Benefits include discounts for legal services, Trade Magazine subscriptions, and consulting, as well as comprehensive information concerning the steps from concept to market. There is a membership fee.

Arkansas

Small Business Development Center
University of Arkansas at Little Rock   800-862-2040 (AR only)
2801 S. University Ave.   501-324-9043
Little Rock, AR 72204   Fax: 501-324-9049
http://asbdc.ualr.edu
The center offers counseling for a wide range of business issues and problems.

California

Greater Sacramento Small Business Development Center
1410 Ethan Way   916-563-3210
Sacramento, CA 95825
www.sbdc.net
The center offers counseling for a wide range of business issues and problems.

Inventors' Alliance
P.O. Box 390219   650-964-1576
Mountain View, CA 94039-390219
www.inventorsalliance.org
They have monthly meetings with guest speakers on topics such as marketing and product development. These meetings are designed to increase the inventors' knowledge and create contacts for a successful production of a product.

Inventors Forum
P.O. Box 8008, 80 Huntington St. #9   714-540-2491
Huntington Beach, CA 92615-8008   Fax: 714-668-0583
www.inventorsforum.org
Email: info@inventorsforum.org
This nonprofit group teaches inventors about the invention process. Some of the products and services they provide are the Invention Showcase, a listing of service providers for a number of different services, and an inventors message base with a range of topics.

Redwood Empire Small Business
Development Center   888-346-SBDC
606 Healdsburg Avenue   707-524-1770
Santa Rosa, CA 95401   Fax: 707-524-1772
www.santarosa.edu/sbdc/
Email: sbdc@santarosa.edu
They have a Patent Information Network where inventor clients perform initial patent searches to help in forming an assessment of an idea or design. They also offer one-on-one professional business consulting. There is no charge for these services.

Central Valley Inventor's Assn.
P.O. Box 1551
Manteca, CA 95336   209-239-8090

Inventors Forum of San Diego
11292 Poblado Road   858-451-1028
San Diego, CA 92127   Fax: 858-451-6154

Sawyer Center
4261 Brookshire Circle
Santa Rosa, CA 95405   707-524-1773

American Inventor Network
1320 High School Rd.   707-823-7909
Sebastopol, CA 95472   Fax: 707-823-0913

Inventors' Alliance of Northern California
22070 Palo Way, Ste. 4
Palo Cedro, CA 96049-3365   530-243-2400
Email: ianc.frontiernet.net   Fax: 530-547-4644
www.inventorsnorcal.org
Established in 1999, the IANC assists inventors in the patent process, and the development and marketing of ideas and products.

Idea to Market Network
P.O. Box 12248
Santa Rosa, CA 95406   1-800-ITM-3210
www.ideatomarket.org
Email: info@ideatomarket.org
Idea to Market is a network of inventors who guide fellow members through the inventive process.

Colorado
Affiliated Inventors Foundation, Inc.
1405 Potter Dr., Ste. 107   719-380-1234

Colorado Springs, CO 80909
To order free Info Kit
www.affiliatedinventors.com
Email: info@affiliatedinventors.com

800-525-5885
Fax: 800-380-3862

This foundation counsels inventors on commercialization and patent processes, and provides detailed information on the steps needed to reach commercialization. Preliminary appraisals, evaluations and other services are available for a fee.

Small Business Development Center
Office of Economic Development
1625 Broadway, Suite 1710
Denver, CO 80202
www.state.co.us/oed/sbdc

303-892-3794
Fax: 303-892-3848

The center offers counseling for a wide range of business issues and problems.

Rocky Mountain Inventors Associations
(RMIA)
P.O. Box 36233
Denver, CO 80236-0233
www.rminventor.org
Email: info@RMinventor.org

303-670-3760
Fax: 720-962-5026

Their mission is to help people with new ideas to fulfill their greatest potential. Their members include new and established inventors, prototypers, manufacturers, marketers, patent attorneys and others connected to the invention process. There are round table meetings, networking sessions, monthly educational meetings and an annual conference. They offer information on the invention process, the tools needed and advice on what to do with the invention.

Connecticut

Small Business Development Center
University of Connecticut
2100 Hillside Road, Unit 1094
Storrs, CT 06269-1094
www.sbdc.uconn.edu
Email: CSBDCInformation@business.uconn.edu

860-486-4135
Fax: 860-486-1576

The center offers counseling for a wide range of business issues and problems.

Inventors Association of Connecticut
9-B Greenhouse Road
Bridgeport, CT 06606-2130
www.inventus.org
Email: IACT@inventus.org

203-866-0720
Fax: 781-846-6448

This is a nonprofit group who has members that include inventors, designers, engineers, attorneys, and business people. They look to nurture, stimulate creativity and advance the image of independent inventors by education, promotion and sharing of member resources. They have monthly meetings with pre-meeting sessions, and a newsletter to accomplish this goal. There is a monthly fee.

Delaware

Small Business Development Center
University of Delaware
One Innovation Way, Suite 301
Newark, DE 19711
www.delawaresbdc.org

302-831-1555
Fax: 302-831-1423

The office offers management counseling and seminars on various topics, and can counsel inventors on areas such as the commercialization and patenting processes. Services are by appointment only.

Delaware Economic Development
99 Kings Highway   302-739-4271
Dover, DE 19901   Fax: 302-739-2028
www.state.de.us/dedo
Assistance is available to any applicant located in Delaware or relocating to Delaware, who has been granted a phase I SBIR award and has submitted a Phase II SBIR application.

Early Stage East
3 Mill Road, Suite 201A
Wilmington, DE 19806   302-777-2460
Email: info@earlystageeast.org

District of Columbia
U.S. Department of Commerce
U.S. Patent and Trademark Office
Crystal Plaza 3, Room 2C02   800-PTO-9199
PO Box 1450   703-308-4357
Alexandria, VA 22313-1450
www.uspto.gov
Email: usptoinfo@uspto.gov

Washington, DC Small Business Development Center
Howard University
2600 6th St., NW, Suite 128   202-806-1550
Washington, DC 20059   Fax: 202-806-1777
www.bschool.howard.edu/sbdc/index.htm
Email: husbdc@cldc.howard.edu
The center offers counseling for a wide range of business issues and problems.

U.S. Small Business Administration
1110 Vermont Ave., NW, 9th Floor   202-606-4000
Washington, DC 20005   Fax: 202-606-4225
www.sba.gov
This office provides general assistance and information on funding.

Inventor's Network of the Capital Area
P.O. Box 15150, Arlington, VA 22215   703-971-9216
http://dcinventors.org
This is a non-profit educational organization offering monthly meetings, guest speakers, and networking with fellow inventors.

Florida
Small Business Development Center
University of North Florida   904-620-2476
12000 Alumni Drive   800-450-4624 (in FL)
Jacksonville, FL 32224   Fax: 904-620-2567
www.sbdc.unf.edu
Email: smallbiz@unf.edu
The center offers counseling for a wide range of business issues and problems.

Small Business Development Center
University of West Florida
1170 Martin L. King, Jr. Blvd.   850-863-6543
Fort Walton Beach, FL 32547   Fax: 850-863-6564
www.sbdc.uwf.edu
The center offers counseling for a wide range of business issues and problems.

Florida SBDC Network
401 E. Chase St.   850-473-7830
Pensacola, FL 32502   Fax: 850-473-7813
www.floridasbdc.com
The network provides general assistance; conducts market/ technical assessments; offers legal advice on patents and licensing; provides funding information; and assists in building a prototype. Inventors get to showcase their inventions and meet with other inventors and investors.

University of Central Florida
Small Business Development Center
315 E. Robinson St., Ste 100   407-420-4850
Orlando, FL 32801   Fax: 407-420-4862
www.bus.ucf.edu/sbdc
The center provides general assistance, funding information and conducts market assessments. Inventors meet other inventors.

Edison Inventors Association
P.O. Box 07398   239-275-IDEA (4332)
Ft. Myers, FL 33919   Fax: 941-267-9746
www.edisoninventors.org
They are a non-profit group whose goal is to aid creativity and assist inventors and entrepreneurs to be successful. They have monthly meetings.

Inventors Society of South Florida
P.O. Box 244306
Boynton Beach, FL 33424   954-486-2426
http://inventorssociety.net
They consider themselves a non-profit educational society. The guest speakers include patent agents, attorneys, government sources, engineers, technicians and more. You will be able to ask questions of the guest and also network with other inventors at monthly meetings.

Tampa Bay Inventors' Council
7441 114th Ave N., Ste 606
Largo FL 33773   727-547-5450 (phone/fax)
http://tbich.us
This non-profit organization educates its members and others about invention product development and marketing. The meetings are a public forum for people who have information for inventors and for inventors that have questions. Members also get a monthly newsletter, a current member directory and reference materials. There is a membership fee.

Space Coast Inventors Guild
1221 Pine Tree Drive
Indian Harbour Beach, FL 32937   321-773-4031 (phone/fax)
They accept the challenge to help people in the development of an idea so they can present for a patent. The monthly meetings are open to the public and there is no charge to attend.

Inventors Council of Central Florida
4855 Big Oaks Ln.
Orlando, FL 32806-7826   407-859-4855

Georgia
University of Georgia, Business Outreach Services/SBDC
Chicopee Complex
1180 East Broad Street   706-542-7436
Athens, GA 30602-5412   Fax: 706-542-6803
www.sbdc.uga.edu
The center offers counseling for a wide range of business issues and problems.

Inventor Associates of Georgia, Inc.
P.O. Box 888163
Dunwoody, GA 30356   478-474-6948
www.geocities.com/iaggroup/   Fax: 478-474-2602
A group of experts and novices that assist independent inventors with the process of developing their ideas so that they can be marketed. Partly, this is accomplished by Q&A with members and impartial evaluations of inventions. There are monthly meetings with roundtable discussions afterwards. There is a membership fee.

Inventor Associates of Georgia, Inc.
PO Box 888163
Dunwoody, GA 30356   770-908-7386 (phone/fax)
Email: tropez99@yahoo.com
www.geocities.com/iaggroup
IAG, Inc. assists independent inventors in getting their product to market.

Hawaii
Small Business Development Center
University of Hawaii at Hilo
308 Kamehameha Avenue, Suite 201   808-974-7515
Hilo, HI 96720   Fax: 808-974-7683
http://hawaii-sbdc.org
The center offers counseling for a wide range of business issues and problems.

Idaho
Idaho Research Foundation, Inc.
University of Idaho
Morrill Hall 103
P.O. Box 443003   208-885-4550
Moscow, ID 83844-3003   Fax: 208-882-0105
www.irf.uro.uidaho.edu
Email: irf@uidaho.edu
This foundation counsels inventors on commercialization and patent processes, and provides critical reviews on inventions. Computerized data searching and marketing service is available. It takes a percentage of intellectual property royalties.

Small Business Development Center
Boise State University   800-225-3815 (in ID)
1910 University Drive   208-426-1640
Boise, ID 83725-1655   Fax: 208-426-3877
www.idahosbdc.org
Email: cchamber@boisestate.edu@idahosbdc.org
The center offers counseling for a wide range of business issues and problems.

Idaho Small Business Development Center
College of Southern Idaho
P.O. Box 1238
315 Falls Ave.   208-732-6221
Twin Falls, ID 83303-1238   Fax: 208-736-3015
www.csi.edu/support/isbdc/sbdc.html
Email: info@csi.edu
The center conducts market assessments and provides funding information.

Idaho Small Business Development Center
Lewis-Clark State College
500 8th Ave.   208-792-2465
Lewiston, ID 83501   Fax: 208-792-2878
www.lcsc.edu/isbdc
The center provides general assistance and funding information. They also conduct market assessments.

Idaho State University
Small Business Development Center
2300 N. Yellowstone   208-523-1087
Idaho Falls, ID 83401   Fax: 208-528-7127
www.idahosbdc.org
The center provides general assistance and funding information, and conducts technical assessments. Inventors meet with other inventors and investors.

Illinois
Small Business Development Center
Department of Commerce and Community Affairs
620 East Adams St., 3rd Floor   217-782-7500
Springfield, IL 62701   Fax: 217-785-6328
www.commerce.state.il.us
The center offers counseling for a wide range of business issues and problems, including commercialization and patent processes.

Small Business Development Center
Evanston Business Investment Corp.
1840 Oak Avenue   847-866-1817
Evanston, IL 60201-3670   Fax: 847-866-1808
The center provides general assistance and funding information.

Western Illinois University
Small Business Development Center
214 Seal Hall   309-298-2211
1 University Circle   Fax: 309-298-2520
Macomb, IL 61455-1390
www.wiusbdc.org
The center provides general assistance; conducts market/technical assessments; provides investment and funding information; and aids in building a prototype. Inventors meet with other inventors and investors, and get the chance to showcase their inventions.

Illinois Innovators and Inventor's Club
P.O. Box 623
Edwardsville, IL 62025   618-288-6275
They are a non-profit group created to exchange useful information and ideas. Membership fees cover monthly meetings, newsletters, and events.

Inventors' Council
431 South Dearborn, Suite 705   312-939-3329
Chicago, IL 60605
www.donmoyer.com
Email: don@donmoyer.com
There is a multitude of information and links to information at this web site. Patent searching tools, how to get a free patent application if you are eligible, technology information, science facts, where to look for money, and so much more is available. Mostly, their workshops are in virtual reality on the web, but they still hold some of them in person, and they are free! They list tips from them, such as The Fool Rule, The secrets Rule and other basics. Mr. Moyer cannot answer questions over the phone, but he will do so through Email.

Indiana

Small Business Development Center   Toll-free: 888-ISBD-244
One North Capitol, Suite 900   317-234-2082
Indianapolis, IN 46204   Fax: 317-232-8872
The center offers counseling for a wide range of business issues and problems.

Indiana Inventors Association
5514 South Adams   765-674-2845
Marion, IN 46953   Fax: 765-733-0579
This is an informal non-profit group. Their members include inventors, engineers, educators and more. They are concerned with the innovation process and look to answer questions and solve problems at the monthly meetings. There is no fee.

Iowa

Small Business Development Center
Iowa State University
2501 N. Loop Drive   515-296-7828
Bldg. 1, Suite 1615   Fax: 515-296-6714
Ames, IA 50010-8283
www.iabusnet.org
The center offers counseling for a wide range of business issues and problems.

Drake Small Business Development Center and
Inventure Program
2429 University Avenue   515-271-2655
Des Moines, IA 50311   Fax: 515-271-1899
The Inventure Program is a program within the Small Business Development Center. In the program, they will evaluate a product so that the inventor can decide if it is feasible to go to market. There is a fee of $125 and it is open to all people in the nation. The Small Business Development Center offers counseling on commercialization and other business aspects. There is no charge for this and it is only open to residents of Iowa.

Kansas

Small Business Development Center
Wichita State University
Campus Box 148
1845 Fairmount   316-978-3193
Wichita, KS 67260-0148   Fax: 316-978-3647
http://webs.wichita.edu/depttools/user_home/?view=ksbdc
Email: wsusbdc@wichita.edu
The center offers counseling for a wide range of business issues and problems.

Inventors' Association of South Central Kansas
2302 Amarado
Wichita, KS 67205   316-721-1866
www.networksplus.net/aledarich
Email: aledarich@networksplus.net
They have monthly meetings with a guest speaker who takes questions after finishing the speech. Reports of important information concerning the group, discussions and workshops are included. Guests and members must sign a non-disclosure agreement to protect the ideas that are discussed. There is a membership fee.

Kentucky

Small Business Development Center
123 E. Main St.   502-625-0123
Louisville, KY 40202   Fax: 502-625-1181
www.louisvillesmallbiz.org
This center counsels inventors on commercialization and patent processes and provides critical reviews of inventions. It provides assistance in technically refining inventions. There are no fees.

Small Business Development Center
Kentucky's Small Business Development Centers
Center for Business Development
College of Business and Economics Building
225 Gatton College of Business & Economics
University of Kentucky   859-257-7668
Lexington, KY 40506-0034   888-475-SBDC
www.ksbdc.org   Fax: 859-323-1907
Kentucky's Small Business Development Centers provide the Commonwealth of Kentucky's entrepreneurs and small businesses with management consulting, environmental consulting, educational training, and business resources needed to maximize their growth. There are 15 centers located throughout the state.

Kentucky Transportation Center
176 Oliver H. Raymond Bldg.   859-257-4513
Lexington, KY 40506-0281   Fax: 859-257-1815
www.ktc.uky.edu
The center works closely with various federal, state and local agencies, as well as the private sector to conduct research supported by a wide variety of sources.

Central Kentucky Inventors Council, Inc.
3060 Pine Ridge Road
Winchester, KY 40391   859-842-4110

Louisiana

Small Business Development Center
University of Louisiana at Monroe
College of Business Administration
700 University Avenue, Room 2-123   318-342-1224
Monroe, LA 71209   Fax: 318-342-3085
Louisiana Economic Development provides referral to and financial support for the 12 Small Business Development Centers. The SBDCs offer assistance by providing a variety of information and guidance to small businesses, entrepreneurs, and small business start-ups.

Louisiana Department of Economic Development
P.O. Box 94185
1051 N. Third St.

Baton Rouge, LA 70802-9185   225-342-3000
www.lded.state.la.us
The department provides general assistance.

Maine
Department of Industrial Cooperation
5717 Corbet Hall, Room 480   207-581-2200
Orono, ME 04469-5717   Fax: 207-581-1479
www.umaine.edu/dic
On March 15, 1984, the Inventors Forum of Maine, Inc. (IFM), was formed and became a nonprofit corporation in the state of Maine. It was organized to stimulate inventiveness and entrepreneurship, and to help innovators and entrepreneurs develop and promote their ideas. It allows inventors and entrepreneurs to join together, share ideas and hopefully improve the chance for success. It gives encouragement, professional expertise, evaluation assistance, confidentiality and moral support of the University of Maine's Network and the University of Southern Maine's Small Business Development Center.

The Inventors Forum of Maine generally meets on the first Tuesday evening of each month at the University of Southern Maine, Campus Center, Room A, B & C on Bedford Street in Portland. Membership is open to all.

Portland Inventors' Forum
5717 Corbet Hall, Room 480
University of Maine   207-581-2200
Orono, ME 04469-5717   Fax: 207-581-1479
www.umaine.edu/DIC/Invent/IFM.htm
This group of inventors and business people offer encouragement, professional expertise, confidentiality and evaluation assistance to its members. At the monthly meeting they have Show & Tell, speakers and open discussions. There is not a membership fee.

Maryland
Inventions and Innovations
Department of Energy
Forrestal Building
1000 Independence Ave., SW
Washington, DC 20585-0121   202-586-2079
www.eere.energy.gov/inventions
The office evaluates all promising non-nuclear energy-related inventions, particularly those submitted by independent inventors and small companies for the purpose of obtaining direct grants for their development from the U.S. Department of Energy.

Small Business Development Center
Meridian Management Group, Inc.
826 E. Baltimore Street   410-333-2548
Baltimore, MD 21202   Fax: 410-333-2552
www.mmggroup.com
Email: contact@mmggroup.com
The center offers counseling for a wide range of business issues and problems.

Massachusetts
Massachusetts Small Business Development Center
Salem State College Enterprise Center
121 Loring Avenue, Suite 310
Salem, MA 01970   978-542-6343
www.salemsbdc.org
The center offers counseling for a wide range of business issues and problems.

Small Business Development Center
227 Isenberg School of Management
121 Presidents Drive
University of Massachusetts   413-545-6301
Amherst, MA 01003-9310   Fax: 413-545-1273
http://msbdc.som.umass.edu
The center provides general assistance and funding information.

Smaller Business Association of New England
1601 Trapelo Rd., Ste. 212   781-890-9070
Waltham, MA 02451   Fax: 781-890-4567
www.sbane.org
The association provides general assistance and funding information.

Inventors' Association of New England (IANE)
P.O. Box 335   978-433-2397
Lexington, MA 02420-0004   Fax: 978-433-3516
www.inventne.org
At the monthly meetings, they discuss things such as patent protection, licensing, manufacturing and avoiding scams. They also have guest speakers and free workshops. Their inventor shows and exhibits showcase member's inventions. Membership dues cover meetings, a monthly newsletter, and discounts to trade shows, and some publications.

Innovators' Resource Network
c/o Pelham West Associates
P.O. Box 137
Shutesbury, MA 01072-0137   413-259-2006
http://pages.prodigy.net/pwassoc/irn.html
Email: info@IRNetwork.org
The center of this group of inventors and business people have either created successful businesses with their invention, or they have been licensed. They focus on getting the product to market. Monthly meetings alternate between public and private. They involve networking, announcements, assistance and a guest speaker.

Cape Cod Inventors Association
Briar Main
P.O. Box 143
Wellfleet, MA 02667   508-349-1629

Inventors Association of New England
P.O. Box 577   978-433-2397
Pepperal, MA 01463   Fax: 978-433-3516
www.inventne.org
Expert speakers and members join together to provide guidance to inventors in the areas of patents, marketing, and product development.

Michigan

Small Business & Technology Development Center
Grand Valley State University
Seidman School of Business
510 W. Fulton Street   616-331-7480
Grand Rapids, MI 49504   Fax: 616-331-7485
www.misbtdc.org
The Small Business & Technology Development Center offers support, training and counsel to small business owners and entrepreneurs throughout the 83 counties in Michigan.

Inventors Club of America
524 Curtis Road
East Lansing, MI 48823   517-332-3561
They meet monthly where a roll call is kept. They have an open quorum and look to help each other with past experiences.

Inventor's Council of Mid-Michigan (ICMM)
Flint-Genesee Economic Growth Alliance
519 South Saginaw Street, Suite 210   810-238-7803
Flint, MI 48502   Fax: 810-238-7866
www.flintchamber.org
The goal is to help members with patents, trademarks, and copyrights and to get their inventions to market without a large cost. The monthly dues cover meetings and a 2 year subscription to Inventors Digest.

Inventors Association of Metropolitan Detroit
749 Clairepointe Circle St.
St. Clair, MI 48081

Minnesota

Minnesota Project Innovation, Inc.
100 Mill Place
111 Third Ave. S.   612-338-3280
Minneapolis, MN 55401   Fax: 612-349-2603
www.mpi.org
This project is affiliated with the Minnesota Dept. of Energy and Economic Development, U.S. Small Business Administration, and private companies. It provides referrals to inventors for sources of technical assistance in refining inventions.

Minnesota Inventors Congress (MIC)
805 E Bridge St., Box 71   507-637-2344
Redwood Falls, MN 56283   Fax: 507-637-8399
www.invent1.org   800-invent1
Email: mic@invent1.org

The Minnesota Inventors Congress (MIC) is a nonprofit organization established in 1958 to promote creativity, innovation, entrepreneurship by assisting the inventor and entrepreneur with education, promotion and referral. It's a professional organization composed of private individuals and corporations, who are creating and developing useful technologies. MIC is for inventors at every development stage - the novice and experienced; male or female; young and old; and supporters of invention and innovation. Workshops are also available. These are for individuals with ideas or inventions not yet successfully on the market; for companies, entrepreneurs looking for such inventions or new products.

"World's Oldest Annual Invention Convention," promotes the spirit of invention and innovation. Each year a 3 day convention presents more than 200 inventions and attracts some 10,000 visitors from around the world. The MIC provides a meeting place for:

1. Inventors to showcase their new products, connecting with manufacturers/investors, product test market, educational seminars, publicity, inventors network, and $1,500 in cash awards.

2. Manufacturers, marketers, investors and licensees seeking new products.

3. Inventors, viewers and exhibitors seeking free counsel and literature on the invention development process.

4. Public to view the latest inventions, by adults and students, purchase MarketPlace products and meet global inventors.

University of Minnesota, Duluth
Center for Economic Development
Duluth Technology Village   Toll free: 888-387-4594
11 East Superior Street, Suite 210   218-726-7298
Duluth, MN 55802   Fax: 218-726-6338
www.umdced.com
The center offers counseling for a wide range of business issues and problems.

Society of Minnesota Inventors
20231 Basalt St.   612-753-2766
Anoka, MN 55303
With two meetings a month, this group aims to educate inventors. They have inventor question and answer, discussion sessions, and conduct general business. There is a small monthly fee.

Inventors' Network (Mpls./St.Paul)
23 Empire Dr., Suite 105
St. Paul, MN 55103   651-602-3175
www.inventorsnetwork.org

Mississippi
Mississippi State University
Small Business Development Center
P.O. Box 5288   662-325-8684
Mississippi State, MS 39762   Fax: 662-325-4016
www.cbi.msstate.edu/cobi/sbdc/sbdc.html
The center provides general assistance; conducts market assessments; and provides funding information.

Small Business Development Center
Meridian Community College
910 Highway 19 North   601-483-8241
Meridian, MS 39307
www.mcc.cc.ms.us
The center provides general assistance and funding information; conducts market/technical assessments; and offers legal advice on patents and licensing. Inventors meet with other inventors and investors.

Society of Mississippi Inventors
B19 Jeannette Phillips Dr.
P.O. Box 1848   800-725-7232 (in MS only)
University of Mississippi   662-915-5001
University, MS 38677-1848   Fax: 662-915-5650
www.olemiss.edu/depts/mssbdc/invent.html
Email: msbdc@olemiss.edu
This Small Business Development Center specializes in assisting inventors. They help inventors to get started with an idea, give them sources for evaluation, patents, trademarks, finance, and specialized assistance. There are also seminars and workshops.

Mississippi SBDC Inventor Assistance
B 19 Jeanette Phillips Dr.   662-915-5001
www.olemiss.edu/depts/mssbdc/invent.html   800-725-7232 (in MS only)
                                             Fax: 662-915-5650
This organization provides a wide range of services to assist Mississippi residents through the invention process.

Missouri

Missouri Innovation Center
Student Health Building
410 South Sixth Street   573-884-0496
Columbia, MO 65211-2290   Fax: 573-884-3600
www.marketmaker.org/aboutus.htm
Email: info@marketmaker.org
This group provides communications among inventors, manufacturers, patent attorneys and venture capitalists, and provides general consultations. It is sponsored by the state, city of Columbia, and the University of Missouri. There are fees for some services.

Inventors Association of St. Louis
P.O. Box 410111
St. Louis, MO 63141   314-432-1291
The group holds monthly meetings, provides communications among inventors, manufacturers, patent attorneys, and venture capitalists. It publishes a newsletter. There are annual dues.

Small Business Development Centers
University of Missouri - Columbia
1205 University Ave.
Suite 300   573-882-0344
Columbia, MO 65211   Fax: 573-884-4297
www.missouribusiness.net/sbdc/index.asp
The center offers counseling for a wide range of business issues and problems.

Women's Inventor Project
7400 Foxmount
Hazlewood, MO 63042

Montana

Small Business Development Center
Montana Department of Commerce
301 South Park Ave.
P.O. Box 200501   406-841-2746
Helena, MT 59620-0501   Fax: 406-841-2728
www.commerce.state.mt.us
The center offers counseling for a wide range of business issues and problems.

Montana Inventors Association
5350 Love Lane   406-586-1541
Bozeman, MT 59178
They have a yearly 2-day meeting for inventors. The guest speaker is a known inventor or a patent officer. They will answer questions and have discussions and some of the inventors talk about the process they used to market their product. They also have a member directory.

Blue Sky Inventors
1200 Blair Lane, Apt. #1
Billings, MT 59102   406-259-9110

Nebraska

University of Nebraska – Lincoln
Engineering Extension
W 189 Nebraska Hall
Lincoln, NE 68588   402-472-5600
                                                     Fax: 402-472-0015
Upon request, the University will send a packet of information so that the individual may go to the location and conduct their own Patent and Trademark search.

Nebraska Business Development Center
University of Nebraska at Omaha
Roskens Hall, CBA, Room 415   402-554-2521
Omaha, NE 68182-0248   Fax: 402-554-3473
http://nbdc.unomaha.edu
The center offers counseling for a wide range of business issues and problems.

Nevada

Nevada Small Business Center
University of Nevada - Reno
College of Business Administration,
Business Building, Room 411
Reno, NV 89557-0100   775-784-1717
www.nsbdc.org   Fax: 775-784-4337
Email: nsbdc@unr.nevada.edu
The center provides general assistance and funding information. Inventors meet with other inventors and get to showcase their inventions.

Nevada Small Business Development Center
851 E. Tropicana, Bldg. 700
UNLV, 4505 Maryland Pkwy.
P.O. Box 456011
Las Vegas, NV 89154   702-895-4270
www.nsbdc.org   Fax: 702-895-4273
Email: nsbdc@unlv.nevada.edu
The center provides general assistance and funding information. Inventors meet with other inventors.

Inventors Society of Southern Nevada
Las Vegas, NV 89121   702-435-7741
Here inventors will learn the process from A to Z. The group will answer questions and send its members in the correct direction to accomplish their goals. They host different speakers from the field at monthly meetings which are open to the public. All ideas are kept confidential. There are yearly dues that cover all of this plus a newsletter.

Nevada Inventors Association
P.O. Box 11008   775-677-0123
Reno, NV 89510-1108   Fax: 775-677-1322
www.nevadainventors.org
Email: inventors@nevadainventors.org
They offer education, assistance, and networking to their members. Anywhere from one to nine guests will show up at the monthly meetings. They also put together a monthly newsletter.

New Hampshire

Small Business Development Center
University of New Hampshire
108 McConnell Hall   603-862-2200
15 College Rd.   Fax: 603-862-4876

Durham, NH 03824
www.nhsbdc.org
The center offers counseling for a wide range of business issues and problems.

Small Business Development Center
33 Commercial Street
Manchester, NH 03101-1796   603-624-2000
www.nhsbdc.org   Fax: 603-647-4410
Email: sbdc_manchester@verizonesg.net
The Small Business Development Center provides general assistance and funding information, and offers legal
advice on patents and licensing. Inventors meet with other inventors.

New Jersey

Small Business Development Center
Rutgers University
49 Bleeker St.   973-353-5950
Newark, NJ 07102-1897   Fax: 973-353-1030
http://njsbdc.com/home
The Small Business Development Center offers counseling for a wide range of business issues and problems.

Jersey Shore Inventors Club
23 Pittenger Pond Rd.   732-407-8885
Freehold, NJ 07728
They have monthly meetings where inventors can learn from each other.

National Society of Inventors
94 North Rockledge Dr.   973-994-9282
Livingston, NJ 07039-1121   Fax: 973-535-0777
This group is "Inventor Friendly". They are inventors helping each other in the
New Jersey area. They offer meetings that either have speakers or round table
discussions that are open to the public. There is a minimal membership fee.

Kean Univ. SBDC
215 North Ave., Room 242   908-737-5950
Union NJ 07083   Fax: 908-737-5955

New Jersey Entrepreneurs Forum
P.O. Box 313   908-789-3424
Westfield, NJ 07091-0313   Fax: 908-789-9761

New Mexico

New Mexico Invention Club
P.O. Box 30062
Albuquerque, NM 87190   505-266-3541 (phone/fax)
The contact is Dr. Albert Goodman, president of the club. The club meets on a monthly basis for speakers and
presentations by different inventors. Members include patent attorneys, investors, and manufacturers.

Small Business Development Center
Santa Fe Community College   800-281-7232
6401 Richards Ave.   505-428-1362
Santa Fe, NM 87505   Fax: 505-428-1469
www.nmsbdc.org
Email: sbdc@sfccn.org
The center offers counseling for a wide range of business issues and problems.

New York

Small Business Development Center
University of Albany
One Pinnacle Place, Suite 218   518-453-9567
Albany, NY 12203-3439   Fax: 518-453-9572
www.nyssbdc.org
Email: albsbdc@nycap.rr.com
The center offers counseling for a wide range of business issues and problems.

New York State Energy Research and Development Authority
17 Columbia Circle   Toll free: 866-NYSERDA
Albany, NY 12203-6399   518-862-1090
www.nyserda.org   Fax: 518-862-1091
The office provides general assistance and investment and funding information. It assists in building a prototype.

SUNY Institute of Technology
Small Business Development Center
P.O. Box 3050, Rte. 12N   315-792-7547
Utica, NY 13504-3050   Fax: 315-792-7554
www.sbdc.sunyit.edu
Email: sbdc@sunyit.edu
The center provides general assistance and funding information; conducts market/technical assessments; offers legal advice on patents and licensing, and assists in building a prototype. Inventors meet with other inventors.

Empire State Development
Division for Small Business
30 South Pearl St.   800-782-8369
Albany, NY 12245
www.empire.state.ny.us/
Email: sbtif@empire.state.ny.us
The program provides financing assistance for technology-based start-up companies with initial investment as much as $300,000.

United Inventors Association of the USA
P.O. Box 23447   585-359-9310
Rochester, NY 14692   Fax: 585-359-1132
www.uiausa.org
This non-profit group helps inventors by educating them to develop their business and offer support and recognition. The members and guest speakers offer useful information and contacts at the monthly meetings.

Long Island Forum for Technology, Inc.
111 West Main St.   631-969-3700
Bay Shore, NY 11706   Fax: 631-969-4489
www.lift.org
Email: info@lift.org

Inventors Society of Western New York
52 Manor Hill Drive
Fairport, NY 14450   585-223-1225
Email: inventnewyork@aol.com

Innovators Resource Network of Central NY
65 Hospital Hill Road
Binghamton, NY 13901   607-648-4626
Email: mvpinnovation@aol.com

North Carolina
Small Business Development Center
University of North Carolina
5 West Target St.   919-715-7272
Raleigh, NC 27601-1348   Fax: 919-715-7777
The center offers counseling for a wide range of business issues and problems.

North Dakota
Center for Innovation
University of North Dakota
4300 Dartmouth Drive
P.O. Box 8372   701-777-3132
Grand Forks, ND 58202-8372   Fax: 701-777-2339
www.innovators.net
This center conducts occasional seminars and workshops with speakers; counsels on the commercialization and patenting process; provides communications among inventors, manufacturers, and patent attorneys. There are fees for services, but the first consultation is free.

Small Business Development Center
University of North Dakota
P.O. Box 7308   701-777-3700
Grand Forks, ND 58202-7308   Fax: 701-777-3225
www.ndsbdc.org
www.und.edu/academics/departments
The center offers counseling for a wide range of business issues and problems.

North Dakota Inventors Congress
2534 South University Drive, Suite 4   800-281-7009
Fargo, ND 58103   701-281-8822
www.ndinventors.com   Fax: 701-237-0544
The NDIC provides inventors and entrepreneurs with all the information needed to see an idea through to fruition.

Ohio
Inventors Council of Dayton
Wright Brothers Station
P.O. Box 611   937-293-2770
Dayton, OH 45409-0611   Fax: 937-293-3061
www.xec.com/invent/index.html
This association meets on a regular basis and provides communication among inventors, manufacturers, patent attorneys, etc., and often publishes newsletters.

Docie Invention Services
73 Maplewood Drive   740-594-5200
Athens, OH 45701-1910   Fax: 740-594-4004 (Limit three pages)
http://docie.com
Email: idea@docie.com
Docie Marketing provides assistance to inventors worldwide, including free educational material, free referrals to legitimate invention service providers, commission-based brokerage, and fee-based services for inventors.

Small Business Development Center
Department of Development
77 S. High Street   800-848-1300
P.O. Box 1001   614-466-4551
Columbus, OH 43216-1001   Fax: 614-644-5167
www.odod.state.oh.us.com

Email: connect@odod.state.oh.us
The center offers counseling for a wide range of business issues and problems.

Inventors Connection of Greater Cleveland, Inc.
P.O. Box 360804   216-226-9681
Cleveland, OH 44136
http://members.aol.com/icgc/index.htm
This is a non-profit organization of inventors helping inventors to make ideas into marketable products. They provide information on patent developments, educate them on things pertaining to the inventing process, and identify needs for those inventions that have a possible market. Monthly meetings cover many topics, but stress the introduction of ideas into the marketplace.

Inventors Council of Canton
303 55th Street, NW
North Canton, OH 44720   330-499-1262
The Council provides an opportunity for inventors to meet and share ideas. They hold monthly meetings to further this goal.

Inventors Network
1275 Kinnear Road
Columbus, OH 43212   614-470-0144
This is a non-profit group with members in varying occupations. Entrepreneurs and inventors are educated on the invention process and production. They meet monthly to network and question various guest speakers. They cover topics like manufacturing, prototyping, and marketing. They also have a yearly seminar.

Inventor's Council of Cincinnati
121 Bradford Drive   513-831-0664
Milford, OH 45150   Fax: 513-831-6328
Email: InventorsCouncil@fuse.net

Youngstown-Warren Inv. Assn.
500 City Center One, P.O. Box 507   330-744-4481
Youngstown, OH 44501-0500

Research

Oklahoma
Small Business Development Center
Southeastern Oklahoma State University
517 University, P.O. Box 2584   508-745-2877
Durant, OK 74701   Fax: 508-745-7471
www.osbdc.org
The center offers counseling for a wide range of business issues and problems.

Inventor's Assistance Program   877-577-7632 (in OK)
395 Cordell South   405-744-8727
Stillwater, OK 74078-8015   Fax: 405-744-8516
http://techweb.ceat.okstate.edu/ias
This is a service to help inventors navigate the process from idea to marketplace using information, education and referrals. The service itself is free.

Oklahoma Inventors Congress
P.O. Box 57464
Oklahoma City, OK 73157-7464   405-947-5782
Email: wbaker@gbronline.com   Fax: 405-947-6950
They are a self-help group that shares knowledge and experience with each other in order to help in the invention process. They hold monthly meetings.

Oregon

Eastern Oregon University
Small Business Development Center
One University Blvd.   541-962-1532 (Phone and Fax)
La Grande, OR 97850
Email: sbdc@eoni.com
www.eoni.com/~sbdc

Oregon Institute of Technology
Small Business Development Center
3201 Campus Dr.
Boivin Hall, Room 119   541-885-1760
Klamath Falls, OR 97601-8801   Fax: 541-885-1761
www.oit.edu/sbdc/5
Email: sbdc@oit.edu

Southern Oregon University
Small Business Development Center
322 W. 6th St.   541-772-3478
Medford, OR 97501   Fax: 541-734-4813
www.sou.edu/business/sbdc.htm
Small Business Development Centers (SBDCs) at three state colleges and the community colleges can counsel
inventors and direct them where to go for patent process, etc.

Oregon Small Business Development Center
1445 Willamette Street, Ste 1   541-463-5255
Eugene, OR 97401-4087   Fax: 541-686-0096
www.bizcenter.org
The center provides general assistance and funding information.

Small Business Development Center
2025 Lloyd Center Mall   503-978-5080
Portland, OR 97232   Fax: 503-288-1366
www.bizcenter.org/portland
The Small Business Development Center offers free business counseling services to small and start-up businesses
throughout the Portland-Metro area. They can help you with planning, marketing, etc.

Oregon State Library
State Library Building
250 Winter St., NE   503-378-4277
Salem, OR 97301-3950   Fax: 503-588-7119
www.osl.state.or.us
Organization's name and address may be given to individual inventors for referrals.

South Coast Inventors Group
c/o Southwestern Business Development Center
2455 Mapleleaf   541-888-7100
North Bend, OR 97459   Fax: 541-756-5735

Pennsylvania

Small Business Development Center
Bucknell University   Toll free: 866-375-6010
125 Dana Engineering Bldg.   570-577-1249
Lewisburg, PA 17837   Fax: 570-577-1768

www.departments.bucknell.edu/sbdc/
Email: sbdc@bucknell.edu
The center offers counseling for a wide range of business issues and problems.

Pennsylvania Small Business Development Centers
University of Pennsylvania, The Wharton School
Vance Hall, 4th Floor
3733 Spruce Street   215-898-4861
Philadelphia, PA 19104-6374   Fax: 215-898-1063
www.pasbdc.org
Email: pasbdc@wharton.upenn.edu
The center provides general assistance and funding information. It also conducts market and technical assessments.
It also oversees all centers in Pennsylvania.

American Society of Inventors
P.O. Box 58426
Philadelphia, PA 19102-5426   215-546-6601
www.asoi.org
Email: info@asoi.org
This group offers members legal, technical, and business information. Some of the services that they have are, the
Information Index, the Inventors Notebook, and the Invention Conception, all provided to help the member become
creative and successful. They have bi-monthly meetings and newsletters. At the Board Meeting, 2 members will be
allowed to have their inventions evaluated.

Pennsylvania Inventors Association
2317 East 43rd
Erie, PA 16510   814-825-5820
"What we are able to conceive, we are meant to create", is the motto of this group. They bring together people with
ideas, link inventors to industry, and get support for inventors. Meetings are open to local inventors and others
interested in promoting creativity.

Central Pennsylvania Inventors Association
9 First Avenue
Lemoyne, PA 17043   717-763-5742

Puerto Rico
Puerto Rico Inventors Association
PO Box 1081
Saint Just, PR 00978   787-760-5074

Rhode Island
Service Corps of Retired Executives (SCORE)
c/o U.S. Small Business Administration
380 Westminster St., Room #511   401-528-4571
Providence, RI 02903   Fax: 401-528-4539
www.sba.gov/ri
Volunteers in the SCORE office are experts in many areas of business management and can offer advice to
inventors in areas including marketing and the commercialization process.

Small Business Development Center
30 Exchange Terrace
Providence, RI 02903   401-831-1330
The center offers counseling for a wide range of business issues and problems.

Small Business Development Center
Bryant College
1150 Douglas Pike   401-232-6111
Smithfield, RI 02917-1284   Fax: 401-232-6933
www.risbdc.org
The Rhode Island Small Business Development Center helps entrepreneurs by providing consulting services. The center helps businesses grow and increase their profitability. These services are free to Rhode Island residents. Contact any one of the RISBDC offices listed in the Directory of Offices.

The Center for Design & Business
169 Weybosset St., Floor #2   401-454-6108
Providence, RI 02903   Fax: 401-454-6559

South Carolina
Small Business Development Center
South Carolina State University
School of Business
300 College Ave.
Orangeburg, SC 29117   803-536-8445
http://belcher.scsu.edu   Fax: 803-536-8066
The center offers counseling for a wide range of business issues and problems.

South Carolina Small Business Development Center
University of South Carolina
1710 College Street
College of Business Administration   803-777-4907
Columbia, SC 29208   Fax: 803-777-4403
The center provides general assistance and funding information.

South Dakota
Small Business Development Center
University of South Dakota
Business Research Bureau
169 Weybosset St., Floor #2
School of Business
414 East Clark St.   605-677-5287
Vermillion, SD 57069-2390   Fax: 605-677-5427
www.usd.edu/brbinfo
Email: brbinfo@usd.edu
The center offers counseling for a wide range of business issues and problems.

South Dakota Inventors Congress
Box 2220
Brookings, SD 57007   605-688-4184
                                          Fax: 605-688-5880

Tennessee
Jackson State Community College
Small Business Development Center
2046 North Parkway Street   731-424-5389
Jackson, TN 38301   Fax: 731-425-2641
The center offers counseling for a wide range of business issues and problems.

Tennessee Inventor's Association
P.O. Box 11225
Knoxville, TN 37939-1225   865-981-2927
www.uscni.com/tia
Their main goal is the advancement of technology through Tennessee by providing guidance, information, and encouragement. They have a TIA Inventor's Guide that has topics such as the Inventors Log, how to market your product yourself, prototypes, and licensing. Their members include inventors, small business developers, research scientists and more to network with. There is a lot more information available with this group.

Inventors' Association of Middle Tennessee and South Kentucky
3908 Trimble Rd.
Nashville, TN 37215   615-269-4346

Texas

Bill J. Priest Institute for Economic Development
Dallas Community College District
1402 Corinth Street   214-860-5900
Dallas, TX 75215   Fax: 214-860-5815
www.billpriestinstitute.org/dallas_sbdc.htm
The center offers counseling for a wide range of business issues and problems.

Texas Tech University
Small Business Development Center   806-745-1637
2579 S. Loop 289, St. 210   800-992-7232
Lubbock, TX 79423   Fax: 806-745-6717
www.lubbock-sbdc.org
The center provides general assistance and funding information.

Amarillo Inventors Association
7000 West 45th Street, Suite 2   806-352-6085
Amarillo, TX 79109   Fax: 806-352-6264
They have monthly meetings in order to inform inventors of steps that they can take to enhance their invention.

Houston Inventors Association
2916 West T.C. Jester Boulevard
Suite 100   713-686-7676
Houston, TX 77018   Fax: 713-686-7676
www.inventors.org
Speakers at monthly meetings discuss their success stories, technical areas, and share tips on making money from inventions. There are also monthly workshops on patent fundamentals, injection moldings and more. They will put together members having a problem with members who can help them.

Technology Advocates of San Antonio
Inventors & Entrepreneurs SIG
112 E. Pecan, Ste. 100
San Antonio, Texas 78205   210-246-5995
Email: tasa@tasa.org   Fax: 210-246-5999
www.tasa.org

Texas Inventors Association
P.O. Box 251248
Plano, TX 75025   972-312-0090
www.asktheinventors.com
Successful inventors providing experienced advice for new inventors.

Utah

Utah Small Business Development Center
9750 S. 300 West MCPC   801-957-3480
Sandy, UT 84070   Fax: 801-957-3488
www.slcc.edu/sbdc
The center provides general assistance and funding information, and conducts market research and strategy.

Vermont

Economic and Development Office
State of Vermont
National Life Bldg.   802-828-3211
North, Drawer 20   Fax: 802-828-3258
Montpelier, VT 05620
www.dca.state.vt.us
Inventors will be given references to businesses that can assist with the commercialization and marketing process.

Small Business Development Center
P.O. Box 188   Toll free: 800-464-7232 (in VT)
Randolph Center, VT 05061-0188   802-728-9101
www.vtsbdc.org   Fax: 802-728-3026
The center offers counseling for a wide range of business issues and problems.

Inventors Network of Vermont
4 Park Street   802-885-5100
Springfield, VT 05156

Invent Vermont
PO Box 82
Woodbury, VT 05681   802-472-8741

Virginia

Virginia Small Business Development Center
Department of Business Assistance
707 E. Main St., Suite 300
P.O. Box 446   804-371-8200
Richmond, VA 23218-0446   Fax: 804-371-8111
www.dba.state.va.us
The center offers counseling for a wide range of business issues and problems.

Small Business Development Center
2000 Holiday Drive, Suite 200   434-295-8198
Charlottesville, VA 22901   Fax: 434-817-0664
http://avenue.org
Email: sbdc@cstone.net
The center provides general assistance, conducts market studies, and refers inventors to companies that conduct market and technical assessments.

Blue Ridge Inventors' Club
P.O. Box 7451   434-973-3708
Charlottesville, VA 22906-7451   Fax: 434-973-2648
www.inventorclub.org
The purpose of this club is to help people protect their innovations, provide information on patents, trademarks, and copyrights, and inform them how the US Patent and Trademark Office operates.

Inventors Network of the Capital Area
6501 Inwood Drive   703-971-7443
Springfield, VA 22150   Fax: 703-971-9216
This is a non-profit educational organization offering monthly meetings, guest speakers, and networking with fellow inventors.

Washington
Innovation Assessment Center
Washington State University   509-335-6843
Pullman, WA 99164-4851   Fax: 509-335-6843
www.wsbdc.org/services/innovation_assessment.htm
Part of the Small Business Development Center, this center performs commercial evaluations of inventions, counseling and provides assistance with patentability searches. There are fees for services.

Small Business Development Center
Washington State University
Spokane, WA 99210   509-358-7765
www.wsbdc.org   Fax: 509-358-7764
Email: sbdc@wsu.edu
The center offers counseling for a wide range of business issues and problems.

Small Business Development Center
Western Washington University
Bellingham Towers
119 N. Commercial St., Suite 195   360-733-4014
Bellingham, WA 98225   Fax: 360-733-5092
www.cbe.wwu.edu/sbdc
The center provides general assistance, and investment and funding information.

Inventors Network
P.O. Box 5575
Vancouver, WA 98668   503-239-8299
This is a nonprofit inventor's self-help club whose goal it is to make an invention a reality. They will not do it for you, but rather help you to do it yourself. There is an annual membership fee.

West Virginia
West Virginia Development Center
Fairmount State College
3040 University Ave.   304-293-5839
Morgantown, WV 26505
The center offers counseling for a wide range of business issues and problems.

West Virginia Small Business Development Office
Marshall University
2000 7th Ave.   304-696-6246
Huntington, WV 25703-1527   Fax: 304-696-4835
www.marshall.edu/ibd/sbdc.htmlx
The Marshall University Small Business Development Center is committed to helping businesses and entrepreneurs by providing management assistance and educational programs. There is no charge for the Marshall University Small Business Development Center's counseling services.

Wisconsin
Wisconsin Innovation Service Center
402 McCutchan Hall
UW-Whitewater   262-472-1365
Whitewater, WI 53190   Fax: 262-472-1600
http://academics.uww.edu/business/innovate/innovate.htm
Provides early stage market research for inventors. There is a flat fee of $595 for services.

Small Business Development Center
University of Wisconsin
975 University Ave., Room 3260   608-263-7680
Madison, WI 53706   Fax: 608-263-0818
www.wisconsinsbdc.org
Email: sbdc@bus.wisc.edu
The center offers counseling for a wide range of business issues and problems.

Wisconsin Department of Commerce
201 W. Washington Ave.
P.O. Box 7970   608-266-1018
Madison, WI 53717   Fax: 608-266-1018
www.commerce.state.wi.us
The office provides information on investment and funding.

Inventors Network of Wisconsin
1066 St. Paul Street
Green Bay, WI 54304   920-429-0331
This group holds monthly meetings to advance the knowledge of its members. They do this through speakers, networking, and other resources.

Wyoming
Small Business Development Center
300 South Wolcott, Suite 300   307-234-6683
Casper, WY 82601   Fax: 307-577-7014
http://uwadmnweb.uwyo.edu/sbdc
Dr. Leonard Holler, who works in the office, is able to help inventors on a wide range of issues including patenting, commercialization and intellectual property rights. There are fees for services.

National Organization
United Inventors Association
Carol Oldenburg
P.O. Box 23447   585-359-9310
Rochester, NY 14692   Fax: 585-359-1132
www.uiausa.com
The MISSION of the UIA is to provide leadership, support and services to inventor support groups and independent inventors.

Government Buys Bright Ideas From Inventors: Small Business Innovative Research Programs (SBIR)

The Small Business Innovative Research Program (SBIR) stimulates technological innovation, encourages small science and technology based firms to participate in government funded research, and provides incentives for converting research results into commercial applications. The program is designed to stimulate technological innovation in this country by providing qualified U.S. small business concerns with competitive opportunities to propose innovative concepts to meet the research and development needs of the Federal government. Eleven federal agencies with research and development budgets greater than $100 million are required by law to participate: The Departments of Defense, Health and Human Services, Energy, Agriculture, Commerce, Transportation, and Education; the National Aeronautics and Space Administration; the National Science Foundation; the Nuclear Regulatory Commission; and the Environmental Protection Agency.

Businesses of 500 or fewer employees that are organized for profit are eligible to compete for SBIR funding. Nonprofit organizations and foreign owned firms are not eligible to receive awards, and the research must be carried out in the U.S. All areas of research and development solicit for proposals, and the 2001 budget for SBIR is $1.158 billion. There are three phases of the program: Phase I determines whether the research idea, often on high risk advanced concepts, is technically feasible; whether the firm can do high quality research; and whether sufficient progress has been made to justify a larger Phase II effort. This phase is usually funded for 6 months with awards up to $100,000. Phase II is the principal research effort, and is usually limited to a maximum of $750,000 for up to two years. The third phase, which is to pursue potential commercial applications of the research funded under the first two phases, is supported solely by nonfederal funding, usually from third party, venture capital, or large industrial firms. SBIR is one of the most competitive research and development programs in the government today. About one proposal out of ten received is funded in Phase I. Generally, about half of these receive support in Phase II. Solicitations for proposals are released once a year (in a few cases twice a year). To assist the small business community in its SBIR efforts, the U.S. Small Business Administration publishes the Pre-Solicitation Announcement (PSA) in December, March, June, and September of each year. Every issue of the PSA contains pertinent information on the SBIR Program along with details on SBIR solicitations that are about to be released. This publication eliminates the need for small business concerns to track the activities of all of the federal agencies participating in the SBIR Program. In recognition of the difficulties encountered by many small firms in their efforts to locate sources of funding essential to finalization of their innovative products, SBA has developed the Commercialization Matching System. This system contains information on all SBIR awardees, as well as financing sources that have indicated an interest in investing in SBIR innovations. Firms interested in obtaining more information on the SBIR Program or receiving the PSA, should contact the Office of Technology, Small Business Administration, 409 3rd St., SW, MC/6470, Washington, DC 20416, 202-205-6450.

SBIR representatives can answer questions and send you materials about their agency's SBIR plans and funding:

Department of Agriculture
SBIR Program, U.S. Department of Agriculture, Stop 2243, Waterfront Centre, Suite 2312, 1400 Independence Avenue, SW, Washington, DC 20250-2243; 202-401-6852, Fax: 202-401-6070.

Department of Commerce
Department of Commerce, 1335 East-West Highway, Room 106, Silver Spring, MD 20910, 301-713-3565, Fax: 301-713-4100.

Department of Defense
SBIR/STTR Program Administrator, Office Under Secretary of Defense, U.S. Department of Defense, 1777 North Kent Street, Rosslyn Plaza North, Suite 9100, Arlington, VA 22209, 703-588-8616, Fax: 703-588-7561.

Department of Education
SBIR Program Coordinator, Department of Education, Room 508 D-Capitol Place, 555 New Jersey Avenue, NW Washington DC 20208, 202-219-2004, Fax: 202-219-1407.

Department of Energy
SBIR/STTR Program Manager, US Department of Energy, SC-32 19901 Germantown Road, Germantown, MD 20874-1290, 301-903-3000, Fax: 301-903-3877.

Department of Health and Human Services
Director OSDBU, Office of the Secretary, U.S. Department of Health and Human Services, 200 Independence Ave., Washington, DC 20201; 202-690-7235, Fax: 202-260-4872.

Department of Transportation
SBIR Program Director, DTS-22, US Department of Transportation, Volpe Center, 55 Broadway, Kendall Square, Cambridge, MA 02142-1093, 617-494-2712, Fax: 617-494-2370.

Environmental Protection Agency
Office of Research and Development, US Environmental Protection Agency, ORD/NCER (8722R), 1200 Pennsylvania Ave., NW, Washington DC 20460, 202-564-6823, Fax: 202-565-2447.

National Aeronautics and Space Administration
SBIR Program, National Aeronautics Space Administration-HQ, 300 E. St, SW, Code RC, Washington, DC 20546-0001; 202-358-2320, Fax: 202-358-3878.

Small Business Administration
US Small Business Administration, 409 3rd Street, SW, Mail Code: #6540, Washington, DC 20416, 202-205-6450, Fax: 202-205-6390.

FEDERAL MONEY FOR HOUSING AND REAL ESTATE

Always dreamed of owning your own home or rehabbing a historic one? These dreams are not impossible to achieve thanks to a wide variety of federal and state programs. You can get money to fix up your house in the country, emergency assistance for natural disasters, weatherization and heating assistance, and much more. Most states have programs for first-time homebuyers that may provide assistance with lower interest rates or help with the closing costs. You may even be considered a first-time homebuyer if you have not owned a home in the previous three years! In addition, don't forget to check out county and city community development organizations that may have programs to help you on your way to home ownership.

Many of these programs take advantage of the Community Development and Block Grant Program from the federal government that allows cities and states to help improve the housing situation.

Now don't forget to read the first part of this book, "Types of Assistance and Grants Sources," as well as "More Help In Finding a Grant." These sections provide some great starting places for your money hunt. In addition, the U. S. Department of Housing and Urban Development has a quite extensive site that provides a wealth of information for those interested in buying a home. The website {www.hud.gov} has everything from how to choose a real estate agent; to calculating your mortgage payments; to finding homes for sale that the government is selling for cheap. There are also links to local HUD offices that can assist you in locating other resources in your area. You can also check out the federal government's website {www.consumer.gov} for a listing of publications and other helpful information regarding your home and community.

Other resources to check out include:

- National Association of Housing and Redevelopment Officials, 630 Eye St., NW, Washington, DC 20001; 202-289-3500, Toll Free 877-866-2476; Fax: 202-289-8181; {www.nahro.org}.
- Information Center, Community Connections, P.O. Box 7189, Gaithersburg, MD 20898-7189; 800-998-9999; Fax: 301-519-5027; {www.comcon.org}.
- National Association of Community Action Agencies, Community Action Partnership, 1100 17th St., NW, Suite 500, Washington, DC 20036; 202-265-7546; Fax: 202-265-8850; {www.communityactionpartnership.com}.

The sections that follow outline the Federal money programs available for housing, followed by each state's programs. Again, don't forget to check out your city or county's programs as well. There is also a section on grants and tax credits to renovate historic homes and buildings, and then a mix of other sources of assistance and help for the homeowner. All that is left for you to do is pack the boxes and you are on your way!

The following is a description of the federal funds available to renters, homeowners, developers, and real estate investors for housing assistance in urban and rural areas. This information is derived from the *Catalog of Federal Domestic Assistance* which is published by the U.S. Government Printing Office in Washington, D.C. The number next to the title description is the official reference for this federal program. Contact the office listed below the caption for further details. The following is a description of some of the terms used for the types of assistance available:

Loans: money lent by a federal agency for a specific period of time and with a reasonable expectation of repayment. Loans may or may not require a payment of interest.

Loan Guarantees: programs in which federal agencies agree to pay back part or all of a loan to a private lender if the borrower defaults.

Grants: money given by federal agencies for a fixed period of time and which does not have to be repaid.

Direct Payments: funds provided by federal agencies to individuals, private firms, and institutions. The use of direct payments may be "specified" to perform a particular service or for "unrestricted" use.

Insurance: coverage under specific programs to assure reimbursement for losses sustained. Insurance may be provided by federal agencies or through insurance companies and may or may not require the payment of premiums.

Money for Conserving the Water and Soil During an Emergency

(10.054 Emergency Conservation Program (ECP))
U.S. Department of Agriculture
Farm Service Agency, Stop 0513
1400 Independence Avenue, SW
Washington, DC 20250-0513
202-720-6221
www.fsa.usda.gov
Objectives: To enable farmers to perform emergency conservation measures to control wind erosion on farmlands, or to rehabilitate farmlands damaged by wind erosion, floods, hurricanes, or other natural disasters and to carry out emergency water conservation or water enhancing measures during periods of severe drought. Types of assistance: direct payments for specified use. Estimate of annual funds available: (Direct payments) $82,000,000.

Money to Improve Your Water and Soil

(10.069 Conservation Reserve Program (CRP))
U.S. Department of Agriculture
Farm Service Agency, Stop 0513
1400 Independence Ave, SW
Washington, DC 20250-0513
202-720-6221
www.fsa.usda.gov
Objectives: To protect the Nation's long-term capability to produce food and fiber; to reduce soil erosion; to reduce sedimentation; to improve water quality; to create a better habitat for fish and wildlife; to curb production of some surplus commodities; and to provide some needed income support for farmers. Types of assistance: direct payments for specified use. Estimate of annual funds available: $1,787,722,000.

Money to Change Your Country Property Into a Wetlands

(10.070 Colorado River Basin Salinity Control Program (CRBSCP))
National Resources
Conservation Service
U.S. Department of Agriculture
P.O. Box 2890
Washington, DC 20013
202-720-1873
www.nrcs.usda.gov
Objectives: To provide financial and technical assistance to: (1) Identify salt source areas; (2) develop project plans to carry out conservation practices to reduce salt loads; (3) install conservation practices to reduce salinity levels; (4) carry out research, education, and demonstration activities; (5) carry out monitoring and evaluation activities; and (6) to decrease salt concentration and salt loading which causes increased salinity levels within the Colorado River and to enhance the supply and quality of water available for use in the United States and the Republic of Mexico. Types of assistance: direct payments for specified use. Estimate of annual funds available: (Direct payments) $832,145.

Loans to Help Your Country Property Recover From an Emergency

(10.404 Emergency Loans)
Loan Making Division
U.S. Department of Agriculture
Farm Service Agency
AG Box 0522
Washington, DC 20250
202-720-1632
www.fsa.usda.gov
Objectives: To assist established (owner or tenant)

family farmers, ranchers and aquaculture operators with loans to cover losses resulting from major and/or natural disasters, which can be used for annual farm operating expenses, and for other essential needs necessary to return disaster victims' farming operations to financially sound bases in order that they will be able to return to private sources of credit as soon as possible. Types of assistance: direct loans. Estimate of annual funds available: $40,571,000.

Money to Build Houses for Your Employees

(10.405 Farm Labor Housing Loans and Grants (Labor Housing))
Multifamily Housing Processing Division
Rural Housing Service
U.S. Department of Agriculture
Washington, DC 20250
202-720-1604
www.rurdev.usda.gov
Objectives: To provide decent, safe, and sanitary low rent housing and related facilities for domestic farm laborers. Types of assistance: project grants; guaranteed/insured loans. Estimate of annual funds available: (Loans) $28,522,532. (Grants) $15,000,000.

Money to Buy, Fix Up or Build Houses in Small Towns

(10.410 Very Low to Moderate Income Housing Loans (Section 502 Rural Housing Loans))
Director
Single Family Housing
Direct Loan Division
U.S. Department of Agriculture
Washington, DC 20250
202-720-1474
Or
Direct Single Family Housing Guaranteed Loan Division
Rural Housing Service
U.S. Department of Agriculture
Washington, DC 20250
202-720-1452
www.rurdev.usda.gov
Objectives: To assist lower income rural families through direct loans to buy, build, rehabilitate, or improve decent, safe, and sanitary dwellings and related facilities for use by the applicant as a permanent residence. Subsidized funds are available only on direct loans for low and very low income applicants. Nonsubsidized Funds (loan making) are available for very low and low income applicants who are otherwise eligible for assistance, but based on the amount of the loan requested, the interest credit

assistance formula results in no interest credit. Nonsubsidized funds (loan servicing) are available to very low, low and moderate income applicants/borrowers who do not qualify for interest credit assistance for: (1) Subsequent loans for repair and rehabilitation; and (2) subsequent loan part only (repair or rehabilitation or the payment of equity) in connection with transfers by assumption or credit sales. Loan guarantees are also available to assist moderate income rural families in home acquisition. Types of assistance: direct loans; guaranteed/insured loans. Estimate of annual funds available: (Direct Loans) $1,037,866,417 (for subsidized low or moderate income loans for servicing and repairs). (Guaranteed loans) $2,845,318,616.

Money to Help Low Income Rural Families Get Housing

(10.441 Technical and Supervisory Assistance Grant)
Rural Housing Service (RHS)
USDA
14th Street and Independence Ave., SW
Washington, DC 20250
202-720-1474
www.rurdev.usda.gov
Objectives: To assist low-income rural families in obtaining adequate housing to meet their families needs and/or to provide the necessary guidance to promote their continued occupancy of already adequate housing. These objectives will be accomplished through the establishment or support of housing delivery and counseling projects run by eligible applicants. This program is intended to make use of any available housing program that provides the low-income rural resident access to adequate rental properties or homeownership. Types of assistance: project grants. Estimate of annual funds available: $1,687,543.

Money for Nonprofits to Build Rental Houses in Small Towns

(10.415 Rural Rental Housing Loans)
Multi-Family Housing Processing Division
Rural Housing Service
U.S. Department of Agriculture
Washington, DC 20250
202-720-1604
www.rurdev.usda.gov
Objectives: To provide economically designed and constructed rental and cooperative housing and related facilities suited for independent living for rural residents. Types of assistance: direct loans. Estimate of annual funds available: (Direct Loans) $49,000,000.

Loans and Grants to Fix Up Your House in the Country ($5,000 Grants)

(10.417 Very Low-Income Housing Repair Loans and Grants) (Section 504 Rural Housing Loans and Grants)
Single-Family Housing Processing Division
Rural Housing Service
U.S. Department of Agriculture
Washington, DC 20250
202-720-1474
www.rurdev.usda.gov
Objectives: To give very low income rural homeowners an opportunity to make essential repairs to their homes to make them safe and to remove health hazards to the family or the community. Types of assistance: direct loans; project grants. Estimate of annual funds available: (Loans) $32,396,000. (Grants) $30,000,000.

Money for Needy Families to Keep Their Homes

(10.420 Rural Self-Help Housing Technical Assistance) (Section 523 Technical Assistance)
Director, Single-Family Housing Processing Division
Rural Housing Service (RHS)
U.S. Department of Agriculture
Washington, DC 20250
202-720-1474
www.rurdev.usda.gov
Objectives: To provide financial support for programs of technical and supervisory assistance that will aid needy and very low and low-income individuals and their families in carrying out mutual self-help housing efforts in rural areas. Types of assistance: project grants. Estimate of annual funds available: (Grants and Contracts) $34,000,000

Help for Low-Income Families to Reduce Their Rent

(10.427 Rural Rental Assistance Payments) (Rental Assistance)
Director, Multi-Family Housing Portfolio Management Division

Rural Housing Service
U.S. Department of Agriculture
Washington, DC 20250
202-720-1600
www.rurdev.usda.gov
Objectives: To reduce the tenant contribution paid by low-income families occupying eligible Rural Rental Housing (RRH), Rural Cooperative Housing (RCH), and Farm Labor Housing (LH) projects financed by the Rural Housing Service (RHS) through its sections 515, 514 and 516 loans and grants. Types of assistance: direct payment for specified use. Estimate of annual funds available: $679,000,000

Application Assistance for Low-Income Rural Residents

(10.442 Housing Application Packaging Grants) (Section 509 Grants)
Director, Single Family Housing Processing Division
Rural Housing Service
Department of Agriculture
Washington, DC 20250
202-720-1474
www.rurdev.usda.gov
Objectives: To package single family housing applications for very low and low-income rural residents into colonials and designated counties who wish to buy, build, or repair houses for their own use and to package applications for organization wishing to develop rental units for lower income families. Types of assistance: project grants. Estimate of annual funds available: (Grants) $755,821

Money for Emergency Assistance for Natural Disasters

(10.444 Direct Housing-Natural Disaster Loans and Grants) (Section 504, Rural Housing Loans and Grants)
Director, Single Family Housing Processing Division
Rural Housing Service
Department of Agriculture
Washington, DC 20250
202-720-1474
www.rurdev.usda.gov
Objectives: To assist qualified recipients to meet emergency assistance needs resulting from natural disaster. Funds are only available to the extent that funds are not provided by the Federal Emergency Management Agency (FEMA) for the purpose of administering these funds, natural disaster will only include those counties identified by a Presidential declaration. Types of assistance: project grants, direct loans. Estimate of annual funds available: (Loans) $1,056,000 (Grants) $4,143,000. Funds under this

program are based on supplemental funding provided by Congress in response to a natural disaster.

Money to Improve Housing After a Natural Disaster

(10.445 Direct Housing-Natural Disaster) (Section 502 Very Low and Low Income Loans)
Director
Single Family Housing Processing Division
Rural Housing Service
Department of Agriculture
Washington, DC 20250
202-720-1474
www.rurdev.usda.gov
Objectives: To assist qualified lower income rural families to meet emergency, assistance needs resulting from natural disaster to buy, build, rehabilitate, or improve dwelling in rural areas. Funds are only available to the extent that funds are not provided by the Federal Emergency Management Agency (FEMA). For the purpose of administering these funds, natural disaster will only include those counties identified by a Presidential declaration. Types of assistance: direct loans. Estimate of annual funds available: (Loans) $10,495,428. Funds under this program are based on supplemental funding provided by Congress in response to a natural disaster.

Money to Conserve Soil and Water in Small Towns

(10.900 Great Plains Conservation)
Deputy Chief
National Resources Conservation Service
U.S. Department of Agriculture
P.O. Box 2890
Washington, DC 20013
202-720-1873
www.nrcs.usda.gov
Objectives: To conserve and develop the Great Plains soil and water resources by providing technical and financial assistance to farmers, ranchers, and others in planning and implementing conservation practices. Types of assistance: direct payments for specified use; advisory services and counseling. Estimate of annual funds available: (Grants) $400,144. (Salaries and expenses) $0.

Money to Fix Up an Abandoned Coal Mine

(10.910 Rural Abandoned Mine Program (RAMP))
Deputy Chief for Programs
Natural Resources Conservation Service
U.S. Department of Agriculture
P.O. Box 2890

Washington, DC 20013
202-720-1873
www.nrcs.usda.gov
Objectives: To protect people and the environment from the adverse effects of past coal mining practices, and to promote the development of soil and water resources of unreclaimed mined lands. Types of assistance: direct payments for specified use; advisory services and counseling. Estimate of annual funds available: (Grants) $164,470. (Salaries and expenses) $10,538.

Money for Farmers and Ranchers to Improve Water and Soil

(10.912 Environmental Quality Incentives Program EQIP)
Deputy Chief for Natural Resources Conservation Programs
Natural Resources Conservation Service
U.S. Department of Agriculture
P.O. Box 2890
Washington, DC 20013
202-720-1845
Fax: 202-720-4265
www.nrcs.usda.gov
Objectives: Technical, education and finance assistance to eligible farmers and ranchers to address soil, water and related natural resource concerns on their lands in an environmentally beneficial and cost-effective manner. This program provides assistance to farmers and ranchers in complying with Federal, State and tribal environmental laws and encourages environmental enhancement. The purpose of this program is achieved through the implementation of structural, vegetative, and land management practices eligible land. This program is funded through the Commodity Credit Corporation (CCC). NRCS provides overall program management and implementation leadership for conservation planning and implementation. The Farm Service Agency provides leadership for administrative processes and procedures for the program. Types of assistance: direct payment and specified use. Estimate of annual funds available: (Grants) $162,000,000 (Salaries and Expenses) $38,000,000 (Education Assistance) not to exceed 1% of grants estimate.

Loans to Fix Up Houses That Are More Than One Year Old

(14.108 Rehabilitation Mortgage Insurance (203(k))
Contact your State Homeownership Center or local HUD office
www.hud.gov/offices/hsg/sfh/ins/singlefamily.cfm
Objectives: To help families repair or improve,

purchase and improve, or refinance and improve existing residential structures more than one year old. Types of assistance: guaranteed/insured loans. Estimate of annual funds available: (Loans insured) $912,000,000.

Loans to Buy Trailers

(14.110 Manufactured Home Loan Insurance-Financing Purchase of Manufactured Homes as Principal Residences of Borrowers (Title I))
Chief
Home Mortgage Insurance Division
451 7th Street, SW, Room 9272
U.S. Department of Housing and Urban Development
Washington, DC 20410
202-708-2121
www.hud.gov/funds/index.cfm
Objectives: To make possible reasonable financing of manufactured home purchases. Types of assistance: guaranteed/insured loans. Estimate of annual funds available: (Loans insured) $71,000,000.

Loans to Co-op Investors

(14.112 Mortgage Insurance for Construction or Substantial Rehabilitation of Condominium Projects (234(d) Condominiums))
Chief
Home Mortgage Insurance Division
Room 9272
U.S. Department of Housing and Urban Development
Washington, DC 20410
202-708-2121
www.hud.gov/funds/index.cfm
Objectives: To enable sponsors to develop condominium projects in which individual units will be sold to home buyers. Types of assistance: guaranteed/insured loans. Estimate of annual funds available: (Mortgages insured) $0.

Loans to Homeowners Anywhere With 1 to 4 Family Units

(14.117 Mortgage Insurance-Homes (203(b)))
Contact your State Homeownership Center or local HUD office.
Objectives: To help people undertake home ownership. Types of assistance: guaranteed/insured loans. Estimate of annual funds available: (Mortgages insured) $139,289,282,000.

Loans to Buy Single Family Homes for Disaster Victims

(14.119 Mortgage Insurance-Homes for Disaster Victims (203(h)))
Contact your State Homeownership Center or local HUD office.
Objectives: To help victims of a major disaster undertake homeownership on a sound basis. Types of assistance: guaranteed/insured loans. Estimate of annual funds available: (Mortgages insured) reported under Program No. 14.117.

Money for Homes in Urban Renewal Areas

(14.122 Mortgage Insurance-Homes in Urban Renewal Areas (220 Homes))
Contact your State Homeownership Center or local HUD office.
www.hud.gov
Objectives: To help families purchase or rehabilitate homes in urban renewal areas. Types of assistance: guaranteed/insured loans. Estimate of annual funds available: (Mortgages insured) Reported under Program 14.133.

Money for Homes in Older Areas of Town

(14.123 Mortgage Insurance-Housing in Older, Declining Areas (223(e)))
Contact your State Homeownership Center or local HUD office.
www.hud.gov
Objectives: To assist in the purchase or rehabilitation of housing in older, declining urban areas. Types of assistance: guaranteed/insured loans. Estimate of annual funds available: (Mortgages insured) Reported under Program 14.133.

Money to Buy a Co-op Apartment

(14.126 Mortgage Insurance-Cooperative Projects (213 Cooperatives))
Office of Multifamily Housing Development
U.S. Department of Housing and Urban Development
451 7th Street, SW

Washington, DC 20410
202-708-1142
www.hud.gov/offices/hsg/hsgmulti.cfm
Objectives: To make it possible for nonprofit cooperative ownership housing corporations or trusts to develop or sponsor the development of housing projects to be operated as cooperatives and to allow investors to provide good quality multifamily housing to be sold to such nonprofit corporations or trusts upon completion of construction or rehabilitation. Types of assistance: guaranteed/insured loans. Estimate of annual funds available: (Mortgages insured) Reported under Program 14.117.

Money to Buy a Trailer-Home Park
(14.127 Mortgage Insurance-Manufactured Home Parks (207(m)
Manufactured Home Parks))
Office of Multifamily Development
U.S. Department of Housing and Urban Development
451 7th Street, SW
Washington, DC 20410
202-708-1142
www.hud.gov/offices/hsg/hsgmulti.cfm
Objectives: To make possible the financing of construction or rehabilitation of manufactured home parks. Types of assistance: guaranteed/insured loans. Estimate of annual funds available: (Mortgages insured) Reported under Program No. 14.135.

Money to Buy a Hospital
(14.128 Mortgage Insurance-Hospitals (242 Hospitals))
Office of Insured Health Care Facilities
U.S. Department of Housing and Urban Development
Washington, DC 20410
202-708-0599
or
Division of Facilities Loans
U.S. Department of Health and Human Services
Rockville, MD 20857
301-443-5317
www.hud.gov/offices/hsg/hosp/hsghospi.cfm
Objectives: To facilitate the affordable financing of hospitals for the care and treatment of persons who are acutely ill or who otherwise require medical care and related services of the kind customarily furnished only or most effectively by hospitals. Types of assistance: guaranteed/insured loans. Estimate of annual funds available: (Mortgages insured) $899,000,000.

Money to Buy a Nursing Home
(14.129 Mortgage Insurance-Nursing Homes, Intermediate Care Facilities, Board and Care Homes (232 Nursing Homes))
Office of Multifamily Development
U.S. Department of Housing and Urban Development
451 7th Street, SW
Washington, DC 20410
202-708-1142
www.hud.gov/offices/hsg/hsgmulti.cfm
Objectives: To make possible financing for construction or rehabilitation of nursing homes, intermediate care facilities and board and care homes, to allow purchase or refinancing with or without repairs of projects currently insured by HUD, but not requiring substantial rehabilitation, and to provide loan insurance to install fire safety equipment. Types of assistance: guaranteed/insured loans. Estimate of annual funds available: (Mortgages/insured) $2,418,750,000.

Money to Buy Your Co-op
(14.132 Mortgage Insurance-Purchase of Sales-Type Cooperative Housing Units (213 Sales))
Contact your State Homeownership Center or local HUD office.
Objectives: To make available, good quality, new housing for purchase by individual members of a housing cooperative. Types of assistance: guaranteed/insured loans. Estimate of annual funds available: (Mortgages insured) Reported under program 14.135.

Money to Buy a Condominium
(14.133 Mortgage Insurance-Purchase of Units in Condominiums (234(c)))
Contact your State Homeownership Center or local HUD office.
www.hud.gov/funds/index.cfm

Objectives: To enable families to purchase units in condominium projects. Types of assistance: guaranteed/insured loans. Estimate of annual funds available: (Mortgages insured) $13,900,000,000.

Housing Money for Middle Income Families

(14.134 Mortgage Insurance-Rental Housing) (207)
Office of Multifamily Development
Department of Housing and Urban Development
451 7th Street, SW
Washington, DC 20410
202-708-1142
www.hud.gov/offices/hsg/mfh/progdesc/progdesc.cfm
Objectives: To provide good quality housing for middle income families. Types of assistance: mortgages insured. Estimate of annual funds available: Reported under Program 14.135.

Money to Invest in Apartment Buildings for Middle Class Families

(14.135 Mortgage Insurance-Rental and Cooperative Housing for Moderate Income Families and Elderly, Market Interest Rate (221(d)(3) and (4) Multifamily - Market Rate Housing))
Office of Multifamily Development
U.S. Department of Housing and Urban Development
Washington, DC 20410
202-708-1142
www.hud.gov/offices/hsg/hsgmulti.cfm
Objectives: To provide good quality rental or cooperative housing for moderate income families and the elderly and handicapped. Single Room Occupancy (SRO) may also be insured under this section (see 14.184). Types of assistance: guaranteed/insured loans. Estimate of annual funds available: (Mortgages insured excluding coinsurance) $6,953,000,000.

Money to Invest in Rental Housing for the Elderly

(14.138 Mortgage Insurance-Rental Housing for the Elderly (231))
Office of Multifamily Development
U.S. Department of Housing and Urban Development
451 7th Street, SW
Washington, DC 20410
202-708-1142
Objectives: To provide good quality rental housing for the elderly. Types of assistance: guaranteed/insured loans. Estimate of annual funds available: (Mortgages insured) Reported under program 14.135.

Money to Invest in Rental Housing in Urban Renewal Areas

(14.139 Mortgage Insurance-Rental Housing in Urban Renewal Areas (220 Multifamily))
Office of Multifamily Development
U.S. Department of Housing and Urban Development
451 7th Street, SW
Washington, DC 20410
202-708-1142
www.hud.gov/offices/hsg/hsgmulti.cfm
Objectives: To provide good quality rental housing in urban renewal areas, code enforcement areas, and other areas designated for overall revitalization. Types of assistance: guaranteed/insured loans. Estimate of annual funds available: (Mortgages insured) Reported under Program 14.135.

Money to Fix Up Your Home

(14.142 Property Improvement Loan Insurance for Improving All Existing Structures and Building of New Nonresidential Structures (Title I))
Contact your State Homeownership Center or local HUD office., 800-440-8647
www.hud.gov/funds/index.cfm

Objectives: To facilitate the financing of improvements to homes and other existing structures and the building of new nonresidential structures. Types of assistance: guaranteed/insured loans. Estimate of annual funds available: $109,000,000.

Money to Fix Up Multifamily Projects
(14.151 Supplemental Loan Insurance-Multifamily Rental Housing (241(a)))
Policies and Procedures Division
Office of Multifamily Development
U.S. Department of Housing and Urban Development
451 7th Street, SW
Washington, DC 20410
202-708-1142
www.hud.gov/offices/hsg/hsgmulti.cfm
Objectives: To finance repairs, additions and improvements to multifamily projects, group practice facilities, hospitals, or nursing homes already insured by HUD or held by HUD. Major movable equipment for insured nursing homes, group practice facilities or hospitals may be covered by a mortgage under this program. Types of assistance: guaranteed/insured loans. Estimate of annual funds available: (Loans insured) $23,750,000.

Money to Investors to Purchase or Refinance Multifamily Housing
(14.155 Mortgage Insurance for the Purchase or Refinancing of Existing Multifamily Housing Projects (Section 223(f) Insured Under Section 207))
Office of Multifamily Development
U.S. Department of Housing and Urban Development
451 7th Street, SW
Washington, DC 20410
202-708-1142
www.hud.gov/offices/hsg/hsgmulti.cfm
Objectives: To provide mortgage insurance to lenders for the purchase or refinancing of existing multifamily housing projects, whether conventionally financed or subject to federally insured mortgages at the time of application for mortgage insurance. Types of assistance: guaranteed/insured loans. Estimate of annual funds available: (Mortgages Insured) $1,775,000,000.

Money to Build Housing for the Elderly That Also Provides Support Services
(14.157 Supportive Housing for the Elderly (202))
Office of Housing Assistance and Grants Administration
U.S. Department of Housing and Urban Development
Washington, DC 20410
202-708-2866
www.hud.gov/offices/hsg/mfh/progdesc/eld202.cfm
Objectives: To expand the supply of housing with supportive services for the elderly. Types of assistance: direct payment for specified use. Estimate of annual funds available: $783,286,000.

Money to Buy a House With Graduated Mortgage Payments
(14.159 Section 245 Graduated Payment Mortgage Program)
Contact your State Homeownership Center or local HUD office.
www.hud.gov/funds/index.cfm
Objectives: To facilitate early home ownership for households that expect their incomes to rise. Program allows homeowners to make smaller monthly payments initially and to increase their size gradually over time. Types of assistance: guaranteed/insured loans. Estimate of annual funds available: Reported under Program 14.117.

Money to Buy a Trailer and Trailer Lot
(14.162 Mortgage Insurance-Combination and Manufactured Home Lot Loans (Title I))
Chief, Mortgage Insurance Division
U.S. Department of Housing and Urban Development
451 7th Street, SW, Room 9272
Washington, DC 20410
202-708-2121
www.hud.gov/funds/index.cfm
Objectives: To make possible reasonable financing for the purchase of a manufactured home and a lot on which to place the home. Types of assistance: guaranteed/insured loans. Estimate of annual funds available: (Mortgages insured) Reported under program No. 14.110.

Money to Finance Coop Buildings
(14.163 Mortgage Insurance-Single Family Cooperative Housing (203(n)))
Contact your State Homeownership Center or local HUD office.
www.hud.gov/funds/index.cfm
Objectives: To provide insured financing for the purchase of the Corporate Certificate and Occupancy Certificate for a unit in a cooperative housing project. Ownership of the corporate certificate carries the right to occupy the unit located within the cooperative project. Types of assistance: guaranteed/insured loans. Estimate of annual funds available: (Mortgages Insured) Reported under program No. 14.117.

Money to Developers in Financial Trouble

(14.164 Operating Assistance for Troubled Multifamily Housing Projects (Flexible Subsidy Fund) (Troubled Projects))
Office of Housing Assistance and Grants Administration
U.S. Department of Housing and Urban Development
Washington, DC 20420
202-708-2866
www.hud.gov/offices/hsg/mfh/progdesc/progdesc.cfm
Objectives: To provide loans to restore or maintain the physical and financial soundness, to assist in the management and to maintain the low to moderate income character of certain projects assisted or approved for assistance under the National Housing Act or under the Housing and Urban Development Act of 1965. Types of assistance: direct payments for specified use. Estimate of annual funds available: (Obligations) $2,151,000.

Money to Buy Houses in Areas Hurt by Defense Cuts

(14.165 Mortgage Insurance-Homes-Military Impacted Areas (238(c)))
Contact your State Homeownership Center or local HUD office.
www.hud.gov/offices/hsg/sfh/ins/singlefamily.cfm
Objectives: To help families undertake home ownership in military impacted areas. Types of assistance: guaranteed/insured loans. Estimate of annual funds available: (Mortgages Insured) Reported under Program 14.133.

Loans to Developers in Trouble During Their First Two Years of Operation

(14.167 Mortgage Insurance-Two Year Operating Loss Loans, Section 223(d) (Two Year Operating Loss Loans))
Office of Multifamily Development
U.S. Department of Housing and Urban Development
451 7th Street, SW

Washington, DC 20410
202-708-1142
www.hud.gov/offices/hsg/hsgmulti.cfm
Objectives: To insure a separate loan covering operating losses incurred during the first two years following the date of completion of a multifamily project with a HUD-insured first mortgage. Types of assistance: guaranteed/insured loans. Estimate of annual funds available: (Loans insured) $3,033,750.

Money to Buy a Home Using Increased Equity Payments

(14.172 Mortgage Insurance-Growing Equity Mortgages (GEMs))
Contact your State Homeownership Center or local HUD office.
www.hud.gov
Objectives: To provide a rapid principal reduction and shorter mortgage term by increasing payments over a 10-year period, thereby expanding housing opportunities to the homebuying public. Types of assistance: guaranteed/insured loans. Estimate of annual funds available: (Mortgages insured) Reported under program 14.117.

Money to Buy a Home Using an Adjustable Rate Mortgage

(14.175 Adjustable Rate Mortgages (ARMS))
Contact your State Homeownership Center or local HUD office.
www.hud.gov/funds/index.cfm
Objectives: To provide mortgage insurance for an adjustable rate mortgage which offers lenders more assurance of long term profitability than a fixed rate mortgage, while offering consumer protection features. Types of assistance: guaranteed/insured loans. Estimate of annual funds available: (Mortgages Insured) Reported under 14.117.

Money to Invest in Houses for Those With Disabilities

(14.181 Supportive Housing for Persons with Disabilities (811))
Office of Housing Assistance and Grants Administration
U.S. Department of Housing and Urban Development
Washington, DC 20410
202-708-2866
www.hud.gov/offices/hsg/mfh/prodesc/disab811.cfm
Objectives: To provide for supportive housing and related facilities for persons with disabilities. Types of assistance: direct payments for specified use. Estimate of annual funds available: $250,515,000

Money to Help Elderly Homeowners Convert Their Equity into a Monthly Income

(14.183 Home Equity Conversion Mortgages (255))
Director
Insured Family Development Division
Office of Single Family Housing
U.S. Department of Housing and Urban Development
Washington, DC 20410
202-708-2121
www.hud.gov/funds/index.cfm
Objectives: To enable elderly homeowners to convert equity in their homes to monthly streams of income or, except for Texas, lines of credit. Types of assistance: guaranteed/insured loans. Estimate of annual funds available: (Mortgages insured): Reported under program 14.133.

Money for Supportive Housing for the Homeless

(14.235 Supportive Housing Program) (Transitional Housing; Permanent Housing for Homeless Persons with Disabilities; Innovative Supportive Housing; Supportive Services for Homeless Persons not in Conjunction with Supportive Housing; and Safe Havens)
Director
Office of Special Needs Assistance Programs
Community Planning and Development
U.S. Department of Housing and Urban Development
451 7th Street, SW
Washington, DC 20410
202-708-4300
www.hud.gov/homeless/index.cfm
Objective: The Supportive Housing Program is designed to promote the development of supportive housing and supportive services to assist homeless persons in the transition from homelessness and to enable them to live as independently as possible. Program funds may be used to provide: (i) transitional housing within a 24 month period as well as up to six months of follow-up services to former residents to assist their adjustment to independent living, (ii) permanent housing provided in conjunction with appropriate supportive services designed to maximize the ability of person with disabilities to live as independently as possible; (iii) supportive housing that is, or is part of, a particularly innovative project for, or alternate method of, meeting the immediate and long-term needs of homeless individuals and families; (iv) supportive services for homeless individuals not provided in conjunction with supportive housing, and (v) safe havens for homeless individuals with serious mental illness currently residing on the streets who may not yet be ready for supportive services. Types of assistance: project grants, direct payment for specified use. Estimate of annual funds available: (Grants) $888,509,000.

Rent Supplements to Building Owners With Tenants That Have Low Incomes

(14.856 Lower Income Housing Assistance Program-Section 8 Moderate Rehabilitation (Section 8 Housing Assistance Payments Program for Very Low Income Families-Moderate Rehabilitation))
Office of the Deputy Assistant Secretary for Public Assisted Housing Development
Real Estate and Housing Performance Division
U.S. Department of Housing and Urban Development
Washington, DC 20410
202-708-0477
www.hud.gov/progdesc/pihindx.cfm
Objectives: To aid very low income families and homeless individuals in obtaining decent, safe and sanitary rental housing. Types of assistance: direct payments for specified use. Estimate of annual funds available: (Outlays) not separately identifiable.

Money to Have Your State Buy Your Old Farm and Turn It into a Park

(15.916 Outdoor Recreation-Acquisition, Development and Planning (Land and Water Conservation Fund Grants))
Chief
Recreation Programs Division
National Park Service (2225)
U.S. Department of the Interior
1849 C Street, NW
Washington, DC 20240
202-354-6900
www.nps.gov/lwcf
Objectives: To provide financial assistance to the States and their political subdivisions for the preparation of Statewide Comprehensive Outdoor Recreation Plans (SCORPs) and acquisition and development of outdoor recreation areas and facilities for the general public, to meet current and future needs. Types of assistance: project grants. Estimate of annual funds available: (Grants) $156,000,000.

Grants to Build Houses on Indian Reservations

(15.141 Indian Housing Assistance)
Division of Human Services
Office of Tribal Services
Bureau of Indian Affairs
MS 4660 MIB
1849 C Street, NW
Washington, DC 20240
202-208-3667
Objectives: To use the Indian Housing Improvement Program (HIP) and Bureau of Indian Affairs resources to substantially eliminate substandard Indian housing. This effort is combined with the Indian Health Service (Department of Health and Human Services). Types of assistance: project grants (contracts); dissemination of technical information. Estimate of annual funds available: (Total amount of award: Self-determination contracts and direct grants) $16,474,000.

Appalachian Local Development District Assistance

(23.009 Appalachian Local Development District Assistance LDD)
Inquiries and proposals for projects should be submitted first to:
Appalachian State Office designated by the Governor
Other inquiries:
Executive Director
Appalachian Regional Commission
1666 Connecticut Avenue, NW, 20235
Washington, DC 20009-1068
202-884-7700
www.arc.gov
Objectives: To provide planning and development resources in multi county areas; to help develop the technical competence essential to land development assistance; and to meet the objectives stated under the program entitled Appalachian Regional Development (23.001). Types of assistance: project grants. Estimate of annual funds available: (Grants) $5,900,000.

Physical Disaster Loans

(59.008 Physical Disaster Loans) (7 (b) Loans (DL))
Office of Disaster Assistance
Small Business Administration
409 3rd Street, SW, Ste. 6050
Washington, DC 20416
202-205-6734
www.sba.gov/disaster_recov/index.html
Objectives: To provide loans to the victims of declared physical type disasters for uninsured losses.

Types of assistance: direct loans. Estimate of annual funds available: (Loans) $814,000,000 (Obligations include funds for 59.002 and 59.008).

Homeless Providers Grant

(64.024 VA Homeless Providers Grant and Per Diem Program)
Program Manager
VA Homeless Providers Grant and Per Diem Program
Mental Health Strategic Healthcare Group (116E)
U.S. Department of Veteran Affairs
810 Vermont Avenue, NW
Washington, DC 20420
202-273-8966
www.va.gov
Objectives: To assist public and nonprofit private entities in establishing new programs and service centers to furnish supportive services and supportive housing for homeless veterans through grants that may be used to acquire, renovate, or alter facilities, and to provide per diem payments, or in-kind assistance in lieu of per diem payments, to eligible entities which established programs after November 10, 1992 that provide supportive services and supportive housing for the homeless veterans. Types of assistance: project grants. Estimate of annual fund available: $31,653,000.

Paraplegic Housing

(64.106 Specially Adapted Housing for Disabled Veteran) (Paraplegic Housing)
U.S. Department of Veterans Affairs
810 Vermont Ave, NW
Washington, DC 20420
202-273-7355
www.va.gov
Objectives: To help certain severely disabled veterans acquire a home which is suitably adapted to meet the special needs of their disability. Types of

assistance: direct payment for specified use. Estimate of annual funds available: (Direct Payments) $22,805,000

Money for Veterans Who Want to Buy a House
(64.114 Veterans Housing-Guaranteed and Insured Loans (VA Home Loans))
U.S. Department of Veterans Affairs
810 Vermont Ave, NW
Washington, DC 20420
202-273-7390
www.va.gov
Objectives: To assist veterans, certain service personnel, and certain unremarried surviving spouses of veterans, in obtaining credit for the purchase, construction or improvement of homes on more liberal terms than are generally available to non-veterans. Types of assistance: guaranteed/insured loans. Estimate of annual funds available: (Closed Loans Guaranteed) $55,000,000,000.

Loans for Disabled Veterans to Buy a House
(64.118 Veterans Housing-Direct Loans for Disabled Veterans)
U.S. Department of Veterans Affairs
810 Vermont Ave., NW
Washington, DC 20420
202-273-7390
www.va.gov
Objectives: To provide certain severely disabled veterans with direct housing credit in connection with grants for specially adaptive housing with special features or movable facilities made necessary by the nature of their disabilities. Types of assistance: direct loans. Estimate of annual funds available: (Loans) $33,000.

Money for Veterans to Buy Mobile Homes
(64.119 Veterans Housing-Manufactured Home Loans)
U.S. Department of Veterans Affairs
810 Vermont Ave., NW
Washington, DC 20420
202-273-7390
www.va.gov
Objectives: To assist veterans, servicepersons, and certain unremarried surviving spouses of veterans in obtaining credit for the purchase of a manufactured home on more liberal terms than are available to non-veterans. Types of assistance: guaranteed/insured loans. Estimate of annual funds available: (Guaranteed Loans) $0.

Loans for Native American Veterans to Buy or Build a Home
(64.126 Native American Veteran Direct Loan Program (VA Native American Home Loan

Program))
U.S. Department of Veterans Affairs
810 Vermont Ave., NW
Washington, DC 20420
202-273-7377
www.va.gov
Objectives: To provide direct loans to certain Native American veterans for the purchase or construction of homes on trust lands. Types of assistance: direct loans. Estimate of annual funds available: (Loans): $3,225,000.

Grants for Storm Windows or to Weatherize Your Home
(81.042 Weatherization Assistance for Low-Income Persons)
Director
Office of Building and Technology Assistance
Mail Stop EE-42
Office of Energy Efficiency and Renewable Energy
U.S. Department of Energy
Forrestal Building
Washington, DC 20585
202-586-4074
www.eere.energy.gov/weatherization
Objectives: To insulate the dwellings of low income persons, particularly the elderly and handicapped low income, in order to conserve needed energy and to aid those persons least able to afford higher utility costs. Types of assistance: formula grants. Estimate of annual funds available: $227,165,966.

Grants for Renovation or Construction of Non-Acute Health Care Facilities
(93.887 Health Care and Other Facilities (Renovation or Construction Projects)

Program:
Director
Division of Facilities Compliance and Recovery
Office of Special Programs
Health Resources and Services Administration
Department of Health and Human Services
Parklawn Building
5600 Fishers Lane
Rockville, MD 20857
301-443-5656

Grants:
Grants Management Specialist
Grants Management Branch
Office of Program Support
HIV/AIDS Bureau
Health Resources and Services Administration
Parklawn Building
5600 Fishers Lane
Rockville, MD 20857
301-443-3376
www.hrsa.gov/osp
Objectives: To renovate, expand, repair, equip, or modernize non-acute health care facilities. Types of assistance: project grants. Estimate of annual funds available: (Grants) $293,253,000

Money For Nonprofits to Provide Rural Housing Site Loans

(10.411 Rural Housing Site Loans and Self-Help Housing Land Development Loans (Section 523 and 524 Site Loans))
Director
Single-Family Housing Processing Division
Rural Housing Service
U.S. Department of Agriculture
Washington, DC 20250
202-720-1474
www.rurdev.usda.gov
Objectives: To assist public or private nonprofit organizations interested in providing sites for housing, to acquire and develop land in rural areas to be subdivided as adequate building sites and sold on a cost development basis to families eligible for low and very low income loans, cooperatives, and broadly based nonprofit rural rental housing applicants. Types of assistance: direct loans. Estimate of annual funds available: (Loans) $5,009,000.

Money to Fix Up Your Home in the Country

(10.433 Rural Housing Preservation Grants)
Multiple Family Housing Processing Division
Rural Housing Service
U.S. Department of Agriculture
Washington, DC 20250
202-720-1660
www.rurdev.usda.gov
Objectives: To assist very low and low income rural residents including individual homeowners and rental property owners (single/multi-unit) or to provide the consumer cooperative housing projects (co-ops) the necessary assistance to repair or rehabilitate their dwellings. These objectives will be accomplished through the establishment of

repair/rehabilitation, projects run by eligible applicants. This program is intended to make use of and leverage any other available housing programs which provide resources to very low and low income rural residents to bring their dwellings up to development standards. Types of assistance: project grants. Estimate of annual funds available: (Grants) $8,000,000.

Money for Homes for Low Income Indian Families

(14.850 Public and Indian Housing)
Assistant Secretary for Public and Indian Housing
U.S. Department of Housing and Urban Development
Washington, DC 20410
202-708-0950
www.hud.gov/progdesc/pihindx.cfm
Objectives: To provide and operate cost-effective, decent, safe and affordable dwellings for lower income families through an authorized local Public Housing Agency (PHA) or Indian Housing Authority (IHA). Types of assistance: direct payments for specified use. Estimate of annual funds available: $3,574,000,000.

Money to Provide Affordable Rental Housing for Low-Income Families

(14.239 HOME Investment Partnerships Program)
Office of Affordable Housing Programs
Community Planning and Development
U.S. Department of Housing and Urban Development
451 7th St., SW, Room 7164
Washington, DC 20410
202-708-2470
www.hud.gov/offices/cpd
Objectives: (1) To expand the supply of decent and affordable housing, particularly rental housing, for low and very low income Americans; (2) To strengthen the abilities of State and local governments to design and implement strategies for achieving adequate supplies of decent, affordable housing; (3) To provide both financial and technical assistance to participating jurisdictions, including the development of model programs for developing affordable low income housing and; (4) To extend and strengthen partnerships among all levels of government and the private sector, including for-profit and nonprofit organizations, in the production and operation of affordable housing. Types of assistance: formula grants. Estimate of annual funds available: (Grants) $2,168,300,000.

Money to Invest in Rental Housing for Lower Income Families

(14.856 Lower Income Housing Assistance Program-Section 8 Moderate Rehabilitation)
Office of the Deputy Assistant Secretary for Public Assisted Housing Delivery
Real Estate and Housing Performance Division
U.S. Department of Housing and
Urban Development
Washington, DC 20410
202-708-0477
www.hud.gov/progdesc/pihindx.cfm
Objectives: To aid very low income families in obtaining decent, safe and sanitary rental housing. Types of assistance: direct payments for specified use. Estimate of annual funds available: (Outlays) not separately identifiable.

Loans to Investors, Builders, Developers of Affordable Housing

(14.189 Qualified Participating Entities QPE Risk Sharing Pilot Program)
Office of Multifamily Development
U.S. Department of Housing and Urban Development
451 7th Street, SW
Washington, DC 20410
202-708-1142
www.hud.gov/offices/hsg/hsgmulti.cfm
Objectives: Under this program HUD will provide reinsurance on multifamily housing projects whose loans are originated, underwritten, serviced, and disposed of by qualified participating entities (QPEs) and/or its approved lenders. The program is a pilot designed to assess the feasibility of risk-sharing partnerships between HUD and QPEs, including Government Sponsored Enterprises, State and local housing finance agencies, financial institutions and the Federal Housing Finance Board, in providing affordable housing for the nation. Types of assistance: guaranteed/insured loans. Estimate of annual funds available: (Loans insured) $57,000,000.

Money for Developers, Investors, and Builders of Low Income Housing

(14.188 HFA Risk Sharing Pilot Program)
Office of Multifamily Development
U.S. Department of Housing and Urban Development
451 7th Street, SW
Washington, DC 20410
202-708-1142
www.hud.gov/offices/hsg/hsgmulti.cfm
Objectives: Under this program, HUD will provide credit enhancement for mortgages for multifamily housing projects whose loans are underwritten, processed, serviced, and disposed of by HFAs, HUD, and the Housing Finance Agencies share in the risk of the mortgage. Types of assistance: guaranteed/insured loans. Estimate of annual funds available: (Loans Insured) $415,000,000.

State Money for Housing and Real Estate

State Initiatives

While affordable housing has long held an important place on the Federal government's policy agenda, budget cutbacks in recent years have forced the government to turn over many housing responsibilities to the states. Housing finance

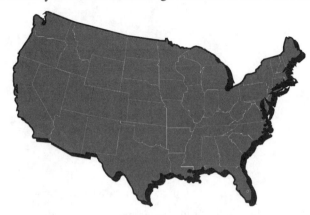

agencies (HFAs) have been created by states to issue tax-exempt bonds to finance mortgages for lower income first-time home buyers and to build multifamily housing.

States are involved in a host of initiatives throughout the broad spectrum of housing finance and development. Interim construction financing programs which can reduce the basic costs of lower income housing projects have been initiated in a number of states, together with innovative home ownership programs and programs directed toward rehabilitation and improved energy conservation.

States are also venturing into areas which have not received as much public sector attention until recently. By encouraging non-traditional types of housing, such as accessory units, shelters, and single room occupancy housing, states are addressing important elements of the housing market.

In Colorado, the state Housing and Finance Authority (CHFA) has issued more than $2.6 billion of bonds and notes since its establishment in 1973, providing housing for more than 47,000 families and individuals of low and moderate income; 27,200 first-time home buyers and over 20,500 rental housing units. In recent years the state has broadened CHFA's authority to allow it to develop finance programs to assist the growth of small business, help exports with insurance on goods sold overseas, and similar projects.

Colorado has done more than simply help its citizens find housing: the programs have resulted in construction employment of more than 20,000 jobs, with wages estimated at almost $20 million in new local real estate taxes and an indirect gain of $1.6 billion for the state.

Wisconsin, Maine and New York each have between 18 and 20 programs including special ones for women and minorities, for disabled persons, and for environmental hazard removal.

Maryland operates 26 programs, including those to help people with closing costs and settlement expenses. It also has special funds available for the elderly and is developing an emergency mortgage fund to help people who have fallen behind in their payments. Nonprofit developers can also tap the state for money to build low cost rental units.

Among Michigan's 29 programs and Minnesota's 25 are several for neighborhood revitalization. Minnesota also offers programs targeting the needs of urban Indians and migrant farm workers. Alaska, Oregon and Vermont offer financing for tenant acquisition of mobile home parks.

Funds are also available for persons who take steps to make their homes more energy efficient, for homeowners and landlords who remove lead paint from dwelling units, for houses without plumbing or those with plumbing that is dysfunctional, for handicapped persons, and to help landlords defray the costs of bringing low income housing into compliance with state and local housing codes. There are also funds for nonprofit organizations to acquire or renovate existing houses and apartments for use as group homes for special needs such as the mentally retarded.

In many states, elderly homeowners can look to the HFA to obtain financing and/or support services they need to remain in their homes and avoid institutionalization. Some of the states have more than one agency dedicated to housing and we have attempted to list them all here. Also, many cities and counties have quasi-federal/quasi-local "housing authorities" with additional programs. Check your local government listings for these.

The following is a complete listing of state housing programs.

Housing Offices

Alabama

Alabama Housing Finance Authority
2000 Interstate Park Dr., Suite 408
Montgomery, AL 36109
Mailing Address:
    P.O. Box 230909
    Montgomery, AL 36123-0909
334-244-9200
800-325-2432
www.ahfa.com
Fax: 334-244-9214
Email: webmaster@ahfa.com

1. Mortgage Revenue Bond Program: low rate loans for income eligible first-time homebuyers. Contact the Alabama Housing Finance Authority for application information.
2. Step Up Program: designed specifically for moderate-income home buyers: those whose incomes can sustain a market-rate mortgage but whose savings fall short of the amount needed for entry costs like a down payment, closing costs and prepaid items. The application can be found in the Appendix Manual, Appendix 45, page 104 at the web site, {www.ahfa.com/StepUpmanuals.htm}.
3. Habitat For Humanity Loan Purchase Program: loan purchasing program in which AHFA purchases loans from Alabama's 32 Habitat affiliates. The affiliate uses the up-front money to build more housing for low-income families.
4. Building Blocks To Homeownership: free seminar that educates Alabama's potential or current homebuyer in money management, credit, financing and home maintenance.
5. Low Income Housing Tax Credit Program: federal tax credits for owners of low-income rental housing. The program increases the supply of affordable housing for economically disadvantaged families. {www.ahfa.com/LIHTCprgm.htm}.
6. HOME Program: provides additional opportunities for the production of affordable housing for low-income families. For an application, fill out the request form on the back of the HOME brochure booklet; {www.ahfa.com/HOMEprgm.htm}.
7. Multifamily Mortgage Revenue Bonds: Lower than market interest rates for developers of multifamily housing that reserve some of their units for very-low income renters. Contact the Alabama Housing Finance Authority for application information.
8. Alabama Multifamily Loan Consortium: long-term financing for affordable multifamily housing development and rehabilitation. To view the Charter Members of the Consortium go to {www.ahfa.com/AMLCmembers.htm}.

Alaska

Alaska Housing Finance Corporation
4300 Boniface Parkway 99504
Anchorage, AK 99510-1020
Mailing Address:
    P.O. Box 101020
    Anchorage, AK 99510-1020

907-338-6100
800-478-2432
www.ahfc.state.ak.us

1. Single Family Lenders Mobile Home Program: low down payment for affordable homes. To view a list of approved lenders, go to {www.ahfc.state.ak.us/Department_Files/Mortgage/approved-lenders.htm}.

2. Veteran Mortgage Program: low interest loans to qualified veterans. To view a list of approved lenders, go to {www.ahfc.state.ak.us/Department_Files/Mortgage/approved-lenders.htm}.

3. Refinance Program: reduce monthly payments on existing loans. To view a list of approved lenders, go to {www.ahfc.state.ak.us/Department_Files/Mortgage/approved-lenders.htm}.

4. Non-Conforming Program: financing for homes which cannot be financed through traditional financing. To view a list of approved lenders, go to {www.ahfc.state.ak.us/Department_Files/Mortgage/approved-lenders.htm}.

5. Senior Housing Plan: potential borrowers may apply for financing to purchase, construct, rehabilitate or improve various kinds of housing that would meet the needs of persons 60 or older. To obtain an application, call 800-478-AHFC, 907-330-8436.

6. Energy Efficient Interest Rate Reduction Program: participants of an AHFC loan may qualify for an interest-rate reduction depending on the energy efficiency of their home. To view a list of approved lenders, go to {www.ahfc.state.ak.us/Department_Files/Mortgage/approved-lenders.htm}.

7. Low-Income Weatherization Program: eligible low-income Alaskans can lower the cost of heating their homes by providing energy-efficient improvements. To view a list of service providers, go to {www.ahfc.state.ak.us/Department_Files/RIC/Energy/weatherization-providers.htm}.

8. Affordable Housing Enhanced Loan Program: down payment assistance to moderate-income borrowers. To view a list of approved lenders, go to {www.ahfc.state.ak.us/Department_Files/Mortgage/approved-lenders.htm}.

9. Assistance Provider interest Rate Reduction: subsidized interest rates for housing with a live-in care provider for physically or mentally disabled occupants. For a loan application, call 907-338-6100.

10. Association Loan Program: funds to Homeowners' Associations for improvements to common-area that if not corrected could threaten the health and safety of the residents. For loan information, call 800-478-AHFC, 907-338-6100.

11. Conventional Loan Program (Taxable Loan Program): loans for borrowers that do not meet the criteria of other special AHFC programs for eligible property. To view a list of approved lenders, go to {www.ahfc.state.ak.us/Department_Files/Mortgage/approved-lenders.htm}.

12. First Time Homebuyer Program: (Tax-Exempt Loan Program) loan program for income eligible first-time homebuyers. To view a list of approved lenders, go to {www.ahfc.state.ak.us/Department_Files/Mortgage/approved-lenders.htm}.

13. Interest Rate Reduction for Low Income Buyer: interest rate subsidy for low-income borrower. To view a list of approved lenders, go to {www.ahfc.state.ak.us/Department_Files/Mortgage/approved-lenders.htm}.

14. Rural Owner-Occupied Loan Program: low interest financing for the construction or rehabilitation of a primary residence to qualified borrowers that live in "small communities" in rural Alaska. To view a list of approved lenders, go to {www.ahfc.state.ak.us/Department_Files/Mortgage/approved-lenders.htm}.

15. Second Mortgage program: funds to qualified borrowers for home improvements or for the purchase of a home subject to an existing first mortgage. To view a list of approved lenders, go to {www.ahfc.state.ak.us/Department_Files/Mortgage/approved-lenders.htm}.

16. Second Mortgage for Health and Safety Repair: funding for health and safety repairs to a financed property of AHFC. To view a list of approved lenders, go to {www.ahfc.state.ak.us/Department_Files/Mortgage/approved-lenders.htm}.

17. Small Building Material Loan Program: financing for qualified borrowers to purchase materials to rehabilitate primary residences in areas that are defined as "small communities". Contact the Alaska Housing Finance Corporation for application information.

18. Streamline Refinance Program: applicants can get financing secured by property that is currently financed by AHFC without income, credit, or appraisal qualifications. To view a list of approved lenders, go to {www.ahfc.state.ak.us/Department_Files/Mortgage/approved-lenders.htm}.

19. Rural Enhanced Loan Program (RELP): offers an interest rate reduction, reduced mortgage requirements, and one step construction loans to low-moderate income borrowers in remote communities. To view a list of approved lenders, go to {www.ahfc.state.ak.us/Department_Files/Mortgage/approved-lenders.htm}.

20. Multifamily, Congregate and Special Needs Housing Loan: assists qualified nonprofit housing providers and for-profit companies in financing multifamily complexes for low- and moderate-income housing. Contact the Alaska Finance Corporation for information.

21. GOAL Program: provides grants, federal tax credits, and zero interest loans to for profit and non-profit developers who build affordable rental housing for low-to-moderate income families and seniors. This program is funded through three programs: For applications to this program, go to {www.ahfc.state.ak.us/Download/download-main-page.htm}.

22. HOME Investment Partnership Program (HOME): funding for the development of affordable housing for low-to-moderate income families.

23. Low-Income Housing Tax Credits (LIHTC): tax credits to owners of rental property where a number of units are set aside for low- to moderate-income families.

24. Senior Citizens Housing Development Fund (SCHDF): grants to non-profit agencies.

25. Senior Housing Loan Program: potential borrowers may apply for financing to purchase, construct, rehabilitate or improve various kinds of housing that would meet the needs of persons 60 or older. To obtain an application, call 800-478-AHFC, 907-338-6100.

26. Assistance Provider Interest Rate Reduction: subsidized interest rates for housing with a live-in care provider for physically or mentally disabled occupants. For a loan application, call 800-478-AHFC, 907-338-6100.

27. Multifamily Federally Insured Loan Program: up to 85% of financing for the acquisition, rehabilitation, or refinance of existing multifamily properties. To view a list of approved lenders, go to {www.ahfc.state.ak.us/Department_Files/Mortgage/approved-lenders.htm}.

28. Loans to Sponsors: funding to sponsors of affordable housing for low to moderate income people or those living in remote, underdeveloped, or blighted areas of the state. For a loan application, call 800-478-AHFC, 907-338-6100.

29. Multi Family Loan Purchase Program: loans for the acquisition, rehabilitation, and refinance of multifamily properties with at least 5 units. For an application, go to {www.ahfc.state.ak.us/Department_Files/Mortgage/MFamily/mfloans.htm}.

30. Taxable First Time Home Buyer Program: reduced interest rate to eligible borrowers, without income limits. To view a list of approved lenders, go to (www.ahfc.state.ak.us/Department_Files/Mortgage/approved-lenders.htm).

31. Rural Teacher Housing Loan Program: conventional loans to purchase or renovate housing occupied by educators in rural "small communities" of Alaska.

32. State Veterans Interest Rate Preference: a one percent rate reduction on the first $50,000 to low-to-moderate income qualified veterans.

33. Public Housing Rental Program: safe, decent, and affordable rental housing to low-income Alaskans. To view a list of available rental housing locations, go to {www.ahfc.state.ak.us/Department_Files/Public_Housing/public-housing-program.htm}.

Arizona

Arizona Department of Housing
1700 West Washington St., Ste 210
Phoenix, AZ 85007
602-771-1000
www.housingaz.com

1. Low Interest Mortgages: affordable mortgages for first-time homebuyers that can include down payment assistance. Contact the Governor's Office of Housing Development for a list of participating lenders.

2. Down Payment Assistance: down payment and closing cost assistance offered in the area in which you live. The Homebuyer Counseling Agencies list is at {www.housingaz.com/homeownershipassistance/default.asp}.

3. Rural Home Purchase Program: assistance to qualified low-income family or individuals purchasing a home. Contact the Governor's Office of Housing Development for information on this program.

4. Weatherization Assistance Program: helps low-income families and individuals reduce their home energy costs. A list of agencies to apply to is located at {www.commerce.state.az.us/Energy/default.asp}.

5. HOME Program: provides help for low-income families with various housing needs from rehabilitation to rental assistance. Applications related to this program are available at {www.housingaz.com/library/#1013}.

6. Special Needs Housing Program: grants to provide planning, technical assistance, and services to groups that serve low-income special needs groups. Contact the Governor's Office of Housing Development for application information.

7. Low Income Housing Tax Credits: federal income tax credits for owners of low income housing units. The application is available at {www.housingaz.com/library/default.asp}.

8. Tenant Based Rental Assistance Program: rental assistance to income eligible households. The application can be downloaded from {www.housingaz.com/library/default.asp}.

9. Project Based Rental Assistance: project based rent subsidies to income eligible households. Contact the Governor's Office of Housing Development for application information.

10. Publicly Assisted Affordable Rental Properties: affordable rental property available to income eligible households. Contact the Governor's Office of Housing Development for application information.

11. Low Income Housing Tax Credits: federal income tax credits for owners of low income housing units. The application is available at {www.housingaz.com/library/default.asp}.

Arkansas

Arkansas Development Finance Authority
423 Main Street, Suite 500
P.O. Box 8023
Little Rock, AR 72203-8023
501-682-5900
www.arkansas.gov/adfa
Email: mdodson@adfa.state.ar.us

1. Home To Own (Mortgage Revenue Bond Program): low interest rate loans to low and moderate income first time homebuyers. For a list of participating lenders, go to {www.arkansas.gov/adfa/programs/H2OProgramGuide.htm}.

2. Down Payment Assistance Program: closing cost assistance for low to moderate-income first time homebuyers. The Homebuyer Counseling Agencies list can be viewed at {www.arkansas.gov/adfa/programs/dpap.html}.

3. Low Income Housing Tax Credit Program: federal tax credits for owners of low-income rental housing. The application can be found at {www.arkansas.gov/adfa/programs/lihtcp.html}.

4. HOME Program: funds are used for a variety of activities to develop and support affordable housing for low-income households. Eligible activities include: Tenant Based Rental Assistance, Rental Rehabilitation, new construction, and assistance to homeowners and homebuyers. Download an application at {www.arkansas.gov/adfa/home_program_2000.htm}.

5. Tax Exempt Multi Family Housing Bonds: below market rate loans for developers that agree to set affordable rental rates for low to moderate-income families. Contact the Arkansas Development Finance Authority for application information.

California

California Housing Finance Agency
1121 L Street, 7th Floor
Sacramento, CA 95814
916-322-3991
www.calhfa.ca.gov
Email: homeownership@calhfa.ca.gov

Visit {www.hcd.ca.gov/clearinghouse/} to find information on over 200 housing programs, government, private leaders and foundation grants. Each program listing identifies the goals, eligible activities and type of funding, as well as such critical and timely information as application deadlines and current funding availability.

1. 100% Loan Program (CHAP): provides low interest financing along with CalHFA down payment assistance to qualified first-time homebuyers.
2. The Affordable Housing Partnership Program (AHPP): assists first-time homebuyers with closing cost and/or down payment. The Approved Subordinate Localities and Programs list can be viewed at {www.calhfa.ca.gov/homeownership/programs/ahpp.htm}.
3. Extra Credit Teacher Program: provides qualified teachers and principals down payment assistance to first-time homebuyers. The documents needed for this program are at {www.calhfa.ca.gov/homeownership/approved/lenders/index.htm}.
4. Oakland Teacher Program: provides affordable loans and down payment assistance to qualified teachers and principals on the purchase of their first home. For a list of approved lenders to apply to, go to {www.calhfa.ca.gov/homeownership/programs/oakland-teacher.htm}.
5. High Cost Area Home Purchase Assistance Pilot Program (HiCAP): designed to assist first-time homebuyers in the highest housing cost areas of the state. Eligible counties are: San Francisco, San Mateo, Santa Clara, Alameda, Contra Costa, and Sonoma. An application can be obtained from an approved lender, see the list at {www.calhfa.ca.gov/homeownership/programs/hicap.htm}.
6. Builder Lock (BLOCK) Program: Builders/Developers may purchase forward commitments for permanent mortgage financing for CalHFA-eligible borrowers tied to their construction/marketing program at single-family new-home developments anywhere in the state. On any day, builders/developers may lock-in, through an approved CalHFA Lender, an interest rate for a pool of funds for terms of 6, 9, or 12 months (nonprofits up to 18 months) into the future for commitment fees of 0.5%, 1.5%, and 2% respectively. Contact the California Housing Finance Agency for application information.
7. Loan to Lender Financing: available to eligible sponsors to help reduce the cost of construction financing for affordable housing projects by providing low cost funds to eligible construction lenders. Contact the California Housing Finance Agency for application information. {www.calhfa.ca.gov/special/help/index.htm}.
8. Multifamily Housing Program: loans for new construction, rehabilitation preservation of permanent and transitional rental housing for lower income households. The application can be downloaded at {www.calhfa.ca.gov/multifamily/financing/index.htm}.
9. Energy Efficient Mortgages: loans to finance energy-efficient improvements to new and existing homes.
10. California Housing Loan Insurance Fund: helps homeowners with the restrictions of conventional mortgage insurance by encouraging lenders to serve borrowers with limited funds for a down payment or closing costs.
11. Self-Help Builder Assistance Program: permanent low interest loans for single family homes built by owner-builders through self-help construction. This gives families with limited down payments the opportunity to use their "sweat equity" to obtain homeownership. To view a list of nonprofit builders who have participated go to {www.calhfa.ca.gov/homeownership/programs/shbap.htm}.

California Department of Housing and Community Development
1800 Third Street
P.O. Box 952050
Sacramento, CA 94252-2050
916-445-4782
www.hcd.ca.gov

1. California Self-Help Housing Program: assists low- and moderate-income families to build and rehabilitate their homes with their own labor. The application can be downloaded at the following website, {www.hcd.ca.gov/ca/calhome}.
2. HOME Program: assists communities and community housing development organization (CHDOs) in activities that create or retain affordable housing. The application can be found at {www.hcd.ca.gov/ca/home/nofa2001}.
3. Emergency Housing Assistance Program: grants to provide emergency shelters, transitional housing and services for the homeless. The forms for this program can be downloaded from the following website, {www.hcd.ca.gov/ca/ehap/ehapforms.html}.
4. California Indian Assistance Program: assists tribal organizations to obtain and administer housing, infrastructure. Call 916-445-4727 to check if funding is available and information on the application procedure.

5. Mobile Home Park Resident Ownership Program: loan to mobile home park resident organizations, nonprofit housing sponsors, or local public agencies that are purchasing the park. Go to {www.hcd.ca.gov/ca/mprop} for the necessary forms.
6. Federal Emergency Shelter Grant Program: grants to fund emergency shelters, services and transitional housing for the homeless. Applications and Request for Proposal (RFP) forms are available at {www.hcd.ca.gov/ca/fesg}.
7. Child Care Facilities Finance Program: loan guarantees and direct loans for the development and or expansion of child care facilities, child development facilities and family child care homes. Call 916-263-0470 for information on funding availability and the application process.
8. Families Moving to Work Program: loans to Cal WORKS welfare reform program recipients for limited-term housing assistance, childcare, employment assistance and other services. The forms can be found at {www.hcd.ca.gov/ca/fmtw}.
9. Housing Assistance Program: rent assistance for extremely low and very-low income households in rural counties without housing authorities. For information on the application process, call 916-324-7696.
10. Office of Migrant Services: loans and grants to provide safe, decent and affordable seasonal rental housing and support services for migrant farm worker families during peak harvest season. Call 916-324-0695 for funding availability and application information.

Colorado

Colorado Housing and Finance Authority
1981 Blake Street
Denver, CO 80202-1272
303-297-2432
800-877-2432
www.colohfa.org

1. HomeStart Program (tax-exempt bond program): first-mortgage financing program for eligible Colorado home buyers that offers a competitive interest rate loan and optional cash assistance to help pay down payment and closing expenses. For a list of participating lenders to apply with, go to {www.colohfa.org/hf_homestart_info.shtml}.
2. HomeStart Plus (taxable bond program): provides competitive interest rates and includes cash assistance. Eligibility Income limits are higher than the CHFA HomeStart program but are still below market. For a list of participating lenders to apply with, go to {www.colohfa.org/hf_homestart_info.shtml}.
3. Home Access and Home Access Plus Program: CHFA can possibly make it easier for those with disabilities to purchase their first home with a low interest rate loan. CHFA also offers a second mortgage program for down payment and closing costs. Call 800-877-2432 ext. 376 or 303-297-7376 for application assistance.
4. Mortgage Credit Certificate Program: reduction of federal income tax for homebuyers to pay their monthly mortgage. Call 303-297-7376 for application information.
5. Down Payment Assistance: low interest second mortgage loan to help eligible homebuyers with down payment and closing costs; only available to those who get CHFA Forward Commitment Loans. Call 303-572-9445 for application information.
6. Tax Exempt Private Activity Bonds: provides tax-exempt financing for construction loans and/or permanent mortgage loans. Call Colorado Housing and Finance Authority for a developer pack; 303-297-7351 or 800-877-2432.
7. Risk Sharing Program: provides long term, fully amortizing loans for new construction or acquisition with rehabilitation of rental housing for families or elderly. Contact the Colorado Housing and Finance Authority for application information.
8. Taxable Loans: combined with the Low Income Housing Tax Credit for new construction, acquisition, or rehabilitation of rental property to house families or the elderly. For an application, go to {www.colohfa.org/rf_main.shtml}.
9. Low Income Housing Tax Credit: federal tax credits for owners of low-income rental housing. For an application, go to {www.colohfa.org/tc_lihtc.shtml}.

10. Small Affordable Rental Transaction (SMART): provides long term financing for small rental housing projects; also minimizes the paperwork, document costs and the time it takes to close the loan. The application is available at {www.colohfa.org/rf_main.shtml}.

Connecticut

Connecticut Housing Finance Authority
999 West Street
Rocky Hill, CT 06067-4005
860-721-9501
www.chfa.org/
Email: info@chfa.org

1. Home of Your Own Program (HOYO): offers 30-year fixed rate mortgages to first time homebuyers with disabilities. Contact the Connecticut Housing Finance Authority for application information.
2. Urban Rehabilitation Home Ownership (UR Home) Program: a 2-year pilot program with hopes of revitalizing 16 targeted urban communities in Connecticut. This program offers a low interest rate, 30-year CHFA mortgage loan with low-cost down payment assistance. For a list of participating lenders to apply with, go to {www.chfa.org/FirstHome/firsthome_HomeownershipProgram.asp}.
3. Military Homeownership Program: a special, low-interest rate mortgage for full-time enlisted military personnel. If you are serving in the military full-time, whether it be U.S. Army, Navy, Air Force, Marine Corps, Coast Guard, or National Guard, you may be eligible. Call 860-571-3502 for application information.
4. Teachers Mortgage Assistance Program: low interest rate mortgage available to Connecticut certified public school teachers. Call 860-571-3502 for application information.
5. Home Buyer Mortgages: below market interest rates for first time low or moderate income homebuyers that purchase moderate priced homes. Call 860-571-3502 for application information.
6. Rehabilitation Mortgage Loan Program: loans to income eligible home buyers that purchase a home that needs to be repaired, refinancing of a home in need of repair for income eligible homeowners. Call 860-571-3502 for application information.
7. Homeownership Program: mortgages for public housing tenants and certain public assisted housing residents that meet income requirements; a home buyer education seminar must be attended. Call 860-571-3502 for application information.
8. Police Homeownership Program: low interest rate mortgages to police officers that purchase a home in certain communities; must not have owned a home within the past 3 years unless they purchase in targeted areas. Call 860-571-3502 for application information.
9. Down Payment Assistance Program: down payment assistance to eligible homebuyers; closing costs assistance to low income buyers in the Homeownership Program. To download an application, go to {www.chfa.org/mainpages/dap_forms.htm}.
10. Apartment Conversion for the Elderly: funding for elderly homeowners so they can renovate or add an addition on their home to create an accessory apartment to provide rental income. Call 860-571-3502 for application information.
11. Reverse Annuity Mortgage Program: elderly low-income homeowners can use the equity in their home as tax-free income which can be repaid after their death or when they no longer occupy the home. Call 860-571-3502 for application information.
12. Common Interest Community Common Element Repair Program: financing for repairs to common elements of condominiums and housing cooperatives where other financing is not available. Call 860-571-4390 for application information.
13. Employer Assisted Housing Tax Credit Program: state tax credits to employers that create loan funds for low and moderate income employees so they can purchase or rent a home. For information on the application, go to {www.chfa.org/TaxCredits/application.pdf}.
14. Community Development and Preservation Loan Fund: financing for developers to acquire, rehabilitate, and/or construct one to four family housing for income eligible buyers. Call 860-571-4275 for application information.

15. Multifamily Rental Housing Program: construction and permanent first mortgages to developers that build or rehabilitate affordable housing where some units are set aside for low income residents. Call 860-571-4216 for application information.
16. Mobile Manufactured Home Parks Pilot Program: financing for resident associations and certain non-profits to purchase mobile home park land to convert it to condominiums or cooperative ownership. Call 860-571-4377 for application information.
17. Low Income Housing Tax Credit: federal tax credits for developers of rental housing for low income tenants. Call 860-571-4216 for application information.
18. Housing Tax Credit Contribution Program: tax credits to non-profits that develop, sponsor or manage housing for very low, low, and moderate income individuals or families. Call 860-571-4216 for application information.

Delaware

Delaware State Housing Authority
18 The Green
Dover, DE 19901
302-739-4263
www2.state.de.us/dsha

1. Home Fix-Up Program: offered in Northeast Wilmington, this program provides housing rehabilitation loans to low- and moderate-income home owners and to landlords renting to low-income persons, to bring properties up to State Housing Code standards or to add handicapped-accessible modifications. Call the Delaware State Housing Authority for application information.
2. Housing Rehabilitation Loan Program: loans to low- to moderate-income homeowners or landlords who rent to low-income tenants of $35,000 for ten years at 3% for repairs or handicapped accessibility modifications. Call the Delaware State Housing Authority for application information.
3. Single-Family Mortgage Revenue Bond Program: low interest loans to first time homebuyers with low and moderate income. For a list of participating lenders to apply with, go to {www2.state.de.us/dsha/sfmrb_frame.htm}.
4. Second Mortgage Assistance Program: down payment and closing costs assistance to persons who have not owned a home in the past year. For a list of participating lenders to apply with, go to {www2.state.de.us/dsha/smal_frame.htm}.
5. Delaware Housing Partnership Program: second mortgages for settlement assistance to low to moderate-income families purchasing homes in targeted new construction subdivisions. For a list of participating lenders to apply with, go to {www2.state.de.us/dsha/home_buy_frame.htm}.
6. Acquisition/Rehabilitation Loan Program: loans for low- and moderate-income first time buyers to purchase homes that are in need of repair and then get a 3% interest loan to make the repairs all with one application. Call the Delaware State Housing Authority for application information.
7. Multifamily Mortgage Revenue Bond Program: tax-exempt mortgage revenue bonds, for the acquisition, new construction or rehabilitation of an apartment, which will be rented to low-income individuals and families. Call the Delaware State Housing Authority for application information.
8. Home Fix-Up Program: offered in Northeast Wilmington, this program provides housing rehabilitation loans to low- and moderate-income homeowners and also to landlords renting to low-income persons, to bring properties up to State Housing Code standards or to add handicapped-accessible modifications. Call the Delaware State Housing Authority for application information.
9. Housing Development Funds: loans to developers of housing for low- and moderate-income persons and families. Call the Delaware State Housing Authority for application information.
10. Community Development Block Grant: funding to maintain or improve housing, in Kent and Sussex counties, of low/moderate income households. Call the Delaware State Housing Authority for application information.
11. Emergency Shelter Grant Program: federal funds for local communities in Kent and Sussex counties, to rehabilitate, expand and operate emergency shelters. Call the Delaware State Housing Authority for application information.
12. HOME Program: designed to expand affordable housing through tenant and homebuyer assistance, rehabilitation, and new construction. Call the Delaware State Housing Authority for application information.

13. Neighborhood Revitalization Fund: low-interest loans to help entire communities restore their homes to State Housing Code standards. To download the application, go to {www2.state.de.us/dsha/nrf_frame.htm}.

14. Low Income Housing Tax Credit: federal income tax credit to owners and investors of affordable rental housing that rent to low-income tenants. For an application, go to {www2.state.de.us/dsha/lihtc2_frame.htm}.

15. Housing Capacity Building Program: a range of assistance to providers of affordable housing to increase their capacity to build and maintain the housing. For an application, go to {www2.state.de.us/dsha/hcbp_frame.htm}.

16. Public Housing (PH): offers low-income persons in Kent and Sussex Counties who are in need of assistance to afford month-to-month rent payments. Call the Delaware State Housing Authority for application information.

17. Section 8 Vouchers (SEC8V): assistance for low-income households to meet costs of rental housing for DSHA-approved private rental residency. Call the Delaware State Housing Authority for application information.

18. Moving to Work Demonstration Program (MTW): Applicants on the two programs (MTW and SEC8V) are placed on a combined waiting list for assistance. They are given the first available subsidy location, whether it is at a public housing site, a DSHA-owned apartment complex, or it is in the form of a Section 8 Voucher for use in the private market. Most residents, with the exception of the elderly and disabled, are eligible to receive subsidy under these programs for a maximum of 5 years (with some one-year extensions) while they take part in a mandatory self-sufficiency program. Call the Delaware State Housing Authority for application information.

19. Resident Services (RS): this self-sufficiency program provides its residents with social workers, counseling and programs to assist them with becoming independent of government housing assistance. Call the Delaware State Housing Authority for application information.

20. Section 8 New Construction (SEC 8 NC): affordable housing to very low-income people at 30 different sites in the state where participants pay about 30% of their income for rent. Call the Delaware State Housing Authority for application information.

District of Columbia

DC Department of Housing and Community Development
801 North Capitol Street, NE, Suite 8000
Washington, DC 20002
202-442-7200
http://dhcd.dc.gov
For application information on the following programs, please contact the Department of Housing and Community Development.

1. Home Purchase Assistance Program: low or no interest loans for low and moderate-income homebuyers.

2. First Right Purchase Assistance Program: low cost loans for low and moderate income individuals and tenant groups to exercise their right to purchase their rental housing that is being offered for sale.

3. Homestead Housing Preservation Program: repossessed properties are sold to eligible District residents at low cost and with deferred payment loans.

4. Handicapped Access Improvements Program: grants to remove barriers and improve accessibility; for homeowners or landlords on behalf of handicapped tenants.

5. D.C. Employer Assisted Housing Program: grants and deferred loans to first-time homebuyers that are employees of the District of Columbia government.

6. D.C. Metropolitan Police Housing Assistance Program: assistance to members of the Metropolitan Police Department for down payment and closing costs.

7. Senior Citizen Home Repair and Improvement Program: loans to senior citizens so that they can make emergency repairs to their home that would otherwise threaten their health and safety.

8. Distressed Properties Improvement Program: tax incentives to encourage the repair of occupied or vacant rental housing and retain low-income residents.

9. Housing Finance for the Elderly, Dependent and Disabled: loans for the development of housing for special needs households.

10. Low Income Housing Tax Credit Program: tax credits for owners of low and moderate income rental housing.

11. Single-Family Housing Rehabilitation Program: low cost financing for the rehabilitation of one to four unit low-income housing in designated areas.

12. Handicapped Access Improvements Program: grants to remove barriers and improve accessibility; for homeowners or landlords on behalf of handicapped tenants.

13 Homeownership Developer Incentive Fund: grant to development entities to lower the development costs so that they are affordable to low and moderate-income residents.

14. Apartment Improvement Program: technical assistance to rental housing owners to make comprehensive property improvement plans that involve a cooperative effort between owners, renters and financial institutions.

15. Construction Assistance Program: assistance to nonprofit land trusts to develop acquired land and buildings to create low- and moderate-income housing.

16. Community Land Acquisition Program: assistance to nonprofits to acquire land and buildings to create low and moderate income housing.

17. Housing Production Trust Fund Program: financial assistance to developers for the planning and production of low- to moderate-income housing and related facilities; there are a wide range of housing initiates concerning housing production and preservation.

Florida

Florida Housing Finance Corporation
227 North Bronough St., Suite 5000
Tallahassee, FL 32301
850-488-4197
www.floridahousing.org

1. First-Time Homebuyer Mortgage Revenue Bond Program: below market rate financing for first-time homebuyers with low/moderate income. Contact the Florida Housing Finance Corporation for application information.

2. Home Ownership Assistance Program: 0% interest, non-amortized 2nd mortgage loans to low-income families; 3% interest rate loan for nonprofit to develop or substantially rehabilitate affordable housing. Contact the Florida Housing Finance Corporation for application information.

3. State Housing Initiative Program (SHIP): funds for the development and maintenance of affordable housing through public/private partnerships. Contact the Florida Housing Finance Corporation for application information.

4. State Apartment Incentive Loan Program (SAIL): low rate financing for developers who build or rehabilitate rental housing that is affordable to very low-income people. For an application, go to {www.floridahousing.org/ViewPage.aspx?page=25}.

5. HOME Program: provides states their opportunity to administer federally funded homeownership housing program. To download an application, go to {www.floridahousing.org/ViewPage.aspx?page=10}.

6. HOME Rental Program: mortgage loans to construct, rehabilitate, or acquire and rehabilitate affordable housing for low-income households. To obtain an application, go to {www.floridahousing.org/ViewPage.aspx?page=10}.

7. Housing Credit Program: federal tax reduction to acquire and rehabilitate or construct rental housing units for low- and very low-income renters. For an application, go to {www.floridahousing.org/ViewPage.aspx?page=33}.

8. Florida Affordable Housing Guarantee Program: issues guarantees on obligation of the financing of affordable housing in order to encourage lending activities. To download an application, go to {www.floridahousing.org/ViewPage.aspx?page=17}.

9. Predevelopment Loan Program: financial assistance to non-profits with limited or no experience that develop affordable housing for very low- or low-income households. Download the Application Package Request Form at {www.floridahousing.org/ViewPage.aspx?page=62}.

10. Multifamily Revenue Bonds: below market rate loans to developers who set aside 20% of the units to low-income or 40% of units to very low-income persons. For an application, go to {www.floridahousing.org/ViewPage.aspx?page=21}.

11. Home Ownership Assistance Program: 0% interest, non-amortized 2nd mortgage loans to low-income families; 3% interest rate loan for nonprofit to develop or substantially rehabilitate affordable housing.

Georgia

Georgia Department of Community Affairs
60 Executive Park South NE
Atlanta, GA 30329
404-679-4940
www.dca.state.ga.us/

1. Own Home Down payment Program: loan to cover most of the down payment, closing costs and prepaid expenses to first time homebuyers. For a list of participating lenders to apply to, go to {www.dca.state.ga.us/housing/SFH/index.asp}.
2. Home Buyer Program: low interest rate mortgages to qualified first-time homebuyers. For a list of participating lenders to apply to, go to {www.dca.state.ga.us/housing/SFH/index.asp}.
3. The Redevelopment Fund Program: provides flexible financial assistance to local governments to assist them in implementing challenging economic and community development projects that cannot be undertaken with existing public sector grant and loan programs. For an application, go to {www.dca.state.ga.us/economic/RedevFund.html}.
4. The CDBG Loan Guarantee Program (Section 108 Program): program is a method of assisting non-entitlement local governments with certain unique and large-scale economic development projects that cannot proceed without the loan guarantee. A pre-application manual can be downloaded from {www.dca.state.ga.us/economic/108manual.html}.
5. Bond Allocation Program: long-term low-interest financing to businesses and individuals for the construction or improvements of manufacturing facilities, single and multi-family housing projects exempt financing is available both at the state and local level. For an application, go to {www.dca.state.ga.us/economic/bond.html}.
6. The Community HOME Investment Program (CHIP): used for the production, acquisition, or rehabilitation of decent, safe, and sanitary housing units which will be occupied by income eligible homebuyers, homeowners, or tenants. For an application, use the "Small Cities" Program application at the website, {www.dca.state.ga.us/grants/homeinvestment.html}.
7. Affordable Rental Housing Development Financing: DCA's rental housing finance programs work with for-profit, nonprofit and government partners to build or rehabilitate rental housing in Georgia. Download the application from the website, {www.dca.state.ga.us/housing/rentalfin.html}.
8. Appalachian Regional Commission: grants for site development and technical assistance for low- and moderate-income housing projects. For an application, go to {www.dca.state.ga.us/economic/arc.html}.
9. Emergency Shelter Grant Program: grants to shelter facilities for their operation and for the essential services for the homeless they service. To download an application, go to {www.dca.state.ga.us/housing/hopwamemo.html}.
10. Housing Opportunities for Persons with AIDS Program: direct subsidies of Federal funds to nonprofit groups that operate housing and provide supportive services to people with AIDS and related diseases. To download an application, go to {www.dca.state.ga.us/housing/hopwamemo.html}.
11. Community Development Block Grant Program: grant program including those for housing improvement projects, and economic development projects. For an application, go to {www.dca.state.ga.us/grants/grantprogram.html}.
12. Local Development Fund: matching grants to fund community improvement projects. {www.dca.state.ga.us/grants/developfund.html}.
13. Downtown Development payment Revolving Loan Fund: loans to eligible applicants to carry out downtown development projects. To download the application, go to {www.dca.state.ga.us/economic/ddrlf2.html}.
14. Housing Opportunities for Persons with AIDS Program: direct subsidies of Federal funds to nonprofit groups that operate housing and provide supportive services to people with AIDS and related diseases. To download an application, go to {www.dca.state.ga.us/housing/hopwamemo.html}.

Hawaii

Housing and Community Development Corporation of Hawaii
677 Queen Street, Suite 300
Honolulu, HI 96813

808-587-0597
www.hcdch.state.hi.us
Email: hcdch@hcdch.state.hi.us

1. Lease to Fee Conversion: provides a method for lessee homeowners to acquire the fee simple title to their house lots. Contact the Housing and Community Development Corporation of Hawaii for application information.
2. Hula Mae Single Family Program: low interest loans to first-time homebuyers. For a list of participating lenders, go to {www.hcdch.state.hi.us/hulamae.htm}.
3. Mortgage Credit Certificate Program: direct federal tax credit to potential homebuyers so that they have more available income to qualify for a loan and to help make payments. For a list of participating lenders, go to {www.hcdch.state.hi.us/mortgagecredit.html}.
4. Housing Alteration Revolving Loan Fund Program: low interest loans to persons with physical disabilities to adapt their home or rental unit. For application information, call 808-587-0567.
5. Down Payment Loan Program: down payment loans for borrowers that meet certain criteria. For a list of participating lenders, go to {www.hcdch.state.hi.us/downpay_loan.html}.
6. Interim Financing: a developer may receive interim construction financing from the Corporation at a reduced interest rate. Contact the Housing and Community Development Corporation of Hawaii for application information.
7. Rental Housing Trust Fund: provides "Equity Gap" low-interest loans or grants to qualified owners and developers constructing affordable housing units. Contact the Housing and Community Development Corporation of Hawaii for application information.
8. Rental Assistance Program: provides qualified owners monthly subsidies to assist eligible tenants who live in rental housing developments to make their rental payments. Also provides for interim construction financing for rental projects. Contact the Housing and Community Development Corporation of Hawaii for application information.
9. Low Income Housing Tax credit: tax credit for developers that construct or rehabilitate affordable rental housing. Contact the Housing and Community Development Corporation of Hawaii for an application.
10. Seed Money Loan: loans or grants to help with the costs to initiate a low- to moderate-income housing project. Contact the Housing and Community Development Corporation of Hawaii for application information.
11. Rental Assistance Program: provides qualified owners monthly subsidies to assist eligible tenants who live in rental housing developments to make their rental payments. Also provides for interim construction financing for rental projects. Contact the Housing and Community Development Corporation of Hawaii for application information.
12. Homeless Program: shelter and social services for homeless families and individuals. Contact the Housing and Community Development Corporation of Hawaii for application information.
13. State Rent Supplement Program: rent subsidies to tenants in approved projects. Contact the Housing and Community Development Corporation of Hawaii for an application.
14. Section 8 Housing Voucher Program: rental housing subsidies. Contact the Housing and Community Development Corporation of Hawaii for application information.
15. Housing Alteration Revolving Loan Fund Program: low interest loans to persons with physical disabilities to adapt their home or rental unit. Contact the Housing and Community Development Corporation of Hawaii for application information.
16. Lease Rent Renegotiation Program: arbitration of a lease renegotiation for one and two family residences leased by cooperative housing corporations. Contact the Housing and Community Development Corporation of Hawaii for application information.

Idaho

Idaho Housing and Finance Association
565 West Myrtle
P.O. Box 7899
Boise, ID 83707-1899
208-331-4882
www.ihfa.org

1. First-Time Home Buyer Program: low interest rate loans for first-time low- to moderate-income homebuyers. Contact the Idaho Housing and Finance Association for application information.
2. Finally Home Program: after completing the education, program participants may be eligible for financial assistance to purchase a home. Contact the Idaho Housing and Finance Association for information.
3. IHFA Housing Bonds: low-interest mortgage loans to first-time homebuyers, developers and nonprofit sponsors of affordable multifamily developments, for both families and seniors. Contact the Idaho Housing and Finance Association for application information.
4. 501(c)(3) Nonprofit Facilities Bonds: provides loans for nonprofit facilities to be owned by qualified nonprofit organizations. Contact the Idaho Housing and Finance Association for application information.
5. HOME Program: funds used for the construction and rehabilitation of affordable rental housing for low-income families across the state. The application can be obtained from {www.ihfa.org/multifamily_taxcredit.html}.
6. Emergency Shelter Grant Program: grants to improve the quality of emergency homeless shelters. For an application go to {www.ihfa.org/grants_homeless.html}.
7. Homeless Program Assistance: provides technical assistance to participants in homeless care programs. For an application go to {www.ihfa.org/grants_homeless.html}.
8. Section 8 Rental Assistance Program: assistance for low-income households to meet costs of rental housing. Contact the Idaho Housing and Finance Association for application information.
9. Family Self-Sufficiency Program: recipients receive assistance to eventually free themselves of federal and state welfare assistance. Contact the Idaho Housing and Finance Association for application information.
10. Public Housing in Idaho: IHFA operated public housing in target areas where lower income renters pay 30% of their income towards rent. Contact the Idaho Housing and Finance Association for application information.
11. Housing Opportunities for Persons Living with HIV/AIDS: 45 units with rental assistance to people who have a family member with HIV/AIDS. To download the application, go to {www.ihfa.org/rental_housingopps.html}.
12. Supportive Housing Program: supportive housing services to help the homeless with the transition to independent living; long-term assisted housing for persons with disabilities; supportive services for hard-to-reach homeless person with severe mental illness. Contact the Idaho Housing and Finance Association for application information.
13. Shelter Plus Care Program: rental and supportive services for seriously mentally ill homeless people. Contact the Idaho Housing and Finance Association for application information.

Illinois

Illinois Housing Development Authority
401 North Michigan Ave., Suite 900
Chicago, IL 60611
312-836-5200
www.ihda.org

1. First-Time Home Buyer Program: low interest mortgages for first-time income eligible homebuyers. For a list of participating lenders, go to {www.ihda.org/sf_search_form.htm}.
2. Mortgage Credit Certificate Program: federal tax credit to first-time income eligible homebuyers. For a list of participating lenders, go to {www.ihda.org/sf_search_form.htm}.
3. Affordable Housing Trust Fund: grants and loans to profit and nonprofit developers of low-income housing projects. For an application, go {www.ihda.org/cd2.htm}.
4. HOME Program: this program is designed to expand the availability of affordable housing for low and very low income persons. The application can be found at the following website; {www.ihda.org/home6.htm}.
5. Low Income Housing Tax Credits: tax credit to investors for new construction and rehabilitation of rental housing for low-income families. For an application, go to {www.ihda.org/lihtc2.htm}.
6. Multifamily Program: low interest loan to build or rehabilitate low-income housing. The application can be downloaded at the following website, {www.ihda.org/mf2.htm}.

Indiana

Indiana Housing Finance Authority
30 South Meridian
Suite 1000
Indianapolis, IN 46204

317-232-7777
800-872-0371
Fax: 317-232-7778
www.IN.gov/ihfa

1. First Time Home Program: loans to first-time homebuyers below the market rate. For a list of participating lenders, go to {www.IN.gov/ihfa/county/county.htm}.
2. Mortgage Credit Certificate Program: tax credit to low and moderate income families to purchase a single-family residence. For a list of participating lenders, go to {www.IN.gov/ihfa/county/county.htm}.
3. First Home 100 Program: works with the First Home and Rural Development Direct Loan Programs for further financial assistance to eligible homebuyers. For a list of Rural Development Offices, go to {www.rurdev.usda.gov/in/}.
4. First Home/One Down Program: 0% interest forgivable loan to assist qualified first-time home buyers with a down payment. For a list of participating lenders, go to {www.IN.gov/ ihfa/county/county.htm}.
5. First Home/Plus Program: a 5%–10% down payment assistance loan 0% in conjunction with a First Home Loan. For a list of participating lenders, go to to {www.IN.gov/ihfa/county/county.htm}.
6. The Housing Opportunities for People with AIDS (HOPWA) Program: provides housing assistance and related services for about 500 low-income persons with HIV/AIDS and their families.
7. Rental Housing Tax Credits: federal tax credit to owners of low-income rental housing. For information on how to request an application, go to {www.IN.gov/ihfa/rental/tax/allo/programs/programs.htm}.
8. HOME Program: funds used for a number of different purposes to create affordable housing. For an application, go to {www.IN.gov/ihfa/comdev/allo/apps/subrecipients/subrec.htm}.
9. Community Development Block Grant: funding to create affordable housing for low and very low income families. Contact the Indiana Housing Finance Authority for information.
10. Build-A-Home: grants to non-profit developers for construction or rehabilitation of single-family homes. Contact the Indiana Housing Finance Authority for information.
11. The Low-Income Housing Trust Fund: uses various State funding sources to provide additional financing options and may be used by not-for-profit housing developers to obtain financing for various kinds of housing development. Contact the Indiana Housing Finance Authority for application information.
12. Market-to-Market: subsidies to bring rent down to market level. Contact the Indiana Housing Finance Authority for application information.
13. First Home Community: enables teachers, fire fighters, law enforcement, state and municipal workers to purchase a home with as little as 1% of the purchase price or $500, whichever is less, of their own funds.
14. First Home Opportunity: enables qualified buyers the ability to purchase a home with as little as 1% of the purchase price or $500, whichever is less, of their own funds.

Iowa

Iowa Finance Authority
200 East Grand, Suite 350
Des Moines, IA 50309
515-242-4989
800-843-0201
Fax: 515-242-4994
www.ifahome.com

1. First-Time Home Buyer Mortgage Loan Program: low interest rate mortgage loans for first-time homebuyers. For a list of participating lenders, go to {www.ifahome.com/docs/sf_lenders.pdf}.
2. First Home Plus Program: designed to help first-time homebuyers or individuals who have not owned a home in the last three years pay for closing costs, down payment and required repairs. For a list of participating lenders, go to {www.ifahome.com/docs/sf_lenders.pdf}.
3. Multifamily Preservation Loan Program: loans available to help preserve the existing supply of affordable rental units at risk of being lost – either from physical deterioration or the need for financial restructuring. Loans are made available to eligible nonprofit and for-profit sponsors. For information on the application, contact the Iowa Finance Authority.

4. Transitional Housing: grants for existing non-profit providers of transitional housing to increase the number of transitional housing units they provide OR for domestic violence shelters/homeless shelters and other non-profits who wish to develop transitional housing units. To download an application, go to {www.ifahome.com/partner_haf.asp}.

5. Transitional Housing Technical Assistance: provide technical assistance for a variety of purposes. To download an application, go to {www.ifahome.com/partner_haf.asp}.

6. LHAP (housing production): loans, grants or combination of loans and grants to focus on the creation of additional units that serve single-family and multi-family rental housing needs. The housing must be affordable to low and moderate income individuals and families. For an application, go to {www.ifahome.com/partner_haf.asp}.

7. Main Street Revitalization Loan Program: partnership between Main Street Iowa, the Iowa Finance Authority and the Federal Home Loan Bank of Des Moines created a program to make available funds for lending to Main Street communities in Iowa. The pre-application form can be downloaded from {www.ifahome.com/partner_mainstreet.asp}.

8. Housing Assistance Funds Program: a flexible program of financial assistance dedicated to a variety of housing projects, programs and activities which contribute to the goal of providing decent, safe and affordable housing for limited income persons. Contact the Iowa Finance Authority for application information.

Kansas

Kansas Department of Commerce
1000 SW Jackson Street, Suite 150
Topeka, KS 66612-1354
785-296-5865
Fax: 785-296-8985
www.kshousingcorp.org
Email: info@kshousingcorp.org

1. Kansas Accessibility Program: assists individuals with disabilities needing funds to make modifications of their primary residence allowing them to better fulfill their abilities to use their home. The KAMP Service Providers list can be viewed at {www.kshousingcorp.org/programs/kamp.shtml}.

2. First Time Homebuyers Down Payment Assistance Program: loan for qualified homebuyers for down payment, closing costs, and legal fees associated with the purchase of a home. Forms for the program are available at the website, {www.kshousingcorp.org/programs/fthb.shtml}.

3. Homeowner Rehabilitation of Existing Property Program: funds to help homeowners to repair and rehabilitate their property, priority is given to elderly homeowners and families with school-age children. Forms for this program are available at the website, {www.kshousingcorp.org/programs/hr.shtml}.

4. Weatherization Assistance Program: a multi-funded program used to increase energy efficiency in low-income homes. A list of what the State provides and income limits is available at {www.kshousingcorp.org/programs/wap.shtml}.

5. State Housing Trust Fund: assists homeownership, rental housing, and housing with supportive services developments. The application can be found at {www.kshousingcorp.org/programs/shtf.shtml}.

6. Private Activity Bond Allocation: provide lower interest and longer term financing which reduces financing costs for multifamily housing. For an application, go to {www.kshousingcorp.org/programs/pab.shtml}.

7. Housing Tax Credits: tax credits for developers who rent to low-income families. For an application, go to {www.kshousingcorp.org/programs/htc.shtml}.

8. Emergency Shelter Grant Program: grants to local government agencies to provide emergency shelters for the homeless. To download the application, go to {www.kshousingcorp.org/programs/esg.shtml}.

9. Interim Development Loan: financial assistance to aid difficult-to-develop rental housing projects. The application can be downloaded from the following website; {www.kshousingcorp.org/programs/idl.shtml}.
10. Community Services Block Grant: funding for community action agencies to combat the causes and condition of poverty in the community. {www.kshousingcorp.org/programs/csbg.shtml}.
11. Tenant Based Rental Assistance Program: grants to the owners of a rental unit to help renters with monthly rent payments. The application is available from the following website; {www.kshousingcorp.org/programs/tbra.shtml}.
12. Rural Housing Incentive District: encourages local governments to develop housing in rural cities and counties. To download the application, go to {www.kshousingcorp.org/programs/rhid.shtml}.
13. Community Housing Development Organization: helps communities, through non-profit housing developers address housing issues. To download the application, go to {www.kshousingcorp.org/programs/chdo.shtml}.

Kentucky

Kentucky Housing Corporation
1231 Louisville Road
Frankfort, KY 40601
502-564-7630
800-633-8896
TTY: 800-648-6056
www.kyhousing.org

1. Home Ownership Program: low interest loans to homebuyers who currently do not own property and meet income requirements. Contact the Kentucky Housing Corporation for application information.
2. Homeownership Trust Fund: low fixed interest rate for very low-income families with special needs. Contact the Kentucky Housing Corporation for application information.
3. Yes You Can...Own a Home Program: free homeownership education program. For the Qualified Counselor list, go to {www.kyhousing.org/homeownership}.
4. Homeownership Counseling Program: homeownership counseling services to eligible potential homebuyers. Contact the Kentucky Housing Corporation for application information.
5. Repair Affair: assistance to homeowners that do not qualify for other existing programs to complete needed home repairs. Contact the Kentucky Housing Corporation for application information.
6. Kentucky Appalachian Housing Program: site development grants and loans for housing development in 49 eastern KY counties. Contact the Kentucky Housing Corporation for application information.
7. New Construction/Substantial Rehabilitation Program: funds to create or substantially rehabilitate housing to make it affordable for very low-income residents. For a list of complexes to apply directly to, go to {www.kyhousing.org/rental/newconstruct.cfm}.
8. Risk Sharing Program: low interest, permanent rate financing to developers of new construction or substantial rehabilitation of apartment units. For an application, go to {www.kyhousing.org/center/programs/RiskSharing/default.cfm}.
9. Assisted Living Program: low interest rate financing to developers of housing/service units for the elderly. To download an application, go to {www.kyhousing.org}.
10. Small Multi Family Affordable Loan Program: loans to be used for construction and/or permanent financing of rental housing development not exceeding 11 units for lower-income people. The application can be downloaded at the following website; {www.kyhousing.org/center/programs/SMAL/default.cfm}.
11. HOME Program: program to fund affordable housing production and rehabilitation. For an application, go to {www.kyhousing.org/homeownership/education/YYC.cfm}.

12. Nonprofit Housing Production and Repair Program: very low-interest loans for the production and repair of lower income housing. To download an application, go to {www.kyhousing.org/center/programs/NHPR/default.cfm}.
13. Housing Development Fund: flexible loan terms and low-interest rates to build affordable housing. Contact the Kentucky Housing Corporation for application information.
14. Affordable Housing Trust Fund: funds to acquire, rehabilitate, and/or build housing for very low-income residents. To download an application, go to {www.kyhousing.org/center/programs/AHTF/default.cfm}.
15. Housing Opportunities for Person with AIDS: funds to meet the housing needs of people with AIDS or related diseases. Download the application at {www.kyhousing.org/center/programs/HOPWA/default.cfm}.
16. Renaissance Kentucky: assists communities to revitalize their downtown. Call the Kentucky Housing Corporation for application information.
17. Housing Credit Program: offer eligible property owners a ten-year tax credit for each unit set aside for low-income families. Download the application at {www.kyhousing.org/center/programs/Credits/default.cfm}.
18. Rental Housing Deposits Program: assistance with utility and security deposits for low-income households. Contact the Kentucky Housing Corporation for application information.
19. Housing Choice Voucher Program: recipients can locate and rent a dwelling that meets the guideline on their own, provides rental assistance. For a list of housing contacts that will provide an application, go to {www.kyhousing.org/rental/voucher.cfm}.
20. Family Self-Sufficiency Program: rental assistance and supportive services for very low-income people that are willing to commit to a goal of being free of government assistance. Contact the Kentucky Housing Corporation for application information.
21. Mark-to-Market: assistance to owners of properties with expiring Section 8 contracts to achieve market-rate rents and affordable rental units. Contact the Kentucky Housing Corporation for application information.
22. Continuum of Care Program: variety of programs that offer transitional housing, rental assistance, supportive services, and permanent housing for disabled homeless persons and operating funds for emergency shelters. Download the application at {www.kyhousing.org/center/programs/Continuum/default.cfm}.
23. New Construction/Substantial Rehabilitation Program: offers rental units throughout the state. For a list of rental complexes, go to {www.kyhousing.org/rental/newconstruction.cfm}.

Louisiana
Louisiana Housing Finance Agency
2415 Quail Drive
Baton Rouge, LA 70808
225-763-8700
888-454-2001
Fax: 225-763-8710
www.lhfa.state.la.us
1. Low Income Housing Tax Credit: federal tax credits to developer/owners of rental units for low-income families. The application can be downloaded from {www.lhfa.state.la.us/programs/rental/htc-dwnlds.html}.
2. HOME Programs
   - Community Housing Development Organizations (CHDOs): Section 231 of the Cranston-Gonzalez National Affordable Housing Act requires that 15% of HOME allocations are to be set-aside for CHDOs. The purpose of the set aside is to be used by CHDOs in housing activities to develop, sponsor or own. Contact the Lousiana Housing Finance Agency for information.
   - Substandard Housing Assistance for Rural Economies (SHARE): funds used for the purpose of rehabilitating owner occupied dwellings. Contact the Louisiana Housing Finance Agency for information.
   - HOME/Mortgage Revenue Bond Program (MRB): offers a lower interest rate to assist those homebuyers whose annual income does not exceed 80 percent of median income (adjusted for family size) in the parish in which the property being purchased is located. The list of participating lenders can be found at {www.lhfa.state.la.us/programs/homeownership/firsthome.html}. The application can be downloaded from {http://204.196.244.8/programs/homeownership/firsthome.html}.
   - HOME Rental Program (5 or more units): provided to non-profits and for profits to develop new construction or rehabilitate existing housing. The application can be downloaded from {www.lhfa.state.la.us/programs/rental/home-dwnlds.html}.

3. First-Time Homebuyer Program: low interest rate loans for first time low-to-moderate income homebuyers. For additional information, go to {www.lhfa.state.la.us/programs/programs.html}.
4. Teachers' Homebuyers Program: designed to help state classroom teachers buy single-family homes. Additional 4% grant to homebuyers to cover closing costs with no repayment. For additional information, go to {www.lhfa.state.la.us/programs/homeownership/teacher/teacherhome.html}.
5. Low Income Housing Energy Assistance Program: assists low-income households meet their energy costs. For additional assistance, go to {www.lhfa.state.la.us/programs/energy/liheap.html}.
6. TANF Energy Assistance Program: energy assistance voucher program to prevent the loss of utility services for families participating in Family Independence Temporary Assistance Program (FITAP) and Kinship Subsidy Program (KSCP). For additional information, go to {www.lhfa.state.la.us/programs/energy/tanf.html}.
7. Weatherization Assistance Program: funds are distributed to nonprofit community agencies to assist low-income households through energy efficiency. For additional information, go to {www.lhfa.state.la.us/programs/energy/wap.html}.

Maine

Maine State Housing Authority
353 Water Street
Augusta, ME 04330-4633
207-626-4600
800-452-4668
Fax: 207-626-4678
TTY: 800-452-4603
www.mainehousing.org

1. hoMEworks program: a network of homebuyer education that gives potential homebuyers an opportunity to sort through the complex process of buying a home, including building good credit, shopping for a home, qualifying for a loan, and life as a homeowner.
    Check the statewide schedule for available classes on the hoMEworks web site at: {www.mainehomeworks.org}.
2. Mortgage Insurance Program for Tribal Land: insures mortgage loans for individuals purchasing or refinancing homes on Passamaquoddy and Penobscot Tribal land where restrictions on ownership prevent lenders from ever taking possession of the property. For a list of participating lenders, go to {www.mainehousing.org/1stbuyer.html}.
3. Home Rehabilitation Program (Pilot): provides loans to income eligible households to perform necessary repairs. Currently offered in four counties (Cumberland, Knox, Hancock and Washington Counties). For a list of contacts that you may apply to, go to {www.mainehousing.org/homerepair.html}.
4. Low Income Assistance Plan (LIAP): bill payment assistance program to eligible low and very low-income households who receive residential electric service. For a list of CAP agencies that will have an application, go to {www.mainehousing.org/liap.html#CAP%20Agencies}.
5. Homeownership Program; low down payment and low rate financing for first-time income eligible homebuyers. For a list of participating lenders, go to {www.mainehousing.org/1stbuyer.html}.
6. Purchase Plus Improvement: home improvement loans for borrowers to make immediate repairs. For a list of participating lenders, go to {www.mainehousing.org/1stbuyer.html}.
7. Low Income Home Energy Assistance Program: offers assistance to fuel vendors to provide heating for low-income homeowners and renters. For a list of CAP agencies, go to {www.mainehousing.org/liheap.html#CAP%20Agencies}.
8. Closing Cost Assistance: a loan of 2% of the mortgage to eligible applicants to cover closing costs. For a list of participating lenders, go to {www.mainehousing.org/1stbuyer.html}.
9. Down Home Loan: allows a minimum cash contribution of $750 or $1,000 in out-of-pocket expenses for income eligible borrowers. For a list of participating lenders, go to {www.mainehousing.org/1stbuyer.html}.
10. New Neighbors Program: special financing to buy a home in inner city, low-income neighborhoods in specified areas. For a list of participating lenders, go to {www.mainehousing.org/1stbuyer.html}.
11. Great Rate Program: low interest rate for low-income applicants; a homebuyer education course must first be completed. For a list of participating lenders, go to {www.mainehousing.org/1stbuyer.html}.

12. Lead Hazard Control Program: grants and loans to low-income homeowners and renters with a child under 6 in the household to get rid of lead-based paint problems. For a list of CAP agencies to apply to, go to {www.mainehousing.org/leadpaint.html}.

13. Low Income Home Energy Assistance Program (LIHEAP): program to help low-income households reduce their energy costs. For a list of CAP agencies to apply to, go to {www.mainehousing.org/homerepair.html}.

14. Weatherization/Central Heating Improvement Program: delivers weatherization and central heating repair/replacement to low-income homeowners and renters. For a list of CAP agencies to apply to, go to {www.mainehousing.org/weather.html#CAP%20Agencies}.

15. Pre-development Loan Program: provides interest-free capital to cover mortgageable pre-development costs to nonprofit borrowers developing affordable housing projects. To download an application, go to {www.mainehousing.org/download/download.html#PDL}.

16. Subsequent Loan Program: provides funds to existing MSHA mortgagors to make capital improvements, including converting electrically heated projects to another energy source; to make major repairs or to create new affordable units within an existing project. Contact the Maine State Housing Authority for application information.

17. Preservation Financing Program: a program to preserve the future affordability of MSHA-financed Section 8 projects. Download an application from the following website, {www.mainehousing.org/download/download.html#Pres}.

18. Project-Based Rental Assistance: offered to housing developers, owners, and managers to maintain financial and physical viability of subsidized housing in order to continue providing affordable housing to very low and low income elderly, disabled and families. Contact the Maine State Housing Authority for application information.

19. Transitional Housing Request for Proposals Program: MSHA solicits proposals for the development of new transitional housing for youth, families and victims of domestic violence who are homeless. These funds may be used for acquisition, acquisition and rehabilitation, and new construction. The application can be downloaded from {www.mainehousing.org/TransHousRFP.html}.

20. Rental Loan Program: below market rate loan for new or rehabilitated rental housing affordable to low- and very-low income households. Download an application at {www.mainehousing.org/download/download.html#RLP}.

21. Homeless Housing Program: funding to operate or improve shelters. For a list of CAP Agencies to apply to, go to {www.mainehousing.org/hhp.html#CAPAgencies}.

22. Low Income Energy Assistance Program: offers assistance to fuel vendors to provide heating for low-income homeowners and renters. For a list of CAP Agencies to apply to, go to {www.mainehousing.org/hhp.html#CAPAgencies}.

23. New Lease Program: reduced interest rate loans for the acquisition and rehabilitation of housing for low- and very low-income renters. To download an application, go to {www.mainehousing.org/download/download.html#NL}.

24. Supportive Housing Program: reduced interest rate mortgage financing and subsidy funding for nonprofits to create housing for persons who need supportive housing and services. For an application, go to {www.mainehousing.org/shp.html}.

25. Low Income Assistance Plan (LIAP): bill payment assistance program to eligible low and very low-income households who receive residential electric service. For a list of CAP agencies to apply to, go to {www.mainehousing.org/liap.html#CAP%20Agencies}.

26. Preservation Financing Program: a program to preserve the future affordability of MSHA-financed Section 8 projects. Download an application from the following website, {www.mainehousing.org/download/download.html#Pres}.

27. Project-Based Rental Assistance: offered to housing developers, owners, and managers to maintain financial and physical viability of subsidized housing in order to continue providing affordable housing to very low and low income elderly, disabled and families. Contact the Maine State Housing Authority for application information.

28. The Continuum of Care Homeless Assistance Program: funds to assist homeless persons move to self-sufficiency and permanent housing. For an application, go to {www.mainehousing.org/download/download.html#CofC}.

29. Shelter Plus Care Program: provides housing and supportive services on a long-term basis for homeless people with disabilities, (primarily those with serious mental illness, chronic problems with alcohol or drugs, or acquired immunodeficiency (AIDS) or related diseases). The program provides rental vouchers that are matched with supportive services. Contact the Maine State Housing Authority for application information.

30. Section 8 Moderate Rehabilitation for Single Room Occupancy (SRO) Dwellings for Homeless Individuals: SRO housing contains units for occupancy for one person. The SRO program provides rental assistance on behalf of homeless individuals in connection with the moderate rehabilitation of SRO dwellings. Contact the Maine State Housing Authority for application information.

31. Low Income Energy Assistance Program: offers assistance to fuel vendors to provide heating for low-income homeowners and renters. For a list of CAP agencies to apply to, go to {www.mainehousing.org/liheap.html#CAP%20Agencies}.

32. Lead Hazard Control Program: grants and loans to low-income homeowners and renters with a child under 6 in the household to get rid of lead-based paint problems. For a list of CAP agencies to apply to, go to {www.mainehousing.org/leadpaint.html}.

33. Low Income Home Energy Assistance Program (LIHEAP): program to help low-income households reduce their energy costs. For a list of CAP agencies to apply to, go to {www.mainehousing.org/homerepair.html}.

34. Weatherization/Central Heating Improvement Program: delivers weatherization and central heating repair/replacement to low-income homeowners and renters. For a list of CAP agencies to apply to, go to {www.mainehousing.org/weather.html#CAP%20Agencies}.

35. Tenant Assistance Program: federal rent subsidies to very low-income elderly, disabled, or families. Contact the Maine State Housing Authority for application information.

Maryland

Department of Housing and Community Development
100 Community Place
Crownsville, MD 21032-2023
410-514-7000
800-756-0119
www.dhcd.state.md.us
Email: customerservice@dhcd.state.md.us

1. The Homeownership for Individuals with Disabilities Program: provides low-interest mortgage loans to eligible disabled homebuyers. Contact the Center for Community Development Association at 800-638-7781 to be referred to a housing counselor.

2. The HotSpot Homeownership Initiative: an initiative to promote homeownership in HotSpot neighborhoods. A HotSpot neighborhood is an at-risks high-crime neighborhood that has been targeted to receive additional federal and State funding for crime control and prevention efforts. Contact the Maryland Department of Housing and Community Development for application information.

3. Mortgage Program: below market interest rate mortgage financing for low- and moderate-income first time homebuyers. For a list of lenders to apply to, go to {www.dhcd.state.md.us}.

4. Housing Rehabilitation Program-Single Family: loans to limited income homeowners and owners of small nonresidential properties to preserve and improve the property. For a list of local housing offices to apply to, go to {www.dhcd.state.md.us/mhrp-sf/index.asp}.

5. Downpayment and Settlement Expense Loan Program: borrowers through the *Mortgage Program* can get a 0% loan to help cover settlement expenses. Contact the Maryland Department of Housing and Community Development for application information.

6. Live Near Your Work Program: employees that purchase a home near their work in targeted areas receive a grant for costs associated with the purchase of a home. For an application, go to {www.dhcd.state.md.us/lnyw/index.cfm}.

7. Lead Hazard Reduction Grant and Loan Program: funds to homeowners and landlords to reduce or eliminate lead-based paint hazard.

8. Weatherization Assistance Program: low interest rate loans assist eligible low-income households to install energy conservation materials. For a list of local government or non-profit organizations to apply to, go to {www.dhcd.state.md.us/weather/index.asp}.

9. Special Targeted Applicant Rehabilitated Program (STAR): funds to help single-family homeowners to bring their property up to code. Contact the Maryland Department of Housing and Community Development for application information.

10. Community Housing Support Program (CHSP): for eligible non-profit organizations to renovate and resell properties to owner/occupants, thus reducing vacancies and encouraging the health and vitality of those neighborhoods. For a list of available properties, go to {www.dhcd.state.md.us/chsp/index.cfm}.

11. Rental Housing Funds: provides loans to nonprofit and profit developers for new construction and rehabilitation projects for the development of affordable multi-family housing in priority funding areas. To download an application, go to {www.dhcd.state.md.us/rhfunds/index.asp}.

12. The Self-Help Homeownership Technical Assistance Program: provides funds to non-profit organizations and local governments that operate self-help housing programs. To download an application, go to {www.dhcd.state.md.us/shhtag/index.asp}.

13. Maryland Affordable Housing Trust (MAHT); a variety of opportunities that promote affordable housing for very low-income households earning less than 50% of area or Statewide median income. To download an application, go to {www.dhcd.state.md.us/maht/index.asp}.

14. Operating Assistance Grants Program: consists of two types of grants—production and capacity building. To download the applications, go to {www.dhcd.state.md.us/oagp/index.asp}.
   - Production Grants: for nonprofit organizations who are engaged in the production and/or rehabilitation of affordable housing.
   - Capacity Building Grants: for inexperienced nonprofit organizations or existing nonprofit organizations that are undertaking new types of affordable housing activities, for the development of affordable housing.

15. Group Home Financing Program: low interest, no interest deferred payment loans to nonprofit organizations to purchase and modify housing for use as group homes and shelters. For information on the application process, call the Maryland Department of Housing and Community Development.

16. Multifamily Bond Program: below-market financing for low-income multifamily rental housing development. For information on the application process, call the Maryland Department of Housing and Community Development.

17. Accessory, Shared and Sheltered Housing Program: low rate loans to finance additions and improvement to create accessory, shared or sheltered housing for low-income households. For information on the application process, call the Maryland Department of Housing and Community Development.

18. Federal Low Income Housing Tax Credit Program: federal tax credit to owners of low-income rental housing. To download an application, go to {www.dhcd.state.md.us/lihtc/index.asp}.

19. Shelter and Transitional Housing Facilities Program: provides grants to improve or create transitional housing and emergency shelters. For information on the application process, call the Maryland Department of Housing and Community Development.

20. Lead Hazard Reduction Grant and Loan Program: funds to homeowners and landlords to reduce or eliminate lead-based paint hazard. For a listing of local housing offices to apply to, go to {www.dhcd.state.md.us/lead/index.asp}.

21. HOME Program: funds for the construction, acquisition and rehabilitation of rental housing, owner occupied housing, and special needs housing. To download an application, go to {www.dhcd.state.md.us/home/index.asp}.

22. Office and Commercial Space Conversion Initiative: financing to convert older offices and commercial space downtown into new affordable rental housing. To download an application, go to {www.dhcd.state.md.us/ocsci/index.asp}.

23. Rental Allowance Program (RAP): provides monthly rent assistance for low income families who are homeless or who have an emergency need for housing. To download the RAP Handbook, go to {www.dhcd.state.md.us/rap/index.asp}.

24. Rental Allowance Program: subsidies to very low-income individuals with emergency needs or that are homeless. To download the RAP Handbook, go to {www.dhcd.state.md.us/rap/index.asp}.
25. Section 8 Existing Certificate/Voucher Program: rent subsidies for low-income households. For application information, contact the Maryland Department of Housing and Community Development.
26. Lead Hazard Reduction Grant and Loan Program: funds to homeowners and landlords to reduce or eliminate lead-based paint hazard. For a listing of local housing offices to apply to, go to {www.dhcd.state.md.us/lead/index.asp}.

Massachusetts
MassHousing
One Beacon Street
Boston, MA 02108-3110
617-854-1000
Fax: 617-854-1029
TDD: 617-854-1025
www.mhfa.com
Email: information@masshousing.com

1. Group Home Financing Program: low interest, no interest deferred payment loans to nonprofit organizations to purchase and modify housing for use as group homes and shelters. Contact the Massachusetts Housing Finance Agency for information.
2. Municipal Mortgage Program: financing available to police, firefighters, school teachers and other municipal employees that requires no down payment. For a list of participating banks, go to {http://mhfadata.com/municipal_results.asp}.
3. Home Improvement Loan Program: loans of up to $50,000 to eligible homeowners to make needed permanent general improvements to their homes. For a list of lenders to apply to, go to {www.mhfa.com/}.
4. General Lending: special loans for income eligible first time homebuyers. Contact the Massachusetts Housing Finance Agency for information.
5. Mortgage Insurance Fund: provides private mortgage insurance on mortgage loan down payments below 20%. Contact the Massachusetts Housing Finance Agency for information.
6. Get the Lead Out Program: provides low cost financing to owners of 1 to 4 family homes to remove lead paint. For a listing of local rehabilitation agencies, go to {www.mhfa.com/}.
7. MassHousing Program: loan of 4% of the loan amount for down payment and closing cost assistance to qualified buyers. For a list of lenders to apply to, go to {www.mhfa.com/sf/sf_lenders.htm}.
8. Septic Repair Loan Program: financial assistance for income eligible homeowners to repair a failed septic system. For a list of lenders to apply to, go to {www.mhfa.com/}.
9. Elder 80/20: Supportive Housing for Seniors Program: for the development of housing that will serve elders who wish to live in independent rental apartments with on-site access to supportive services as needed. At least 20% of the units must be reserved for low-income occupancy. Contact the Massachusetts Housing Finance Agency for application information.
10. Construction Loan Program: loans available to builders who agree to price 25% of their units at or below MHFA's acquisition cost limits, thus creating homeownership opportunities for low- and moderate-income persons and assisting small-scale home builders who may not be able to access conventional sources of construction financing. Contact the Massachusetts Housing Finance Agency for application information.
11. Low Income Housing Tax Credit Program: federal tax credits for owners of low-income rental housing. Contact the Massachusetts Housing Finance Agency for application information.
12. Get the Lead Out Program: provides low cost financing to owners of 1 to 4 family homes to remove lead paint. For a listing of local rehabilitation agencies, go to {www.mhfa.com}.

13. The Massachusetts Affordable Housing Trust Fund: designed to provide resources to create or preserve affordable housing throughout the state for low-income households. To download an application, go to {www.mhfa.com/}.
14. Expanding Rental Affordability Program (ERA): assistance for rental housing where at least 20% of the units are set aside for low-income renters. For information, contact the Massachusetts Housing Finance Agency.
15. Demonstration Disposition Program: funding to renovate development in specified areas. To download an application, go to {www.mhfa.com/dev/dp_ddfactsheet.htm}.
16. Options for Independence Program: financing to community based residences for previously mentally institutionalized persons, homeless mentally ill, and other special needs persons. For information, contact the Massachusetts Housing Finance Agency.
17. Bridge Loan Financing: for developers of low-income rental housing in conjunction with construction/permanent financing. For information, contact the Massachusetts Housing Finance Agency.
18. 504/ADA Technical Assistance: technical assistance for housing providers, residents, applicants, and service providers. For information, contact the Massachusetts Housing Finance Agency.
19. Project TAP (Tenant Assistance Program): training for project residents and management for drug and alcohol-related problems. For information, contact the Massachusetts Housing Finance Agency.
20. Get the Lead Out Program: provides low cost financing to owners of 1 to 4 family homes to remove lead paint. For a listing of local rehabilitation agencies, go to {www.mhfa.com/sf/sf_lra.htm}.
21. Expanding Rental Affordability Program: assistance for rental housing where at least 20% of the units are set aside for low-income renters. For information, contact the Massachusetts Housing Finance Agency.
22. 504/ADA Technical Assistance: technical assistance for housing providers, residents, applicants, and service providers. For information, contact the Massachusetts Housing Finance Agency.
23. Youth Resident Activities Program: programs and activities for youths that reside in MHFA properties in specified areas. For information, contact the Massachusetts Housing Finance Agency.
24. MassAdvantage: below-market-rate mortgages or home improvement loans available to low-to-moderate income first-time homebuyers. For additional information, go to {www.mhfa.com}.
25. MassAdvantage100: 100% financing available to low-to-moderate first-time homebuyers. For additional information, go to {www.mhfa.com}.
26. Purchase and Rehabilitation Program: program covering purchase price plus necessary rehabilitation costs for first-time homebuyers. For additional information, go to {www.mhfa.com}.
27. RHS Loan Guarantee Loan: mortgage program for low-to-moderate income borrowers in identified rural areas. For additional information, go to {www.mhfa.com}.
28. Take the "T" Home Mortgage Program: provides 100% financing to qualified regular public transportation ("T") riders buying a home in close proximity to public transportation. For additional information, go to {www.mhfa.com}.

Massachusetts Department of Housing and Community Development
100 Cambridge Street, Ste. 300
Boston, MA 02114
617-573-1100
www.state.ma.us/dhcd
The following websites provide location listings:
- Local Housing Authorities: {www.state.ma.us/dhcd/publications/HOW_TO2K.HTM#LHAs}
- Department of Transitional Assistance (DTA): {www.state.ma.us/dhcd/publications/HOW_TO2K.HTM#DTAs}
- Neighborhood Housing Services Offices: {http://www.state.ma.us/dhcd/publications/HOW_TO2K.HTM#NHS}
- Community Development Corporations: {www.state.ma.us/dhcd/publications/HOW_TO2K.HTM#CDCs}
- Community Action Agencies: {www.state.ma.us/dhcd/publications/HOW_TO2K.HTM#CAAs}
- Area Agencies on Aging: {www.state.ma.us/dhcd/publications/HOW_TO2K.HTM#AaonA}

- Independent Living Centers: {www.state.ma.us/dhcd/publications/HOW_TO2K.HTM#ILC}
- Shelter Referral / Placement Services: {www.state.ma.us/dhcd/publications/HOW_TO2K.HTM#SR/PS}
- Temporary Shelters: {www.state.ma.us/dhcd/publications/HOW_TO2K.HTM#TSs}

Other available resources:
For The Elderly:
> Statewide Elder Hotline: 1-800-882-2003
> Massachusetts Executive Office of Elder Affairs: 617-727-7750

For Special Needs Housing:
> Massachusetts Department of Mental Health: 617-626-8000
> Massachusetts Department of Mental Retardation: 617-727-5608, {www.dmr.state.ma.us/}

1. The State Soft-Second Mortgage Program: a state funded program that will help first time homebuyers purchase a home. For more information, contact the Massachusetts Housing Partnership at 617-330-9955 or visit their website at {www.mhp.net}.
2. Homebuyer Counseling: educates first-time home buyers of the home buying process.
   - Contact the *Massachusetts Homeownership Collaborative*, part of the Citizens' Housing and Planning Association for information on homebuyer counseling agencies across the state. Call 800-HOME-111 (or 617-742-0820) or visit the web site at {www.chapa.org/housing_programs.htm}.
   - The *City of Boston* operates the Boston Home Center. Call 617-635-4663 or visit the web site at {www.ci.boston.ma.us/dnd}.
   - The *Massachusetts Housing Finance Agency* has a list of homebuyer counseling agencies. Call 617-854-1000 or visit the web site at {www.mhfa.com}.
3. Home Rehabilitation Loans: loans made available to moderate and low income homeowners.
4. Low Income Home Energy Assistance Program (LIHEAP): helps low-income households to pay winter heating bills. Contact the Massachusetts Department of Housing and Community Development for an application.
5. Weatherization Assistance Program: funds for full-scale energy conservation services in low-income households. Contact the Massachusetts Department of Housing and Community Development for information.
6. Heating Emergency Assistance Retrofit Task Weatherization Assistance Program (HEARTWAP): provides heating system repair and replacement services to low-income households. Contact the Massachusetts Department of Housing and Community Development for information.
7. Low Income Sewer and Water Assistance Program: financial assistance to homeowners that have excessive water and sewer bills. Contact the Massachusetts Department of Housing and Community Development for information.
8. Homeownership Opportunity Program (HOP): reduced rate first mortgage loans to buyers of HOP units. Call 617-573-1300 for application information.
9. Community Development Block Grant Program: variety of programs that fund housing and/or public facilities and infrastructure programs. Contact the Massachusetts Department of Housing and Community Development for application information.
10. Community Enterprise Economic Development Program: assistance for residents and their local community development corporation to revitalize their neighborhoods. Contact the Massachusetts Department of Housing and Community Development for application information.
11. HOME Program: funds available for rental housing production and rehabilitation, first time homebuyer assistance, rehabilitation assistance for homeowners, and tenant based rental assistance. Contact the Massachusetts Department of Housing and Community Development for application information.
12. Housing Innovations Fund: Deferred payment loans to non-profit developers who reserve at least 50% of the housing units to low-income families. Contact the Massachusetts Department of Housing and Community Development for application information.

13. Housing Stabilization Fund Program: funding for three specific programs. Contact the Massachusetts Department of Housing and Community Development for application information.
    - Neighborhood Restoration Initiative (NRI): funds used for neighborhood revitalization to support affordable rental housing and affordable homeownership.
    - The Rehabilitation Initiative (RI): funds to support the acquisition, rehabilitation, and reuse of distressed, reused, or abandoned properties as affordable housing.
    - Soft Second Loan Program: creates homeownership opportunities by subsidizing mortgages, or providing closing cost assistance and down payments.
14. Local Initiative Program: technical assistance to communities and developers that are working together to create housing that sets aside 25% of its units for low and moderate income households.
15. Neighborhood Housing Services Program: support for agency or individual housing rehabilitation projects. Contact the Massachusetts Department of Housing and Community Development for application information.
16. Contact the Massachusetts Department of Housing and Community Development for application information on these programs.
    - Rental Voucher Program (MRVP): subsidies for very low-income families.
    - Section 8 Certificate/Voucher Program: rent subsidies for very low-income families, the elderly and the disabled.
    - Section 8 Designated Housing Program: tenant based subsidies for non-elderly disabled individuals who are on waiting lists at MHFA developments.
    - Section 8 Family Self-Sufficiency Program: assists eligible families to achieve economic independence.
    - Section 8 Family Unification Program: eligible families are issued a Section 8 voucher. The family is then given up to 180 days to locate their own rental housing.
    - Section 8 Housing Choice Voucher Program: eligible families are issued a Section 8 voucher. The family is then given up to 180 days to locate their own rental housing.
    - Section 8 Housing Options Program: Section 8 vouchers for eligible low-income disabled individuals that are living in transitional housing.
    - Section 8 Mainstream Housing Program: available to eligible families where the head of household is disabled.
    - Section 8 Moderate Rehab Single Room Occupancy Program: available to very low-income homeless individuals that may or may not have a need for supportive services.
    - Section 8 Raising Next Generation Program: targeted for low-income families living independently in the community but need special support services for both the elderly and young children.
    - Section 8 Tenant Based Rental Assistance for Persons Living with HIV/AIDS: section 8 vouchers, and supportive services for those eligible very low-income persons living with HIV/AIDS.
    - Section 8 Veterans Administration Supported Housing Program: provides section 8 rental vouchers along with ongoing case management and clinical services administered by the Veterans Administration Supportive Housing (VASH) to homeless disabled veterans.
    - Alternative Housing Voucher Program (AHVP): provides rental assistance to people with disabilities under age 60 who either live in, or are eligible to live in elderly/disabled state-assisted public housing.
    - Low Income Home Energy Assistance Program (LIHEAP): helps low-income households to pay winter heating bills.
    - Weatherization Assistance Program: funds for full scale energy conservation services in low-income households.
    - Heating Emergency Assistance Retrofit Task Weatherization Assistance Program (HEARTWAP): provides heating system repair and replacement services to low-income households.
    - Homeless Intervention and Housing Services Program: supportive services that help people in a housing crisis situation find housing.
    - McKinney Emergency Shelter Grant Program: provides emergency shelter and homelessness prevention to low-income families and individuals.
    - McKinney Local Housing Authority Transitional Housing Program: transitional housing and individual service plans that include job training, education, counseling, employment assistance, daycare, and life skills enhancements.

- McKinney Shelter Plus Care Program: provides rental assistance and support services for homeless families or individuals with disabilities—primarily those with mental illness, chronic substance abuse, and/or HIV/AIDS.
- Mcattered Site Transitional Apartment Program (SSTAP): transitional housing provided to individuals, and their families, who are victims of domestic violence, and are homeless as a result of domestic violence.

Michigan

Michigan State Housing Development Authority
735 East Michigan Avenue
P.O. Box 30044
Lansing, MI 48912
517-373-8370
Fax: 517-335-4797
TTY: 800-382-4568
www.michigan.gov/mshda

1. Property Improvement Loan: home improvement loans for owner and non-owner occupied homes over 20 years old at a low interest rate. Contact the Michigan State Housing Development Authority for application information.
2. Homeownership Counseling Network: free counseling for potential MSHDA borrowers. To use the counselor locator, go to the following web site: {www.michigan.gov/mshda/1,1607,7-141-5485_5498-29223--,00.html}.
3. Mortgage Credit Certificate: federal income tax credits that give homebuyers more income to qualify for a mortgage. To view the list of participating lenders, go to {www.michigan.gov/mshda/0,1607,7-141-5485_5494-29465--00.html}.
4. Single Family Mortgage Program: low interest loans for the purchase single family homes and condominiums. For a list of participating lenders to apply with, go to {www.michigan.gov/mshda/1,1607,7-141-5485_5486---00.html}.
5. Housing Resource Fund: funds for nonprofit and local government to create affordable housing projects. Contact the Michigan State Housing Development Authority for application information.
6. Community Development Block Grant: grants to small communities and counties so that lower income homeowners can upgrade their homes and carry out other housing activities. Contact the Michigan State Housing Development Authority for application information.
7. Habitat for Humanity Housing Grant Fund: grants to Habitat for Humanity to build or rehabilitate homes. Contact the Michigan State Housing Development Authority for information on this program.
8. Contractor's Assistance Program: provides working capital loans to small contractors who have been selected to work on rental housing projects. Contact the Michigan State Housing Development Authority for application information.
9. Low Income Housing Tax Credit Program: federal tax credit for owner/developers of low-income rental housing. Contact the Michigan State Housing Development Authority for application information.
10. More Independence Through HOME: funds used to finance nonprofit projects that provide rental units for disabled people. Contact the Michigan State Housing Development Authority for application information.
11. Section 8 Existing Rental Allowance Program: rent subsidies for very low-income persons who find their own housing in private homes and apartment buildings. Contact the Michigan State Housing Development Authority for application information.
12. Tax Exempt Apartment for Michigan (TEAM): program for rental units where 20% of the units are for low income people and another 20% for very low income people. Contact the Michigan State Housing Development Authority for application information.
13. Family Self Sufficiency Program (FSS): help for families in assisted housing that contract to be off of government support. Contact the Michigan State Housing Development Authority for application information.
14. Taxable Bond Program: loans for rental housing where most tenants will have very low incomes. Contact the Michigan State Housing Development Authority for application information.
15. Acquisition Rehabilitation Mortgages: available to qualified homebuyers with repair costs or improvements of at least $5,000. Contact the Michigan State Housing Authority for application information.

Minnesota

Minnesota Housing Finance Agency
400 Sibley Street, Suite 300
St. Paul, MN 55101-1998
651-296-7608
800-657-3769
TDD: 651-297-2361
www.mhfa.state.mn.us
Email: mhfa@state.mn.us

1. Minnesota Mortgage Program (MMP): below market rate loans for low/moderate income first-time homebuyers. For a list of lenders, go to {www.mhfa.state.mn.us/homes/MMP.htm}.
2. Minnesota City Participation Program (MCPP): low interest mortgage loans for low to moderate income first-time homebuyers. For a list of communities and lenders, go to {www.mhfa.state.mn.us/homes/MCPP.htm}.
3. Urban Indian Housing Program: loans at below market interest rates for low to moderate income Indian families buying their first home in an urban area. Contact the Minnesota Housing Finance Agency for application information.
4. Home Equity Conversion Counseling (HECC): a Home Equity Conversion or Reverse Mortgage is designed to assist primarily senior homeowners (as defined by the participating lender), to be able to spend the equity in their home while still continuing to live there. In order to receive this type of mortgage, homeowners are required to receive counseling specifically designed to educate the homeowner on the options available under a reverse mortgage. Contact the Minnesota Housing Finance Agency for program information.
5. Home Ownership Assistance Fund (HAF): down payment and monthly payment assistance to low to moderate income MHFA mortgage recipients. Contact the Minnesota Housing Finance Agency for application information.
6. Entry Cost Homeownership Opportunity (ECHO): provides down payment and closing cost assistance to those purchasing a home through a community lending program. Contact the Minnesota Housing Finance Agency for application information.
7. Fix Up Fund Loans: loans offering below market interest rates to fix up your home. Contact the Minnesota Housing Finance Agency for application information.
8. Rehabilitation Loan Program: loans to low to moderate-income homeowners for home improvements directly affecting the safety, habitability, energy efficiency and accessibility of their home. Contact the Minnesota Housing Finance Agency for application information.
9. Community Fix-Up Fund: home improvement loans offered to low to moderate income homeowners who occupy the property to be improved, in participating communities. Eligible homeowners must also meet any additional targeting criteria established by the community. Contact the Minnesota Housing Finance Agency for application information.
10. Foreclosure Prevention Assistance Program: provides case management services and, if applicable, mortgage payment, or other financial assistance to homeowners facing foreclosure, due to a temporary financial crisis. For a list of FPAP Administrators, go to {www.mhfa.state.mn.us/homes/homes_foreclosure.htm}.
11. Urban Indian Housing Program: loans at below market interest rates for low to moderate income Indian families buying their first home in an urban area, low interest rate loans for rental housing development for Indian families that have a low income. Contact the Minnesota Housing Finance Agency for application information.
12. Preservation of Federally Assisted Housing: a statewide program that will provide zero to one percent interest-deferred loans to help cover the costs of preserving permanent affordable rental housing with long term project-based federal subsidies that are in jeopardy of being lost. To download an application, go to {www.mhfa.state.mn.us/multifamily/multifamily_preserving.htm}.
13. Economic Development and Housing Challenge Program: supports economic development activities by providing loans and grants for construction, acquisition, rehabilitation, construction financing, permanent financing, interest rate reduction, refinancing, and gap financing of both single and multi-family homes. Contact the Minnesota Housing Finance Agency for application information.
14. Housing Trust Fund (HTF): zero interest deferred loans for acquisition, contraction or rehabilitation of a development of low-income rental and co-op housing. To download an application, go to {www.mhfa.state.mh.us/multifamily/RAFS.htm}.

15. Low to Moderate Income Rental Program: funds for the refinance or rehabilitation OR acquisition/rehabilitation or new construction of existing properties for low income people; funds for the acquisition and rehabilitation or new construction/conversion of rental housing for low and moderate income people. To download an application, go to {www.mhfa.state.mn.us/multifamily/RRLP.htm}.

16. Rental Rehabilitation Loan Program: low interest loans to rental property owners to rehabilitate the property. For an application, go to {www.mhfa.state.mn.us/multifamily/RRLP.htm}.

17. HOME Rental Rehabilitation Program: grants to rental property owners to rehabilitate property so that it is safe and affordable for low-income people. To download an application, go to {www.mhfa.state.mn.us/multifamily/HomeRRG.htm}.

18. Family Homeless and Prevention Assistance Program: grants to support or establish support systems relating to homelessness, funds can be used in an existing home, shelter, or with the transition to permanent affordable housing. To download an application, go to {www.mhfa.state.mn.us/multifamily/FHPAP.htm}.

19. Rental Assistance for Family Stabilization: rental assistance to families on public service enrolled in self-sufficiency programs that reside in specified counties. To download an application, go to {www.mhfa.state.mn.us/multifamily/RAFS.htm}.

20. Bridges: housing subsidy for low-income households that have at least one adult member with a serious and persistent mental illness. To download an application, go to {www.mhfa.state.mn.us/multifamily/bridges.htm}.

21. Section 8 New Construction: subsidized housing to assist low and moderate income families in need of housing. Contact the Minnesota Housing Finance Agency for application information.

22. Section 8 Existing Housing (Certificate Voucher Program): administered by local, county, or regional housing and redevelopment authorities (HRA) to help pay the rent on housing the applicant can find in the private market. For a list of local HRAs, go to {www.mhfa.state.mn.us/renters/renter_programs.htm}.

23. Housing Opportunities for Persons with AIDS: grants for housing assistance and services to people with AIDS and/or related diseases and their families. Contact the Minnesota Housing Finance Agency for application information.

24. 4d Property Tax Classification: property tax reduction for owners of residential rental property that pledge to comply with 4d requirements for 5 years. To download an application, go to {www.mhfa.state.mn.us/managers/property_4d.htm}.

25. Accessibility Home Fund: provides loans to borrowers with a disabled family member to buy, remodel or refinance a home.

Mississippi

Mississippi Home Corporation
735 Riverside Dr., Jackson, MS 39202
P.O. Box 23369
Jackson, MS 39225-3369
601-718-4636
Fax: 601-718-4643
www.mshomecorp.com

1. Down Payment Assistance Program: for lower income buyers who can afford mortgage payments but not a down payment. Contact the Mississippi Home Corporation for application information.

2. Mortgage Revenue Bond Program: interest rate at or below market rate and 3% down payment assistance. For a list of participating lenders to apply to, go to {www.mshomecorp.com/homebuyers/mortgage%20revenue%20bond.htm}.

3. Mortgage Credit Certificate Program: reduction of the amount of Federal Income Tax paid by income eligible borrowers. For a list of participating lenders to apply to, go to {www.mshomecorp.com/homebuyers/mortgage%20credit/%20certificate.htm}.

4. HomeRun: loan for down payment and closing costs to low to moderate income for first time homebuyers. For a list of participating lenders to apply to, go to {www.mshomecorp.com/homebuyers/homerun%20mortgage.htm}.

5. Housing Assistance for Teachers Program: down payment and closing cost assistance to licensed teachers that teach in a specified area. For a list of participating lenders to apply to, go to {www.mshomecorp.com/homebuyers/hat%20program.htm}.

6. Mississippi Affordable Housing Development Fund: loans to owners for construction, mortgage, predevelopment costs and rehabilitation of housing for moderate income households. To download an application, go to {www.mshomecorp.com/development/development.htm}.

7. Housing Tax Credit Program: tax credits for owners of low-income rental housing. For an application, go to {www.mshomecorp.com/htc/htc%20application.htm}.

8. Mississippi Affordable Housing Development Fund: loans to owners for construction, mortgage, predevelopment costs and rehabilitation of housing for moderate income households. To download an application, go to {www.mshomecorp.com/development/development.htm}.

9. Get on the Track Mortgage: provides prospective homebuyers with impaired credit a predetermined lease period to establish their credit reputation. For additional information, contact the Mississippi Home Corporation.

10. Mississippi Home of Your Own Project (HOYO): assistance for persons with disabilities to locate financial counseling which may allow them to purchase a home. For additional information, contact the Mississippi Home Corporation.

Missouri

Missouri Housing Development Commission
3435 Broadway
Kansas City, MO 64111-2459
816-759-6600
TTY: 816-758-6839
www.mhdc.com
Email: info@mhdc.com

1. Mortgage Revenue Bond Program: mortgage financing at interest rates below conventional market rates. For a list of participating lenders, go to {www.mhdc.com/homebuyer_programs/MRB_guidelines.htm}.

2. MHDC Rental Housing Production Program: funding to developers who acquire, rehabilitate, and/or construct rental housing for low- and moderate-income families. For an application, go to {www.mhdc.com/rental_production/forms/default.htm}.

3. HOME Rental Housing Program: provides financing for the acquisition and rehabilitation of housing for low- to very low-income families. For an application, go to {www.mhdc.com/rental_production/forms/default.htm}.

4. MISSOURI Housing Trust Fund: funds for eligible activities to meet the housing needs of very low income families; activities include rental housing production, housing and related services for the homeless, and rental subsidies. Contact the Missouri Housing Development Commission for an application package.

5. Affordable Housing Assistance Program (AHAP): tax credit for firms that donate cash, services, or property to a non-profit community organization that develops affordable housing. To download an application, go to {www.mhdc.com/rental_production/ahap/ahapapplication.doc}.

6. More Help Program "Home Repair": assistance for low-to-moderate income families to make improvements and repairs to their homes. To download an application, go to {www.mhdc.com/rental_production/pdf/home%20repair%20app%20packet.pdf}.

7. Cash Assistance Payment: 4% cash assistance to eligible homebuyers of their loan amount that does not have to be repaid. The payment may be applied to down payment, closing costs, prepaid taxes or other loan expenses. For additional information, go to {www.mhdc.com/homebuyer_programs/MRB_guidelines.htm}.

Montana

Montana Board of Housing
Department of Commerce
301 S. Park Ave.
Helena, MT 59601
Mailing Address:
    P.O. Box 200501
    Helena, MT 59620-0501
406-841-2700
Fax: 406-841-2701
http://commerce.state.mt.us/Housing/hous_prog_bhb.html

1. Reverse Annuity Mortgage Loan: home equity loans for lower income senior 68+ homeowners. Contact the Board of Housing for application information.
2. Single Family Bond Program: assists low and moderate income people in the purchase of a first home; in targeted areas it does not need to be a first time purchase. Contact a participating lender in your area for application information.
3. Disabled Accessible Affordable Homeownership Program: assists people with disabilities to acquire affordable architecturally accessible homes enabling them to live independently. Contact the Board of Housing for application information.
4. Recycled Single Family Mortgage Program: below market rate funds are often coupled with federal grants or local funds to make purchasing a home more affordable for lower income families and individuals. Contact the Board of Housing for application information.
5. HOME Program: funds to government and community housing organizations to create affordable housing and provide financial and technical assistance for low-income persons. To download an application, go to {http://commerce.state.mt.us/HOUSING/Hous_Prog_HOME.html}.
6. Risk Sharing Program: permanent mortgage financing for affordable rental housing to low income people. Contact the Board of Housing for application information.
7. Section 8 Housing Program: subsidies for rent and utilities to very low-income families. Contact the Board of Housing for application information.
8. Low Income Housing Tax Credit Program: federal tax credits for owners of low-income housing. Contact the Board of Housing for application information.
9. Risk Sharing Program: permanent mortgage financing for affordable rental housing to low-income people. Contact the Board of Housing for application information.

Nebraska
Nebraska Investment Finance Authority
200 Commerce Court
1230 "O" Street, Ste 200
Lincoln, NE 68508-1402
402-434-3900
800-204-6432
www.nifa.org/
Email: info@nifa.org
1. Agricultural Finance Programs: low interest rate loans to farmers and ranchers. Contact a local financial institution or a NIFA office for an application.
2. Single Family Home Ownership Program: loans for first time homebuyers that are income eligible. For a list of participating lenders, go to {www.nifa.org/programs}.
3. Affordable Housing Trust Fund: funds to help low and moderate income households obtain affordable housing. Contact the Nebraska Investment Finance Authority for application information.
4. Technical Assistance Review Process (TARP): provides technical assistance on financial resources, application, housing projects and more. Contact the Nebraska Investment Finance Authority for application information.
5. Low Income Housing Tax Credit Program: Federal tax credits for owners of low income housing. To download an application, go to {www.nifa.org/programs/}.
6. Super-Targeted Mortgage Program: low interest loans for low-to-moderate income potential homeowners to purchase a home. Homebuyer education is required. For additional information, contact the Nebraska Investment Finance Authority.
7. Community Empowerment Resource Funds (CERF): funds for the development of affordable housing development projects for low-to-moderate income individuals. Certain restrictions may apply. For additional information, contact the Nebraska Investment Finance Authority.

8. Credits to Own (CROWN): provides qualified low-income individuals the resources to plan and save to buy a home. The 15-year rental period in affordable housing allows time for the tenant to participate in homebuyer education, build equity and correct credit problems. For additional information, contact the Nebraska Investment Finance Authority.

Nevada
Nevada Housing Division
1802 North Carson St., Suite 154
Carson City, NV 89701
775-687-4258
Fax: 775-687-4040
http://nvhousing.state.nv.us
Email: nhd@nvhousing.state.nv.us

1. Single Family Mortgage Program: loans to moderate-income families with no previous home ownership interest in the past 3 years. For a list of participating lenders, go to {www.nvhousing.state.nv.us/single_family/participatinglenders.htm}.
2. Low Income Housing Trust Fund: funds available to homeowners for down payment assistance or rehabilitation of owner-occupied housing. Funds can also be used by developers to develop and support affordable rental housing through Acquisition, New Construction, Reconstruction, Moderate or Substantial Rehabilitation, Site Improvements, Conversion, Demolition and certain finance costs. Trust Funds may also be used for technical assistance. The application for developers can be found at {www.nvhousing.state.nv.us/low_income/developer%20information.htm}.
3. Low Income Weatherization Program: assist eligible low-income households with their utility bills by providing for various energy conservation measures. Contact the Nevada Housing Division for application information.
4. Emergency Shelter Grant Program: provides funding to help improve existing shelters, make available additional emergency shelters, as well as provide social and supportive services to homeless individuals. The forms for this program can be found at {www.nvhousing.state.nv.us/emer_shelter/Forms.htm}.
5. Low Income Housing Tax Credit Program: tax credits to developers of low and very low income housing. To download an application, go to {www.nvhousing.state.nv.us/tax_credit/tax%20credit%20index.htm}.
6. Multi-Family Project Bond Financing Program: funding to developers of affordable housing projects. For an application, go to {http://nvhousing.state.nv.us/bond_program/mfindex.htm}.
7. Low Income Housing Trust Fund: funds available to homeowners for down payment assistance or rehabilitation of owner-occupied housing. Funds can also be used by developers to develop and support affordable rental housing through Acquisition, New Construction, Reconstruction, Moderate or Substantial Rehabilitation, Site Improvements, Conversion, Demolition and certain finance costs. Trust Funds may also be used for technical assistance. The application for developers can be found at {www.nvhousing.state.nv.us/low_income/developer%20information.htm}.
8. HOME Program: federally funded programs to expand the number of rental housing and improve ownership opportunities for low income people. To download an application, go to {www.nvhousing.state.nv.us/fed_home/HOMEindex.htm}.
9. Down Payment and Closing Cost Loan Program: provides second mortgage loans to qualified buyers for down payment and closing cost assistance. For a list of participating lenders, go to {www.nvhousing.state.nv.us/single_family/participatinglenders.htm}.

New Hampshire
New Hampshire Housing Finance Authority
P.O. Box 5087
Manchester, NH 03108

603-472-8623
800-640-7239
Fax: 603-472-8501
TDD: 603-472-2089
www.nhhfa.org

1. Single-Family Mortgage Program: low interest mortgage funds to qualifying individuals and households. For a list of participating lenders, go to {www.nhhfa.org/sfmp.htm}.
2. Cash Assistance Option: provides cash assistance grant to help defray down payment, closing, and prepaid escrow expenses. Contact the New Hampshire Financing Authority for application information.
3. First Time Homebuyers Seminar: free seminars on the process of buying a home. To view the seminar schedule, go to {www.nhhfa.org/homeown.htm#1sttime}.
4. HELP (Housing Expense Loan Program): closing cost funds to income eligible homebuyers. For a list of participating lenders, go to {www.nhhfa.org/sfmp.htm}.
5. Philip S. Rader Divorced Borrower Initiative: qualifying borrowers with minor children can refinance and retain their principal residence in connection with a divorce. Contact the New Hampshire Financing Authority for information.
6. Voucher Assisted Mortgage Option: uses *Housing Choice (Section 8 Vouchers)* as a portion of the monthly mortgage payment to provide very-low income families the opportunity to purchase a home. For a list of participating lenders, go to {www.nhhfa.org/ho_vamo.htm}.
7. Emergency Home Repair Loan (EHRL): affordable loans to borrow with existing mortgages through the Single-Family Mortgage program to cover costs of repairs when an emergency occurs in their home that is not covered by insurance and that affects the livability of the home. Contact the New Hampshire Financing Authority for application information.
8. Purchase/Rehab Program: loans to eligible new homebuyers to make improvements to a home in need of repair. For a list of participating lenders, go to {www.nhhfa.org/sfmp.htm}.
9. Home of Your Own Program (HOYO): homeownership opportunities for developmentally disabled people that are income eligible. Contact the New Hampshire Financing Authority for application information.
10. HomeAccess Program: helps low and moderate-income borrowers acquire a home and/or make it accessible for a permanently disabled household member. For a list of participating lenders, go to {www.nhhfa.org/sfmp.htm}.
11. Low Income Housing Tax Credit Program: tax credits for owners of low income rental housing. To download a MultiFamily application, go to {www.nhhfa.org/lihtc.htm}.
12. HOME Rental Housing Production Program: provides funds to support the development of rental housing opportunities for low- and very-low income households. To download an application, go to {www.nhhfa.org/mf_home.htm}.
13. Special Needs Housing: permanent financing for the development of rental housing for low and very low income special needs people that also provide social services. An application can be downloaded from {www.nhhfa.org/mf_specialneeds.htm}.
14. Affordable Housing Fund: funds to support rental housing, group homes and manufactured housing co-ops for low income people. An application can be downloaded from {www.nhhfa.org/mf_aht.htm}.
15. Housing Finance Fund: funds for short-term construction and bridge financing for new or rehabilitated rental housing. An application can be downloaded from {www.nhhfa.org/multifam.htm}.
16. Tax Exempt Bond Financing: for multifamily housing that rents to moderate, low and very low income people. An application can be downloaded from {www.nhhfa.org/mf_bond.htm}.
17. Multi-Family Housing Production Initiative and the Senior Housing Production Initiative: in an effort to meet the demands for new affordable housing units, funding is available for the construction, or the adaptive reuse of non-residential structures. An application can be downloaded from {www.nhhfa.org/multifam.htm}.
18. Section 8 Existing Housing Program: Rental assistance for low income households. For an application, go to {www.nhhfa.org/rent_htw.htm}.
19. Housing to Work Rental Assistance Program: rental assistance to families that either are eligible or are currently receiving *TANF (Temporary Assistance to Needy Families)* funds and sign an employment agreement. Request an application at {www.nhhfa.org/rent_htw.htm}.

20. Family Self-Sufficiency Program: families receiving *Section 8* rental assistance that participate in a program to become economically self-sufficient. An application can be downloaded from {www.nhhfa.org/fss.htm}.

21. Section 8 New Construction/Substantial Rehabilitation (Project-Based Rental Assistance): rental assistance to eligible persons that live in housing complexes financed by NHFA's tax exempt bonds or other public, private sources. Contact the New Hampshire Financing Authority for application information.

22. Supportive Services Program: technical assistance and training to managers of senior housing complexes so that they can provide quality supportive services for seniors. The Service Directory can be viewed at {www.nhhfa.org/}.

23. Emergency Housing Program: short term rental assistance to eligible households when municipalities cannot help them. Contact the New Hampshire Financing Authority for application information.

24. Manufactured Housing Program: financing to low-to-moderate-income borrowers to purchase new manufactured homes located in a NHHFA approved Housing Community. For a list of participating lenders, go to {www.nhhfa.org/sfmp.htm}.

New Jersey

New Jersey Housing and Mortgage Finance Agency
637 S. Clinton Avenue
P.O. Box 18550
Trenton, NJ 08650-2085
609-278-7400
800-NJ-HOUSE
www.state.nj.us/dca/hmfa/

1. Home Buyer Mortgage Program: low interest loans to urban area, income eligible, first-time buyers with a 3% down payment. For a list of lenders, go to {www.state.nj.us/dca/hmfa/singfam/lenderlist070201.htm}.

2. Home Ownership for Performing Employees (HOPE): employer guaranteed below market, fixed rate loans to eligible employees. Contact the New Jersey Housing and Mortgage Finance Agency for application information.

3. Home Plus Program: low rate financing for income-eligible first time homebuyers in urban areas that need immediate home improvements. For a list of approved lenders, go to {www.state.nj.us/dca/hmfa/singfam/homeplus.htm}.

4. One Hundred Percent Mortgage Program: no down payment, no mortgage insurance, mortgage loans for qualified first time and urban area buyers at pre-approved single family housing developments. For a list of approved lenders, go to {www.state.nj.us/dca/hmfa/sinfgam/ndpfact.htm}.

5. Police and Firemen's Retirement System Mortgage Program: loans for active members of the New Jersey Police and Fireman's Retirement System with at least 1 year of active duty for purchase or refinancing of a home. For a list of approved lenders, go to {www.state.nj.us/dca/hmfa/singfam/pfrsfact.htm}.

6. Potable Water Loan Program: loans available to owners of single family residences to pay for an alternative water supply or adequate treatment of drinking water that comes from a private well that violates the State's Primary Drinking Water standards or the standards for sodium, chloride, lead, mercury, iron or manganese. Contact the New Jersey Housing and Mortgage Finance Agency for application information.

7. Purchase or Refinance/Rehabilitation Mortgage Program: below market rate financing to qualified first time buyers and urban target area buyers that purchase and rehabilitate a home or rehabilitate a presently owned home. For a list of approved lenders, go to {www.state.nj.us/dca/hmfa/singfam/buy&fix.htm}.

8. Reverse Mortgage Program: allows seniors to access the equity in their home without a monthly repayment schedule. Counseling is required. To view the list of lenders, go to {www.state.nj.us/dca/hmfa/singfam/lenderlist070201.htm}.

9. Upstairs-Downtown Mortgages: below market rate funds to acquire and rehabilitate, or refinance and rehabilitate residential structures with a storefront commercial component. To view the list of lenders, go to {www.state.nj.us/dca/hmfa/singfam/lenderlist070201.htm}.

10. Urban Home Ownership Recovery Program: construction financing for developers of urban for sale housing. For information on the application process, contact the New Jersey Housing and Mortgage Finance Agency.

New Mexico
New Mexico Mortgage Finance Authority
344 4th Street, SW
Albuquerque, NM 87102
505-843-6880
800-444-6880
Fax: 505-243-3289
TTY: 800-659-8331
www.nmmfa.org

1. Help Program: loans to first-time, income eligible homebuyers who participate in the Mortgage Saver Home Program for down payment and closing costs. To view the list of lenders, go to {www.nmmfa.org/consumer/lender.asp}.

2. Helping Hand Program: down payment and closing cost assistance to low income families where a member has a disability. Contact the New Mexico Mortgage Finance Authority for application information.

3. Mortgage Saver Program: loans to first time homebuyers at two interest rates; one below market value and one about even with conventional market rate. To view the list of lenders, go to {www.nmmfa.org/consumer/lender.asp}.

4. Mortgage Saver Plus: buyers that choose the higher rate in the *Mortgage Saver Program*, get credit towards closing costs up to 3.5% of the principal. To view the list of lenders, go to {www.nmmfa.org/consumer/lender.asp}.

5. Payment Saver Program: first time, income eligible, buyers get a below market interest rate and a 2nd zero percent interest loan to pay for up-front costs. To view the list of lenders, go to {www.nmmfa.org/consumer/lender.asp}.

6. "Take 5" Program: down payment assistance to low-income first-time homebuyers. To download the forms for this program go to {www.nmmfa.org/forms/formsLentake5.htm}

7. Weatherization Assistance Program: assistance to low-income homeowners to improve the energy efficiency of their homes. The forms for this program can be downloaded at {www.nmmfa.org/consumer/conswap.htm}.

8. Low Income Energy Assistance Program: assistance for low-income households to pay their energy bills. Call 800-285-4465 for information on this program.

9. Housing Opportunities for Persons with AIDS: provides housing and supportive services to persons with AIDS/HIV; funding to enhance and expand housing opportunities for people with AIDS/HIV. The application can be downloaded at {www.nmmfa.org/communityService/commHOPWA.htm}.

10. Building Trust: assistance for Native Americans interested in buying, building or repairing a home on trust land. For additional information, go to {www.nmmfa.org/consumer/consBuildingTrust.asp}.

11. Section 8 Assisted Housing Program: permanent financing for 5 multi-family housing projects in specified areas. Call the New Mexico Mortgage Finance Authority for application information.

12. 501(c) (3) Bond Program: funds for the acquisition, new construction, rehabilitation, or refinance of residential rental projects of nonprofit corporations. Call the New Mexico Mortgage Finance Authority for application information.

13. Build It: guaranties of conventional interim loans to nonprofit organizations, tribal, or public agencies to develop affordable housing. Call the New Mexico Mortgage Finance Authority for application information.

14. Primero Investment Fund: seed money to nonprofit, tribal, and public agencies to develop multifamily rental or special needs housing projects. Call the New Mexico Mortgage Finance Authority for application information.

15. Rental HOME: gap financing for projects that create low income housing and special needs projects. The application for this program can be downloaded at {www.nmmfa.org/multifamily/rentalhomeprogram.htm}.

16. Emergency Shelter Grants Program: assistance to improve the quality of emergency shelters, help with operational costs, and of providing essential services to the homeless. Contact the New Mexico Mortgage Finance Authority for application information.

17. State Homeless Assistance Program: assistance to shelters that provide emergency shelter or short-term services to homeless people and their families. The application can be downloaded at {www.nmmfa.org/consumer/conshomelessassist.htm}.

18. Housing Opportunities for Persons with AIDS: provides housing and supportive services to persons with AIDS/HIV; funding to enhance and expand housing opportunities for people with AIDS/HIV. The application can be downloaded at {www.nmmfa.org/communityService/commHOPWA.htm}.

19. State Homeless Assistance Program: assistance to shelters that provide emergency shelter or short-term services to homeless people and their families. The application can be downloaded at {www.nmmfa.org/consumer/conshomelessassist.htm}.
20. Housing Tax Credits: federal tax credits for owners of low-income rental housing. The application can be downloaded from {www.nmmfa.org/multifamily/htc/allocations.htm}.
21. Emergency Shelter Grants Program: assistance to improve the quality of emergency shelters; help with operational costs, and of providing essential services to the homeless. Contact the New Mexico Mortgage Finance Authority for application information.
22. Shelter Plus Care Program (S+C): funding to service providers to help disabled homeless persons through supportive services. Contact the New Mexico Mortgage Finance Authority for application information.
23. Supportive Housing: funding for transitional housing with supportive services enabling the homeless to live more independently. Contact the New Mexico Mortgage Finance Authority for application information.
24. Tenant Based Rental Assistance Program: one time cash assistance for security deposits, utility deposits, and/or first month's rent, and up to 6 months of rent subsidy to low income tenants in order to obtain permanent or transitional housing.
25. Special Needs Rental Program: below market rate loans to develop affordable rental housing projects with a maximum of 20 units where half are set aside for special needs people.

New York

New York State Division of Housing and Community Renewal
Hampton Plaza
38-40 State Street
Albany, NY 12207
518-402-3728
www.dhcr.state.ny.us

1. Weatherization Assistance Program: services to low-income households include life-saving health and safety tests and fuel consumption analysis to identify the potential to save energy.
2. Residential Emergency Services to Offer Repairs to the Elderly Program (RESTORE): funds to make emergency repairs in order to eliminate hazardous conditions in elderly owned homes when the homeowner cannot afford to make the repairs.
3. Rural Preservation Program: funds to local not-for-profit organizations engaging in a variety of activities for the benefit of low and moderate income persons in rural areas.
4. Neighborhood Preservation Program: funding to defray administrative costs of nonprofit agencies performing neighborhood preservation activities.
5. HOME Program: provides funds for a variety of housing needs for low-income families.
6. Disaster Recovery Initiative Grant: grants to help cities, counties, and States recover from declared disasters, especially in low income areas.
7. Farmworker Housing Program: low-cost loans for the improvement of existing housing or construction of new housing for seasonal farmworkers.
8. Homes for Working Families Initiative: substantial rehabilitation or new construction of affordable rental housing.
9. Senior Housing Initiative: funding for projects that substantially rehabilitate or construct rental housing for seniors.
10. Housing Development Fund: loans to nonprofits for development of low-income housing projects.
11. Low-Income Housing Credit Program: reduction in federal income tax liability for project owners that develop, rehabilitate, and acquire rental housing for low-income families.
12. Residential Emergency Services to Offer Repairs to the Elderly Program (RESTORE): funds to make emergency repairs in order to eliminate hazardous conditions in elderly owned homes when the homeowner cannot afford to make the repairs.

13. Low Income Housing Trust Fund: funds to nonprofit sponsors to rehabilitate existing properties into affordable low income housing.
14. Rural Rental Assistance Program: rent subsidies for multifamily project development of rental housing for elderly, and family, low-income tenants.
15. Mitchell-Lama Housing Program: low-interest mortgage loans to build affordable housing for middle-income people.
16. Rural Rental Assistance Program: rent subsidies for multifamily project development of rental housing for elderly, and family, low-income tenants.
17. Section 8 Statewide Program: rent subsidies for low income households.

New York Housing Finance Agency
641 Lexington Avenue
New York, NY 10022
212-688-4000
www.nyhomes.org/

1. 80/20 Program: loans for projects that will rent 80% of the units to individuals or families at market-rate rents, while the other 20% must be rented to low income households. Contact the New York Housing Finance Agency for application information.
2. The All Affordable Program: for production of new construction or rehabilitation of multi-family rental housing that all the units are affordable to low-income families. Contact the New York Housing Finance Agency for application information.
3. The Senior Housing Financing Program: financing for new construction or acquisition/rehabilitation of senior housing; Assisted Living, Rental or State Licensed housing. Contact the New York Housing Finance Agency for application information.
4. 501(c) (3) Bond Program: funds to nonprofit organizations for new construction, or rehabilitation of existing multi-family rental housing projects, or residential rental projects of nonprofit organizations. Contact the New York Housing Finance Agency for application information.
5. Manufactured Homes Cooperative Fund Program: technical and financial assistance to encourage and facilitate cooperative ownership of mobile home parks. Contact the New York Housing Finance Agency for application information.
6. Low Income Housing Tax Credit Program: federal tax credits for owners of low-income housing. Contact the New York Housing Finance Agency for application information.
7. Empire Housing Fund Program: low interest or no-interest loans made to developers to subsidize costs for the construction or rehabilitation of low-income housing. Contact the New York Housing Finance Agency for application information.

North Carolina
North Carolina Housing Finance Agency
3508 Bush Street
Raleigh, NC 27609-7509
919-877-5700
www.nchfa.com

1. Low Interest Home Loans: below market, fixed rate loans for first-time homebuyers with low/moderate income. For a list of participating lending institutions, go to {www.nchfa.com/lib/html/Homeownership%20Programs/For%20Individuals/low_interest_rates.htm}.
2. Mortgage Credit Certificate: federal tax-credit for first-time income eligible homebuyers. {www.nchfa.com/lib/html/Homeownership%20Programs/For%20Individuals/mortgage%20participating_lenders. htm}.
3. Urgent Repair Program: grants to fix housing conditions that pose a threat to health and safety in low-income homes. The application can be downloaded from {www.nchfa.com/lib/html/Urgent%20Repair%20&%20Rehab/URP2003_application_guidelines.doc}.

4. Mortgage Revenue Bond (MRB) Program: reduced rate loans to low and moderate-income first-time homebuyers. Contact the North Carolina Housing Finance Agency for application information.
5. Self-Help Housing Program: funding for nonprofit organizations building 1–5 homes a year. Homebuyer sweat equity and volunteer labor must be used to reduce the construction costs by at least 30% from the cost of conventional construction. The application can be downloaded at {www.nchfa.com/lib/html/Homeownership%20Programs/For%20Govts%20&%20Nonprofits/Self-Help%20Housing%20Program.htm}.
6. Supportive Housing Development Program: loans for the production of transitional and permanent housing and for the rehabilitation of emergency housing for people with special needs. An application can be downloaded at {www.nchfa.com/lib/html/Special%20Needs%20Housing/Supportive%20Housing%20Page.htm}.
7. Multifamily Rental Development Program: federal and state tax credits for developers of low-income housing and below market rate loans to develop the housing. The application can be downloaded at {www.nchfa.com/lib/html/rental/Rental%20Programs%20Home%20Page.htm}.
8. Low Income Housing Tax Credit Program: federal tax credit for owners of low-income housing. The application can be downloaded at {www.nchfa.com/lib/html/rental/Tax%20Credit/Application%20Forms%20Page.htm}.
9. Affordable Homeownership Program: loans for the purchase of newly constructed, rehabilitated, or existing homes for income-eligible homebuyers. Contact the North Carolina Housing Finance Agency for information.
10. Rental Production Program: financing for the construction of rental housing for low income households. The application can be downloaded at {www.nchfa.com/lib/html/rental/Tax%20Credit/Application%20Forms%20Page.htm}.
11. Low Income Housing Tax Credit Program: federal tax credit for owners of low income housing. The application can be downloaded at {www.nchfa.com/lib/html/rental/Tax%20Credit/Application%20Forms%20Page.htm}.

North Dakota

North Dakota Housing Finance Agency
1500 E. Capitol Ave.
P.O. Box 1535
Bismarck, ND 58502-1535
701-328-8080
800-292-8621
Fax: 701-328-8090
TTY: 800-366-6888
www.ndhfa.org

1. HomeSmart Homebuyer Education Incentive Program: after completion of the course to help first-time homebuyers prepare for home ownership, borrowers may receive a $100 grant to be used towards closing costs. A listing of the homebuyer education providers is available at {www.ndhfa.org/default.asp?nMenu=03010}.
2. Home Mortgage Finance Program: low interest rate mortgages for first-time income eligible homebuyers. Contact the North Dakota Housing Finance Agency for application information.
3. Rural Real Estate Mortgage Program: creates a secondary market for residential real estate mortgages for purchases of a single-family, owner occupied, non-farm, principal residence. Contact the North Dakota Housing Finance Agency for application information.
4. Start Program: a low interest second mortgage for first-time homebuyers for down payment assistance. Contact the North Dakota Housing Finance Agency for application information.
5. Down Payment and Closing Cost Assistance Program: zero percent interest loans to participants of a single-family mortgage loan from NDHFA for down payment and closing costs.
6. HomeWork: down payment and closing cost assistance to employees of those employers that have partnered with the North Dakota Housing Finance Agency (NDHFA). Contact the North Dakota Housing Finance Agency for application information.
7. Major Home Improvement Program: low interest rate loans to income eligible borrowers to buy and rehabilitate single-family homes or to rehabilitate their existing homes. Contact the North Dakota Housing Finance Agency for application information.

8. Homeownership Acquisition and Rehabilitation Program: low-income households receive home owner education, assistance in finding an affordable home, rehabilitation funds to make the property safe and sanitary and if necessary, help in acquiring the home. For a list of Community Action Agencies to contact, go to {www.ndhfa.org/Default.asp?nMenu=03135}.

9. HomeKey Program: one-percent interest rate reduction for the first three years of a Home Mortgage Finance Program loan. Borrowers must meet income-eligible guidelines.

10. Rental Rehab Assistance Program: funds for property improvement to rental units that address the needs of physically disabled people. The application can be downloaded at {www.ndhfa.org/Default.asp?nMenu=0520}

11. Helping Housing Across North Dakota (Helping Hand): funds to Habitat for Humanities Affiliates, Native American Reservations, and North Dakota Community Action Agencies to support new or existing single family or multi-family housing rehabilitation programs for low-income housing. The application can be downloaded from {www.ndhfa.org/Default.asp?nMenu=0553}.

12. Moderate Rehabilitation Program: provides low-income households the ability to acquire affordable, safe and decent housing through the use of rent subsidies available to qualified individuals in specified locations. Contact the North Dakota Housing Finance Agency for application information.

13. Low Income Housing Tax Credit Program: federal tax credits for owners of low-income rental housing. The application can be downloaded from {www.ndhfa.org/Default.asp?nMenu=03010}.

14. Rental Rehab Assistance Program: funds for property improvement to rental units that address the needs of physically disabled people. The application can be downloaded at {www.ndhfa.org/Default.asp?nMenu=0520}.

Ohio

Ohio Housing Finance Agency
57 E. Main St.
Columbus, OH 43215-5135
614-466-7970
Fax: 614-644-5393
TDD: 614-466-1940
www.odod.state.oh.us/ohfa

1. First-Time Homebuyer Program: below market financing for first-time, low- to moderate-income homebuyers. A listing of participating lenders to apply to is available at {www.odod.state.oh.us/ohfa/homebuyer/default.htm}.

2. Housing Credit Program: federal tax credits for owners of low-income rental housing. The application can be downloaded at {www.odod.state.oh.us/ohfa/lihtc/default.htm}.

3. Affordable Housing Loan Program: loans to developers of low- to moderate-income residents. The application can be downloaded at {www.odod.state.oh.us/ohfa/RENTAL/AHL/downld2.htm}.

4. Housing Development Assistance Program: financing available for eligible housing projects to expand housing for very low-income individuals and households. The application can be downloaded at {www.odod.state.oh.us/ohfa/hdap/default.htm}.

5. Multifamily Bond Program: financial assistance with the acquisition, construction, and substantial rehabilitation of multifamily dwelling units and single-family housing. The application can be downloaded at {www.odod.state.oh.us/ohfa/hdap/default.htm}.

6. Loan Guarantee Program: the OHFA may guarantee the repayment of all or part of a loan for costs of development housing for low- and moderate-income families and the elderly. The application is located in Appendix B of the Affordable Housing Loan application. To download that form, go to {www.odod.state.oh.us/ohfa/loanguar/default.htm}.

7. CHDO Competitive Operating Grant Program: funding to develop self-sufficient organizations with the capacity to create affordable housing. For additional information, go to {www.odod.state.oh.us/ohfa/chdo/default.htm}.

8. Housing Credit Program: federal tax credits for owners of low-income rental housing. The application can be downloaded at {www.odod.state.oh.us/ohfa/lihtc/default.htm}.

9. Section 8 Rental Assistance Program: rent subsidies on behalf of low-income people and families including the elderly and handicapped. Contact the Ohio Housing Finance Agency for application information.

Oklahoma

Oklahoma Housing Finance Agency
100 NW 63rd Street, Suite 200
P.O. Box 26720
Oklahoma City, OK 73126-0720
405-848-1144
800-256-1489
TDD: 405-848-7471
www.ohfa.org

1. Mortgage Revenue Bond Program (OHFA Advantage): low rate loans to first-time home buyers. For a list of participating lenders, go to {www.ohfa.org/HDT/Bond1/ohfahmby.html}.
2. 1st Four: statewide down payment and closing cost assistance for first-time homebuyers and non-first time homebuyers in Targeted areas. For additional information, go to {www.ohfa.org/HDT/Bond1/Types/1stfour.html}.
3. Market Best: statewide low interest rate assistance for first-time homebuyers and non-first time homebuyers in Target areas. For additional information, go to {www.ohfa.org/HDT/Bond1/Types/Market.html}.
4. Future Foundation: statewide low interest rate assistance for first-time homebuyers and non-first time homebuyers in Target areas that want to build a new home. For additional information, go to {www.ohfa.org/HDT/Bond1/Types/Future.html}.
5. HOME Plus: low interest rate loans for homebuyers with limited or fixed income. Loans not available in Norman, Lawton, Tulsa or Oklahoma City. For additional information, go to {www.ohfa.org/HDT/Bond1/Types/HOMEPlus.html}.
6. Housing Tax Credit Program: tax credits for new construction and rehabilitation of existing rental properties. The application can be downloaded from {www.ohfa.org/hdt/tcredits1/ohfalihp.html}.
7. HOME Program: funding for programs that increase the supply of housing and single family new construction. The application can be downloaded from {www.ohfa.org/hdt/home1/homepage.html}.
8. Section 8 Rental Assistance Program: rent subsidies for low-income households who locate their own housing. The application can be downloaded at {www.ohfa.org/rental/preapp/works.html}.
9. Transitional Housing Pilot Program: pays maintenance and utility bills at transitional homes. Contact the Oklahoma Housing Finance Agency for application information.
10. Housing Opportunities for People with AIDS (HOPWA): provides assistance that can help a family find a place to rent, provide utility or rental assistance, or provide housing counseling to people with AIDS that are homeless or at risk of becoming homeless. Contact the Oklahoma Housing Finance Agency for application information.
11. Moderate Rehabilitation "Mod Rehab": section project based rental assistance. For additional information, go to {www.ohfa.org/Rental/Modrehab/contact.htm}.
12. Family Self-Sufficiency Program: helps families work towards economic independence. The application can be downloaded from {www.ohfa.org/Rental/FSS/ohfafsspsk.html}.

Oregon

Oregon Housing and Community Services
P.O. Box 14508
Salem, OR 97309-0409
503-986-2000
Fax: 503-986-2020
TTY: 503-986-2100
www.hcs.state.or.us/

1. Residential Energy Assistance Challenge Program (REACH): provides low-income households assistance with utility payments, energy education, weatherization assistance, and family services related to budget management. A list of participating lenders can be viewed at {www.hcs.state.or.us/community_resources/energy_wx/reach.html}.

2. Low-Income Energy Assistance Program: helps low-income households pay heating bills. A listing of local Community Action Agencies can be viewed at {www.hcs.state.or.us/community_resources/energy_wx/lieap.html}.

3. Low-Income Weatherization Assistance Program: free weatherization and energy conservation services to income eligible households. A listing of local Community Action Agencies can be viewed at {www.hcs.state.or.us/community_resources/energy_wx/liwap.html}.

4. Energy Rated Home of Oregon (ERHO): provides Oregon home-builders and home-buyers with Home Energy Ratings which can be used to qualify for certain mortgages and programs. Contact the Oregon Housing Agency for application information.

5. Homebuyer Training: classes offered to help the first-time homebuyer understand the home buying process. Contact the Oregon Housing Agency for program information.

6. Downpayment and Closing Cost Assistance Program: assistance to low-income, first-time homebuyers with down payment and closing costs. A list of participating lenders can be viewed at {www.hcs.state.or.us/housing/homebuying/downpayment.html}.

7. Residential Loan Program: below market interest rate loans to low and moderate-income homebuyers. Contact the Oregon Housing Agency for application information.

8. Manufactured Dwelling Park Ombudsman Program: assists park owners and residents to resolve conflicts and provides technical assistance. Contact the Oregon Housing Agency for application information.

9. Multi-Family Housing Finance Program: financing for multi-unit rental housing for moderate, low, and very low-income families. Contact the Oregon Housing Agency for application information.

10. Elderly and Disabled Loan Program: offers below market rate permanent mortgages to profit and non-profit developers for the development of newly constructed properties or the acquisition / rehabilitation of existing properties for elderly and/or disabled residents. The application can be downloaded at {www.hcs.state.or.us/housing/multi_family_finance/elderly_disabled.html}.

11. Loan Guarantee Program: provides partial loan repayment guarantees to assist the financing of new housing construction or the acquisition and/or rehabilitation of existing housing for low- and very low-income families. A list of Regional Advisors to the Director can be viewed at {www.hcs.state.or.us/rads/rads.html}.

12. Oregon Rural Rehabilitation Loan Program: funding specifically for the construction or rehabilitation of farm worker housing. A list of Regional Advisors to the Director can be viewed at {www.hcs.state.or.us/rads/rads.html}.

13. Seed Money Advance Loan: loans to help cover predevelopment costs for the production of housing for low-income individuals and families. A list of Regional Advisors to the Director can be viewed at {www.hcs.state.or.us/rads/rads.html}.

14. Risk Sharing Program: below market financing for the development of affordable housing for low- and very low-income individuals or families. The application can be downloaded from {www.hcs.state.or.us/housing/multi_family_finance/risk_sharing.html}.

15. HELP Program: assistance for the development of housing for very-low income families. The Consolidated Funding Cycle form can be downloaded from {www.hcs.state.or.us/housing/help}.

16. HOME Investment Partnership: provides funding for the development of affordable housing for low and very low-income families and individuals. The Consolidated Funding Cycle form can be downloaded from {www.hcs.state.or.us/housing/home}.

17. Housing Development Grant Program: funding for the acquisition, construction, and/or rehabilitation of housing for low and very low-income families. The Consolidated Funding Cycle form can be downloaded from {www.hcs.state.or.us/housing/hsgdevgrant}.

18. Low Income Housing Tax Credits: federal income tax credit to developers who construct, rehabilitate, or acquire qualified low-income rental housing. The application can be downloaded at {www.hcs.state.or.us/housing/lihtc}.

19. Oregon Affordable Housing Tax Credits: tax credits for housing projects or community rehabilitation projects for low-income people, savings must be passed on to the tenants by reduced rents. The application can be downloaded at {www.hcs.state.or.us/housing/oahtc}.

20. Residential Energy Assistance Challenge Program (REACH): provides low-income households assistance with utility payments, energy education, weatherization assistance, and family services related to budget management. A list of participating lenders can be viewed at {www.hcs.state.or.us/community_resources/energy_wx/reach.html}.

21. Low-Income Energy Assistance Program: helps low-income households pay heating bills. A listing of local Community Action Agencies can be viewed at {www.hcs.state.or.us/community_resources/energy_wx/lieap.html}.
22. Low-Income Weatherization Assistance Program: free weatherization and energy conservation services to income eligible households. A listing of local Community Action Agencies can be viewed at {www.hcs.state.or.us/community_resources/energy_wx/liwap.html}.
23. Emergency Housing Account: assistance to homeless people or those at risk of becoming homeless to pay for emergency shelter, services and housing assistance. A list of participating agencies is available at {www.hcs.state.or.us/community_resources/housing_shelter/index.html}.
24. Emergency Shelter Grant: money to increase the number of beds in emergency shelters. A list of participating agencies is available at {www.hcs.state.or.us/community_resources/housing_shelter/index.html}.
25. HOME Tenant Based Assistance (TBA): rental assistance to very low-income tenants for housing costs and security deposits. A list of service agencies can be viewed at {www.hcs.state.or.us/community_resources/housing_shelter/hometba.html}.
26. Housing Stabilization Program: assistance to households with children that are at risk of becoming homeless or are homeless. Contact the Oregon Housing Agency for application information.
27. Low Income Rental Housing Fund: rental assistance to very low-income families. A list of local service providers is available at {www.hcs.state.or.us/community_resources/housing_shelter/lirhf.html}.
28. State Homeless Assistance Program: funding to emergency shelters and services directly related to them. Contact the Oregon Housing Authority for application information.
29. Low Income Housing Tax Credits: federal income tax credit to developers who construct, rehabilitate, or acquire qualified low-income rental housing. The application can be downloaded from {www.hcs.state.or.us/housing/lihtc}.
30. Manufactured Dwelling Park Ombudsman Program: assists park owners and residents to resolve conflicts and provides technical assistance. Contact the Oregon Housing Agency for application information.

Pennsylvania

Pennsylvania Housing Finance Agency
211 North Front Street
P.O. Box 8029
Harrisburg, PA 17105-8029
717-780-3800
TTY: 717-780-1869
www.phfa.org

1. Future Home Buyer Program: teaches high school students the importance of budgeting, the use of credit and the ramifications of credit abuse and some of the everyday legal issues they may face in the near future. Contact the Pennsylvania Housing and Finance Agency for information on this program.
2. Homeowners Emergency Assistance Program: loans to keep delinquent homeowners from losing their homes to foreclosure. A list of counseling agencies is available at {www.phfa.org/programs/hemap/index.htm}.
3. PennVest Individual On-Lot Sewage System Loans: very low interest rate loan up to $25,000 for homeowners to repair or upgrade malfunctioning on-lot sewer systems in rural areas. The Participating Lending Institutions list can be viewed at {www.phfa.org/programs/singlefamily/pennvest.htm}.
4. Access Down Payment and Closing Cost Assistance Loan Program: loans for down payment and closing cost assistance for those persons with disabilities or who have a family member(s) living in the household with disabilities who are purchasing a home. Contact the Pennsylvania Housing and Finance Agency for application information.
5. Access Home Modification Program: no-interest accessibility improvement loans ranging from $1,000 to $10,000 in conjunction with PHFA first mortgage financing. Contact the Pennsylvania Housing and Finance Agency for application information.
6. Closing Cost Assistance Program: pays up to $2,000 toward closing costs for homes that are bought by participants in the Lower Income Home Ownership Program, qualified participants must have dependent children or be disabled. Contact the Pennsylvania Housing and Finance Agency for application information.

7. FHA 203(k) Program: loans to acquire property in need of repair and to finance the improvements. Contact the Pennsylvania Housing and Finance Agency for application information.
8. Homestead Second Mortgage Program: non-interest loans from $1,000 to $10,000 to income eligible families with at least one child or a member with a disability, for down payment and closing costs. Contact the Pennsylvania Housing and Finance Agency for application information.
9. Joint Financing Program: below-market interest rate loans to first-time buyers in specified areas of the Commonwealth. Contact the Pennsylvania Housing and Finance Agency for application information.
10. Low Income Homeownership Program: provides mortgage loans to low income first time homebuyers that have children or a member with a disability and meet income and home purchase price guidelines. Contact the Pennsylvania Housing and Finance Agency for application information.
11. PHFA/Fannie Mae Disability Access Modification Loan Program: provides mortgage assistance to those with disabilities or who have a family member(s) with a disability to retrofit the home to meet accessibility needs of the household member with the disability. To view a list of lenders, go to {www.phfa.org/programs/singlefamily/lenders/index.htm}.
12. Purchasing-Improvement Program: allows up to $15,000 in improvements in conjunction with an Agency first mortgage loan. Contact the Pennsylvania Housing and Finance Agency for application information.
13. Statewide Homeownership Program: low interest financing for first-time qualified home buyers or buyers of property in targeted areas. To view a list of lenders, go to {www.phfa.org/programs/singlefamily/lenders/index.htm}.
14. Construction Loan Program: construction loans to sponsors of low-income rental housing who have permanent take-out financing from other lenders. To view a list of lenders, go to {www.phfa.org/programs/singlefamily/lenders/index.htm}.
15. Low Income Housing Tax Credit Program: tax credits to owners and investors of affordable rental housing. To download an application, go to {www.phfa.org/programs/multifamily/taxcredit.htm}.
16. PennHOMES Program: provides interim and permanent mortgage financing to developers of low income rental housing. An application can be downloaded at {www.phfa.org/mfapg/index.htm}.
17. Taxable and Tax Exempt Bond Financing: below market loans for the development of or rehabilitation of affordable rental units. To view a list of lenders, go to {www.phfa.org/programs/singlefamily/lenders/index.htm}.
18. Low Income Housing Tax Credit Program: tax credits to owners and investors of affordable rental housing. To download an application, go to {www.phfa.org/programs/multifamily/taxcredit.htm}.
19. Supportive Services Program: provides on-site supportive housing services for residents of PHFA-financed rental developments. Contact the Pennsylvania Housing and Finance Agency for application information.

Rhode Island

Rhode Island Housing and Mortgage Finance Corporation
44 Washington Street
Providence, RI 02903-1721
401-751-5566
TDD: 401-427-9799
www.rihousing.com/
Contact the Rhode Island Housing and Mortgage Finance Corporation for application information for the following programs.
1. First HOMES: low interest rates with low down payment requirements for first time home buyers, assistance with down payment costs for lower income first time homebuyers.
2. Jump Start Program: low interest rate loans with up to $5,000 in down payment and closing cost assistance.
3. Opening Doors Program: first mortgages from other banks with down payment and closing cost assistance from RIHMFC for minority purchases; employment and credit history requirements are relaxed.
4. Purchase Plus Program: loans for income-eligible, first time homebuyers to purchase a home and make up to $10,000 worth of repairs or improvements.
5. Buy It/Fix It Program: low-interest mortgage with construction financing to first time income eligible purchasers; current income eligible homeowners can refinance their mortgage providing they make at least $5,000 worth of needed repairs.

6. Zero Down Program: low-interest loans with federal loan guarantees that allow you to borrow up to 100% of the purchase price for down payment assistance to first-time, income-eligible buyers.

7. Equity Rebate: a grant to income eligible homebuyers that equals 2% of the purchase price of the home you buy or $1,000, whichever is less, to be used to pay closing costs.

8. Silent Second Mortgage: a deferred payment second mortgage that must be repaid when you sell your home.

9. Closing Costs Assistance Loan: income eligible homebuyers can borrow up to 5% of the purchase price, or $5,000, whichever is less, to pay closing costs.

10. Home Repair: fixed rate loans to make needed repairs to owner occupied homes and on one to four unit dwellings that meet income requirements.

11. Lead Hazard Reduction: loans to income eligible homeowners and landlords who rent to income eligible tenants to make eligible repairs so their homes/units are lead safe.

12. EquiSense Program: low interest rate, second mortgage based on home equity that has no points or application, title, credit report or appraisal fees.

13. Reverse Mortgages Program: elderly income eligible home owners can use their home equity to provide them with tax-free income; no monthly payments and no repayment as long as they own the home.

14. Access Independence Program: low-interest loans and grants for qualified low- and moderate-income owner-occupied single family homes so they can remodel for persons with functional disabilities.

15. HOME: grants and low interest loans to encourage the construction or rehabilitation of affordable housing.

16. Low Income Housing Tax Credit Program: tax credits for owners of rental housing for low income households.

17. Predevelopment Loan: qualified nonprofit developers can get short-term loans to cover pre-closing costs incurred in determining development feasibility.

18. Preservation Loan Program: below market rate loans to preserve affordability of existing subsidized rental housing.

19. Rental Housing Production Program: a combination of financing programs to construct or rehabilitate affordable housing where portions of the units are rented to low income people.

20. Targeted Loans Program: loans for the construction or rehabilitation of affordable apartments; generally available only with first mortgage financing.

21. Technical Assistance Program: technical help and short-term loans to individuals, municipalities, and nonprofit groups to help preserve affordable housing.

22. Thresholds Program: grants for the development of housing that introduces persons with long-term mental illness into the community.

23. Home Repair: fixed rate loans to make needed repairs to owner occupied homes and on one to four unit dwellings that meet income requirements.

24. Lead Hazard Reduction: loans to income eligible homeowners and landlords who rent to income eligible tenants to make eligible repairs so their homes/units are lead safe.

25. Low Income Housing Tax Credit Program: tax credits for owners of rental housing for low income households.

26. Next Step Program: loans to nonprofit social service agencies for the development of transitional apartments for people in crisis.

27. Family Self Sufficiency Program: education and training available to Section 8 certificate and voucher holders to help them move from welfare into a job that will give them financial independence.

28. Foundation for Senior Health Program: funding for homemaker services to frail elderly and disabled residents of specified Section 8 apartments.

29. Youth RAP: funding for tutoring, employment and self-esteem building activities for disadvantaged children living in RIHMFC financed apartments.

South Carolina

South Carolina State Housing Finance and Development Authority
919 Bluff Road
Columbia, SC 29201
803-734-2000
www.sha.state.sc.us

1. Homeownership Mortgage Purchase Program: below market rate financing for income eligible homebuyers funded through the sale of bonds. A list of participating lenders is available at {www.sha.state.sc.us/Programs/HomeOwnership/lenders/lenders.html}.
2. Mortgage Assistance Loan Program: loans for down payment and for up-front closing costs not in excess of $2,000 for qualified home buyers that participate in one of the Homeownership Programs. The list of participating lenders is located at {www.sha.state.sc.us/Programs/HomeOwnership/lenders/lenders.html}.
3. MultiFamily Tax-Exempt Bond Financing Program: permanent financing for property being developed for low- to moderate-income multifamily rental projects. The application can be downloaded at {www.sha.state.sc.us/Programs/Rental/Multifamily/multifamily.html}.
4. Low Income Housing Tax Credit Program: tax credits for developers of low-income rental housing. An application can be downloaded at {www.sha.state.sc.us/Programs/Rental/Tax_Credit/tax_credit.html}.
5. HOME Program: affords state and local government the flexibility to fund a wide range of low income housing activities. An application can be downloaded from {www.sha.state.sc.us/Programs/Other/HomeInvest/homeinvest.html}.
6. Section 8 Rental Assistance Program: rental subsidies for low-income households. The application is available at {www.sha.state.sc.us/Programs/Rental/Section-8/section-8.html}.

South Dakota

South Dakota Housing Development Authority
221 South Central Ave.
P.O. Box 1237
Pierre, SD 57501-1237
605-773-3181
Fax: 605-773-5154
TTY: 605-773-6107
www.sdhda.org

1. First-Time Homebuyer Program: below market rates to income qualified first-time homebuyers. For a list of participating lenders, go to {www.sdhda.org/hofthb.htm}.
2. Mortgage Assistance Program: provides down payment and closing costs assistance up to $6,000 to qualified first-time homebuyers. For a list of participating lenders, go to {www.sdhda.org/homap.htm}.
3. Employer Mortgage Assistance Program (EMAP): provides down payment and closing cost assistance to income eligible employees with a participating employer. For a list of current participating employers, go to {www.sdhda.org/hoemap.htm}. For a list of participating lenders, go to {www.sdhda.org/hofthb.htm}.
4. Cooperative Home Improvement Program: low interest loans for up to seven years for the improvement, repair, or addition to the borrower's home.
5. Housing Tax Credit: tax credits for the construction and rehabilitation of rental housing for low-income households. The application can be downloaded from {www.sdhda.org/planapp.htm#htc}.
6. HOME Program: designed to expand the supply of affordable housing for very low- and low-income families. The application is available at {www.sdhda.org/planapp.htm#home}.
7. Multifamily Bond Financing Program: mortgage loans to finance the construction of multifamily housing. The application can be downloaded from {www.sdhda.org/planapp.htm#bond}.
8. Emergency Shelter Grant Program: financing of shelters for homeless people. The application can be downloaded from {www.sdhda.org/planapp.htm#esg}.
9. Rural Site Development Program: funding for the development of new affordable housing in rural areas. Contact the South Dakota Housing Development Authority for a pre-application meeting.
10. The Governor's House: provides reasonably sized, affordable, energy efficient homes to income eligible families. Contact the South Dakota Housing Development Authority for information on this program.
11. Services to the Aging Residents Program: owners of SDHDA financed housing developments targeted for the elderly can provide supportive services to their residents. Housekeeping, transportation, meals, service coordination, and other services are available. Contact the South Dakota Housing Development Authority for information.

Tennessee

Tennessee Housing Development Agency
404 James Robertson Parkway, Suite 1114
Nashville, TN 37243-0900
615-741-2400
www.state.tn.us/thda

1. Great Rate Mortgage Program: loans for low- and moderate-income first-time homebuyers for homes that meet certain requirements. Contact the Tennessee Housing Development Authority for application information.
2. Great Start Mortgage Program: loans for low and moderate-income first-time homebuyers at a slightly higher interest rate, but offers down payment and closing cost assistance. Contact the Tennessee Housing Development Authority for application information.
3. New Start 0% Mortgage Loan Program: loans for nonprofit organizations for the construction of new single-family homes for very low-income families. An application can be downloaded from {www.state.tn.us/thda/Programs/Mortgage/0startmemo.htm}.
4. HOME Programs: federal funding to create affordable housing programs for income eligible people. An application can be downloaded from {www.state.tn.us/thda/Programs/grants00/grants.htm}.
5. Low Income Housing Tax Credit: tax credits for 10 years to owners of low-income housing. An application can be downloaded from {www.state.tn.us/thda/Programs/lihtc/lihtccvr.html}.
6. Tax Exempt Multi Family Bond Authority: loans for development of multifamily housing that sets aside units for certain income households. An application can be downloaded from {www.state.tn.us/thda/Programs/temfba/mfcvr.html}.
7. Family Self-Sufficiency Program: provides access to the supportive services families need to become free of public assistance within five years. Contact the Tennessee Housing Development Authority for application information.
8. Housing Choice Voucher Program: subsidy funds to low-income households that find their own dwelling. An application can be downloaded from {www.state.tn.us/thda/Programs/s8ca/s8cacvr.html}.

Texas

Texas Department of Housing and Community Affairs
Waller Creek Office Building
507 Sabine Street
Austin, TX 78701
Mailing Address:
   P.O. Box 13941
   Austin, TX 78711-3941
512-475-3800
www.tdhca.state.tx.us
Email: info@tdhca.state.tx.us

1. Comprehensive Energy Assistance Program (CEAP): case management, education, and financial assistance to very low- and extremely low-income families to help reduce utility bills to comfortable levels. Services include utility payment assistance, energy education and budget counseling. A list of service providers is available at {www.tdhca.state.tx.us/ea.htm#consumerCEAP}.
2. Weatherization Assistance Program: provides energy related improvements to homes, and also provides education about energy conservation. Priority is given to those families with children, the elderly and/or disabled, and those households with the highest energy costs, and the lowest income. The Service Provider list is at {www.tdhca.state.tx.us/ea.htm#consumerWAP}.
3. Down Payment Assistance Program: assists low and very low-income families with an interest free loan to be used for a down payment and certain closing costs on a home purchased through the First Time Homebuyer Program. Contact the Texas Department of Housing and Community Affairs for application information.
4. First time Homebuyer Program: low interest revenue bonds channeled through certain Texas lenders to eligible families purchasing their first home. For a list of participating lenders, go to {www.tdhca.state.tx.us/hf_sfbp.htm}.

5. HOME Program: To download the application for this program, go to {www.tdhca.state.tx.us/HOMEApps2004.htm}.
    - Owner Occupied Housing Assistance Program: funds to rehabilitate single family, owner occupied, homes where the owner meets income requirements.
    - Homebuyer Assistance Program: loans up to $10,000 to income eligible borrowers for down payment, closing costs and gap financing.
6. Housing Trust Fund Program: funds to nonprofit, local government, public housing authorities, community housing developments and income eligible families to acquire, rehabilitate, or construct affordable housing for low and very low income people. The application can be downloaded at {www.tdhca.state.tx.us/htf.htm}.
7. "Bootstrap" Homebuilder Loan Program: loans to low-income families who agree to help build their house. An application is available at {www.tdhca.state.tx.us/oci/bootstrap.jsp}.
8. Contract for Deed Consumer Education Program: class to teach consumers about contract for deed sales. Contact the Texas Department of Housing and Community Affairs for information on this program.
9. Contract for Deed Conversion Initiative: available to residents who are currently purchasing residential property within 150 miles of the Texas-Mexico border and reside in a colonia identified by the Texas Water Development Board or meet the Department's definition of a colonia. Residents interested in converting their contract for deed into a traditional note and deed of trust may apply. Contact the Texas Department of Housing and Community Affairs for information on this program.
10. Mortgage Revenue Bond Program: finances below market loans to nonprofit and for profit developers of apartment projects that agree to set aside units for rental to low income families and special needs people. The application can be downloaded from {www.tdhca.state.tx.us/hf_mfbp.htm}.
11. HOME Program:
    - Rental Housing Development Program: funds to build, acquire, and/or rehabilitate rental property for mixed income, mixed use, single room occupancy, or transitional housing. The application is available at {www.tdhca.state.tx.us/HOMEApps2004.htm}.
12. Housing Trust Fund Program: funds to nonprofit, local government, public housing authorities, community housing developments and income eligible families to acquire, rehabilitate, or construct affordable housing for low and very low income people. The application can be downloaded from {www.tdhca.state.tx.us/htf.htm}.
13. Low Income Housing Tax Credit Program: tax credit to developers of low-income rental housing used to offset a portion of their federal tax liability in exchange for the production of affordable rental housing. The application can be downloaded from {www.tdhca.state.tx.us/lihtc.htm}.
14. Emergency Nutrition/Emergency Relief Program (ENERP): provides Texans with emergency and energy related assistance to low-income households. Services include utility assistance, housing, clothes, food, medical assistance and transportation. Contact the Texas Department of Housing and Community Affairs for application information.
15. Emergency Shelter Grants Program: provides grants to entities that provide shelter and related services for the homeless. Also provides grants to assist those at risk of becoming homeless. An application can be downloaded from {www.tdhca.state.tx.us/cs.htm#esgp}.
16. HOME Program:
    - Tenant Based Rental Assistance Program: rent subsidies and security deposit payments to tenants that participate in a self-sufficiency program. The application is available at {www.tdhca.state.tx.us/HOMEApps2004.htm}.
17. Section 8 Housing Assistance Program: rental assistance via subsidies for low income households, elderly, disabled and handicapped people. Contact the Texas Department of Housing and Community Affairs for application information.

Utah

Utah Housing Corporation
554 South, 300 East
Salt Lake City, UT 84111
801-521-6950
800-284-6950 (UT only)
800-344-0452 (outside UT)
Fax: 801-359-1701

www.utahhousingcorp.org
Email: info@utahhousingcorp.org

1. First Home Program: below market rate mortgage loans to qualifying first time home buyers; purchases made in targeted areas do not need to meet the first time homebuyer requirements. The list of participating mortgage lenders is located at {www.utahhousingcorp.org/}.
2. Low Income Housing Tax Credits Program: tax credits for developers/owners of rental housing for income eligible people. The application can be downloaded at {www.utahhousingcorp.org/}.
3. Tax Exempt Bond Financing: financing for the development of multifamily housing for low to moderate income persons. The application is available at {www.utahhousingcorp.org/}.
4. Low Income Housing Tax Credit Program: tax credits for developers/owners of rental housing for income eligible people. The application can be downloaded at {www.utahhousingcorp.org/}.
5. Low Income Housing Tax Credit Program: tax credits for developers/owners of rental housing for income eligible people. The application can be downloaded at {www.utahhousingcorp.org/}.

Vermont

Vermont Housing Finance Agency
164 St. Paul St.
Burlington, VT 05401-4364
P.O. Box 408
Burlington, VT 05402-0408
802-864-5743
Fax: 802-864-5746
www.vhfa.org
Email: home@vhfa.org

1. Mortgages for Vermonters (MOVE): offers several interest rate and point options with flexible down payment requirements. A list of participating lenders is at {www.vhfa.org/homeownership/loanprograms.htm}.
2. Cash Assistance Rate Option: provides up to 3% of the loan amount to be used towards down payment and closing costs associated with a VHFA loan. Contact the Vermont Housing Finance Authority for application information.
3. Homeownership Opportunities Using Shared Equity: loans with stepped interest rates to nonprofit housing organizations that work together to reduce the purchase price and related costs; they agree to keep the property affordable to future home buyers by sharing any profit when it is sold. A list of participating lenders is at {www.vhfa.org/homeownership/loanprograms.htm}.
4. Limited Refinance: provides qualified homeowners the opportunity to replace high interest rate mobile home loan and all other property types can replace shared appreciation financing. Borrowers can also finance the cost of property improvements, and all associated closing costs. A list of participating lenders is at {www.vhfa.org/homeownership/loanprograms.htm}.
5. Construction and Permanent Loan Financing Program: financing for the development and preservation of affordable rental housing where at least 51% of the units are rented to low and moderate income people. The application can be downloaded at {www.vhfa.org/development/index.htm}.
6. Nonprofit Housing Predevelopment and Bridge Loan Program: low cost financing to eligible nonprofit housing developers for projects such as transitional housing, nursing homes, co-op housing, single family homes and more. Call the Vermont Housing Finance Agency for an application.
7. Low Income Housing Tax Credit Program: tax credits for developers/owners of rental housing for low-income households. The application is available at {www.vhfa.org/development/lihtc.htm}.

Vermont State Housing Authority
One Prospect Street
Montpelier, VT 05602
802-828-3295
Fax: 802-828-3248
www.vsha.org

1. Section 8 HomeOwnership Program: allows some people to convert Section 8 Rental vouchers into HomeOwnership vouchers. This can provide those eligible, assistance meeting monthly costs associated with owning a home. The Questionnaire and Mutual Release can be downloaded from {www.vsha.org/homeown.htm}.
2. Development Program: assistance for the development and preservation of affordable multi-unit complexes and mobile home parks. Contact the Vermont State Housing Authority for application information.
3. New Construction/Substantial Rehabilitation Program: creates new and rehabilitated housing in communities without safe and sanitary housing for low-income families and the elderly. Contact the Vermont State Housing Authority for application information.
4. Section 8 Rental Assistance Program: rental assistance to eligible persons who choose their own housing. An application can be downloaded at {www.vsha.org/ra.htm}.
5. Shelter Plus Care Program: rental assistance to disabled homeless people. Contact the Vermont State Housing Authority for application information.
6. Project Based Certificates and Moderate Rehabilitation Program: a rent subsidy that is attached to the unit and not the tenant. The application can be downloaded from {www.vsha.org/ra.htm}.
7. Family Unification Program: promotes family unification by providing rental assistance to families for whom the lack of adequate housing is a primary factor in the separation, or threat of imminent separation, of children from their families. The Department of Social and Rehabilitative Services refer eligible households to VSHA. Contact the Vermont State Housing Authority for application information.
8. Mainstream Housing: rental assistance for disabled families. Contact the Vermont State Housing Authority for application information.

Virginia

Virginia Housing Development Authority
601 South Belvidere Street
Richmond, VA 23220
804-782-1986
800-968-7837
www.vhda.com

1. Home Ownership Education: helps prepare first-time homebuyers with the purchase of their first home. A list of class schedules is located at {www.vhda.com/sf/singlefam.asp}.
2. Fresh Start Loan Program: offers low rate interest loans to qualified first-time homebuyers that have had difficulty purchasing a home due to past credit issues. The list of housing counseling agencies is at {www.vhda.com/sf/freshstart.asp}.
3. FHA Plus Loan Program: assists qualified borrowers who need down payment assistance. Contact a local VHDA originating lender (www.vhda.com/sf/singlefam.asp) for information.
4. Flexible Alternative Program: optioning for a slightly higher interest rate, allows up to 100% loan-to-value financing without mortgage insurance to eligible buyers. The application can be downloaded at {www.vhda.com/sf/SF_Flex_Apply_right.asp}.
5. Flexible Alternative Step Rate Program: couples the flexible features of the *Flexible Alternative Program* with the lower interest rate loan of the Step Rate program; lower interest rate for the first two years of the loan. Contact the Virginia Housing Development Authority for application information.
6. Flexible Alternative Home Enhancer Program: offers qualified borrowers the same features as the *Flexible Alternative Program*. But also offers financing for modest home improvements. Contact the Virginia Housing Development Authority for application information.
7. Flexible Alternative Home Access Program: a variation of the *Flexible Alternative Program* offering up to 100% of the sale price, but also offers an additional 10% more to be used for home modifications for accessibility. Contact the Virginia Housing Development Authority for application information.
8. Fixed Rate Loan: lower interest fixed rate loans for eligible homebuyers. Contact the Virginia Housing Development Authority for application information.
9. Step Rate Loan Program: lower interest rate for the first two years of the loan creating lower mortgage payments for those years. Contact the Virginia Housing Development Authority for application information.

10. Home Improvement Loan: loan for home improvement with a lower interest rate, low closing costs, and no points for low and moderate income homeowners. Contact the Virginia Housing Development Authority for application information.
11. Low Income Housing Tax Credits Program: federal tax credits for owners of low-income rental housing. The application can be downloaded at {www.vhda.com/multifam/taxcredframes.htm}.
12. Virginia Housing Fund: low interest rate funds for multi-family projects available to for-profits and non-profits for minority, and rural area developers. The application can be downloaded from {www.vhda.com/multifam/mfvhf.htm}.
13. Bond-Funded Loan program: funding for multi-family projects that rent to low and very low-income tenants. An application is available at {www.vhda.com/multifam/mfbond.htm}.
14. Low Income Housing Tax Credit Program: federal tax credits for owners of low-income rental housing. The application can be downloaded at {www.vhda.com/multifam/taxcredframes.htm}.
15. State Credit Rent Reduction Program: tax credit to property owners who fill vacant units and/or reduce rent amounts for elderly, disabled, and homeless persons. Contact the Virginia Housing Development Authority for application information.

Washington

Washington State Housing Finance Commission
1000 Second Avenue, Suite 2700
Seattle, WA 98104-1046
206-464-7139
800-767-4663
Fax: 206-587-5113
www.wshfc.org
Email: askus@wshfc.org

1. Home Choice Program: down payment assistance and lower interest rates for low and moderate income people with a disability, or that have a family member with a disability that are first time buyers or are buying in a targeted area; must complete an education counseling course. For the Service Provider list, go to {www.wshfc.org/buyers/homechoice.htm}.
2. House Key Program: below market rate loans for income eligible first time home buyers and buyers of residences in target areas. The list of participating lenders is at {www.wshfc.org/buyers/key.htm#lenders}.
3. House Key Plus Program: loans to income eligible buyers to help pay down payment and closing costs in conjunction with the *House Key Program*. The list of participating lenders is at {www.wshfc.org/buyers/keyplus.htm}.
4. House Key Teacher Program: offers lower down payment requirements to eligible full-time employed teacher, administrator, principal, vice-principal, librarian, or health care professional (such as nurse or counselor) who is a first-time homebuyer or buying in a targeted area. For a list of House Key Loan originators, go to {www.wshfc.org/buyers/teacher.htm}.
5. House Key Extra: mortgage loan for income eligible first time home buyers with a disability, or a family member with a disability in a rural area and the home is within the specified price range. Contact the Washington State Housing Finance Commission for application information.
6. House Key Rural (Pilot Program): down payment and closing cost assistance available to first time homebuyers buying in a rural area. If buying in a rural targeted area, you do not need to be a first time homebuyer. The list of participating lenders is at {www.wshfc.org/buyers/hkrural.htm}.
7. Open Door Second Mortgage Loan Program: down payment and closing cost assistance to eligible first time homebuyers in the city of Tacoma. The list of participating lenders is at {www.wshfc.org/buyers/open.htm}.
8. Low Income Housing Tax Credit Program: federal tax credits to developers/owners of low-income rental housing. The application can be downloaded at {www.wshfc.org/tax-credits/index.htm}.
9. For Profit Multifamily Developer Program: financing for developers of rental projects or new construction, acquisition and/or rehabilitation, and predevelopment costs. The application can be downloaded from {www.wshfc.org/bonds/multifamily.htm}.
10. Bonds for Nonprofit Capital Projects: funding to nonprofits for a range of real estate and capital equipment projects. {www.wshfc.org/bonds/npfacilitiesApp.htm}.

11. Bonds for Nonprofit Housing: funding to nonprofits for housing projects such as transitional housing, group homes, independent living apartments and more. The application is available at {www.wshfc.org/bonds/nphousingApp.htm}.
12. Low Income Housing Tax Credit Program: federal tax credits to developers/owners of low-income rental housing. The application can be downloaded at {www.wshfc.org/tax-credits/index.htm}.

West Virginia

West Virginia Housing Development Fund
814 Virginia Street East
Charleston, WV 25301
304-345-6475
800-933-9843
www.wvhdf.com
Email: wvhdf@wvhdf.com

1. Teacher and Education Employee Loan Assistance Program: designed for employees of the West Virginia school system who have sufficient income to support a monthly payment, but have limited funds to cover down payment and closing cost expenses. Contact a local banking or financial institution for application information.
2. Single Family Bond Program: low interest rate financing for low- and moderate-income families to buy a home in a specified price range. For a list of participating lenders, go to {www.wvhdf.com/programs/limits.cfm}.
3. Secondary Market Program: below market rate loans or refinancing for eligible homebuyers. For a list of participating lenders, go to {www.wvhdf.com/programs/limits.cfm}.
4. Closing Cost Assistance Program: assistance with closing costs for participants of the *Single Family Bond Program*. For a list of participating lenders, go to {www.wvhdf.com/programs/limits.cfm}.
5. Closing Cost and Down Payment Assistance Loan: loan to be used towards down payment and closing costs available to income eligible participants in the *Secondary Market Program*. For a list of participating lenders, go to {www.wvhdf.com/programs/limits.cfm}.
6. HOME Program: a mortgage program providing funding for low-income families. The application is available when funding is available. It can be downloaded at {www.wvhdf.com/programs/homebuying.cfm}.
7. Housing Emergency Loan Program (HELP): funding for structural or construction problems that threaten the health and safety of low-income homeowners. For a list of participating lenders, go to {www.wvhdf.com/programs/limits.cfm}.
8. Mini-Mod Rehabilitation Program (MMRP): offers landlords affordable financing for upgrading rental units for low-income households. The Area Manager list is available at {www.wvhdf.com/area_managers/index.cfm}.
9. Constructing Affordable Sensible Homes (CASH) Program: provides a guaranteed sales program for single-family homebuilders. This program is only offered in counties affected by the 2001 flood. Contact the West Virginia Housing Development Fund for application information.
10. Construction Loan Incentive Program (CLIP): construction loans for low- and moderate-income multifamily or elderly housing in designated rural areas. Contact the West Virginia Housing Development Fund for application information.
11. Low Income Housing Tax Credit Program: federal tax credits for developers/owners of low-income multifamily housing. Contact the West Virginia Housing Development Fund for application information.
12. Low Income Housing Tax Credit Program: federal tax credits for developers/owners of low-income multifamily housing. Contact the West Virginia Housing Development Fund for application information.

Wisconsin

Wisconsin Housing and Economic Development Authority
201 West Washington, Suite 700
Madison, WI 53703
P.O. Box 1728
Madison, WI 53701-1728
608-266-7884
800-334-6873
Fax: 608-267-1099

www.wheda.com
Email: info@wheda.com
1. HOME Loan: mortgage loans with low interest rates for low- and moderate-income people for first time home buyers. The list of lenders is at {www.wheda.com/Cat_SFL/home.asp}.
2. CROP Program: loan guarantees for agricultural production loans. The list of lenders is at {www.wheda.com/cat_ag/c_product.asp}.
3. FARM Program: guarantees for agricultural expansion and modernization loans.
4. Beginning Farmer Bond Program: low interest rate funding for the first time purchase of a farm, including land, equipment, livestock, or buildings. The list of lenders is at {www.wheda.com/cat_ag/bfb_product.asp}.
5. Home Improvement Loans: home improvement loans of up to $17,500 to low-to-moderate-income Wisconsin homeowners. For additional information, go to {www.wheda.com/cat_sfl/home_imp.asp}.
6. Tax-Exempt Bond Financing: below-market-rate loans for development of multifamily rental housing. Loans can be used for new construction, acquisition and rehabilitation of one-to-three story apartment buildings. For additional information, go to {www.wheda.com/cat_mf/tax_ex.asp}.
7. Affordable Housing Tax Credit: federal tax incentive to encourage the creation of affordable rental housing. For additional information, go to {www.wheda.com/Cat_TCA/tca.asp}.
8. Section 8 Preservation Options: offer mortgage-restructuring options that provide incentive for owners to maintain affordable Section 8 housing for low-income tenants.

Wyoming

Wyoming Community Development Authority
155 North Beech
Casper, WY 82601
307-265-0603
Fax: 307-266-5414
www.wyomingcda.com
Email: info@wyomingcda.com
1. Qualified Rehabilitation Loan: low interest rate loans for rehabilitation projects from extensive major structural repair to major disrepairs. Contact the Wyoming Community Development Authority for application information.
2. Mortgage Revenue Bond (MRB): low interest rate mortgages for first-time Wyoming homebuyers with low and moderate incomes. For additional information, go to {www.wyomingcda.com/Homebuyer/Homebuyer.html}.
3. HOME Investment Partnership Program: funds for the development of affordable housing for low and very low income households. The application can be downloaded at {www.wyomingcda.com/Housing_Dev/Housing_Invest_Programs.html}.
4. Low Income Housing Tax Credit Program: tax credits for owners of rental housing affordable to low income households. The application can be downloaded at {www.wyomingcda.com/Housing_Dev/Housing_Low_Income.html}.
5. Housing Trust Fund: financing of non-traditional affordable housing.
6. Community Development Block Grant (CDBG): loans for housing-related programs that benefit low-income households of Wyoming. For additional information, go to {www.wyomingcda.com/Housing_Dev/Housing_CDBG.html}.
7. Low Rent Public Housing: rental program of single family detached units for very-low income large families. Contact the Wyoming Community Development Authority for application information.
8. Section 8 Rental Assistance Program: certificates and vouchers to assist low income rental households.

Free Grants, Low Interest Loans, and Tax Credits to Renovate Historic Homes and Buildings

Renovating an old house can be very time consuming and expensive. If only there were a way to get someone else to pay

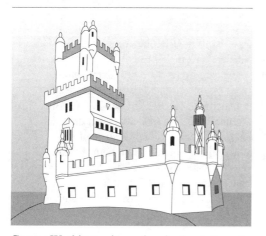

for all that time consuming work...well, there is, if you know where to look. About 20 states offer some kind of grant or loan program for individual homeowners who are renovating historic homes. Here are a few examples:

♦ Iowa offers matching grants for renovation projects
♦ Kansas offers up to $75,000 in matching grants for renovation
♦ South Carolina offers up to $25,000 in matching grants
♦ Maryland offers low interest loans for historic renovation
♦ Tennessee offers 50/50 matching grants for renovation

To qualify for these grant and loan programs, you first need to have your house qualify for the National Register of Historic Places. This isn't as difficult as it might seem. Your house doesn't have to have national significance, such as at one time being George Washington's weekend retreat. It can have local historic or architectural significance to qualify for the National Register. It could be an early example of 18th century Greek Revival style—or have been owned at one time by a locally significant family. You'd be surprised how many older houses have some sort of local significance, and that might be just enough to qualify for these programs. Contact your State Office of Historic Preservation listed below for more information about how to get your property qualified for historic status.

Federal Tax Credits

If you happen to live in one of the 30 states that don't offer renovation grants to individual homeowners, you still may be able to qualify for some types of financial benefits. Under the Federal Tax Credit Program, individuals who have rehabilitated an income producing building used for commercial or industrial purposes can receive a 20% tax credit on expenses incurred during that renovation. To be eligible for funding, buildings must be listed on the National Register of Historic Places or be eligible for membership into that organization.

What this means is that if you renovate your house and use part of it to run your own business, like a gift shop, you may be able to receive a federal tax deduction of 20% of the renovation costs. If you spent $50,000 on renovations, that comes out to a $10,000 tax deduction on next year's taxes. Not bad. Not only would you get the benefit of writing off 20% of your renovation expenses, but you'll also be able to write off part of your mortgage as a business expense.

Nonprofits Get The Breaks

Starting up a nonprofit, or looking to relocate an existing one? Think of moving into an historic building in need of renovation. Most states offer nonprofits matching grant money and low interest loans to buy and renovate historic buildings. Yes, that's right — some states actually offer nonprofits money to buy historic buildings.

Check In Often

The availability of money for historic renovation changes from year to year, depending on the state in which you live. Just because your state isn't awarding grants or loans this year, they may change within the next year or two, so continue to check the resources. Don't forget that some states, like South Dakota and Iowa, allow renovating homeowners of historic places up to 8 years of not having to pay property taxes—in the long run that could be even better for you than getting grant money.

Alabama

State Historic Preservation Office
Alabama Historical Commission
468 South Perry St.
Montgomery, AL 36104
334-242-3184
Fax: 334-240-3477
www.preserveala.org
There are no state grant funds available to individual homeowners. However, owners of commercial property listed in the National Register of Historic Places are eligible for a 50% reduction in property taxes. Nonprofits, local government, and universities are eligible to apply for the Alabama Cultural Resources Preservation Trust Fund, a 50/50 matching grant program. Eligible funding categories include survey and registration, education and public awareness, planning for historic rehabilitation, and planning archaeological project and eligible projects are those that encourage good community preservation. The agency also administers the Federal Rehabilitation Tax Credit Program. Individuals who have rehabilitated an income producing building used for commercial or industrial purposes can receive a 20% tax credit on eligible expenses incurred during renovation. To be eligible for funding, buildings must be listed on the National Register of Historic Places or be eligible for membership.

Alaska

State Historic Preservation Office
Alaska Department of Natural Resources
Office of History and Archaeology
550 West 7th Avenue, Suite 1310
Anchorage, AK 99501-3565
907-269-8721
Fax: 907-269-8908
www.dnr.state.ak.us/parks/oha/index.htm
Email: oha@alaska.net
There are no funding programs available to individual property owners. Communities can become eligible for matching grant funds for historic preservation activities through Alaska's Historic Preservation

Program. In order to qualify, the community must first become a Certified Local Government. As such, they can share in the 10% of federal funds that are passed on to the State Historic Preservation Office. The Federal Tax Rehabilitation Tax Credit is also available, it offers a 20% tax credit on money spent on an eligible rehabilitation of an income producing building that will be used for commercial or industrial purposes. Buildings must be listed on the National Register of Historic Places or be eligible for membership to qualify.

Arizona

State Historic Preservation Office
Arizona State Parks
1300 West Washington
Phoenix, AZ 85007
602-542-4009
Fax: 602-542-4180
www.pr.state.az.us
Although $1.7 million is available in historical renovation grants, funds are not directly awarded to individual property owners. Homeowners must have the support of a sponsoring agency to apply for funding. This may include a certified local government, nonprofit organization, Indian tribe, or a national register listed district or educational institution. Matching funds of 40% are usually required. The office also administers the Federal Investment Tax Credit Program. Through this program, individuals receive a 20% tax credit on expenses they incurred while rehabilitating an income producing building that will be used for commercial or industrial purposes. There is also a State property tax reduction program for non-income producing properties and a State property tax incentive program for commercial or industrial properties. Buildings must be listed on the National Register of Historic Places or be eligible for membership to qualify.

Arkansas

Arkansas Historic Preservation Office
1500 Tower Building
323 Center Street
Little Rock, AR 72201
501-324-9880
Fax: 501-324-9184
www.arkansaspreservation.org
Email: info@arkansaspreservation.org
Owners of historic homes can apply for a 50/50 matching grant from the Historic Preservation Restoration Program. The property must be listed on the Arkansas Register of Historic Places and if the grant will make it eligible for the National Register of Historic Places, the owner must follow through with the listing. The Federal Rehabilitation Tax Credit Program offers a 20% tax credit to individuals who have spent money rehabilitating an income producing building to be used for commercial, industrial, or residential rental purposes. Federal tax deductions can be gained through the donation of a conservation easement of a historic structure. Buildings must be listed on the National Register of Historic Places to qualify for either of these benefits. The Arkansas city governments that participate in the Certified Local Government (CLG) program are eligible for federal pass-through grants. These funds can be used for local historic preservation projects which include the rehabilitation of local historic structures. Individuals that are currently renovating or considering a renovation can receive technical assistance. The agency will provide on-site visits, consultations, and explanations. While cemeteries are not generally included in the National Register of Historic Places, they can be eligible under some circumstances. The Cemetery Preservation Program will consider assistance to those cemeteries where there are a significant amount of older markers and where the graves contain people of historic importance, or if there is a distinctive design feature.

California

State Historic Preservation Office
Office of Historic Preservation
Department of Parks and Recreation
P.O. Box 942896
Sacramento, CA 94296-0001
916-653-6624
Fax: 916-653-9824
http://ohp.parks.ca.gov
Email: calshpo@ohp.parks.ca.gov

There are occasionally state grants available to nonprofit organizations, local governments, and educational organizations. Various cities in California are Certified Local Governments. As such, they are eligible for 10% of the federal funds given to this agency. That money is used for historic preservation actives in each of their communities. The Mills Act provides property tax relief for owners of historic buildings. If the owner pledges to rehabilitate and maintain the historical and architectural character of their building, for a 10 year period they may receive a property tax savings of around 50%. This is not a state program, it is adopted by city and county governments. Another program the agency administers is the Federal Historic Preservation Tax Incentive program. Individuals who have rehabilitated an income producing building used for commercial or industrial purposes can receive a 20% tax credit on expenses incurred during renovation. To be eligible for funding, buildings must be listed on the National Register of Historic Places or be eligible for membership.

Historical Society

Colorado

State Historic Preservation Office
Colorado Historical Society
1300 Broadway
Denver, CO 80203
303-866-3395
Fax: 303-866-2711
www.coloradohistory-oahp.org
Email: oahp@chs.state.co.us
The State Historical Fund awards grants to public and non-profit entities. Individuals can obtain funding if they find a public or non-profit organization to apply for and administer funds on their behalf. Eligible categories include acquisition and development, education, and survey and planning projects. Funding is divided into four types: 1) General Grant: Competitive grants from $25,000 or less or greater than $25,000 to multi-year grants; 2) Preservation Initiative Grants: No dollar amount specified; 3) Historic Structure Assessment Grants: Non-competitive grants of $10,000 or less whose purpose is to prepare a historic building for

assessment; 4) Emergency Grants: Non-competitive grants that generally do not exceed $10,000 for historic properties in danger of being destroyed or seriously damaged. The agency also administers the Colorado Historic Preservation Income Tax Credit. Approved preservation/ rehabilitation projects that cost more than $5,000 and are completed within a 24 month period can receive a 20% credit on state income taxes. Properties must be over 50 years old and listed on the State Register of Historic Places or be landmarked by a Certified Local Government. Another tax savings can be attained through the donation of a preservation easement to this agency. The property must be listed on the National or State Registers of Historic Places to be eligible. There is also the Federal Rehabilitation Tax Credit Program. This is a 20% tax credit on the expenses incurred during the renovation of an income producing building that is used for commercial or industrial purposes. The building must be listed on the National Register of Historic Places or be eligible for a membership.

Connecticut

State Historic Preservation Office
Connecticut Historical Commission
59 South Prospect Street
Hartford, CT 06106
860-566-3005
Fax: 860-566-5078
www.chc.state.ct.us
There are no state grants or loans for homeowner's renovation projects at this time. There is a state tax incentive program, but it is only available to corporations that purchase homes in certain census tracts. There is however, the Federal Rehabilitation Tax Credit Program. This is a 20% tax credit on the expenses incurred during the renovation of an income producing building that is used for commercial or industrial purposes. The building must be listed on the National Register of Historic Places or be eligible for a membership. Another program available is the federally funded program called the Certified Local

Government Program. The CLG's receive 10% of the funds passed on to the Historical Commission to be used for local restoration projects.

Delaware

State Historic Preservation Office
Division of Historical and Cultural Affairs
Hall of Records
Tudor Industrial Park
604 Otis Drive
Dover, DE 19901
302-739-5313
Fax: 302-739-6711
www.state.de.us/shpo/default.shtml
There are no funding programs available to individuals. The office does administer the Federal Rehabilitation Tax Credit Program. Through this program individuals receive a 20% tax credit on expenses they incurred while rehabilitating a commercial or industrial building. Buildings must be listed on the National Register of Historic Places or be eligible for membership to qualify. The Certified Local Government Program is a federally funded program. The CLG's receive 10% of the funds passed on to the Department of Consumer and Regulatory Affairs to be used for local restoration projects.

District of Columbia

Historic Preservation Division
1350 Pennsylvania Ave. NW
Washington, DC 20004
202-442-8818
Fax: 202-535-2497
http://planning.washingtondc.gov/preservation/index2.shtm
At this time there are no funds available from the District of Columbia for individuals to complete restoration projects. However, the agency does administer the Federal Rehabilitation Tax Credit Program. Individuals who have rehabilitated an income producing building used for commercial or industrial purposes can receive a 20% tax credit on expenses incurred during renovation. To be eligible for funding, buildings must be listed on the national Register of Historic Places or be eligible for membership. A federally funded program is the Certified Local Government Program. The CLG's receive 10% of the funds passed on to the Department of Consumer and Regulatory Affairs to be used for local restoration projects.

Florida

State Historic Preservation Office
Division of Historical Resources
Department of State
R.A. Gray Building
500 S. Bronough Street
Tallahassee, FL 32399-0250
850-245-6300
Fax: 850-488-3353
http://dhr.dos.state.fl.us/
State agencies, units of local government, and nonprofit organizations are eligible to submit applications and compete for funding. Funding categories include acquisition and development, survey and planning and community education. In general, grants will provide 50/50 matching assistance. The agency also administers the Federal Rehabilitation Tax Credit Program. Individuals who have rehabilitated an income producing building used for commercial or industrial purposes can receive a 20% tax credit on expenses incurred during renovation. To be eligible for funding, buildings must be listed on the National Register of Historic Places or be eligible for membership. Another federal program is the Certified Local Government Program. With this, the CLG's receive 10% of the funds passed on to the Division of Historical Resources to be used for local restoration projects.

Georgia

State Historic Preservation Office
Georgia Department of Natural Resources
47 Trinity Avenue, SW, Suite 414-H
Atlanta, GA 30334-9006
404-656-2840
Fax: 404-657-1040
http://hpd.dnr.state.ga.us
There are no state grant programs available to home owners. However, this office does administer two federal and one state tax incentive programs. The Federal Rehabilitation Tax Credit Program allows for a 20% tax credit on expenses incurred while rehabilitating an income producing building used for commercial or industrial purposes. The Historic Preservation State Tax Incentive Program offers an 8 year freeze on property tax assessments when a substantial rehabilitation has been done to an individual or business property. There is also a Charitable Contribution Deduction that gives a one time tax deduction to the owner of a historic property that donates a conservation easement.

For all of these programs the building must be listed in the National Register of Historic Places or be eligible for membership and have approval for the project to qualify. There are also cities that are Certified Local Governments in Georgia. Those cities are eligible for a portion of the federal funding to be used for their communities' historic preservation projects and technical assistance.

Hawaii

Department of Land and Natural Resources
State Historic Preservation Division
Kalanimoku Bldg.
1151 Punchbowl St., Rm 130
Honolulu, HI 96813
808-587-0405
Fax: 808-587-0390
www.hawaii.gov/dlnr/
Email: dlnr@exec.state.hi.us
A state grant program provides funding, if funds are available, to local and county governments, nonprofit organizations and responsible corporations and individuals. These are 50/50 matching grants, although there are rarely funds for historic property renovation. The agency also administers the Federal Rehabilitation Tax Credit Program. Individuals who have rehabilitated an income producing building used for commercial or industrial purposes can receive a 20% tax credit on expenses incurred during renovation. To be eligible for funding, the building must be listed on the National Register of Historic Places or be eligible for membership. There is also a property tax exemption available to individuals who won homes listed on the Historic Register. Local county tax offices can provide information and materials. A local government that is deemed a Certified Local Government becomes eligible for federal funding to fund historic renovation projects and technical assistance.

Idaho

State Historic Preservation Office
Idaho State Historical Society
1109 Main Street, Suite 250
Boise, ID 83702
208-334-2682
Fax: 208-334-2774
http://idahohistory.net
There are no funding programs available to individuals in Idaho. However, this office does administer the Federal Tax Credit Program.

Through this program individuals receive a 20% tax credit on expenses they incurred while rehabilitating a building used for commercial or industrial purposes. Buildings must be listed on the National Register of Historic Places or be eligible for membership to qualify. They also have the Certified Local Government Program in which CLG's receive 10% of the federal funds passed on to the Historical Society in the form of matching grants. The funds are used for local preservation projects in the CLG's community.

Illinois

Illinois Historic Preservation Agency
1 Old State Capitol Plaza
Springfield, IL 62701-1507
217-785-4512
217-785-9045
TDD: 217-524-7128
Fax: 217-524-7525
www.state.il.us/HPA
Email: info@ihpa.state.il.us
Homeowners must have a sponsoring agency to apply for state grant funding. Sponsoring agencies include nonprofit organizations or Certified Local Governments. The agency administers the Federal Tax Credit Program. Individuals who have rehabilitated a building used for commercial or industrial purposes can receive a 20% tax credit on approved expenses that were incurred. Another tax incentive program for owner-occupied residences is the State Property Tax Assessment Freeze. When at least 25% of the fair market value of the property is spent on a rehabilitation project, the owner can receive a freeze of the assessed valuation of the property at the pre-rehabilitation level for 8 years. After that time, the assessed value will increase in quarter increments for 4 years. Buildings must be listed on the National Register of Historic Places or be eligible for membership to qualify. They also have the Certified Local Government program. With this, a CLG will receive 10% of the federal funds given to the Historic Preservation Agency to be used for historic preservation of their community.

Indiana

Division of Historic Preservation & Archaeology
402 W. Washington Street, W274
Indianapolis, IN 46204-2739
317-232-1646

Fax: 317-232-0693
www.in.gov/dnr/historic
Email: dhpa@dnr.state.in.us
Grants are available to public agencies, nonprofit organizations with a ceiling up to $30,000. These are 50/50 matching grants. The agency also administers the Federal Rehabilitation Tax Credit Program. Individuals who have rehabilitated an income producing building used for commercial or industrial purposes can receive a 20% tax credit on approved expenses incurred during renovation. To be eligible for funding, the building must be listed on the National Register of Historic Places or be eligible for membership. With the Certified Local Government Program, local communities that have preservation zoning ordinances receive 10% of the federal funds passed on to the Historic Preservation Office. With these matching grants, the CLG's fund local preservation activities in their community.

Iowa

State Historic Preservation Office
State Historical Society of Iowa
Capitol Complex
600 E. Locust Street
Des Moines, IA 50319-0290
515-281-5111
515-281-7471
Fax: 515-242-6498
www.iowahistory.org/preservation/
The Historic Resource Development Program offers matching grants for work on historic properties, museums and their collections, and documentary collections. The program is open to individuals, nonprofit organizations, Certified Local Governments, businesses, state agencies, school districts and Native American tribes. There is another matching grant available to nonprofits, government bodies and Indian Tribes. For both the

buildings must be listed on the National Register of Historic Places or be reviewed by the State Preservation Office to determine eligibility. Local government agencies that become Certified Local Governments receive federal matching grants to fund local preservation planning activities in their communities. This agency also offers a state tax incentive for substantial rehabilitation. This is a combination of a 4 year exemption from any increase of property valuation because of the project and 4 years of decreasing exemptions. Buildings must be evaluated as eligible for membership on the National Register of Historic Places. There is a Federal Rehabilitation Tax Credit Program for rehabilitated income producing buildings used for industrial or commercial purposes. They will receive a 20% tax credit for approved renovations to the buildings. The property must be listed on the National Register of Historic Places or be eligible for membership to participate in the program.

Kansas

State Historic Preservation Office
Kansas State Historical Society
6425 SW Sixth Avenue
Topeka, KS 66615-1099
785-272-8681
TTY: 785-272-8683
Fax: 785-272-8682
www.kshs.org/
Nonprofit organizations, city or county governments, or individuals may apply for the Heritage Trust Fund Program, an annual grant with a funding ceiling of $75,000. This is a matching grant with 80% provided in grant money and a 20% cash match required on the part of the recipient. The deadline for applications is in February. Eligible properties must be listed on national or state registers of historic places. The agency also administers the Federal Rehabilitation Tax Credit Program. Individuals who have rehabilitated an income producing building used for commercial or industrial purposes can receive a 20% tax credit on approved expenses incurred during renovation. To be eligible for funding, the building must be listed on the National Register of Historic Places or be eligible for membership. With the Certified Local Government Program, local communities that have preservation zoning ordinances receive 10% of the federal funds passed on to the Historic Preservation Office. With these matching grants, the CLG's fund local preservation activities in their community.

Kentucky

Kentucky Heritage Council
300 Washington Street
Frankfort, KY 40601
502-564-7005
Fax: 502-564-5820
www.state.ky.us/agencies/khc/khchome.htm
The State Restoration Grant Program is available to all owners of historic properties, including individuals. However, nonprofit organizations and government agencies that restore structures for public use generally take precedence. It is a 50/50 matching grant. They have an African American Heritage Grant Program that has funding for projects relating to African American sites. The grants are sometimes used for building restoration, otherwise, it is for research and exhibits. The agency also administers the Federal Tax Credit Program from which individuals may benefit. Individuals who have rehabilitated an income producing building used for commercial or industrial purposes can receive a 20% tax credit on approved expenses incurred during renovation. To be eligible for the credit, buildings must be listed on the National Register of Historic Places or be eligible for membership. With the Certified Local Government Program, local communities that have preservation zoning ordinances receive 10% of the federal funds passed on to the Historic Preservation Office. With these matching grants, the CLG's fund local preservation activities in their community.

Louisiana

Laurel Wyckoff
State Historic Preservation Officer
Department of Culture, Recreation & Tourism
Division of Historic Preservation
P.O. Box 44247
1051 N. Third St.
Baton Rouge, LA 70804
225-342-8200
Fax: 225-342-8173
www.crt.state.la.us/crt/ocd/hp/ocdhp.htm
E-mail: ocd@crt.state.la.us
At present, state funding is not available to individual property owners. They may however, apply to a Certified Local Government for renovation funding. The CLG's receive a portion of the federal funds given to the Division of Historic Preservation to be

used for renovation programs in their communities. These are generally matching grants. The agency does administer the Federal Preservation Tax Credit Program. Individuals who have rehabilitated an income producing building used for commercial or industrial purposes can receive a 20% tax credit on approved expenses incurred during renovation. They also have the Restoration Tax Abatement Program available for business and owner occupied properties that are going to improve, renovate, or create an addition on their buildings. The program creates a freeze on the assessed value and property taxes at the re-improvement level for 5 years. That can be renewed for an additional 5 years in many parishes. This state program can be used in addition to the Federal Tax Credit Program. To be eligible for funding, the building must be listed on the National Register of Historic Places or be eligible for membership.

Maine
State Historic Preservation Office
Maine Historic Preservation Commission
55 Capitol Street
State House Station 65
Augusta, ME 04333-0065
207-287-2132
Fax: 207-287-2335
www.state.me.us/mhpc
Email: Historic.Preservation@Maine.gov
At present, federal and state funding is not available to individual property owners, nonprofit organizations or local county governments. The agency does administer the Federal Historic Preservation Tax Credit Program. Individuals who have rehabilitated an income producing building used for commercial or industrial purposes can receive a 20% tax credit on approved expenses incurred during renovation. To be eligible for funding, the building must be a certified historic structure. With the Certified Local Government Program, local communities that have preservation zoning ordinances receive 10% of the federal funds passed on to the Historic Preservation Office. With these matching grants, the CLG's fund local preservation activities in their community.

Maryland
State Historic Preservation Office
Maryland Historical Trust

100 Community Place
Crownsville, MD 21032-2023
410-514-7601
Fax: 410-987-4071
www.marylandhistoricaltrust.net
There is a loan and a grant program available to individuals for projects to acquire, rehabilitate or restore eligible properties. The Historic Preservation Grant Fund has awards of $40,000 per year, per project. In order to participate in this program, the owner must give a perpetual historic preservation easement to the Trust before receiving any funds. The Historic Preservation Loan Fund is a low interest loan. They are available on a first come, first serve basis. A perpetual historic preservation easement must be conveyed for this program also. The agency also administers the Federal Rehabilitation Tax Credit Program. Individuals who have rehabilitated an income producing building used for commercial or industrial purposes can receive a 20% tax credit on approved expenses incurred during renovation. To be eligible for funding, the building must be listed on the National Register of Historic Places or be eligible for membership. The state tax incentive program is the Heritage Preservation Tax Credit Program. The owner of a certified heritage structure can receive a tax credit equal to 25% of the qualified capital costs of the rehabilitation project. It also includes a mortgage credit certificate option. With this, a property owner can choose to transfer the credit to his/her mortgage lender for a reduction in the principal amount or interest rate of the loan. There is also a Certified Local Government Program where those local governments receive a portion of the federal funds given to the Historical Division for historic preservation programs.

Historical Commission

Massachusetts
State Historic Preservation Office
Massachusetts Historical Commission
220 Morrissey Boulevard
Boston, MA 02125-3314
617-727-8470

Fax: 617-727-5128
www.state.ma.us/sec/mhc
Email: mhc@sec.state.ma.us
At present, state grants are not available to individual property owners. The Massachusetts Preservation Projects Fund will provide approximately $9 million in matching grants over the next 3 years available to municipalities and non-profits. Money will be used to support the preservation and maintenance of properties and sites listed in the State Register of Historic Places. Eligible categories will include pre-development, development and acquisition projects. Request for pre-development costs range from $5,000 to $30,000; requests for development or acquisition projects can range from $7,500 to $100,000. Local governments that become Certified Local Governments will receive 10% of the federal funds given to the Historical Commission for renovation projects in their communities. Individual property owners may benefit from the Federal Rehabilitation Tax Credit Program. Individuals who have rehabilitated an income producing building used for commercial or industrial purposes can receive a 20% tax credit on approved expenses incurred during renovation. To be eligible for funding, the building must be listed on the National Register of Historic Places or be eligible for membership.

Michigan
State Historic Preservation Office
Michigan Historical Center
P.O. Box 30738
Department of History, Arts and Libraries
702 W. Kalamazoo St.
Lansing, MI 48909-8238
517-373-6362
Fax: 517-241-3647
www.michigan.gov/hal/0,1607,7-160-17455_19277_19523---,00.html
State grants are not available to individual property owners. The agency does, however, administer the Federal Rehabilitation Tax Credit Program.

Individuals who have rehabilitated an income producing building used for commercial or industrial purposes can receive a 20% tax credit on expenses incurred during renovation. There is also the Michigan Historic Preservation Tax Incentive. This is an income tax credit of up to 25% for owners of a historical home that are going to start a rehabilitation project. To be eligible for funding, buildings must be listed on the National Register of Historic Places or be eligible for membership. There is a federal funding program for Certified Local Governments. They receive 10% of the State Historical Center's federal appropriation in the form of matching grants. These funds are used for local preservation projects in the CLG's community.

Minnesota
State Historic Preservation Office
Minnesota Historical Society
345 West Kellogg Boulevard
St. Paul, MN 55102-1903
651-296-6126
800-657-3773
TTY: 651-282-6073
Fax: 651-282-2374
www.mnhs.org
Email: mnshpo@mnhs.org
There is no state funding program available to individual property owners. The agency does, however, offer technical advice concerning restoration projects. They do administer a Federal Rehabilitation Tax Credit Program to individuals that have rehabilitated an income producing building. The credit is for 20% of eligible expenses incurred during renovation and the building must be used for commercial or industrial purposes. In order to be eligible, the building must be listed on the National Register of Historic Places, or be eligible for membership. They also have the Certified Local Government Program. With this program, cities, townships, and counties with qualified local historic preservation ordinances receive federally funded matching grants to be used for local preservation projects.

Mississippi
State Historic Preservation Office
Mississippi Department of Archives and History
618 East Pearl Street
Jackson, MS 39201
Mailing Address:
   P.O. Box 571
   Jackson, MS 39205-0571

601-576-6940
Fax: 601-576-6955
www.mdah.state.ms.us/hpres/hprestxt.html
Email: msshpo@mdah.state.ms.us
They do have a pending program called the
Mississippi Landmark Program. If a property is
designated as a Landmark it can be eligible for
funding, however, it is not clear if individual
property owners will be able to benefit from the
grants. They do have the Certified Local
Government Program. With this program, cities,
townships, and counties with qualified local historic
preservation ordinances receive federally funded
matching grants to be used for local preservation
projects. They also administer a Federal
Rehabilitation Tax Credit Program to individuals that
have rehabilitated an income producing building. The
credit is for 20% of eligible expenses incurred during
renovation and the building must be used for
commercial or industrial purposes. In order to be
eligible, the building must be listed on the National
Register of Historic Places, or be eligible for
membership.

Missouri

State Historic Preservation Office
State Department of Natural Resources
Division of State Parks
205 Jefferson
P.O. Box 176
Jefferson City, MO 65102
573-751-4732
Fax: 573-751-7627
www.dnr.mo.gov/shpo/index.html
The Historic Preservation Fund Grant is a federal
60/40 matching grant that is open to individuals, state
agencies, municipal governments, incorporated
organizations, non-profits and educational
institutions. The eligible activities for funding are
survey, National Register, predevelopment,
development and planning. These activities must be
directly related to the protection of historical or
architectural resources, among other things. The
recipient of the grant must fund the entire project and
then receive a reimbursement up to the total amount
of the grant. The agency also administers the Federal
Tax Credit Program. It offers a 20% tax credit on
money spent on approved rehabilitation of an income
producing building that will be used for commercial
or industrial purposes. There is a state investment tax
credit for 25% of qualified rehabilitation efforts.
Homeowners as well as developers of income

producing buildings can qualify for this credit
and it can be used in combination with the federal
credit for owners of eligible buildings. The
Certified Local Government is a federal program
administered through local communities. The CLG's
receive 10% of the federal funds passed on to the
Historical Division to be used for local renovation
projects.

Montana

Mark Baumler, Program Manager
State Historic Preservation Office
225 North Roberts
P.O. Box 201201
Helena, MT 59620-1201
406-444-7715
Fax: 406-444-6575
www.his.state.mt.us/
There is not any funding available for individual
homeowners. The Certified Local Government
Program is a federal program administered through
local communities. The CLG's receive 10% of the
federal funds passed on to the Historical Division to
be used for local renovation projects. The agency also
administers the Federal Tax Credit Program. It offers
a 20% tax credit on money spent on approved
rehabilitation of an income producing building that
will be used for commercial or industrial purposes.
There is a state investment tax credit for 25% of
qualified rehabilitation efforts. Homeowners as well
as developers of income producing buildings can
qualify for this credit and it can be used in
combination with the federal credit for owners of
eligible buildings.

Nebraska

State Historic Preservation Office
Nebraska State Historical Society
P.O. Box 82554
1500 R Street
Lincoln, NE 68501
402-471-4746
Fax: 402-471-3316
www.nebraskahistory.org
Email: nshs@nebraskahistory.org
There are no state grant programs that provide
funds for historic preservation to homeowners.
Individual property owners may apply for the
Federal Tax Credit Program if they have rehabilitated
an income producing property used for commercial
or industrial purposes. They would receive a 20% tax

credit on expenses they incurred during the project. To be eligible, the building must be either listed on the National Register of Historic Places, or be eligible for membership. With the Certified Local Government Program, local communities that have preservation zoning ordinances receive 10% of the federal funds passed on to the Historic Preservation Office. With these matching grants, the CLG's fund local preservation activities in their community.

Nevada
State Historic Preservation Office
Historic Preservation Office
100 N. Stewart Street
Carson City, NV 89701-4285
775-684-3448
Fax: 775-684-3442
www.nevadaculture.org
Presently, there are no state grant programs for individuals. They do have a program to rehabilitate buildings that are used for cultural purposes. However, they do have the Certified Local Government Program. With this program, cities, townships, and counties with qualified local historic preservation ordinances receive federally funded matching grants to be used for local preservation projects. Individuals may be able to become sponsored through the CLG Program for their restoration project. Individual property owners may also apply for the Federal Rehabilitation Tax Credit Program. Rehabilitation of an income producing building that is used for commercial or industrial purposes can receive a 20% tax credit on expenses incurred during renovation. To be eligible for funding, buildings must be listed on the National Register of Historic Places or be eligible for membership.

New Hampshire
State Historic Preservation Office
Division of Historical Resources and
State Historic Preservation Office
19 Pillsbury Street
P.O. Box 2043
Concord, NH 03301-2043
603-271-3483/3558
TDD: 800-735-2964
Fax: 603-271-3433
www.nh.gov/nhdhr
Email: preservation@nhdhr.state.nh.us

Presently, there are no state grants available for individuals or nonprofit organizations. However, they do have the Certified Local Government Program. With this program, cities, townships, and counties with qualified local historic preservation ordinances receive federally funded matching grants to be used for local preservation projects. There is also the Federal Rehabilitation Tax Credit Program that may benefit individual property owners. They can receive a 20% tax credit on eligible expenses incurred during a renovation of an income producing building used for commercial or industrial purposes. To qualify, the building must be listed on the National Register of Historic Places or be eligible for membership.

New Jersey
State Historic Preservation Office
New Jersey Historic Trust
P.O. Box 404
Trenton, NJ 08625-0404
609-292-2023
Fax: 609-984-0578
www.state.nj.us/dep/hpo
E-mail: NJHPO@DEP.STATE.NJ.US
The state has both grant and loan programs for nonprofits, government agencies, and educational institutions, however, none for individual homeowners. There are two programs that individuals can use as tax benefits. With the New Jersey Legacies Program, the charitable donation of a historic property allows for reduced estate tax as well as other tax benefits. The Preservation Easement Program gives legal protection to a historic property by the donation of an easement. It also has property and federal tax benefits. The property must be listed on the National Register of Historic Places. There is also the Federal Rehabilitation Tax Credit Program that may benefit individual property owners. They can receive a 20% tax credit on eligible expenses incurred

during a renovation of an income producing building used for commercial or industrial purposes. To qualify, the building must be listed on the National Register of Historic Places or be eligible for membership. With the Certified Local Government Program, local communities that have preservation zoning ordinances receive 10% of the federal funds passed on to the Historic Preservation Office. With these matching grants, the CLG's fund local preservation activities in their community.

New Mexico

State Historic Preservation Office
Historic Preservation Division
Office of Cultural Affairs
Room 320, LaVilla Rivera
228 East Palace Avenue
Santa Fe, NM 87501
505-827-6320
505-827-4045
Fax: 505-827-6338
www.museums.state.nm.us/hpd
While there are no state grants currently available, funds from the federal Historic Preservation Fund are being administered by this division through categorical projects. There are ten small grants of up to $2,000 for the promotion of preservation activities available to individuals, local governments, historic and archaeological and preservation groups. The New Mexico Historic Preservation Loan Fund offers rehabilitation incentives to owners of registered cultural properties. This revolving loan fund combines monies of the state and participating local lenders. To obtain funding, projects must be on the State and/or National Register of Historic Places and reviewed for compliance with the Secretary of the Interior's Standards for Rehabilitation and with the Historic Preservation Division Staff. Borrowers are subject to the lending criteria applied by the participating bank. The maximum principal for a loan is $200,000 with a low interest rate and a term of 5 years. Individual property owners can also apply for the Federal Tax Credit Program. Through this program building owners receive a 20% tax credit on allowed expenses they incurred while rehabilitating a building used for commercial or industrial purposes. Buildings must be listed on the National Register of Historic Places or be eligible for membership to qualify. There is a state tax credit program that is available to homeowners and

business owners for expenses incurred during a restoration/rehabilitation project. Those projects that have been approved by the Cultural Properties Review Committee are eligible for a 50% credit for expenditures up to a maximum credit of $25,000. Certified Local Governments get a portion of the federal funding received by the Historic Preservation Division in the form of matching grants. The grants fund local preservation actives in the CLG's community.

New York

Deputy State Historic Preservation Office
Field Services Bureau
New York State Parks, Recreation and
Historic Preservation
New York State Parks
Albany, NY 12238
Physical Address:
    P.O. Box 189
    Peebles Island
    Waterford, NY 12188
518-237-8643
http://nysparks.state.ny.us/
There are no state funds available to individual property owners. Funding to nonprofit organizations and local municipal governments is made available by the Environmental Protection Act of 1993 and provides up to 50% matching grants for acquisition and restoration. Also, the Historic Barn Tax Credit has established a state income tax credit which provides a reduction in state income tax to barn owners based on the rehabilitation of the barn. This office administers the Federal Rehabilitation Tax Credit Program. Through this program individuals receive a 20% tax credit on allowable expenses they incurred while rehabilitating a building used for commercial or industrial purposes. Buildings must be listed on the National Register of Historic Places or be eligible for membership to qualify. New York also has two tax abatement programs that allow local municipalities to establish property tax abatement programs for locally designated landmarks. These will allow for the increase in assessed value of a rehabilitated historic building or barn to be phased-in over time. With the Certified Local Government Program, local communities that have preservation zoning ordinances receive 10% of the federal funds passed on to the Historic Preservation Office. With these matching grants, the CLG's fund local preservation activities in their community.

North Carolina

State Historic Preservation Office
Department of Culture Resources
Division of Archives and History
4610 Mail Service Center
Raleigh, NC 27699-4610
919-733-4763
Fax: 919-733-8653
www.hpo.dcr.state.nc.us
hpo@ncmail.net

North Carolina has no state funding program for individual property owners. The Division of Archives and History provides grants to nonprofit organizations and local county governments for historical preservation activities. Individual property owners can, however, benefit from the Federal Tax Credit Program. Through this program individuals receive a 20% tax credit on expenses they incurred while rehabilitating a building used for commercial or industrial purposes. Buildings must be listed on the National Register of Historic Places or be eligible for membership to qualify. Private residences that are going to take on a substantial rehabilitation of their historic home may take advantage of a 30% state tax credit. The project must be certified and the home must be listed on that National Register or be located within a National Register district. The Certified Local Government Program funds local community preservation activities in communities that have preservation zoning ordinances.

North Dakota

State Historic Preservation Office
State Historical Society of North Dakota
Archeology & Historic Preservation Division
Heritage Center
612 East Boulevard Ave.
Bismarck, ND 58505-0830
701-328-2666
Fax: 701-328-3710
www.state.nd.us/hist
Email: histsoc@state.nd.us

The Restoration Grant Program is available to individuals, but it is offered sporadically. The matching grant comes from federal sources and can be used for approved rehabilitation projects of homes listed on the National Register of Historic Places. The agency also administers the Federal Preservation Tax Credit Program. Individuals who have rehabilitated an income producing building used for commercial or industrial purposes can receive a 20% tax credit on eligible expenses incurred during renovation. To be eligible, the building must be either listed on the National Register of Historic Places, or be eligible for membership. With the Certified Local Government Program, local communities that have preservation zoning ordinances receive 10% of the federal funds passed on to the Historic Preservation Office. With these matching grants, the CLG's fund local preservation activities in their community.

Ohio

State Historic Preservation Office
Ohio Historical Society
Historic Preservation Office
1982 Velma Ave.
Columbus, OH 43211-1030
614-297-2300
Fax: 614-298-2037
www.ohiohistory.org/resource/histpres

There is no state funding available to individual property owners. However, they do have the Certified Local Government Program. With this program, cities, townships, and counties with qualified local historic preservation ordinances receive federally funded matching grants to be used for local preservation projects. Individual property owners may benefit from the Federal Tax Credit Program. Individuals who have rehabilitated an income producing building used for commercial or industrial purposes can receive a 20% tax credit on expenses incurred during renovation. To be eligible for funding, buildings must either be listed on the National Register of Historic Places or be eligible for membership.

Oklahoma

State Historic Preservation Office
2704 Villa Prom
Shepherd Mall
Oklahoma City, OK 73107-2441
405-521-6249
Fax: 405-947-2918
www.ok-history.mus.ok.us

There is no state or federal funding available to individual property owners at the present time. The agency does, however, administer the Federal Tax

Credit Program. Individuals who have rehabilitated an income producing building used for commercial or industrial purposes can receive a 20% tax credit on eligible expenses incurred during renovation. They also have a state tax credit that can be used on top of the federal credit for historic hotels and historic economic development areas. To be eligible for funding for both credits, the buildings must be listed on the National Register of Historic Places, or be eligible for membership. They have another federal program called the Certified Local Government Program. With this program, cities, townships, and counties with qualified local historic preservation ordinances receive federally funded matching grants to be used for local preservation projects.

Oregon

State Parks and Recreation Department
State Historic Preservation Office
725 Summer St. NE
Ste. C
Salem, OR 97301
503-378-6305
Fax: 503-986-0794
www.shpo.state.or.us
Email: shpo.info@state.or.us
They offer competitive grants programs for assistance to National Register properties when they have funding available. Currently, there is no funding but they hope to have it available next year. However, they do have the Certified Local Government Program. With this program, cities, townships, and counties with qualified local historic preservation ordinances receive federally funded matching grants to be used for local preservation projects. Individual property owners may also benefit from the Special Assessment for Historic Properties Program which provides a fifteen year tax abatement on increases in land and improvement. Properties must be listed on the National Register of Historic Places and be approved by a State Historic Preservation committee. This office also administers the Federal Rehabilitation Tax Credit Program. Income producing buildings that are used for commercial or industrial purposes can receive a 20% tax credit for eligible expenses incurred during a renovation. To be eligible, the building must be listed on the National Register of Historic Places, or be eligible for membership.

Pennsylvania

Historical and Museum Commission
Bureau for Historic Preservation
300 North Street
Harrisburg, PA 17120
717-783-8946
Fax: 717-772-0920
www.phmc.state.pa.us
There are no state funds available to residential homeowners at the present time. Nonprofit organizations and public agencies may apply for the Keystone Historic Preservation Grant to renovate/restore historic properties that are open to the public. This is a 50/50 matching grant program. The agency also administers the Federal Tax Credit Program. There is also the Certified Local Government Program. With this program, cities, townships, and counties with qualified local historic preservation ordinances receive federally funded matching grants to be used for local preservation projects. Individuals who have rehabilitated an income producing building used for commercial or industrial purposes can receive a 20% tax credit on approved expenses incurred during renovation. To be eligible for funding, buildings must be listed on the National Register of Historic Places or be eligible for its membership.

Rhode Island

State Historic Preservation Office
Historical Preservation & Heritage Commission
Old State House
150 Benefit Street
Providence, RI 02903
401-222-2678
401-222-4130
Fax: 401-222-2968
www.rihphc.state.ri.us
E-mail: info@preservation.ri.gov
While there are no state grant programs, they do

have a low interest loan program that individual homeowners can apply to for restoration projects. The Historical Preservation Loan Fund has an interest rate of 2% less than prime. The maximum loan is for $200,000 with a term of 5 years. The agency also administers the Federal Rehabilitation Tax Credit Program. Individuals who have rehabilitated an income producing building used for commercial or industrial purposes can receive a 20% tax credit on expenses incurred during renovation. To be eligible for funding, buildings must be listed on the national Register of Historic Places or be eligible for membership. The state's Historic Preservation Residential Tax Credit Program provides a 10% income tax credit for eligible rehabilitation and maintenance costs for homeowners. With the Certified Local Government Program, local communities that have preservation zoning ordinances receive 10% of the federal funds passed on to the Historic Preservation Office. With these matching grants, the CLG's fund local preservation activities in their community.

HISTORIC PRESERVATION

South Carolina
Historic Preservation Office
Department of Archives and History
8301 Parklane Rd.
Columbia, SC 29223
803-896-6100
Fax: 803-896-6198
www.state.sc.us/scdah
This office administers both federal and state grant programs to support preservation efforts of individuals, organizations, institutions and local governments. Owners of South Carolina properties that are listed in the National Register of Historic Places or determined eligible for membership may apply for State Development Grants and Federal Survey & Planning Grants. Funds from State Development grants assist preservation work on historic structures. Awards generally range from $5,000 to $20,000. The Federal Survey & Planning Grant assists historic preservation projects in a variety of categories. The work must be done by professionals and must comply with the agencies'

guidelines and standards. Both of these are reimbursable 50/50 matching grants. They do also have the Certified Local Government Program. With this program, cities, townships, and counties with qualified local historic preservation ordinances receive federally funded matching grants to be used for local preservation projects. There are two tax incentive programs available. The Special Property Tax Assessments for Rehabilitated Historic Buildings encourages the revitalization of neighborhoods and downtown commercial districts. Municipal and county governments can freeze tax assessments when a property owner finishes a substantial rehabilitation of a historic building and low and moderate income rental properties. The freeze is in effect for up to 2 years if the rehabilitation is completed within those years. For the following 8 years, it will be taxed at the greater of 40% of the post-rehabilitation assessment, or 100% of the pre-rehabilitation assessment.

South Dakota
State Historical Society Historic Preservation Center
900 Governors Drive
Pierre, SD 57501-2217
605-773-3458
Fax: 605-773-6041
www.sdhistory.org
Email: sdshswebmaster@state.sd.us
There are no state grants available to individual property owners at the present time. However, individuals, public agencies and nonprofits are eligible to apply for the Deadwood Fund which makes loans and grants available to purchase, restore, or develop historic property for residential, commercial, or public purposes. The agency also administers the Federal Rehabilitation Tax Credit Program. Individuals who have rehabilitated an income producing building used for commercial or industrial purposes can receive a 20% tax credit on expenses incurred during renovation. There is an additional 10% credit for the renovation of buildings that were constructed before 1936. To be eligible for funding, buildings must be listed on the national Register of Historic Places or be eligible for membership. The South Dakota Legislature has also approved an eight year moratorium on property tax assessment for improvements on historical buildings. Buildings must be on the National Register of Historic Places to qualify. There is also the Certified Local Government Program. With this program, cities, townships, and counties with qualified local

historic preservation ordinances receive federally funded matching grants to be used for local preservation projects.

Tennessee
State Historic Preservation Director
Tennessee Historical Commission
Clover Bottom Mansion
2941 Lebanon Road
Nashville, TN 37243-0442
615-532-1550
Fax: 615-532-1549
www.state.tn.us/environment/hist/
The Federal Preservation Grant is open to individuals, local governmental bodies, private organizations or educational institutions. While historic survey projects will be emphasized, funding is also available for other projects that are needed to undertake a restoration. The agency also administers the Federal Renovation Tax Credit Program. Individuals who have rehabilitated an income producing building used for commercial or industrial purposes can receive a 20% tax credit on expenses incurred during renovation. To be eligible for funding, buildings must be listed on the National Register of Historic Places or be eligible for its membership. There is also the Certified Local Government Program. With this program, cities, townships, and counties with qualified local historic preservation ordinances receive federally funded matching grants to be used for local preservation projects.

Texas
State Historic Preservation Office
Texas Historical Commission
P.O. Box 12276
Austin, TX 78711-2276
512-463-6100
Fax: 512-463-8222
www.thc.state.tx.us
Email: thc@thc.state.tx.us
The Texas Preservation Trust Fund Grant Program provides funding to public or private entities in the form of two for one matching grants. Although individuals may apply, the large majority of grants are awarded to nonprofit organizations and municipal governments. There is also the Certified Local Government Program. With this program, cities, townships, and counties with qualified local historic preservation ordinances receive federally funded matching grants to be used for local preservation

projects. This agency administers the Federal Renovation Tax Credit Program. Individuals who have rehabilitated an income producing building used for commercial or industrial purposes can receive a 20% tax credit on expenses incurred during renovation. To be eligible for funding, buildings must be listed on the national Register of Historic Places or be eligible for its membership.

Utah
State Historic Preservation Office
Utah State Historical Society
Office of Preservation
300 South Rio Grande St.
Salt Lake City, UT 84101-1143
801-533-3500
801-533-3552
TDD: 801-533-3502
Fax: 801-533-3503
http://history.utah.gov
At present, there are no state or federal funds directly available to individual property owners. However, individuals may be able to apply for funding through Utah's Certified Local Government Program. Homeowners qualify if they have support of a sponsoring agency. Matching funds are usually required. The agency also administers the State and Federal Tax Credit Programs. Through these programs individuals can receive a 20% tax credit on expenses they incurred while rehabilitating a building that will be used for residences (state tax credit only), commercial or industrial purposes. Buildings must be either listed on the National Register of Historic Places, or be eligible for membership to qualify.

Vermont
State Historic Preservation Office
Vermont Division for Historic Preservation
National Life Building, Drawer 20
Montpelier, VT 05620-0501
802-828-3211
Fax: 802-828-3206
www.historicvermont.org
Vermont has no state funding for privately owned properties other than a state grant program that provides funding for the renovation of old barns. There is a 50/50 matching grant program available to nonprofit organizations and municipalities. The agency also administers the Federal Tax Credit Program. Individuals who have rehabilitated an income producing building used for commercial or

industrial purposes can receive a 20% tax credit on expenses incurred during renovation. To be eligible for funding, buildings must be listed on the National Register of Historic Places or be eligible for its membership. There is also the Certified Local Government Program. With this program, cities, townships, and counties with qualified local historic preservation ordinances receive federally funded matching grants to be used for local preservation projects.

Virginia

State Historic Preservation Office
Department of Historic Resources
Commonwealth of Virginia
2801 Kensington Avenue
Richmond, VA 23221
804-367-2323
Fax: 804-367-2391
www.dhr.virginia.gov
The state grant program is available for local governments, nonprofit historical associations, and museum organizations. However, individuals with state tax liability may benefit from the State Rehabilitation Tax Credit Program which provides a 25% credit for eligible rehabilitation expenses. The agency also administers the Federal Tax Credit Program. Individuals who have rehabilitated an income producing building used for commercial or industrial purposes can receive a 20% tax credit on expenses incurred during renovation. To be eligible for funding, buildings must be listed on the National Register of Historic Places or be eligible for its membership. There is also the Certified Local Government Program. With this program, cities, townships, and counties with qualified local historic preservation ordinances receive federally funded matching grants to be used for local preservation projects.

Washington

State Historic Preservation Office
Office of Archeology and Historic Preservation
1063 S. Capitol Way, Suite 106
P.O. Box 48343
Olympia, WA 98504-8343
360-586-3065
360-586-3066
Fax: 360-586-3067
www.oahp.wa.gov/
At present, state grant funding is not available to individual property owners, nonprofit organizations or local county governments, although, there is the Certified Local Government Program. With this program, cities, townships, and counties with qualified local historic preservation ordinances receive federally funded matching grants to be used for local preservation projects. This agency administers the Federal Rehabilitation Tax Credit Program. Individuals who have rehabilitated an income producing building used for commercial or industrial purposes can receive a 20% tax credit on expenses incurred during renovation. To be eligible for funding, buildings must be either listed on the National Register of Historic Places, or be eligible for membership.

West Virginia

Deputy State Historic Preservation Office
West Virginia Division of Culture and History
1900 Kanawha Boulevard, East
Charleston, WV 25305-0300
304-558-0220
TDD: 304-558-3562
Fax: 304-558-2779
www.wvculture.org/shpo/index.html
State Development Grants are available to individuals who wish to renovate a historical home. Grants range from $1,000 to $20,000 depending upon the scope of the project. There is also the Certified Local Government Program. With this program, cities, townships, and counties with qualified local historic preservation ordinances receive federally funded matching grants to be used for local preservation projects. The Federal Rehabilitation Tax Credit Program is administered by this agency. Individuals who have rehabilitated an income producing building used for commercial or industrial purposes can receive a 20% tax credit on expenses incurred during

renovation. In addition, there is a state tax credit program for both residential and commercial property owners that undergo a rehabilitation project. To be eligible for funding, buildings must be either listed on the National Register of Historic Places, or be eligible for membership.

Wisconsin
State Historic Preservation Office
Historic Preservation Division
State Historical Society
816 State St.
Madison, WI 53706-1482
608-264-6500
Fax: 608-264-6504
www.wisconsinhistory.org/
There are no state or federal grants available to individual homeowners. Individuals can, however, apply for tax assistance under the Federal Tax Credit Program. Individuals who have rehabilitated an income producing building used for commercial or industrial purposes can receive a 20% tax credit on expenses incurred during renovation. To be eligible for funding, buildings must be either listed on the National Register of Historic Places, or be eligible for membership. There is also the Certified Local Government Program. With this program, cities, townships, and counties with qualified local historic preservation ordinances receive federally funded matching grants to be used for local preservation projects.

Wyoming
State Historic Preservation Office
2301 Central Avenue, 3rd Floor
Barrett Building
Cheyenne, WY 82002
307-777-5497
Fax: 307-777-6421
http://wyoshpo.state.wy.us
E-mail: shpoweb@state.wy.us
There are currently no state or federal grant programs available to individuals. Individuals can, however, apply for tax assistance under the Federal Tax Credit Program. Those who have rehabilitated an income producing building used for commercial or industrial purposes can receive a 20% tax credit on expenses incurred during renovation. To be eligible for funding, buildings must be either listed on the National Register of Historic Places, or be eligible for membership. There is also the Certified Local Government Program. With this program, cities, townships, and counties with qualified local historic preservation ordinances receive federally funded matching grants to be used for local preservation projects.

More Housing Money

Just when you thought there were no other places to turn, we have uncovered even more resources and services you can use for all your housing needs. Need help with your heating bill? What about a new paint job on your house? Is your house a safe place to live? All these questions are answered and more. There are even places you can call if you are falling behind in your mortgage payments!

"WOW!...The Government Will Pay My Mortgage"

You'd never have thought to ask, would you?

There are now programs that will make your mortgage payments for you when you get into financial trouble. For example, Pennsylvania law, 35 P.S. § 1680.401 et seq., states it will provide *"mortgage assistance payments to homeowners who are in danger of losing their homes through foreclosure and through no fault of their own and who have a reasonable prospect of resuming mortgage payments within the prescribed time frame."* Pennsylvania calls it the ***"Homeowners' Emergency Mortgage Assistance Program."***

One of the best ways to find out if there are programs like this in your area is to contact the local HUD approved Housing Counseling agencies. To find your closest agency, contact your state housing office, the Housing Counseling Center locator at 800-569-4287; {www.hud.gov/offices/hsg/sfh/hcc/hccprof14.cfm}.

Free Home Owner Calculators at {www.fanniemae.com/homebuyers/ homepath/index.jhtml?p=Homepath}

- How Much Is Your Monthly Payment?

- How Much House Can You Afford?

- What Monthly Payment Is Needed for a House with a Specific Sales Price?

- How Much House Can You Afford with a Specific Monthly Payment?

- Is Now A Good Time To Refinance?

If your local agency doesn't have money to pay your mortgage, they will certainly help you work out other arrangements with your mortgage company.

FREE MONEY FOR CLOSING COSTS AND A DOWN PAYMENT

Houston has a program that offers $4,000 in down-payment and closing costs through their First-Time Homebuyers Program. Iowa offers up to $2,750 in grants for a down-payment. You can be earning up to $65,000 a year and still be eligible for the money in their Down Payment/Closing Cost Grant Program. Many cities, like Minneapolis, will offer interest free loans, called Equity Participation Loans, for up to 10% of the cost of the home. You pay back the money when you sell the house.

Programs vary from state to state and city to city. Contact your city government, your county government, and your local community development office to learn about local programs. If you have trouble locating your local community development office, the following organizations may be able to help:

❑ National Association of Housing and Redevelopment Officials, 630 Eye St, NW, Washington, DC 20001; 202-289-3500, 877-866-2476; Fax: 202-289-8181; {www.nahro.org}

❑ Information Center, Office of Community Planning and Development, Community Connections, P.O. Box 7189, Gaithersburg, MD 20898; 800-998-9999, Fax: 301-519-5027; {www.comcon.org}

❑ Also be sure to contact your state housing office listed in the blue pages of your phone book.

Make Money Going To Housing Classes

A HUD-approved housing counseling agency in Philadelphia offers $1,000 in settlement costs to certain people who attend pre-purchase house counseling sessions. A counseling agency in Boston offers new home buyers access to special low down-payment mortgages if they attend pre-housing classes.

There are over 350 HUD-approved counseling agencies that offer free classes and help in housing related issues including:

"The Best Way To Buy And
Finance A Home"
"Is A Reverse Mortgage For You?"
"Foreclosure and Eviction Options"
'The Best Way To Finance A
Home Fix-Up"

**Who Qualifies As A
First Time Homebuyer?**

Most government programs define a first time homebuyer as someone who has not owned a home during the past 3 years or who is legally separated or divorced.

These non-profit agencies are trained and approved by the U.S. Department of Housing and Urban Development (HUD). To find your closest agency, contact your State housing office, the Housing Counseling Center locator at 800-569-4287; {www.hud.gov/offices/hsg/sfh/hcc/hcc_home.cfm}, or Housing Counseling Clearinghouse, P.O. Box 10423, McLean, VA 22102; 800-569-4287.

CUT YOUR RENT BY 50%

Studies show that people with less income pay a higher portion of their salary on housing than people in higher income categories. It is not unusual for a single mom to pay 70% of her salary in rent. The government has a program called Housing Choice Vouchers (formerly called Section 8 Rental Assistance Program) that offers vouchers and direct payments to landlords. This will, in turn, cut your rent down to only 30% of your income.

Of course, there are income requirements for this program. For example, in Arlington Country, VA, a one-person household with an income of $23,000 qualifies for the program. Arlington County also has housing grant rental assistance for low-income elderly, disabled, and working families with children. Some of these programs have waiting lists, but it could be worth the wait.

To apply for these federal programs, contact your state housing authority, your local housing authority, or a community services agency. If you have trouble getting the help you need, you can contact Information Center, Office of Community Planning and Development, Community Connections, P.O. Box 7189, Gaithersburg, MD 20898; 800-998-9999, Fax: 301-519-5027; {www.comcon.org}.

"Get The Lead Out"
And Get Your House Or Apartment Painted For Free

If you are living in a house or apartment that was built before 1978, you, or even your landlord, may be eligible for grant money and other assistance to make sure that you do not suffer the effects of lead poisoning from lead-based paint.

Chips or dust from this type of paint can be highly dangerous to humans, especially children. The U.S. Department of Housing and Urban Development spends over $60 million a year helping home owners and apartment owners eliminate the problems that may be caused by lead paint.

Contact your state department of housing to see if your state has money for lead paint removal.

How Lead Paint Can Affect Your Kids

Houses and apartments built before 1978 may contain lead contaminated surface dust and paint chips, which, if consumed by children, can result in reduced intelligence, behavioral problems, learning disabilities, and even permanent brain damage. Government sponsored programs can help you inspect your home for lead paint and even get a blood test for your children for potential problems. To find out more about these programs or the effects of lead-based paint, contact the following:

☞ *National Lead Information Center*, 1200 Pennsylvania Ave., NW, Mail Code 7404T Washington, DC 20460; 800-424-LEAD; {www.epa.gov/lead}.

☞ *Office of Lead Hazard Control*, U.S. Department of Housing and Urban Development, 451 7th Street, SW, Room B-133, Washington, DC 20410; 202-755-1785; Fax: 202-755-1000; {www.hud.gov/offices/lead/index.cfm}.

Lead Poisoning and Your Children

This publication is free along with three fact sheets, and a list of state and local contacts for additional information. Specific lead questions can be answered by an information specialist at 800-424-LEAD.

For more information, contact National Lead Information Center, 1200 Pennsylvania Ave., NW, Mail Code 7404T Washington, DC 20460; 800-424-LEAD; {www.epa.gov/lead}.

Free Money To Fix Up Your Home

States, cities, and counties, as well as local community development agencies are providing grants, loans, and even supplies and technical assistance for homeowners who want to fix up the inside or outside of their homes. Many of these have income requirements you must meet. Others offer forgivable loans if you stay in the house a certain number of years. Here are some examples of what communities are offering to their residents:

☞ *Sunnyvale, CA*: Up to $5,000 grant for disabled homeowners to retrofit their homes for handicapped access through the Home Access Grant Program.

☞ *Houston, TX*: loans and grants for major repairs through their Housing Assistance Program for the Elderly and Disabled.

☞ *Tacoma, WA*: Up to $3,500 loan at 0% interest with no monthly payments through the Major Home Repair Program.

☞ *Minneapolis, MN*: $15,000, no interest, and no payments until you sell in their Deferred Rehabilitation Loans.

☞ *Baton Rouge, LA*: $22,000 grant to fix up your home through the Housing Rehabilitation Grant Program.

☞ *Los Angeles, CA*: Free help with roofing, plumbing, electrical and heating work, painting, deadbolt locks, smoke alarms, screens, windows, and yard maintenance for seniors or disabled persons through the Handy Worker Program.

☞ *Michigan*: $1,000 to $10,000 at zero interest, to be paid back when you sell your home through the Rehabilitation Assistance Program.

☞ *Nashville, TN*: $18,000 at 3% to fix up your home.

☞ *Lane County, OR*: offers grants for weatherization assistance for weatherstripping, storm doors and windows, and insulation.

☞ *Des Moines, IA*: offers emergency repair loans.

☞ *Greensboro, NC*: has low interest loans for people with incomes over $30,000 and $8,500 grants for people with incomes up to $20,000.

Programs vary from state to state and city to city. Contact your city government, your county government, and your local community development office to learn about local programs. If you have trouble locating your local community development office, the following organizations may be able to help:

❑ National Association of Housing and Redevelopment Officials, 630 Eye St., NW, Washington, DC 20001; 202-289-3500, 877-866-2476; Fax: 202-289-8181; {www.nahro.org}

*Help To Fix Up
A Home For A Senior*

*The Home Modification
Action Project at:*

www.homemods.org

❑ Information Center, Office of Community Planning and Development, Community Connections, P.O. Box 7189, Gaithersburg, MD 20898; 800-998-9999, Fax: 301-519-5027; {www.comcon.org}
❑ Also be sure to contact your state housing office.

Your Rich Uncle Will Cosign A Loan To Buy or Fix Up a Home

Both the U.S. Department of Housing and Urban Development (HUD) and the Rural Housing Service of the U.S. Department of Agriculture offer loan guarantees to lending agencies around the county. A loan-guarantee assures the lending agency that the government will pay for the loan if you can't. In addition, the Rural Housing Service has a direct loan program that provides loans to lower income families to buy, build, repair, renovate, or relocate their home. This is called the Section 502 Program.

To investigate the programs available in your area, contact your local HUD office listed in the blue pages of your telephone book, or U.S. Department of Housing and Urban Development (HUD), 451 7th Street, SW, Washington, DC 20410; 202-708-1112, 800-245-2691; {www.hud.gov}.

To find your local Rural Housing Service, look in the blue pages of your telephone book, or contact Single Family Housing Programs, USDA Rural Housing Service, Room 5037, South Building, 14th Street and Independence Ave., SW, Washington, DC 20250; 202-720-4323; {www.rurdev.usda.gov/rhs/index.html}. In addition, you may contact your state housing office.

Money For Seniors And Those With A Disability To Buy or Fix Up A Home

The city of Houston offers $5,000 fix up money for the disabled and elderly in their Emergency Repair Program. Minneapolis offers home repair grants of $10,000 to people with disabilities who have incomes under $18,000. Nebraska has a special low interest loan program to help people with disabilities buy a home.

The Rural Housing Service of the U.S. Department of Agriculture offers special grants through their Section 504 program of up to $7,500 if you're over 62, and need to fix up your home. Programs vary from state to state and city to city, and obviously, many have eligibility requirements.

Contact your city government, your county government and your local community development office to learn about local programs. If you have trouble locating your local community development office, contact *National Association of Housing and Redevelopment Officials*, 630 Eye St., NW, Washington, DC 20001; 202-289-3500, 877-866-2476; Fax: 202-289-8181; {www.nahro.org}, or *Information Center, Office of Community Planning and Development*, Community Connections, P.O. Box 7189, Gaithersburg, MD 20898; 800-998-9999, Fax: 301-519-5027; {www.comcon.org}.

To find your local *Rural Housing Service*, look in the blue pages of your telephone book, or contact Single Family Housing Programs, USDA Rural Housing Service, Room 5037, South Building, 14th Street and Independence Ave., SW, Washington, DC 20250; 202-720-4323; {www.rurdev.usda.gov/rhs/index.html}. In addition, you may contact your state housing office.

$4,000 Grant To Paint Your Home

That's what Canton, Ohio offers to very low-income residents — grants to paint their house or put on new siding. They feel that an investment like this improves the value of all the properties in the area.

Sunnyvale, California offers some of their residents $400 in grant money to paint their homes. And if you're over 60 or have a disability, you can get a $1,200 grant.

See if your city or state offers a program like this.

Money To Buy or Fix Up a Mobile Home

The city of Sunnyvale, CA will lend you up to $7,500 at 0-5% interest for a mobile home. New York State offers loans to help you buy a mobile home park or the land your mobile home sits on through their *Manufactured Home Cooperative Fund Program.* And the U.S. Department of Agriculture has what is called *Section 504 funds* that allow loans of up to $20,000 to fix a mobile home or to move it from one site to another. Here is how to contact the major programs for manufactured (mobile) homes.

♦ VA-Guaranteed Manufactured Home Loan

Contact your local office of the Department of Veterans Affairs, or U.S. Department of Veterans Affairs, 1120 Vermont Avenue NW, Washington, DC 20421; 800-827-1000; {www.va.gov/}.

♦ FHA Insured Title I Manufactured Home Loan

Contact your local office of Housing and Urban Development listed in the blue pages of your telephone book, or your state housing office, or the Housing Counseling Clearinghouse, P.O. Box 10423, McLean, VA 22102; 800-569-4287}

♦ Section 504 Rural Housing Loans and Grants

To find your local Rural Housing Service, look in the blue pages of your telephone book, or contact Single Family Housing Programs, USDA Rural Housing Service, Room 5037, South Building, 14th Street and Independence Ave., SW, Washington, DC 20250; 202-720-4323; {www.rurdev.usda.gov/rhs/index.html}.

HUD-man Goes After The Mobile Home Salesman

If your mobile home is not all that was promised, call HUD. The U.S. Department of Housing and Urban Development regulates the construction of mobile homes and investigates complaints about their performance.

Contact: Manufactured Housing and Standards, Office of Consumer and Regulatory Affairs, U.S. Department of Housing and Urban Development, 451 7th St., SW, Room 9152, Washington, DC 20410; 800-927-2891, Fax: 202-708-4213; Email: {mhs@hud.gov}; {www.hud.gov/offices/hsg/sfh/mhs/mhshome.cfm}.

Home Repair Programs

Here are a few *HOME REPAIR* programs we found that were available at the time we were doing research. Things change, but make sure to contact local agencies to see what may be available to you!

City of Sunnyvale
Community Development Department
Housing Division
456 West Olive Ave.
Sunnyvale, CA 94088
408-730-7444
www.sunnyvale.ca.gov/

Tacoma Community Redevelopment Authority
747 Market St., Room 1036
Tacoma, WA 98402
253-591-5213
www.cityoftacoma.org

Community Development
City of Canton
P.O. Box 24218
218 Cleveland Ave., SW 5th Floor
Canton, OH 44701-4218
330-489-3040
www.cityofcanton.com

Minneapolis Community Development Agency
Crown Roller Mill
105 Fifth Ave. S, Suite 200
Minneapolis, MN 55401-2534
612-673-5095
www.mcda.org

Los Angeles Housing Department
3550 Wilshire Blvd.#1500
Los Angeles, CA 90010
866-557-7368
www.cityofla.org/LAHD

Dept. of Housing and Community Development
300 W. Washington St.
P.O. Box 3136
Greensboro, NC 27402
336-373-2349
www.ci.greensboro.nc.us/HCD/

Metropolitan Development and Housing Agency
701 S. 6th St.
Nashville, TN 37206
615-252-8503
www.nashville.gov/mdha

Department of Community Development
Neighborhood Conservation Services Division
602 Robert D. Ray Drive
Des Moines, IA 50309
515-283-4787
www.ci.des-moines.ia.us

Low-Income Weatherization Program
Housing and Community Services Agency
177 Day Island Rd.
Eugene, OR 97401
541-682-3999
www.hacsa.org

Money For Buying a Co-op

The U.S. Department of Housing and Urban Development finances the purchase of condominiums. The program is called *Mortgage Insurance — Purchase of Units in Condominiums (234c)*. They also have a special program for units in co-op buildings called *Single-Family Cooperative Mortgage Insurance (203n)*.

Contact your local office of Housing and Urban Development listed in the blue pages of your telephone book, or your state housing office, or the Housing Counseling Clearinghouse, P.O. Box 10423, McLean, VA 22102; 800-569-4287.

Free Houses

Well, maybe they're not free, but they can cost you as little as a few hundred dollars a month. And maybe they're not in good shape, but many of the programs will also offer you a low interest loan to fix up the house. Some states refer to the program as an ***Urban Homesteading Act***. The idea of the program is that the government gets you a home for next to nothing and you agree to live there for a certain number of years.

Minnesota has a program. Baltimore had a very active program for many years. Davenport, Iowa purchases homes, completely rehabs them, and then offers the houses in a lottery each May. You must get a mortgage, but your monthly payments are under $400 a month for a completely rebuilt house! There are some states, like Alaska, that still offer wilderness land for homesteading. Because the houses are so cheap, there is usually a lottery for eligible buyers. Contact your city government, your county government and your local community development office to learn about local programs. If you have trouble finding your local community development agency, the following organizations may be able to help:

✦ National Association of Housing and Redevelopment Officials, 630 Eye St., NW, Washington, DC 20001; 202-289-3500, 877-866-2476, Fax: 202-289-8181; {www.nahro.org}.

✦ Information Center, Office of Community Planning and Development, Community Connections, P.O. Box 7189, Gaithersburg, MD 20898; 800-998-9999; Fax: 301-519-5027; {www.comcon.org}.

✦ You can also contact your state housing office.

Free Legal Help For Renters and Home Buyers

It's illegal for landlords, realtors, bankers and others to discriminate against you because of your race, religion, sex, family status, or handicap. Landlords also have rules to follow in dealing with you as a tenant. With the proper free help you can find out how to:

＊ Stop paying the rent if your toilet doesn't work.
＊ Get the government to sue your landlord for discriminating against your child.
＊ Break a lease and not pay a penalty.
＊ Get your eviction stopped.
＊ Force a bank to give you a loan for a new home.
＊ Get your landlord to widen your doorways to fit your wheelchair.
＊ Get a third party to fight your landlord for you.

To file a complaint or to learn more about your rights in dealing with landlords and people in the housing industry, contact any of the following:

★ Your state housing office.
★ Your state Attorney General's office.

★ Fair Housing and Equal Opportunity, U.S. Department of Housing and Urban Development, Room 5204, 451 7th St, SW, Washington, DC 20410; 800-669-9777; {www.hud.gov/complaints/housediscrim.cfm}.

Use Your Sweat as a Down Payment and Get a No-Interest Loan

One of the biggest providers of this type of program is the non-profit organization called **Habitat for Humanity**. You've probably seen them in the news with Ex-President Jimmy Carter helping them build houses. They have even received government money to help support their program. The typical arrangement is for people with incomes between $9,000 and $30,000. You and your family work an average of 300 to 500 hours building your home or other people's homes, and in return you get a home with no down-payment and a very low mortgage payment. Because people provide free labor to build the home, you only pay about $60,000 for a $100,000 home, and you get the money interest free. A typical bank loan can cost you over $700 per month, but through this program you pay only about $200 a month.

Other local or national organizations may run similar programs in your area, with or without government financing. To find programs in your area, you can contact:

⇨ Habitat for Humanity International, 121 Habitat Street, Americus, GA 31709; 229-924-6935; {www.habitat. org}. To find a local affiliate, call 229-924-6935, ext. 2551 or ext. 2552.

⇨ Information Center, Office of Community Planning and Development, Community Connections, P.O. Box 7189, Gaithersburg, MD 20898; 800-998-9999, Fax: 301-519-5027; {www.comcon.org}.

Free Housing Books

- *A Consumer's Guide to Mortgage Settlement Costs*

- *Home Mortgages: Understanding the Process*

- *A Consumer's Guide to Mortgage Refinancings*

- *Consumer Handbook on Adjustable Rate Mortgages*

For your copies, contact Board of Governors of the Federal Reserve System, Publications Services, MS-127, Washington, DC 20551; 202-452-3244; {www.federalreserve.gov/}.

Staying Clear Of Deadly Radon Gases

Nowadays when you buy a home, you often have a radon level reading taken, but what do the numbers mean? The *National Radon Information Hotline* has a free brochure that explains what radon is, how to test for it, and more.

There is also a Radon FIX-IT Program operated by the Consumer Research Council, a nonprofit consumer organization that provides free guidance and encouragement to consumers who are trying to fix their homes that have elevated radon levels. The Program operates from noon to 8

FREE HOUSING EXPERTS

The HUD website includes text of over 20 helpful guides, such as: *How To Buy a Home*, *How to Get A Mortgage*, **and** *HUD-approved Lenders*, **as well as listings of government homes for sale. These are not just HUD homes, but also those from the Department of Veteran Affairs, General Services Administration, and more.**

Although the houses are not steals, you can find some great deals. For housing information, call HUD USER, P.O. Box 23268, Washington, DC 20026-3268; 800-245-2691; {www.hud.gov}.

p.m. EST and has information on reducing elevated radon levels, referrals to experts, and names of contractors who are qualified to help.

For more information, contact National Radon Information Hotline at 800-767-7236 (SOS-RADON) and the Radon Fix-It Program at 800-644-6999; or Indoor Air Quality Information Clearinghouse, IAQ Info, P.O. Box 37133, Washington, DC 20013-7133; 800-438-4318; {www.epa.gov/iaq/iaqinfo.html}.

Is Your Drinking Water Safe?

According to the National Consumer Water Survey, 75% of those surveyed have concerns about the quality of the water they drink. Many people are purchasing bottled water or water purification devices for drinking water, but is it a wise use of your money?

The *Safe Drinking Water Hotline* can answer any question or concern you may have regarding drinking water, and can provide you with publications such as: *Is Your Drinking Water Safe?*, *Home Water Testing*, *Home Water Treatment Units*, *Bottled Water* fact sheet, and more. Contact Safe Drinking Water Hotline, U.S. Environmental Protection Agency, MC 4601, Ariel Rios Building, 1200 Pennsylvania Ave. NW, Washington, DC 20460-0003; 800-426-4791; {www.epa.gov/safewater}.

How To Save Up To $650/Year On Fuel Bills

The average family spends close to $1300 a year on their home's utility bills, and a large portion of that energy is wasted. By using a few inexpensive energy efficient measures, you can reduce your energy bills by 10% to 50%.

With the publication, *Energy Savers: Tips on Saving Energy and Money at Home*, you can go step by step through your home to learn energy saving tips. Topics covered include insulation/ weatherization, water heating, lighting, appliances, and more. There is even a major appliance shopping guide that explains the energy labels on appliances and shows you how to choose the best one for you.

The Energy Efficiency and Renewable Energy Clearinghouse can answer your questions on all these topics and has publications and easy to understand fact sheets. Contact the Energy Efficiency and Renewable and Energy Information Center, P.O. Box 43165, Olympia, WA 98504-3165; 877-337-3463; {www.eere.energy.gov}.

Volunteers Will Fix Up Your (Or Your Mom's) Home For Free

Many service organizations have begun to organize community service days, where the town is beautified along with certain homes in need of repair. *Christmas in April* is a national organization with over 185 affiliates that gather together volunteers to help rehabilitate the homes of low-income homeowners. The work is done for free with the goal being to provide a safe and secure home for those in need.

An example of a program in the Dallas area is the Volunteer Home Repair and Weatherization Program. This program provides home repairs that improve the health, safety, and energy efficiency of a home for low-income homeowners. Contact your city government, your county government and your local community development office to learn about local programs.

- In the Dallas area, contact Volunteer Home Repair and Weatherization Program, Center for Housing Resources' Mission, 3103 Greenwood, Dallas, TX 75204-6011; 214-828-4390, Fax: 214-828-4412; {www.chrdallas.org}.

GOVERNMENT FORECLOSED HOMES AT BARGAIN PRICES

No, they are not giving away the kitchen sink, but you may be able to find some good deals nonetheless. The government sells foreclosed homes all across the country, and even in your neighborhood. You don't need to know someone to get in on these deals. All are sold through real estate agents. Contact your agent, ask about government repossessed homes and they can do a search for you. These are not just HUD homes, but also those from the V.A., Fannie Mae, IRS, Federal Deposit Insurance Corporation, and more.

I want to be able to say that they give you these houses at 50% off, but I can't. Most want fair market value, but the government does not want to carry the real estate taxes for all these houses either. You can make a deal that works out best for everyone. For more information, contact HUD USER, P.O. Box 23268, Washington, DC 20026-3268; 800-245-2691; {www.hud.gov/homes/homesforsale.cfm}. (Note: this website has links to all the major government home sale programs); U.S. Department of Veterans Affairs, 810 Vermont Ave., NW, Washington, DC 20420; 800-827-1000; {www.va.gov}.

MONEY TO PAY YOUR HEATING BILL

Storm windows, insulation, and even weatherstripping, can help reduce your fuel bill. Families can receive assistance to weatherize their homes and apartments at no charge if you meet certain income guidelines. States allocate dollars to nonprofit agencies for purchasing and installing energy-related repairs, with the average grant being $2,000 per year. The elderly and families with children get first dibs.

Contact your State Energy Office or the Weatherization Assistance Programs Branch, EE2K, U.S. Department of Energy, 1000 Independence Ave., SW, Washington, DC 20585; 202-586-4074; {www.eere.energy.gov/EE/buildings-state.html}.

$2,000 GRANTS OR 2% INTEREST LOAN
TO FIX UP YOUR HOME

A family of 4 can be making close to $30,000 per year and still be eligible for a 2% interest loan from the local Community Action Agency. Some agencies also offer grants or are aware of other local organizations that provide grants. There are about 1,000 of them around the country to help neighborhoods.

To find an agency near you, contact Community Action Partnership, 1100 17th St., NW, Suite 500, Washington, DC 20036, 202-265-7546; Fax: 202-265-8850; {www.communityactionpartnership.com/default.asp}.

50% Discount
On a New Heating System

The California Energy Commission offers residences and small businesses up to 50% of the cost of a new heating or air conditioning system if it meets their standards for "emerging renewable technologies," like solar heating, but more. Their program is called the Emerging Renewables Program.

To learn more, contact California Energy Commission, 1516 Ninth St., MS-45, Sacramento, CA 95814; 800-555-7794; {www.energy.ca.gov and www.consumerenergycenter.com/erprebate}. Check with your state utility commission to see if your state offers similar programs.

How To Keep Your Air Clean Of Asbestos, Carbon Monoxide, and Second Hand Smoke

You don't need to hire some high priced consultants to find how to keep the air in your home clean of pollution and other toxic substances. The Indoor Air Quality Information Clearinghouse is the expert on all forms of indoor air pollution. They have publications and information on second hand smoke, asbestos, carbon monoxide, air cleaners, and more.

You can contact them at Indoor Air Quality Information Clearinghouse, IAQ Info, P.O. Box 37133, Washington, DC 20013-7133; 800-438-4318; {www.epa.gov/iaq/iaqinfo.html}.

Free Mortgage Publications

The Federal Trade Commission has compiled several brochures to get you started. Some of the titles include:

Looking for the Best Mortgage?, Mortgage Discrimination, Mortgage Servicing: Make Sure your Payments Count and More.

To receive your copies, contact Public Reference, Room 130, Federal Trade Commission, Washington, DC 20580; 202-326-2222, 877-FTC-HELP; {www.ftc.gov}.

Free Weatherization, Fuel Bills, and Rent for Incomes Up to $50,000

If you are within a certain income and need help paying your heating bills, need money to make your house more energy efficient, or need funds for urgent repairs, call your local Community Action Agency. There are about 1,000 of them around the country to help neighborhoods. They will also come out and check if your home or apartment needs to be more energy efficient. To find an agency near you, contact Community Action Partnership, 1100 17th St., NW, Suite 500, Washington, DC 20036; 202-265-7546; Fax: 202-265-8850; {www.communityactionpartnership.com/default.asp}.

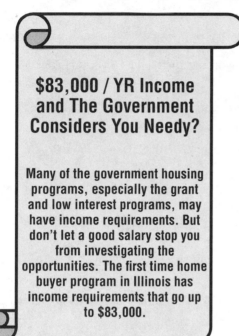

$83,000 / YR Income and The Government Considers You Needy?

Many of the government housing programs, especially the grant and low interest programs, may have income requirements. But don't let a good salary stop you from investigating the opportunities. The first time home buyer program in Illinois has income requirements that go up to $83,000.

Also, your local utility can provide you with or refer you to other programs in your area to analyze your energy usage, recommend energy saving measures, provide fuel and utility assistance to retain or restore service, establish payment discounts based on income and usage, or establish affordable payment plans if you are in arrears. Contact your local utility company to take advantage of these services.

FREE NUTRITION COUNSELING AND CLASSES

Nutrition counseling, menu planning, cooking instruction and comparison shopping is available from your local County Cooperative Extension Service. Group instruction is free of charge, but persons requesting individual lessons are asked to pay for the lesson materials.

They also help neighborhoods establish and maintain community gardens, which provide fresh vegetables to area residents. To find an office near you, look in the blue pages of your local telephone book under county government for County Cooperative Extension Service.

Get Money For Down Payments And Closing Costs Here

The following are examples of financial assistance programs offered by states, cities and counties at the time we were doing our initial research for this book. Be aware that these programs are constantly changing and all have some form of eligibility requirements, but don't let that stop you! New ones are added and old ones may be discarded.

To be sure that you are aware of all the programs available in your area, contact your state office on housing, your city housing office, your county housing office, as well as any local community development offices that may be in your area. If you need help locating your community development office, the following may be of assistance: National Association of Housing and Redevelopment Officials, 630 Eye St., NW, Washington, DC 20001; 202-289-3500, 877-866-2476; Fax: 202-289-8181: {www.nahro.org}.

✖ *Houston*: $3,500 to help with a down payment and closing costs in the First-Time Homebuyers Program.

✖ *Iowa*: 5% of your mortgage in grant money for a down payment and closing costs through Down Payment/ Closing Cost Grant Program.

✖ *Minneapolis, MN*: $3,000 at 0% interest due when you sell the home.

✖ *Michigan*: $5,000 at 0% interest and no monthly payments.

✖ *Baton Rouge, LA*: $10,000 at 0% interest and no payments for 20 years through Home Buyers Assistance Program.

✖ *Georgia*: $5,000 for a down payment at 0% interest through Own HOME Program.

✖ *Hawaii*: $15,000 loans at 3% for down payments, but you only pay interest for the first 5 years in the Down Payment Loan Program.

✖ *Kansas*: You only need $500 and Kansas will assist with down payment, closing costs, and legal fees in First Time Homebuyers Downpayment Assistance Program.

✖ *Maine*: Buy a house with only $750, and finance your down payment at 0% through Down Home Program.

✖ *La Miranda, CA*: 10% loan for down payment for first time homebuyers in the Down Payment Assistance Program.

✖ *Tacoma, WA*: A $5,000 loan for your down payment and settlement costs in Down Payment Assistance Program.

✖ *Indianapolis, IN*: Put 1% down and your closing costs go into a 2nd mortgage in Good Neighbor II Loan Program.

✖ *Los Angeles, CA*: 2% forgivable loan for closing costs money, plus $35,000 loan for repairs with no payments for 30 years or until the house is sold through Home WORKS! Program.

✖ *New York State*: 0% down payment in Low Down Payment, Conventional Rate Program.

✖ *Walnut Creek, CA*: Get a second mortgage for half of the closing costs and 2% of down payment with nothing due until you sell or refinance.

✖ *Washington County, OR*: $19,300 loan with no interest and no payment for the first 5 years in First-Time Home Buyer Program.

✖ *Michigan*: Move into a $60,000 home with only $600 in your pocket in the Down Payment Assistance Program.

✖ *New Hampshire*: $5,000 low interest loan for closing costs through HELP Program.

✖ *Nashville, TN*: Nashville Housing Fund provides down payments, closing costs and low interest loans for first time home buyers.

✖ *Tucson, AZ*: $3,000 loan for down payment and they will pay all closing costs with the Tucson Metropolitan Ministry.

✖ *Oregon*: $500 to $6,000 grant for closing costs, down payment, or minor repairs in their First-Time Homebuyer Program.

Free Furniture

The Community Action Agency in Albany, New York, Albany County Opportunity, Inc., offers free furniture for those with a need because of fire or other hardship reasons. Other agencies offer free furniture if you are moving into a Community Action Agency's afford-able housing or housing units operated by the agency. See if your local agency offers free furniture. There are about 1,000 of them around the country to help neighborhoods.

To find an agency near you, contact Community Action Partnership, 1100 17th St., Suite 500, Washington, DC 20036; 202-265-7546; Fax: 202-265-8850; {www.communityactionpartnership.com/ default.asp}; {www.acoi.com}.

✖ *Missouri*: Move into a home with only $750 through Down Payment Assistance for Homebuyers.

✖ *Canton, OH*: Renters can apply for $5,000 loan for first time home buyers that's forgiven after 5 years through the Down Payment Assistance Program.

✖ *South Carolina*: Loans for SINGLE PARENTS for a down payment and closing costs in their Single Parent Program.

NEW HOME HELP

Here's a listing of programs we found that were available at the time we were doing research. Don't forget to contact state and local housing agencies to see what may be available for you.

Nashville Housing Fund
305 11th Ave., S
Nashville, TN 37203
615-780-7016
www.nashvillehousingfund.org

Washington County
Department of Housing Services
111 NE Lincoln St.
Suite 200-L, MS 63
Hillsboro, OR 97124-3072
503-846-4794
www.co.washington.or.us/deptmts/
hse_serv/housmain.htm

Indianapolis Neighborhood Housing Partnership
3550 N. Washington Blvd.
Indianapolis, IN 46205
317-925-1400
www.inhp.org

Department of Community Affairs
60 Executive Park South, N.E.
Atlanta, GA 30329
404-679-4940
www.dca.state.ga.us

State of New York Mortgage Agency
641 Lexington Ave.
New York, NY 10022
800-382-HOME
212-688-4000
www.nyhomes.org/sony/sonyma.html

Housing Hotline
Division of Housing
Kansas Department of Commerce and Housing

1000 SW Jackson St., Suite 100
Topeka, KS 66612-0481
785-296-5865
http://kdoch.state.ks.us/ProgramApp/index_mm.jsp

Homes For Houston
P.O. Box 1562
Houston, TX 77251-1562
713-868-8300
www.ci.houston.tx.us/departme/housing/

Iowa Finance Authority
100 E. Grand Ave., Suite 250
Des Moines, IA 50309
515-242-4990
800-432-7230
www.ifahome.com

Minncsota Housing Finance Agency
400 Sibley St., Suite 300
St. Paul, MN 55101
800-657-3769
651-296-7608
www.mhfa.state.mn.us

Missouri Housing Development Commission
3435 Broadway
Kansas City, MO 64111-2459
816-759-6600
www.mhdc.com

Office of Community Development
P.O. Box 1471
Baton Rouge, LA 70821
225-389-3039
http://brgov.com/dept/ocd/
Housing/housing.htm

New Hampshire Housing Finance Authority
32 Constitution Dr.
Bedford, NH 03110
P.O. Box 5087
Manchester, NH 03108
800-640-7239
603-472-8623
www.nhhfa.org

Oregon Housing and Community Services
725 NE Summer St., Ste B
Salem, OR 97301
503-986-2000
www.hcs.state.or.us

Maine State Housing Authority
353 Water St.
Augusta, ME 04330-4633
207-626-4600
800-452-4668
www.mainehousing.org

Community Development Department
1666 N. Main St.
Walnut Creek, CA 94596
925-943-5800
www.ci.walnut-creek.ca.us

South Carolina State Housing Finance and
Development Authority
919 Bluff Rd.
Columbia, SC 29201
803-734-2000
www.sha.state.sc.us

Housing and Community Development Corporation
677 Queen St., Suite 300
Honolulu, HI 96813
808-587-0641
www.hcdch.state.hi.us

MONEY FOR YOUR TRAVELS

If your dream is to become an international jet setter, don't let a little problem like money stand in your way. The Federal government has over 60 programs devoted to travel within the U.S. and abroad, spending over 65 million dollars a year to send you packing. They will even pay to have foreign relatives come and study here. No matter if you are 16 or 65, there is something in these programs for everyone.

You can be like:

- Ryan Louis from California, a Fulbright fellow who conducted research in biochemistry in Japan.
- Mark Door, who conducted workshops in criminal law in Tirana, Albania.
- AmeriCorps members that restored a polluted swamp into a natural lake.
- Laura DeLuca herded cattle and worked on crops in Tanzania.
- Rudolph Ware, who studied Lived Histories of Islamic Education and the State in Senegal.
- Laurel Anderson, who cut marks as evidence of pre-Columbia human sacrifice and postmortem bone modification on the North Coast of Peru.
- Dwayne Ball, who spent 10 weeks in Portugal lecturing.
- An American Fulbrighter, who studied molecular biology in Morocco.
- Cowboy artists from the Western Folklife Center of Elko, NV who shared their lore at a festival in Melbourne, Australia with a grant from the National Endowment for the Arts.
- Nancy Friese of Cranston, RI who went to Japan for six months to explore relationships between natural and man-made environments in Japanese landscape gardens through the United States/Japan Artist Exchange Program at the Japan/US Friendship Commission.
- Carl A. Chase, a steel drum maker and tuner from Brooksville, MA who was able to visit Trinidad and Tobago for a residency with one of the islands' foremost steel drum makers through the Travel Grants Program at the National Endowment for the Arts.
- William Ulfelder who spent a year studying the rain forest in Costa Rica as a Fulbright Scholar.
- A police officer from Los Angeles who helped in the creation of D.A.R.E. (Drug Awareness Resistance Education) in several Latin American countries through the U. S. Thematic Programs.
- Piano/violin duo Susan Keith and Laura Kobayashi who toured Latin America and the Caribbean together as Artistic Ambassadors for the U.S. Information Agency.
- Tamara Astor from Northfield, IL who spent a year teaching grades 1-3 in London, England through the Fulbright Teacher Exchange Program at the U.S. Information Agency.
- Central Washington University who sent thirteen K-12 teachers from the state of Washington to Chile for a four-week seminar on the country through the Fulbright-Hays Group Projects Abroad through the U.S. Department of Education.
- Columbia University in New York City acting as the host of seven different humanities seminars for college teachers with grants from the National Endowment for the Humanities.
- Maria Marotti from Santa Barbara, CA who was awarded a $3,000 grant from the National Endowment for the Humanities to study Italian feminism.

Now don't forget to read the first part of this book, "Types of Assistance and Grants Sources," as well as "More Help In Finding a Grant." These sections provide some great starting places for your money hunt. Many of the programs listed below were taken from the *Catalog of Federal Domestic Assistance*. When you see a five digit number like 10.078 after a program title, that refers to the program number in the Catalog. Most libraries have a copy of the Catalog that lists every program the Federal government offers. You can also search the Catalog by number or keyword at {www.cfda.gov}.

Don't forget that you vote for your Senator and your Representative. They want you to vote for them again, so they will do whatever they can to assist you in your cause. You can contact their local office, again by looking in the blue pages of your phone book, or Your Senator, The Senate, Washington, DC 20510; 202-224-3121; {www.senate.gov}; or your Representative, The United States House of Representatives, Washington, DC 20515; 202-224-3121; {www.house.gov}. The federal government has even created a special website called U.S. Consumer Gateway at {www.consumer.gov} that provides links to information by type, topic, current issues, hotlinks, and more. This is a great resource for gathering contacts.

Happy hunting!

High School Students And Teachers Can Visit Russia

(Secondary School Partnership Program)
Youth Programs Division
Office of Citizen Exchanges
Bureau of Educational and Cultural Affairs
301 4th St., SW, Room 568
Washington, DC 20547
202-619-6299
Fax: 202-619-5311
http://exchanges.state.gov/education/citizens/students
The program objective is to sponsor the exchange of high school students and teachers between the U.S. and the former Soviet Union through grants to private not-for-profit organizations and public institutions. Grants are awarded to fund projects in two program areas: academic year in the U.S., and short-term exchanges of groups of students and teachers between linked schools. The total amount of money available is $15 million. Contact the office listed above for information on organizations to which you need to apply or for more information on the programs available.

Spend A Year In Europe On A Mid-Career Break

(Hubert Humphrey Fellowship)
Hubert H. Humphrey Fellowship Program
Humphrey Fellowships and Institutional Linkages
Branch (ECA/A/S/U)
Institute of International Education
U.S. Department of State
SA-44, 301 4th Street, SW
Washington, DC 20547
202-619-5289
202-326-7701
Fax: 202-326-7702

http://exchanges.state.gov/education/hhh
www.iie.org/template.cfm?&Template=/programs/hhh/default.htm
The program provides opportunities for accomplished mid-career professionals from designated countries of Africa, Asia, Latin America, the Caribbean, the Middle East, and Eurasia, to come to the United States for a year of study and related practical professional experiences. The program provides a basis for establishing lasting ties between citizens of the United States and their professional counterparts in other countries, fostering an exchange of knowledge and mutual understanding throughout the world. Fellows are placed in groups at selected U.S. universities and design individualized programs of academic coursework and professional development activities. The total amount of money available is $5 million. Applications must be submitted in the candidates' home countries to the United States Embassy, Public Affairs Section or Fulbright Commissions. Applicants must have an under-graduate degree, five years of substantial professional experience, demonstrated leadership qualities, and fluency in English. Contact the office listed above for more information on the application process.

Money For Artists, Filmmakers, Playwrights, And Museum Professionals To Go Overseas

(Creative Arts Exchange Program)
Cultural Programs Division
Bureau of Educational and Cultural Affairs
U.S. Department of State
SA-44
301 4th St., SW, Room 568
Washington, DC 20547

202-619-4779
Fax: 202-619-6315
http://exchanges.state.gov/education/citizens/culture
The program supports
projects by U.S.
nonprofit
organizations for
exchanges of
professionals in the
arts and museum
fields. Priority is given
to institutionally-based
projects involving
artists in the creation

of their particular art forms and projects which will
lead to institutional linkages. Two way exchanges are
encouraged and cost sharing is required. This
exchange program is designed to introduce American
and foreign participants to each other's cultural and
artistic life and traditions. It also supports
international projects in the United States or overseas
involving composers, choreographers, filmmakers,
playwrights, theater designers, writers and poets,
visual artists, museum professionals, and more. The
program operates through biannual Federal Register
requests for proposals. For more information on the
application process and program eligibility, contact
the office listed above.

Money For Students, Teachers, Bankers, Lawyers, And Journalists To Travel Overseas

(Fulbright Scholar Program)
Council for International Exchange of Scholars
3007 Tilden St., NW, Suite 5L
Washington, DC 20008-3009
202-686-4000
Fax: 202-362-3442
www.iie.org/cies
The program provides grants to U.S. students, teachers, and scholars to study, teach, lecture, and conduct
research overseas, and to foreign nationals to engage
in similar activities in the United States to increase
mutual understanding and peaceful relations between
the people of the United States and the people of
other countries. Fields of study and subjects taught
include the arts and humanities, social sciences, and
physical sciences. In addition to the exchange of
students and scholars, the program includes
professional exchanges in journalism, law,
management, banking, and public administration.
Participants take part in degree programs, nondegree
and self-study courses, internships, and professional

seminars. The total amount of money available is
$119 million. Contact the office listed above for
application information.

Money For English, Law, And Journalism Professionals To Go Abroad

(Professional Exchanges)
Office of Citizen Exchanges
Bureau of Educational and Cultural Affairs
U.S. Department of State
SA-44
301 4th St., SW
Washington, DC 20547
202-619-5348
Fax: 202-619-4350
http://exchanges.state.gov/education/citizens/
professl/
This program sends Americans overseas to aid
foreign institutions seeking professional assistance in
such academic disciplines as English teaching, law,
and journalism. Experts on the United States can
consult with academic and professionals at foreign
educational or other relevant institutions about special
issues, or to conduct seminars/workshops for
professional personnel. The total amount of money
available is $2 million. Contact the office listed above
for guidelines and application information.

Foreign High School Teachers Can Spend Six Weeks In The U.S.

(Fulbright American Studies Institutes — Study Of
The United States)
Study of the U.S. Branch
U.S. Department of State, SA-44
301 4th St., SW, Room 252
Washington, DC 20547
202-619-4557
Fax: 202-619-6790
http://exchanges.state.gov/education/amstudy/fasi.htm
This program provides grants to foreign secondary
and postsecondary school educators for a 4 to 6 week
program of academic workshops in U.S. history,
culture, and institutions to enhance and update the
content of what is taught about the United States
abroad. The total amount of money available is $2.2
million. Contact the office listed above for guidelines
and application information.

Exchange Program For English Teachers

(English Language Specialist Program)
Office of English Language Programs
U.S. Department of State

Annex #44
301 4th St., SW, Room 304
Washington, DC 20547
202-619-5869
Fax: 202-401-1250
http://exchanges.state.gov/education/engteaching
The program promotes the study and teaching of
English abroad, in host country institutions, and
through American educational and binational centers
in 41 countries. TEFL/TESL English teaching
programs concentrate on training teachers through
seminars, exchanges of foreign and American English
specialists, and the development and distribution of
curricula and materials for teaching the English
language and American culture. The total amount of
money available is $341,500. Contact the office listed
above for application information.

Teach School Overseas

(Dependent Schools)
U.S. Department of Defense
Teacher Recruitment Section
4040 N. Fairfax Dr.
Arlington, VA 22203-1635
703-696-3067
Fax: 703-696-2699
www.odedodea.edu
The U.S. Department of Defense is responsible for
providing schooling to dependent children of military
personnel. There are employment positions for
elementary and secondary teachers, as well as those that
can provide support services. The schools are located in
14 countries around the world, with an enrollment of
approximately 102,600 students, and are staffed with
about 8,785 teachers. Contact the office listed above for
an application and program information.

Volunteer In The U.S.

(Corporation for National and Community Service
AMERICORPS - 94.006)
Corporation for National and Community Service
1201 New York Ave., NW
Washington, DC 20525
800-942-2677
202-606-5000
www.cns.gov
The objective of this program is to supplement efforts of
private, nonprofit organizations and federal, state, and
local government agencies to eliminate poverty and
poverty-related problems by enabling persons from all
walks of life and all age groups to perform meaningful
and constructive service as volunteers throughout the

U.S. AmeriCorps volunteers receive a modest
subsistence allowance, an end-of-service stipend, health
insurance, and money for college. The total amount of
money available is $284,000,000. Applications are
available through AmeriCorps State Offices or contact
the office listed above for additional information.

$45,000 To Study Farming Internationally

(Scientific Cooperation and Research — 10.961)
U.S. Department of Agriculture
International Collaborative Research Program
USDA/FAS/ICD/RSED
Ag Box 4314
Room 3230 South Building
1400 Independence Ave., SW, STOP 1084
Washington, DC 20250-1084
202-720-0618
www.fas.usda.gov/
This program
enables American
scientists to work
with foreign
researchers to help
solve critical
problems that are
affecting the food
systems, agriculture, fisheries, forestry and the
environment in the U.S. and the collaborating
country. Contact the office listed above for an
application form. U.S. researchers from USDA
agencies, universities, and private nonprofit
agricultural research institutions are eligible. A
maximum of $45,000 is available for each 3-year
research project.

Your Friends In The Ukraine Can Come To The U.S. To Learn Free Enterprise

(Special American Business Internship Training
Program (SABIT) 11.114)
U.S. Department of Commerce
Special American Business Internship Training
Program
1401 Constitution Ave., NW
FCB-4th Floor-4100 W
Washington, DC 20230
202-482-0073
www.mac.doc.gov/sabit/index.html
This program awards internships in U.S. firms to
business managers and scientific workers from the
independent states of the former Soviet Union.
SABIT provides the intern with a hands-on training
program in the business skills necessary to operate in

a market economy. A counselor is provided to help with cultural adjustments. Companies provide medical insurance, housing, and any other living expenses beyond those covered by the daily stipend provided by the U.S. The amount of money available varies, but averages $18,000. Apply to the program through the U.S. Department of Commerce which considers applications through a competitive process. A SABIT fact sheet is also available.

Money For Students And Teachers To Travel Together Overseas

(International: Overseas Group Projects Abroad-84.021)
International Studies Team
International Education and Grants Programs Service
Office of Postsecondary Education
U.S. Department of Education
1990 K Street, NW, 6th Floor
Washington, DC 20006-8521
202-502-7700
Fax: 202-502-7859
www.ed.gov/HEP/iegps/fr
This program is designed to contribute to the development and improvement of the study of modern foreign languages and area studies in the United States, and provide opportunities for American teachers, advanced students, and faculty to study in foreign countries. Grants allow groups to conduct overseas group projects in research, training, and curriculum development. Money can be used for international travel, maintenance allowances, rent of instructional materials in the country of study, and more. The total amount of money available is $4,415,000. Contact the office listed above for application information.

Finish Your Doctorate Research Abroad

(Fulbright-Hays Doctoral Dissertation Research Abroad - 84.022)
Higher Education Programs
U.S. Department of Education
1990 K St., NW, 6th Floor
Washington, DC 20006
202-502-7700
www.ed.gov/HEP/iegps
This program is designed to provide opportunities for graduate students to engage in full-time dissertation research abroad in modern foreign language and area studies with the exception of Western Europe. This program is designed to develop research knowledge and capability in world areas not widely included in

American curricula. Money can be used for a basic stipend, round trip air fare, baggage allowance, tuition payments, local travel, and more. The total amount of money available is $4.5 million. Candidates apply directly to the institutions at which they are enrolled in a Ph.D. program.

Money For College Teachers To Do Research Overseas

(Fulbright-Hays Faculty Research Abroad - 84.019)
Higher Education Programs
U.S. Department of Education
1990 K St., NW, 6th Floor
Washington, DC 20006
202-502-7700
www.ed.gov/HEP/iegps
This program is designed to help develop modern foreign language and area studies in U.S. higher educational institutions. This program enables faculty members to maintain expertise in specialized fields through support of research in the non-Western areas of the world. Fellowships of 3 to 12 months are available. The total amount of money available is $1,575,000. Candidates should apply directly to their institution. More information is available on this program through the office listed above.

Money For Teachers To Take A Sabbatical Overseas

(Fulbright-Hays Seminars Abroad - 84.018)
Higher Education Programs
U.S. Department of Education
400 Maryland Ave., SW
Washington, DC 20202
800-USA-LEARN
www.ed.gov/
This program is designed to improve understanding and knowledge of people and culture of a different country. There are 7 to 10 seminars that last 4 to 6 weeks held in countries outside of Western Europe. Eligible persons are teachers in social sciences and humanities,

administrators, and curriculum specialists of state and local education agencies, college faculty, librarians and museum teachers who are primarily responsible for teaching undergraduates in the social sciences, humanities, and area studies. The total amount of money available is $2,200,000. Contact the office listed above for application information, as well as a listing of the seminars available.

Grants To College Teachers Who Want To Create Programs In International Business
(Business And International Education - 84.153)
Higher Education Programs
U.S. Department of Education
1990 K St., NW, 6th Floor
Washington, DC 20006
202-502-7700
www.ed.gov/HEP/iegps
This program is designed to promote innovation and improvement in international business education curricula at institutions of higher education and promote linkages between these institutions and the business community. Institutions must enter into an agreement with a business enterprise, trade organization, or association engaged in international economic activity, or a combination or consortium of the named entities. The total amount of money available is $4,620,000. Contact the office listed above for application information.

Conduct Cancer Research In A Different Country
(Short-Term Scientist Exchange Program)
National Cancer Institute
Office of International Affairs
6130 Executive Boulevard, Suite 100
Bethesda, MD 20892-7301
301-496-4761
www.cancer.gov/about_nci/oia
This program is designed to promote collaborative research between established U.S. and foreign scientists

by supporting exchange visits to each country's laboratories. Visits may last from one week to six months time. Candidates must have at least three years postdoctoral experience in cancer research and an invitation from a qualified sponsor. Contact the office listed above for application forms including instructions and other requirements.

Visit The U.S. To Do Health Research
(NIH Visiting Program)
International Services Branch
Office of Research Services
National Institutes of Health (NIH)
13 South Dr., MSC 5774
Bethesda, MD 20892-5774
301-496-6166
www.nih.gov/od/ors/dirs/isb/isb.htm
This program provides talented scientists throughout the world with the opportunity to participate in the varied research activities of the National Institutes of Health. There are two categories of Visiting Program participants: Visiting Fellows and Visiting Scientists. Each participant works closely with a senior NIH investigator who serves as supervisor or sponsor during the period of award or appointment. The Visiting Fellow award is for obtaining research training experience. Fellows must have a doctoral degree, not more than 3 years of relevant postdoctoral research experience, and cannot be U.S. citizens. Visiting Scientists are appointed to conduct health-related research and are considered employees of NIH, and receive a salary and benefits. Individuals interested in a Visiting Program fellowship award or appointment should write to NIH senior scientists working in the same research field, enclosing a resume and brief description of his/her particular research area. Information about the research being conducted by NIH scientists and their names may be obtained from the NIH's Scientific Directory and Annual Bibliography, which can be obtained from the office listed above.

New U.S. Researchers Can Continue Research In Developing Countries
(International Research Scientist Development Award-IRSDA)
International Research Scientists Development Award
Fogarty International Center
Division of International Training and Research
National Institutes of Health
Building 31, Room B2C39
31 Center Drive, MSC 2220
Bethesda, MD 20892-2220

301-496-8733
Fax: 301-402-0779
www.fic.nih.gov/programs/irsda.html
This program provides opportunities for foreign
postdoctoral biomedical or behavioral scientists who are
in the formative stages of their career to extend their
research experience in a laboratory in the United States.
The total amount of money available is $4.4 million. To
learn more about the requirements and application
process, contact the office listed above.

Conduct Medical Research With Foreign Scientists

(Fogarty International Research Collaboration
Award)
Division of International Research and Training
Fogarty International Center
Building 31, Room B2C39
31 Center Drive, MSC 2220
Bethesda, MD 20892-2220
301-496-1653
Fax: 301-402-0779
www.fic.nih.gov/programs/firca.html
This program provides for collaborative research
between U.S. biomedical scientists and investigators in
foreign countries. These awards are made for research
projects that, for the most part, will be carried out at the
foreign research site. Its purpose is to promote discovery
and reduce global health disparities. The foreign
countries involved are Africa, Asia, Latin America, the
Caribbean Region, the Former Soviet Union, and Central
and Eastern Europe. Information and application
instructions are available from the office listed above.

Research Internationally

(International Training and Research Program in
Emerging Infectious Diseases-ITREID)
Division of International Training and Research
Fogarty International Center
National Institutes of Health
Building 31, Room B2C39
31 Center Drive, MSC 2220
Bethesda, MD 20892-2220
301-496-7614
Fax: 301-402-0779
www.fic.nih.gov/programs/erid.html
This program provides the opportunity for research and
training needs in emerging and re-emerging infectious
diseases in developing countries. ITREID is designed to,
among other things, train laboratory scientists and public
health workers in developing countries and the U.S. in
research, control and prevention strategies, and their
implementation and evaluation related to these diseases.
For a list of program directors, refer to the address above.

Money To Study In Japan

Japan-U.S. Friendship Commission
1110 Vermont Ave., NW, Suite 800
Washington, DC 20005
202-418-9800
Fax: 202-418-9802
www.jusfc.gov/commissn/commissn.html
This program provides grants to institutions and
associations to support American studies in Japan,
Japanese studies in the United States,
exchange programs in the arts,
policy-oriented research, and
public affairs, and education.
In addition, the Commission is
interested in sponsoring research on
Japan-US economic relations and
activities in Asia, with priority given to
Japanese investment in Asia and its
effect on Japan-US economic, trade
and political relations. The total
amount of money available is
$8.6 million. Contact the
office listed above for more
information about the various
grant programs, as well as a
biennial report which lists previous
grants recipients and their projects.

Go To Japan For 6 Months

(United States/Japan Creative Artists' Program)
Japan-U.S. Friendship Commission
1110 Vermont Ave., NW, Suite 800
Washington, DC 20005
202-418-9800
Fax: 202-418-9802
www.jusfc.gov/commissn/commissn.html
The program is designed to allow artists who create
original work to pursue their individual artistic goals and
interests by living in Japan for six months, observing
developments in their field, and meeting with their
professional counterparts in Japan. The total amount of
money available is $200,000. Contact the office listed
above for guidelines and an application packet.

Money For Artists To Work With the Newly Independent States

(Artslink)
CEC International Partners
12 West 31st St., Suite 400
New York, NY 10001-4415
212-643-1985
Fax: 212-643-1996
http://godai.comset.net/cecip
Artslink encourages artistic exchange with the newly
independent states in Central and Eastern Europe, the
former Soviet Union, and Eurasia by offering three
categories of support: Artslink Projects, which provides
funding to U.S. artists to work on mutually beneficial
projects with counterparts abroad; Artslink Residencies,
which supports U.S. arts organizations wishing to host a
visiting artist or arts manager for a five-week residency;
and Independent Projects, where artists and art managers
can work on projects in the U.S. The total amount of
money available varies. Contact the office listed above
for guidelines and an application packet.

Artists Can Travel To Improve Their Art

(Fund for U.S. Artists at International Festivals and
Exhibitions)
Cultural Programs Division
Bureau of Educational and Cultural Affairs
U.S. Department of State
SA-44, 301 4th St., SW, Room 568
Washington, DC 20547
202-619-4779
Fax: 202-619-6315
http://exchanges.state.gov/education/citizens/culture/p
erffest.htm
Arts International, Inc.

251 Park Ave. S, 5th Flr.
New York, NY 10010
212-674-9744
Fax: 212-674-9092
www.artsinternational.org
This program is designed to enable U.S. artists to
pursue opportunities abroad that further their artistic
development. Grant decisions will be based on artistic
excellence, the applicant's reasons for wanting to travel
to a particular country, as well as his or her sensitivity
to the culture and country to which he or she wants to
travel. The grants will support artists pursuing a wide
variety of activities abroad including the development
or expansion of relationships with artists and arts
organizations and the exploration of significant
developments in their field. The total amount of money
available is $100,000. Contact the office listed above
for guidelines and an application packet.

Summer Seminars For Teachers

(Promotion of the Humanities – Seminars and
Institutes – 45.161)
Summer Seminars and Institutes Programs
Division of Education Programs
National Endowment for the Humanities
1100 Pennsylvania Ave., NW, Room 302
Washington, DC 20506
202-606-8446
www.neh.gov/grants/guidelines/seminars.html
Email: info@neh.gov
School teachers, college and university teachers, along
with selected foreign secondary teachers, can engage
in intensive study of basic humanities texts and
documents and work closely with outstanding
scholars for 2 to 6 weeks at colleges, universities, and
other appropriate sites, some of which may be located
in a foreign country. Contact the office listed above
for a list of seminar offerings, as well as an
application packet.

Money For Teachers To Study

(Promotion of the Humanities – Fellowships and
Stipends - 45.160)
Fellowships and Stipends
Division of Research
National Endowment for the Humanities
1100 Pennsylvania Ave., NW, Room 318
Washington, DC 20506
202-606-8200
Fax: 202-606-8204
www.neh.gov/grants/guidelines/stipends.html
Email: stipends@neh.gov

Grants provide support for college and university teachers; individuals employed by schools, museums, libraries, etc.; and others to undertake full-time independent study and research in the humanities for two consecutive summer months. Recipients must work full-time on their projects during the two-month period. Contact the office listed above for guidelines and an application packet.

$40,000 To Study And Conduct Research

(Fellowship Programs at Independent Research Institutions)
Division of Research Programs
National Endowment for the Humanities
1100 Pennsylvania Ave., NW, Room 318
Washington, DC 20506
202-606-8200
Fax: 202-606-8204
www.neh.gov/grants/guidelines/fpiri.html
Email: fpiri@neh.gov
Grants provide support for fellowship programs for post doctorates and independent scholars. It is administered by one of two groups: Independent centers for advanced studies, libraries, and museums in the U.S., or American overseas research centers and other organizations that have expertise in promoting research on foreign cultures. Programs that provide long-term fellowships, four months or longer, are given priority. Individuals looking to pursue research at the centers should apply directly to that center. The maximum amount of the stipend is $40,000.

Become A Humanities Fellow

(Fellowships)
Division of Research Programs
National Endowment for the Humanities
1100 Pennsylvania Ave., NW, Room 318
Washington, DC 20506
202-606-8200
Fax: 202-606-8204
www.neh.gov/grants/guidelines/fellowships.html
Email: fellowships@neh.gov
Grants support postdoctoral fellowship programs at independent centers for advanced study which offer scholars opportunities to pursue independent research in the humanities while benefiting from collegial association with scholars in other areas or disciplines of study. Fellowships in this program are awarded and administered by the centers themselves. Tenure of the fellowships may run from six to twelve consecutive months, and stipends vary at the different centers.

Eligibility also varies from center to center, but neither candidates for degrees nor persons seeking support for work toward degrees are eligible to apply. Contact the office listed above for more information on theses programs, as well as a list of centers which accept applications.

Scientific Collaboration

(International Opportunities for Scientists and Engineers)
International Programs Division
National Science Foundation
4201 Wilson Blvd., Ste. 935
Arlington, VA 22230
703-292-5111
www.nsf.gov/sbe/int
Email: info@nsf.gov
This program is designed to advance and benefit U.S. interests by enabling U.S. scientists and engineers to avail themselves of research opportunities in other countries. The Division of International Programs supports efforts to initiate international cooperation involving new foreign collaborators, or new types of activities with established partners. Contact the office listed above for guidelines and application information.

Research In The Tropics

(Short-Term Fellowships)
Office of Fellowships
Smithsonian Tropical Research Institute
750 9th St. NW, Suite 9300
Washington, DC 20560-0902
202-275-0655
Fax: 202-275-0489
www.si.edu/ofg
Email: siofg@si.edu
The objective of this program is to enable selected candidates to work in the tropics and explore research possibilities at the Smithsonian Tropical Research Institute. Fellowships are primarily for graduate students, but awards are made occasionally to undergraduate and postdoctoral candidates. Contact the office listed above for guidelines and application procedures.

Teachers Can Study Abroad

(Fulbright Teacher and Administrator Exchange
Program)
Fulbright Teacher and Administrator Exchange
Program
ATTN: NSL
600 Maryland Ave., SW, Suite 320
Washington, DC 20024-2520
202-314-3520
800-726-0479
Fax: 202-479-6806
www.fulbrightexchanges.org
The program is designed to promote mutual understanding between citizens of the United States and
other countries through educational and cultural
exchanges. It is open to teachers and administrators from
the elementary through the postsecondary levels,
allowing for classroom-to-classroom exchange of
teaching positions between U.S. teachers and counterpart
teachers from selected countries worldwide. Exchange
grants may include full or partial travel grants and cost of
living supplements, depending on the country. The total
amount of money available is $527,000. Contact the
office listed above for guidelines and an application
packet.

Money To Attend Workshops Overseas

(Citizens Exchanges)
Office of Citizen Exchanges
Bureau of Educational and Cultural Affairs
U.S. Department of State
SA-44
301 4th St., SW
Washington, DC 20547
202-619-5348
Fax: 202-619-4350
http://exchanges.state.gov/education/citizens
This program awards grants to U.S. nonprofit
organizations for projects that link their international
exchange interests with counterpart institutions/groups in
other countries. Subject areas include environmental
protection, trade unionism, education administration and
curriculum reform, protection, small business

development and management training, and more.
Programs are normally multi-phase and extend over
more than one fiscal year. Programs usually consist of
sending American specialists on 2–3 week visits to a
country for workshops and meetings, followed by a visit
to the U.S. by foreign counterparts. The total amount of
money available is $2 million. The Office of Citizen
Exchanges develops a series of Requests for Grant
Proposals (RFGPs) during the course of the fiscal
year. Specific application and review guidelines are
available upon written request to the office listed
above. RFGPs are also published in the Federal
Register.

Spend Six Weeks In A Foreign Country Working With Art Colleagues

(American Cultural Specialists)
Cultural Programs Division
Bureau of Educational and Cultural Affairs
U.S. Department of State
SA-44
301 4th St., SW
Washington, DC 20547
202-619-4779
Fax: 202-619-6315
http://exchanges.state.gov/education/citizens
This is not a grant program from which individuals can
request financial assistance for overseas projects, but as
a response to a specific request from embassies abroad.
Participants in this program spend two to six weeks in
one country working with foreign colleagues. Among
other activities, they may conduct workshops or master
classes, direct a play, rehearse a ballet, or advise on arts
management. Specialists are provided with economy
international travel and an honorarium of $200 per
day plus limited allowances for educational and
miscellaneous expenses by the Department of State. The
U.S. embassy and/or the local co-sponsor provide per
diem domestic travel and all local program costs. The
total amount of money available is $380,000. To learn
more on how to have your resume reviewed so your
name can be placed on the Cultural Specialist roster,
contact the office listed above.

Eight Week Foreign Tours For Jazz Musicians

(Jazz Ambassador Program)
Cultural Programs Division
Bureau of Educational and Cultural Affairs
U.S. Department of State/Kennedy Center-Jazz
Ambassadors
2700 F Street NW
Washington, DC 20566

202-619-4779
Fax: 202-619-6315
http://exchanges.state.gov/education/citizens/culture
This program is designed to use the wealth of often undiscovered musical talent in the U.S. to enhance the mission of promoting cross-cultural understanding. Jazz Ambassadors travel to four or five countries for a period of four to eight weeks. In addition to public performances, they may conduct workshops and master classes. The total amount of money available is $169,000. Nominations of classical musicians in various categories are sought from music schools, conservatories, colleges and universities throughout the U.S. Artistic Ambassadors may not be under management and are selected through live auditions on the basis of their musical ability and suitability as "goodwill ambassadors." To learn more about the application process, contact the office listed above.

Foreign Leaders Can Study In The U.S.

(International Visitors Program – 19.402)
Office of International Visitors
U.S. Department of State
301 4th St., SW, Room 255
ECA/PE/V
Washington, DC 20547
866-283-9090
202-619-5217
Fax: 202-619-4655
http://exchanges.state.gov/education/ivp
This office arranges programs for foreign leaders and potential leaders designed to develop and foster professional contacts with their colleagues in the United States and provide a broader exposure to American social, cultural, and political institutions. Areas of expertise government, politics, media, education, science, labor relations, the arts, and other fields. The total amount of money available is $10,800,000. Participants are nominated by U.S. embassies. For more information on the program contact the office listed above.

Do Your Part To Help The World

(Peace Corps)
Peace Corps
1111 20th St., NW
Washington, DC 20526
800-424-8580
202-692-2000
www.peacecorps.gov
The program objective is to promote world peace and friendship, to help other countries in meeting their needs for trained manpower, and to help promote understanding

between the American people and other peoples served by the Peace Corps. Volunteers serve for a period of 2 years, living among the people with whom they work. Volunteers are expected to become a part of the community and to demonstrate, through their voluntary service, that people can be an important impetus for change. Volunteers receive a stipend and health insurance. Contact the office listed above for information on how to become a Peace Corps volunteer.

Money For Engineering Students To Travel The Country Visiting DOE Laboratories

(Faculty and Student Teams Program)
Science Education Programs
Office of Science Education
U.S. Department of Energy
Washington, DC 20585
202-586-0987/7174
Fax: 202-586-0019
www.scied.science.doe.gov/scied/fast/about.html
The program objective is to provide college and university science and engineering faculty and students with energy-related training and research experience in areas of energy research at the U.S. Department of Energy research facilities. Funds can be used to conduct energy research at one  of the DOE research facilities. Students can also participate in energy-related workshops and conferences. Successful candidates receive a stipend of $900 per week for each week at the lab, as well as travel and housing expenses. Students must apply to a participating laboratory or university. Contact the office listed above for information on laboratories and universities that take part in this program.

Community College Students Can Intern at Energy Laboratories

(Community College Institutes)
Science Education Programs
Office of Science Education
U.S. Department of Energy
Washington, DC 20585
202-586-0987/7174
Fax: 202-586-0019
www.scied.science.doe.gov/scied/CCI/about.html
The objective of this program is to give community college students the opportunity to participate in hands-on research at the cutting edge of science at the Department of Energy Laboratories, and to provide

training and experience in the operation of sophisticated state-of-the-art equipment and instruments. College students who are majoring in an energy-related field can spend a semester using some of the Federal government's equipment and instruments at many of the Department of Energy's labs. The energy research must be in an area of the laboratory's ongoing research. Students receive a weekly stipend of $400, complimentary housing or a housing allowance, and a round-trip ticket to the lab. Applications may be obtained by writing to the address above.

The Military Could Be Your Ticket Overseas
(U.S. Department of Defense)
U.S. Air Force Recruiting Service
1922 Patbooker Rd.
Randolph Air Force Base, TX 78148
800-423-USAF
210-652-5993
www.airforce.com/

Commander
Naval Recruiting Command
7609-B Richmond Highway
Alexandria, VA 22306
703-325-9740
800-USA-NAVY
www.navy.com/

Commanding General
Marine Corps Recruiting Command
2 Navy Annex
Washington, DC 20380-1775
800-MARINES
www.usmc.mil/

Army Opportunities
881 Corporate Drive, Suite 203
Lexington, KY 40503
859-224-7822
800-USA-ARMY
www.goarmy.com/

U.S. Coast Guard Information Center
4200 Wilson Blvd., Suite 450
Arlington, VA 22203
877-NOW-USCG
www.uscg.mil
The Army, Navy, Marine Corps, Air Force, and the Coast Guard (part of U.S. Department of Transportation) are responsible for protecting the security of the U.S. There are 2.87 million men and women on active duty,

with over 600,000 serving outside the United States. Length of service does vary, as does pay and types of jobs available. You can even earn the chance to go to college. The military has bases all around the country and the world, and your local recruiter can answer all your questions about the opportunities they have to offer.

Join The Foreign Service
(Foreign Service with the Department of State)
Recruitment Branch
Employment Division
U.S. Department of State
HR/REE/REC
2401 E St., NW, Room 518-H
Washington, DC 20522
202-261-8888
www.state.gov
Professionals in the Foreign Service advance and protect the national interests and security of the United States, both overseas and at home. Foreign Service Officers are generalists who perform administrative, consular, economic and political functions. Foreign Service Specialists perform vital technical, support, and administrative services overseas and in the United States. You must be a U.S. citizen, between the ages of 20 and 59, a high school graduate, and be available for assignment anywhere in the world. Contact the office listed above for information and application procedures.

Thousands Of Government Jobs In Foreign Countries
(Office of Personnel Management)
Federal Job Information Center
Office of Personnel Management
1900 E St., NW
Washington, DC 20415
202-606-1800
www.usajobs.opm.gov
The Federal government hires personnel to do everything from typing to spying, and there are posts all around the world. Those interested in jobs overseas can contact the Office of Personnel Management to  learn current job openings and the skills required. Other government agencies also hire for jobs abroad, and you could contact them directly for information on employment opportunities. Contact the office listed above for more information. Other agencies that hire for overseas employment include:

Agency For International Development
Recruitment Division
Ronald Reagan Building
Washington, DC 20523-1000
202-712-4810
www.usaid.gov

U.S. Customs Service
1300 Pennsylvania Avenue, NW
Washington, DC 20229
202-927-1250
www.customs.treas.gov

Central Intelligence Agency
Office of Personnel
Washington, DC 20505
703-482-1100
Fax: 703-613-8165
www.cia.gov

U.S. Department of Commerce
Human Resources Management Office
U.S. and Foreign Commercial Service
1401 Constitution Ave., NW
Room 3227
Washington, DC 20230
202-482-4938
Fax: 202-482-1629
www.commerce.gov

U.S. Department of Agriculture
Foreign Agricultural Service
Personnel Division
1400 Independence Ave., SW
Washington, DC 20250
703-812-6339
www.fas.usda.gov

Sell Your Goods Overseas
(U.S. Department of Commerce)
Trade Information Center
U.S. Department of Commerce
Washington, DC 20230
800-USA-TRADE
www.trade.gov/td/tic
The Trade Information Center is a comprehensive "one-stop-shop" for information on U.S. government programs and activities that support exporting efforts. This hotline is staffed by trade specialists who can provide information on seminars and conferences, overseas buyers and representatives, overseas events, export financing, technical assistance, and export

counseling. They also have access to the National Trade Data Bank. They offer trade missions to help you find local agents, representatives, distributors, or direct sales. Their Trade Shows promote U.S. products with high export potential. The Agent/Distributor Service will locate, screen, and assess agents, distributors, representatives, and other foreign partners for your business. Matchmaker Trade Delegations prescreen prospects interested in your product and assist with meetings. If you cannot afford the cost of traveling overseas, the Trade Information Center can refer you to several programs that offer loans to help you start exporting. You can also receive assistance from your own state's Department of Economic Development. Contact the office listed above for more information on exporting in general, and for more specific information on your product or service.

Work On Assignment for U.S. Embassies
(English Language Specialist Program)
Office of English Language Programs
U.S. Department of State, Annex #44
301 4th Street, SW, Room 304
Washington, DC 20547
202-619-5869
Fax: 202-401-1250
http://exchanges.state.gov/education/engteaching/speciali
sts.htm
This program recruits American academics in the fields of TEF:/TES: and Applied Linguistics to complete assignments needed by overseas American Embassies. These assignments may include curriculum projects, for Specific Purposes and program evaluation. If a candidate is not specified by the Embassy, one will be recruited by the Office of English Language Programs. Eligible Specialists will hold a MA or Ph.D., and have overseas and teacher training experience. Benefits include an honorarium of $200 per day, round-trip airfare, materials allowance, and basic health insurance. To find out how to become a Specialist, contact the office above.

FREE SCHOLARSHIPS

Organizations are continuously initiating, ending or changing scholarship programs. We have attempted to gather information on some scholarships available, but because of the perpetual changes you will want to check directly with the organization for details and the most up-to-date information. When possible, we have included the website of the organization offering the scholarship for your convenience.

Using the Internet!

Half the battle of scholarships is FINDING them! Thanks to the advent of the Internet, it has become increasingly easy to find scholarships and financial aid information. If you have Internet access, you will want to consider exploring the following websites first. All allow free searches of their databases. Some allow you to "save" your search results, others automatically notify you of new or updated scholarship offerings, and some provide excellent advice on how to improve your odds of winning scholarships. To maximize your information, it is recommended to try all of them because each database offers different information and services.

FreSch! Free Scholarship Search
www.freschinfo.com

FastWeb
http://fastweb.monster.com

FastAID
www.fastaid.com

SallieMae
http://salliemae.collegeanswer.com/paying/scholarship_search/pay_scholarship_search.jsp

The Princeton Review
www.princetonreview.com

GoCollege
www.gocollege.com

The CollegeBoard
http://apps.collegeboard.com/cbsearch_ss/welcome.jsp

CollegeNet
www.collegenet.com

International Service and Travel Center
www.istc.umn.edu/

General Financial Aid Information Websites

FinAid
www.finaid.org

Financial Aid Resource Center
www.theoldschool.org/scholars.asp

Employers

If you have a job, ask your own human resources department if they offer scholarships or tuition reimbursement programs. If you are still in high school, have your parents ask their employers.

Professional or Social Organizations

Of what professional or social organizations are you or your parents members? Association for Internet Addiction? If you or your parents are a member of an organization, ask them and see if they offer any kind of scholarships. If you are NOT a member of any organizations, the next thing to check with is organizations that represent what you are planning on studying. Many such organizations offer scholarships to students who are studying what they support. For example, the American Health Information Management Association's Foundation of Research and Education offers several scholarships for those planning on making a career in health information administration and health information technology. In addition, many organizations permit non-members to apply for scholarships, but expect you to join the organization after receiving the scholarship.

Labor Unions

Are you or your parents a member of a union? All the major labor unions offer scholarships for members and their dependent children (AFL-CIO, Teamsters, etc.).

Church

Check with your church. Your local parish may or may not have any scholarships for their members, but the diocese or headquarters may have some available. And if you have been very active in your local church, they may be able to help you in other ways.

High School

If you are still in high school, it is very important that you speak with your guidance counselor or administration office and ask about scholarships that are available to students at your school.

College

If you are already attending college, or are planning on attending, the financial aid office at your college can be an excellent resource for scholarships and financial aid. You will also find applications for most of the state and federal level aid programs available at your financial aid office.

Scholarships
Full Tuition Scholarships From Microsoft

Women or minorities studying computers can receive full-tuition scholarships and will be required to complete a paid summer internship of 12 weeks or more that allow you to help develop products for Bill Gates. Contact Microsoft Scholarship Program, Microsoft Corporation, One Microsoft Way, Redmond, WA 98052; {www.microsoft.com/college/scholarships}.

$1,000 FOR MINORITIES IN SCIENCE AND ENGINEERING

Xerox Technical Minority Scholarship Program provides funding to minorities enrolled in technical science or engineering majors including computer and software engineering, and information management. Contact: Xerox Corp., 150 State St., 4th Floor, Rochester, NY 14614, Technical Minority Scholarship Program; {www.xerox.com/employment}.

WOMEN IN SCIENCE AND ENGINEERING SCHOLARSHIP

Program Intel offers a Minority Engineering Scholarship Program for undergraduates interested in computer science or engineering and a Women in Science and Engineering Scholarship Program. They also provide internships and mentors to scholarship recipients. Scholarships are only available at selected colleges and universities, and Intel does not accept applications directly from students. Students must be nominated by their school for a scholarship. For more information, contact {www.intel.com}.

Scholarships For Mature Women

The Women's Opportunity Award's intent is to assist mature women who need additional skills, training and education to upgrade their employment status in order to enter or return to the job market. Applicant should be the head of her household with financial responsibility for her dependents, indicate that specific training is necessary to enter or re-enter the job market, demonstrate financial need and be entering vocational or technical training, or be completing an undergraduate degree. Contact Women's Opportunity Award Soroptimist International of the Americas, 1709 Spruce St., Philadelphia, PA 19103-6103; 215-893-9000; Fax: 215-893-5200; {www.soroptimist.org}.

SCHOLARSHIP FOR HEALTH MAJOR

The makers of the Tylenol® Family of Products will award ten $10,000 scholarships and 150 $1,000 scholarships for higher education to students who show leadership in community and school activities. The student's intention must be to major in areas that will lead to health related fields. Contact Tylenol® Scholarship, Citizens' Scholarship Foundation of America, Inc., One Scholarship Way, P.O. Box 88, Saint Peter, MN 56082 {http://scholarship.tylenol.com/}; 800-537-4180.

Scholarships for Composers

Young composers and musicians may apply for a variety of different awards, some of which include the John Lennon Scholarship that is awarded for excellence in vocal/instrumental composition and has been established by Yoko Ono Lennon; the Annual Student Composer Awards ($500–$10,000) for which young composers of concert music may compete; and the Jerry Harrington Jazz Composition Award to encourage composition of musical theatre works.

Contact BMI Foundation, 320 West 57th Street, New York, NY 10019; 212-586-2000; Email: {info@bmifoundation.org}, {www.bmifoundation.org/home.asp}.

Scholarships Available For Family Of Fleet Reserve

This association offers various scholarships. In order to be eligible, the applicant must either be a daughter/granddaughter of Naval, Marine Corps, and Coast Guard personnel, active Fleet Reserve, Fleet Marine Corps Reserve, and Coast Guard Reserve, retired with pay or deceased. Children/grandchildren of deceased FRA members or persons who had eligibility for FRA membership at the time of death, plus children/grandchildren of members of LA FRA are also eligible for these scholarships. Awarding of scholarships is based on financial need, scholarship proficiency and character.

Contact Fleet Reserve Association, Ladies Auxiliary, LA FRA Scholarship Administrator, c/o Fleet Reserve Association, 125 N. West Street, Alexandria, VA 22314-2754; 703-683-1400; 800-FRA-1924; Email: {FRA@FRA.ORG}; {www.fra.org}.

$1,000 Scholarships For Smart Women Pursuing Science Majors

Approximately, 5–10 AWIS graduate fellowships in the amount of $1,000 are awarded to a graduate woman pursuing scientific studies. Preference is given to applicants pursuing research. Applicant must be enrolled in a Ph.D program at the time of application. If you are not a U.S. citizen, you must be enrolled at a U.S. institution. Graduate opportunities include four awards: Amy Lutz Rechel Award for plant biology students; Luise Meyer-Schutzmeister Award for women students in physics; Ruth Satter Memorial Award for women who have had to interrupt their education for 3 or more years in order to raise a family; The Diane H. Russell Award for graduate students in the biochemistry of pharmacology fields. Additionally, there are Citations of Merit given in the amount of $300.

Contact Association For Women In Science (AWIS), AWIS National Headquarters, 1200 New York Ave., NW Suite 650, Washington, DC 20005; 202-326-8940; 800-886-AWIS; Email: {awis@awis.org}; {www.awis.org}.

$1,500 Scholarships For Children Of Air Force Members

This successful program has been awarding grants since 1988. The AFAS provides $1,500 grants for undergraduate study to selected daughters and sons of active duty, retired or deceased Air Force members, stateside spouses of active duty members and surviving spouses of deceased personnel. The Society considers family income and education cost factors for its awards. Contact the AFAS for the current deadline.

Contact Air Force Aid Society (AFAS), Education Assistance Department, 1745 Jefferson Davis Hwy., Suite 202, Arlington, VA 22202; 703-607-3072; {www.afas.org}.

Up to $5,000 For Library Science Graduate Students

Each year, MLA awards up to $5,000 to qualified students to apply for the MLA Scholarship and up to $5,000 for minority students to apply for the MLA Minority Scholarship. Students must be entering or enrolled in an ALA-accredited graduate library science program. Money is also available to practicing health science librarians to help them continue professional development. Contact Medical Library Association (MLA), 65 E. Wacker Place, Suite 1900, Chicago, IL 60601; 312-419-9094 Ext. 28; Email: {info@mlahq.org}. Additional information and applications can also be found at {http://www.mlanet.org/awards/grants}.

Garden Club Awards Up To $8,000/Year

In order to stimulate knowledge of gardening and to restore, protect and improve the environment, this club offers a variety of scholarships and fellowships. Undergraduate and graduate students are eligible for awards up to $8,000/year. Each scholarship varies in its focus and student eligibility. Contact the GCA for details and deadlines. Contact The Garden Club Of America (GCA), 14 East 60th Street, New York, NY 10022; 212-753-8287, Fax: 212-753-0134; Email: {scholarship@gcamerica.org}; {www.gcamerica.org}.

Money For Physical Therapy Doctoral Students

Physical therapist doctoral students pursuing scientific and clinical research are eligible for scholarships from this organization. Awards are based on the distinct phases of education and funding may vary from year to year depending on available resources. Contact the Foundation for details and deadlines. Contact Foundation For Physical Therapy, 1111 North Fairfax Street, Alexandria, VA 22314-1488; 800-875-1378; Fax: 703-706-8519; Email: {foundation@apta.org}; {www.apta.org/foundation}.

Up To $1,500 For Federal Employees And Dependents

Civilian federal and postal employees, with a minimum of three years of federal service, and their dependent family members are eligible for scholarships from FEEA. Applicants may be high school seniors or students who are continuing their college education and have a minimum GPA of 3.0. Awards range from $300–$1,500 and are based on merit. Academic achievement, community service, a recommendation and a two-page essay are included in criteria for selection of recipients. A total of $2.75 million has been awarded in college scholarships. Contact Federal Employee Education And Assistance Fund, 8441 W. Bowles Ave., Suite 200, Littleton, CO 80123-9501; 303-933-7580; Fax: 303-933-7587; {www.feea.org}.

The American Dietetic Association Foundation Scholarhip Program

The ADAF provides scholarships to dietetics students and professionals, with more than $320,000 awarded each year. Scholarships are available for dietetic technicians and undergraduate and graduate students. Students who are participating in internships and dietetics professions who are in continuing education are also eligible for the scholarship. The number of scholarships available and the dollar amount vary from year-to-year. For the 2004-2005 academic year, approximately 166 scholarships will be awarded in amounts ranging from $200 to $5,000. Contact ADA Foundation, 120 South Riverside Plaza, Suite 2000, Chicago, IL 60606; 800-877-1600; Email {Foundation@eatright.org}; {http://webdietitians.org/Public/7713.cfm}.

$2,000 For Women Over 35 Years Of Age Pursuing Below Graduate Level Education

The Foundation offers forty-five competitive awards of $2,000 each to low-income U.S. female citizens over the age of thirty-five years of age who are enrolled or accepted in either an accredited program of technical/vocational training or an undergraduate program. This is not for graduate work or to pursue a second degree. Send a self-addressed stamped business envelope with your sex, age, level and/or year of study written on the envelope. Contact Jeannette Rankin Foundation, PO Box 6653, Athens, GA 30604-6653; 706-208-1211; Fax: 706-548-0202, Email: {info@rankinfoundation.org}; {www.rankinfoundation.org}.

Up To $5,000 For Health Information Management

AHIMA's Foundation of Research and Education (FORE) offers a variety of scholarships ranging from $1,000–$5,000 to members. Field of study must be in health information management or health information technology. Applicant must be a full time student in a program accredited by the Commission on Accreditation of Allied Health Education Programs (CAAHEP). Scholarships are available for undergraduate and graduate study. Contact American Health Information Management Association (AHIMA), 233 N. Michigan Ave., Suite 2150, Chicago, IL 60601-5800; 312-233-1100; Email: {info@ahima.org}; {www.ahima.org}.

Money For Female Artists And Writers

This organization gives small grants that are designed to support feminists who are active in art, fiction, non-fiction and poetry. For more information, contact the organization. Grants range from $250–$1,500. Contact Money for Women/Barbara Deming Memorial Fund, P.O. Box 630125, Bronx, NY 10463.

Up To $10,000 For RN's To Pursue Graduate Nursing Education

Scholarships ranging from $2,500–$10,000, with the amount varying each year depending on contributions to the organization, are available to U.S. registered nurses. The RN must be a member of a national, professional nursing organization, enrolled in or applying to a National League for

Nursing accredited masters program in nursing, or at the doctoral level. The applicant must also be either a full time master's student or full or part time doctoral level student. The first criteria considered is academic excellence. Contact Nurses Educational Funds, Inc., 304 Park Ave. S., 11th Floor, New York, NY 10010; 212-590-2443; Fax: 212-590-2446; {www.n-e-f.org}.

$1,000 For Students Interested In Medical Assisting

The AAMA offers the Maxine Williams Scholarship of $1,000 for one school year. High school graduates who are enrolled in or soon to be enrolled in a post-secondary medical assisting program which is accredited by the Commission on Accreditation of Allied Health Education Programs are eligible. Scholarships are awarded based on interest, need, and aptitude. Contact American Association Of Medical Assistants (AAMA), 20 North Wacker Drive, Suite 1575, Chicago, IL 60606-2903; 312-899-1500; 800-228-2262; {www.aama-ntl.org}.

Scholarships For Medical And Dental Assistant Studies

High school graduates interested in pursuing studies in medical technology, medical laboratory technician, medical assisting, dental assisting, phlebotomy or office laboratory technician may apply for a scholarship with this organization. Applicants must plan on studying at an accredited college or university in the United States. There is an April 1 deadline for submitting applications. Call for an application. Contact American Medical Technologists, 710 Higgins Road, Park Ridge, IL 60068-5765; 847-823-5169 Fax: 847-823-0458; Email: {mail@amt1.com}; {www.amt1.com}.

$1,000 For A Woman In Surveying And Mapping

The Cady McDonnell Memorial Scholarship Award of $1,000 recognizes a woman enrolled in the surveying field who is a legal resident of one of the following western states: Montana, Idaho, Washington, Oregon, Wyoming, Colorado, Utah, Nevada, California, Arizona, New Mexico, Alaska, and Hawaii. This organization also offers a variety of other awards ranging from $500–$2,000 and according to level of education.

Contact American Congress On Surveying And Mapping, 6 Montgomery Village Ave., Suite 403, Gaithersburg, MD 20879; 240-632-9716; Fax: 240-632-1321; Email: {info@acsm.net}; {www.acsm.net/scholar.html}.

Money For Law Librarians

If you are in library school to get your law librarian degree, or are already a librarian and getting your law degree, then the American Association of Law Libraries has scholarships for you. The Association provides scholarships in eight different scholarships to help further the profession of law librarianship. For more information contact American Association of Law Libraries, 53 W. Jackson, Suite 940, Chicago, IL 60604; 312-939-4764; Fax: 312-431-1097; {www.aallnet.org}.

$500 Available For Masters And Doctoral Level Health Education

The AAHE has scholarships available in the amount of $500. There are separate awards for doctoral and masters level students who are currently enrolled in a health education program. Applicants must have a minimum 3.5 GPA on a 4.0 scale and prior AAHE scholarship recipients may not apply. Contact American Association For Health Education (AAHE), 1900 Association Drive, Reston, VA 20191-1598; 703-476-3437; 800-213-7193; Fax: 703-476-9527; Email: {aahe@aahperd.org}; {www.aahperd.org/aahe/template.cfm}.

Money For Women Builders

This foundation awards over $50,000 to worthy recipients each year! Award amounts range from $500–$2,000. Applicants must be in a construction related degree program for a bachelor's or associate degree. You must have at least a 3.0 grade point average and be enrolled full-time in school. Application forms are available by sending a self-addressed stamped envelope to the address listed below.

Contact National Association Of Women In Construction (NAWIC) Founders' Scholarship Foundation, 327 South Adams, Fort Worth, TX 76104; 817-877-5551; 800-552-3506; Fax: 817-877-0324; Email: {nawic@nawic.org}; {www.nawic.org}.

Creative Mothers Can Win Money!

This organization's goal is to assist mothers in educating their children. The American Mothers Cultural and Creative Arts Awards program grants monetary prizes to mothers in three different categories: arts and crafts, literature and vocal music. The intent of the program is to encourage mothers to develop talents that will uplift, teach and share with children. Financial awards are given to the winners in the contests.

Contact American Mothers Inc., 15 Dupont Circle, NW, Washington, DC 20036; 202-234-7375; 877-242-4AMI; Fax: 202-234-7390; Email: {info@americanmothers.org}; {www.americanmothers.org}.

$2,000 Available For Civil Engineers

The ASCE has many different scholarships available. Undergraduate freshmen, sophomores, or juniors who are National ASCE Student members are eligible for the Samuel Fletcher Tapman Scholarship. Twelve recipients may be selected for this award. Past awards have been approximately $2,000 each.

Contact American Society Of Civil Engineers (ASCE), Member Scholarships and Awards, 1801 Alexander Bell Drive, Reston, VA 20191-4400; 800-548-2723; {www.asce.org/inside/stud_scholar.cfm}.

$250–$1,500 For Full Time Food Majors

The Worthy Goal Scholarship Fund awards $250–$1,500 scholarships for those interested in food service. Applicant must be a full time student who is either enrolled in or accepted in a food service related major or vocational training program for the fall following the award. In addition, local scholarships are available through IFSEA Senior branches.

Information regarding Senior branches may be obtained by calling IFSEA headquarters. A total of $116,000 in scholarships is available. Contact International Food Services Executives Association, IFSEA Headquarters, 836 San Bruno Ave., Henderson, NV 89015; 702-564-0997; 888-234-3732; Fax: 702-564-4836; Email: {info@ifsea.com}; {www.ifsea.com}.

Creative Women Over 35 Are Eligible For $1,000 Award

Women artists, photographers, writers and composers who are 35 years or older are eligible for scholarships of $1,000. The intent of the scholarship is to support professional development. A portfolio of work is required with entry. Contact The National League Of American Pen Women, Branch President, 66 Willow Road, Sudbury, MA 01776-2663; 978-443-2165; Email: {info@juno.com}; {www.americanpenwomen.org}.

Bright Broadcasters Eligible For $1,250–$5,000 In Scholarships

College juniors, seniors and graduate students attending a BEA Member university and preparing for a career in broadcasting are eligible for a variety of awards offered by BEA. Eleven scholarship awards, which range from $1,250–$5,000, are awarded to full time students to be used exclusively for tuition, student fees, books, and university dorm room and board. Applicants must possess evidence of high integrity and have a strong academic record.

Contact Broadcast Education Association, 1771 N St., NW, Washington, DC 20036-2891; 202-429-3935; 888-380-7222; Email: {beainfo@beaweb.org}; {www.beaweb.org}.

$1,000 For Women In Advanced Agriculture Or Horticulture Study

The Association offers the Sarah Bradley Tyson Memorial Fellowship to properly qualified women for advanced study in agriculture, horticulture, and related subjects. The $1,000 award is to be used for advanced study at an educational institution of recognized standing within the U.S.A. A letter of application should be sent to the chairman, Mrs. Harold Matyn. Contact Women's National Farm and Garden Association, Inc., 3801 Riverview Terrace S., E. Chinatownship, MI 48054.

Up To $2,500 For Veterinarian Students

The AAEP has two scholarships available. Fourth-year veterinary students are eligible for The AAEP/American Livestock Insurance Company Scholarship, which awards eight $2,500 scholarships each year. AAEP student members attending colleges of veterinary medicine either in the US or Canada are eligible. The second scholarship, The AAEP/United States Pony Club Scholarship, awards one $1,000 scholarship to a current or graduate Pony Club member who is entering veterinary school.

Contact American Association Of Equine Practitioners, 4075 Iron Works Parkway, Lexington, KY 40511; 859-233-0147; Fax: 859-233-1968; Email: {aaepoffice@aaep.org}; {www.aaep.org}

$1,000 AVAILABLE FOR TECHNICAL COMMUNICATION STUDENTS

STC awards four $1,000 scholarships each year toward school tuition and expenses. Applicants must be full time students, either graduate students pursuing a master's or doctor's degree or undergraduate students pursuing a bachelor's degree. They should be studying communication or information about technical subjects such as technical writing, editing, graphical design, interface design, and web design. Awards are made to the school for the benefit of the selected student.

Contact Society For Technical Communication (STC), 901 N. Stuart Street, Suite 904, Arlington, VA 22203-1822; 703-522-4114; Fax: 703-522-2075; Email: {stc@stc.org}; {www.stc.org}.

Money Available For Business Majors

The Kemper Foundation offers its scholarships to students enrolled in one of nineteen different colleges and universities. Contact the Foundation for a list of participating schools, as you apply for the scholarships through the schools. Eligibility consists of students interested in pursuing a career in business and is based on financial need.

The Foundation also awards a limited number of merit scholarships, $3,000 per academic year, to scholars who show no financial need. The current maximum annual scholarship awarded is $8,000. Those who obtain scholarships agree to work for pay during their summers for Kemper Insurance Companies in a variety of capacities and offices. Sixty to seventy scholarships are awarded each year. Contact Kemper Foundation, 20 N. Wacker Drive, Chicago, IL 60606; 312-332-3114; {www.jskemper.org}.

Scholarships Starting At $2,000 For Physician Assistants Students

Since 1989, the Foundation has awarded over $1,000,000. Student members of the AAPA who are currently enrolled in an accredited PA program are eligible to apply. Awards, which start at $2,000, are intended to help students complete their education. Contact American Academy Of Physician Assistants, 950 N. Washington St., Alexandria, VA 22314-1552; 703-836-2272; Fax: 703-684-1924; Email: {aapa@aapa.org}; {www.aapa.org}.

Scholarship from Coca-Cola

The Coca-Cola two-year colleges scholarship program was created in 2000 through a grant from the Joseph B. Whitehead Foundation. Mr. Whitehead was one of the original bottlers of Coca-Cola. This program recognizes students attending two-year degree institutions for community service and academic excellence. Applicants must be U.S. citizens or permanent residents, must maintain a GPA of 2.5 on a 4.0 scale, must have completed 100 hours of community service within the previous 12 months. Contact Coca-Cola Two-Year Colleges Scholarship Program, P.O. Box 1615, Atlanta, GA 30301-1615; 800-306-2653; {www.coca-colascholars.org}.

$500–$2,500 Available For Architectural Students

A variety of scholarships, ranging from $500–$2,500, are available to architectural students who are pursuing a professional degree in architecture. The scholarship applied for depends upon the student's level of education, starting from those just entering and proceeding to postgraduates and professionals.

The AIA/AAF Minority/Disadvantaged Scholarship program offers college freshmen and others twenty scholarships of $500–$2,500 based on financial need for bachelor of architecture majors. The AIA/AAF Scholarship Program for First Professional Degree Candidates awards $500–$2,500 for the final two years of a professional architecture degree program. The RTKL Traveling Fellowship offers one $2,500 award to a student who is almost finished with their program to encourage foreign travel to further their education.

Contact The American Institute Of Architects, The American Architectural Foundation, and the Academy of Architecture for Health, 1735 New York Ave., NW, Washington, DC 20006-5292; 202-626-7511; Email: {info@archfoundation.org}; {www.archfoundation.org/scholarships}.

Many Opportunities For Orthopedic Nurses

NAON Foundation offers a variety of grant and scholarship opportunities to NAON members, ranging from $1,000–$5,000 in value. Scholarships support attendance at NAON programs and continuing college education in the field of orthopedic nursing. Contact National Association Of Orthopedic Nurses (NAON) Foundation, 401 N. Michigan Ave., Ste. 2200, Chicago, IL 60611; 800-289-NAON (6266); Fax: 312-527-6658; Email: {naon@smithbucklin.com}; {www.orthonurse.org}.

Elks National Foundation Scholarships

The Elks National Foundation provides more than $3.3 million in college scholarships each year to graduating high school seniors. There are four scholarships, "Most Valuable Student," "Eagle Scout Award," "Gold Awards," and "Legacy Awards." The value of the scholarships ranges from $1,000 per year to $15,000 per year for graduating high school seniors based on financial need, leadership and scholarship. Contact Elks National Foundation, Scholarship Department, 2750 N. Lakeview Ave., Chicago, IL 60614-1889; 773-755-4732; Fax: 773-755-4733; Email: {scholarship@elks.org}; {www.elks.org/enf/scholars/ourscholarships.cfm}.

$1,500 Available For Students Pursuing Critical Care

The American Association of Critical-Care Nurses offers scholarships of $1,500 to promote nursing professionalism and to advance the science of critical care nursing. Students completing a generic baccalaureate-nursing program, as well as AACN members who are registered nurses completing a baccalaureate or graduate degree program in nursing, are eligible. The funds may be used for tuition, books, supplies and/or fees while the student is enrolled in a baccalaureate program accredited by the National League for Nursing or a graduate program.

Contact American Association of Critical-Care Nurses, Educational Advancement Scholarship, AACN, 101 Columbia, Aliso Viejo, CA 92656-4109; 800-899-2226; 949-362-2000; Fax: 949-362-2020; Email: {info@aacn.org}; {www.aacn.org}.

$500–$1,500 Scholarships Available To Court Reporting Students

The NCRA has three CASE (Counsel on Approved Student Education) scholarships available to students attending an NCRA approved court reporter education program. Lists of schools are available from NCRA on request. Applicants must be nominated by their program and are required to submit an essay on a predetermined subject. The awards range from $500–$1,500. The NCRA also awards six $500 tuition grants to student members of the Association who are chosen by a drawing. Contact National Court Reporters Association (NCRA), 8224 Old Courthouse Road, Vienna, VA 22182-3808; 703-556-6272; 800-272-6272; Fax: 703-556-6291; Email: {msic@ncrahq.org}; {www.ncraonline.org}.

Up To $2,500 In Grants Available For English Teachers

Grants up to $2,500 are awarded by the Research Foundation for 1–12 classroom teachers. Grants are intended for teachers to explore questions related to teaching English/Language Arts. Research questions should be related to work, and have arisen due to questions, concerns or ideas in the classroom. Members of NCTE may apply.

Contact National Council Of Teachers Of English (NCTE), 1111 W. Kenyon Road, Urbana, IL 61801-1096; 217-328-0977; 800-369-6283; Fax: 217-328-0977; {www.ncte.org/}.

Opportunity To Receive College Tuition From NSA

Stokes Educational Scholarship Program is available through NSA. They will consider any student who meets the requirements below and who chooses a full-time college major in either computer science, electrical or computer engineering, languages or mathematics. Requirements consist of having a minimum SAT score of 1100 and a minimum composite ACT score of 25. Chosen students can receive college tuition, reimbursement for books, year-round salary, summer work and have a guaranteed job with the NSA after graduation. Students must work for NSA for one and a half times their length of study, which is usually about five years. Contact National Security Agency,

Manager, Undergraduate Training Program, Attn: S232R (UTP), 9800 Savage Rd., Suite 6740, Ft. Meade, MD 20755-6740; 800-669-0703; {www.nsa.gov}.

Opportunity For An RN To Win $3,000 Toward Occupational Health Education

The AAOHN offers a $3,000 award. Applicant must be a registered nurse who is either a full-time or part-time student in a nationally accredited school of nursing baccalaureate program and demonstrate an interest in occupational and environmental health. The Association also offers a variety of research grants for environmental and health registered nurses. Contact the Association for details.

Contact American Association Of Occupational Health Nurses (AAOHN), AAOHN Foundation, 2920 Brandywine Road, Suite 100, Atlanta, GA 30341-4146; 770-455-7757; Fax: 770-455-7271; Email: {aaohn@aaohn.org}; {www.aaohn.org}.

Opportunity For $1,200–$20,000 For Manufacturing Engineering Students

The SME Education Foundation offers scholarships based on degree of education. High school students in their senior year are eligible to apply for scholarships ranging from $1,200–$2,500 if they are planning to enroll full-time in a manufacturing engineering or manufacturing engineering technology program. Full-time college students with 30 completed hours and a minimum GPA of 3.5 who are pursuing a career in manufacturing engineering, manufacturing engineering technology, automated systems or robotics may apply for scholarships ranging from $1,000–$3,500. Graduate fellowships are available to eligible applicants accepted in a manufacturing engineering or industrial engineering graduate program with a minimum GPA of 3.5. New this year is a program offered by SME for grandchildren and children of SME members providing up to $20,000 annually for graduating high school seniors. Contact Society Of Manufacturing Engineers (SME), Education Foundation, One SME Drive, PO Box 930, Dearborn, MI 48121-0930; 313-271-1500; 800-733-4763; Fax: 313-271-2861; {www.sme.org}.

$3,000 For Audio Engineers

The Audio Engineering Society provides scholarships to those college graduates who are entering graduate studies in the field of audio engineering. Award recipients are allowed to renew the scholarship for a second year. For information on how to apply, contact Audio Engineering Society, 60 East 42nd St. Room 2520, New York, NY 10165; 212-661-8528; Fax: 212-682-0477; {www.aes.org}.

$1,000–$5,000 Available For Smart Women Engineers

The SWE administers over 90 scholarships per year ranging from $1,000–$5,000. Women majoring in engineering or computer science in a college or university with an ABET-accredited program or in a SWE approved school are eligible. There are a variety of scholarships available. Applicants for sophomore, junior, senior and graduate scholarships must have a minimum GPA of 3.5.

SWE also offers re-entry scholarships to assist women, who have been out of the engineering job market as well as out of school for a minimum of two years, in obtaining the credentials necessary to re-enter the job market as engineers. Contact Society Of Women Engineers (SWE), 230 E. Ohio Street, Suite 400, Chicago, IL 60611-3265; 312-596-5223; Fax: 312-596-5252; {www.swe.org}; Email: {hq@swe.org}.

Money Available For Therapists

AMBUCS offers scholarships ranging from $500–$1,500 annually to students in their junior/senior year in a bachelor's degree program, or a graduate program leading to a master's or doctoral degree. There is also one two-year award in the amount of $6,000 offered. Applicants must be accepted in an accredited program in physical therapy, occupational therapy, speech language pathology, and hearing audiology. Applications available online only from January 15th through April 15th. Since inception over $6,000,000 has been given to over 12,000 students. Contact AMBUCS Scholarship Committee, 3315 N. Main St., 27265 P.O. Box 5127, High Point, NC 27262; 336-869-2166; Fax: 336-887-8451; Email: {ambucs@ambucs.org}; {www.ambucs.org}.

Funeral Service Scholarship Opportunities Available

The NFDA provides a list of State Funeral Directors Associations, National Funeral Service Organizations and Mortuary Colleges that offer scholarships to funeral service students. The list provided has over 60 associations, organizations and colleges listed and provides amounts of scholarships available. Contact National Funeral Directors Association (NFDA), 13625 Bishop's Drive, Brookfield, WI 53005-6607; 262-789-1880; 800-228-6332; Fax: 262-789-6977; {www.nfda.org}; Email: {nfda@nfda.org}.

Opportunity For Pharmacy Students

The ASHP Student Leadership Award and Scholarship recognizes students who are interested in pharmacy practice and who have shown academic excellence and leadership ability. This award is offered annually to one student in each participating college of pharmacy. The award is made up of a congratulatory letter from the ASHP president, an award certificate, a copy of both the Pharmacist's Drug Handbook and ASHP's PharmPrep and a $250 scholarship. Contact ASHP Pharmacy Student Forum; 301-657-3000; 7272 Wisconsin Ave., Bethesda, MD 20814; {www.ashp.org}.

$3,000 Scholarship Opportunity For School Librarian Media

The AASL /School Librarian's Workshop Scholarship offers $3,000 for the professional education of persons who are pursuing school library media specialist standing at the preschool through high school levels in public or private educational settings. Applicants are required to have received bachelor's degree with proven academic excellence and to have the intention to pursue full-time graduate level education in an ALA accredited library school program. Contact the Association for details.

Contact Graduate Education, American Library Association, AASL/Scholarship Recommendation, 50 E. Huron St., Chicago, IL 60611-2795; 312-280-4386; 800-545-2433; Fax: 312-664-7459; Email: {scholarships@ala.org}; {www.ala.org}.

$4,000 Scholarship For Communication Science Graduate Students

The Foundation offers full-time graduate students in communication sciences and disorders programs, who demonstrate outstanding academic achievement, the opportunity to compete for $4,000 scholarships. Graduate students with disabilities and minority students, and international students who are enrolled in a communication sciences or disorders program, can compete for a $2,000 scholarship. Contact American Speech-Language-Hearing Foundation, 10801 Rockville Pike, Rockville, MD 20853; 301-897-5700; 800-638-8255; Email: {foundation@asha.org}; {www.ashfoundation.org}.

Women Music Majors Eligible For $300 Scholarship

WBDI offers five annual scholarships to women who are currently enrolled in a music education program and are pursuing a career as a band director. Each award is a non-renewable $300 scholarship. Contact Women Band Directors International (WBDI), Scholarship Chair, Robyn Wilkes, 296 Dailey Hills Circle, Ringgold, GA 30736; Email: {robyn509@aol.com}.

National Security Related Careers Eligible For Scholarship

The Horizons Foundation offers scholarships valued at $500 and up to encourage women to pursue careers related to the national security interests of the U.S. Applicants must be currently enrolled at an accredited university/college either full or part-time. Undergraduate (at least junior level status) and graduate students are eligible. Applicants must also have a minimum GPA of 3.25 and be a U.S. citizen. Women in engineering, computer science, physics, mathematics, business, law, international relations, political science, operations research, and economics fields have preference.

Contact Horizons Foundation Scholarship Program, WID Horizons Foundation, c/o National Defense Industrial Association (NDIA), 2111 Wilson Boulevard, Suite 400, Arlington, VA 22201-3061; 703-247-2552; Fax: 703-522-1885; {http://wid.ndia.org}; Email: {wid@ndia.org}.

$1,000 Scholarship Opportunity For Women In Business or Economic Education

The Foundation generally grants three $1,000 scholarships per year. Women students who are pursuing a career in the business and/or economics field of study are eligible to apply. Applicants must be a full-time student at an approved college/university in the U.S. in pursuit of a business and/or economics degree and must have completed at least one semester or two quarters of college level study. Selection is based on scholastic achievement, leadership potential, motivation and financial need. Contact Phi Chi Theta Foundation, 5215 N O'Connor Blvd. #200, Irving, TX 75039; 972-443-9889; Fax: 214-350-8011 {www.phichitheta.org/foundation/foundation.htm}.

DAUGHTERS OF A CAREER OFFICER ELIGIBLE FOR SCHOLARSHIPS

This program is for seniors in high school who are the daughters of a career officer commissioned in the regular Army, Navy, Air Force, Coast Guard, or Marine Corps (active, retired or deceased). Selection is based on merit and need. Awards are for up to four years and are granted at the college of the candidate's choice. Contact Daughters Of The Cincinnati, Scholarship Program, 122 East 58th Street, New York, NY 10022; 212-319-6915; {http://fdncenter.org/grantmaker/cincinnati}.

John L. Carey Scholarships

The John L. Carey Scholarship Program provides financial assistance to liberal arts degree students pursuing graduate studies in accounting. The amount of the scholarship is $5,000 for one year and is renewable for an additional year if certain requirements are met. Contact American Institute of Certified Public Accountants (AICPA), 1211 Avenue of the Americas, New York, NY 10036-8775; 212-596-6200; Fax: 212-596-6213 {www.aicpa.org}.

Money To Study The Earth And Sky

The AMS offers an array of graduate fellowships and undergraduate scholarships to help further the education of outstanding graduate and undergraduate students. Students must plan to pursue careers in the atmospheric or related oceanic and hydrologic sciences. The amount of the award depends on education level, with a range from $700–$22,000. Contact American Meteorological Society (AMS), 45 Beacon Street, Boston, MA 02108; 617-227-2426; Fax: 617-742-8718 {www.ametsoc.org}; Email: {armstrong@ametsoc.org}.

Scholarship Of $2,500 Available To High School Seniors With Inter-Scholastic Sports

This program offered by ESPN is not an athletic scholarship program. ESPN presents awards to eight graduating seniors, one male and one female in each of the four regions of the U.S.A., each year. The one time $2,500 grants are made to defray the cost of tuition, room and board at an accredited college/university. Selection criteria includes academic achievement, service to school and community, and leadership in interscholastic sports. Applicants must be legal U.S. citizens. Employees of ESPN, Inc., Walt Disney Co., the Hearst Corp. or their respective subsidiaries are not eligible. Contact Sports Leadership, ESPN Sportsfigures Scholarship, P.O. Box 5439, Blair, NE 68009-5439; {http://sportsfigures.espn.com/sportsfigures/stu_theTicket.jsp?iAm=s}.

Scholarships To Students
Who Have Hearing Impairment Or Loss

Optimist International, a volunteer organization devoted to providing services for youth, announces its scholarship contests. Enter each contest through the local Optimist Clubs. Topics change each year.

The Optimist International Essay contest is open to students under 19 years of age as of December 31 of the current school year and attend school in the U.S., Canada, or Caribbean. Essays will be judged at the entry level by February 28 of each year. Winners progress to the next level. Club prize, medallion; District prize, plaque and a $650 college scholarship; International prize, 1st place plaque, $5,000 college scholarship, trip to Optimist International Convention for winner and parents to read essay; 2nd place plaque, $3,000 college scholarship; 3rd place plaque, $2,000 college scholarship.

The Communication Contest for the Deaf and Hard of Hearing is open to students up to and including grade 12 in the United States and Canada, to CEGEP in Quebec and grade 13 in the Caribbean, who are identified by their school as deaf or hard of hearing and educated in the United States, Canada, or Caribbean. Students attending either public school or schools providing special services are eligible to enter if criteria are met. Students may use sign language, oral presentation, or a combination of both. Contests run at various times in each state/province. Club prize, medallion; District prize, plaque; and $1,500 college scholarship for 1st place winner. Contact Optimist International, 4494 Lindell Blvd., St. Louis, MO 63108; E-mail {programs@optimist.org} Website: {www.optimist.org}; 800-500-8130; 314-371-6000; Fax: 314-371-6006.

SCHOLARSHIPS FOR YOUNG BLACK WOMEN

The Association provides financial assistance to young Black women interested in pursuing post-secondary education. Applicants must be graduating high school seniors or enrolled in an accredited college or university and have a minimum GPA of 3.0. All recipients must be full-time students and be either citizens of the U.S. or enrolled in an accredited college in the U.S.

Contact National Association Of Negro Business & Professional Women's Clubs, Inc., 1806 New Hampshire Avenue, Washington, DC 20009-3298; 202-483-4206; {www.nanbpwc.org}.

$1,000 and $2,000 Scholarships
For Spouses And Children Of Blind Veterans

The Blinded Veterans Association offers its Kathern F. Gruber Scholarship Program to dependent children and spouses of blinded veterans of the U.S. Armed Forces. The veteran must be legally blind, but the blindness need not be service-connected. There are eight $2,000 scholarships and eight $1,000 scholarships available. Applicants must either be already enrolled in or accepted for admission, as a full-time student in an accredited institution of higher education, or business, secretarial or vocational school. Contact Blinded Veterans Association, 477 H Street, NW, Washington, DC 20001-2694; 202-371-8880; 800-669-7079; Email: {bva@bva.org}; {www.bva.org}.

Junior Miss Competition Rewards Winners With College Scholarships

This nationwide scholarship program's purpose is to recognize, reward and encourage excellence while promoting self-esteem in young women. Winners of local competition advance to state competition and all 50 state winners will travel to Mobile, AL to compete for the title of America's Junior Miss. The recipient of the America's Junior Miss title will receive a $30,000 college scholarship. More than $1.8 million in cash scholarships and $32 million in college-granted scholarships are available each year. High school girls who are U.S. citizens are eligible to take part in the competition if they have never been married, however it is advisable to inquire during her sophomore year because the local competition may take place prior to her senior year. Contact America's Junior Miss, P.O. Box 2786, Mobile, AL 36652-2786; 251-438-3621; 800-256-5435; Fax: 251-431-0063; Email: {ajmiss@ajm.org}; {www.ajm.org}.

$4,000 Scholarship For Industrial Engineering

The Institute supports the advancement of engineering education and research through a variety of scholarships and awards. The United Parcel Service Scholarship for Female Students awards $4,000 annually. Applicants must be undergraduate students pursuing an industrial engineering degree enrolled in any school in the U.S., Canada and Mexico which is accredited by an agency recognized by IIE. Applicants must be full-time students with an overall minimum 3.4 GPA who are active Institute members and have at least five full quarters or three full semesters of school remaining from the date of nomination. Please contact the Institute for details and other scholarship and award programs not limited to females only. Contact United Parcel Service Scholarship For Female Students, Institute of Industrial Engineers, 3577 Parkway Lane, Suite 200, Norcross, GA 30092; 770-449-0460; 800-494-0460; Fax: 770-441-3295; {www.iienet.org}.

$500–$2,000 Scholarship For Chemistry Students

This National Honor Society for Women in Chemistry offers scholarships for women pursuing a chemistry degree in an accredited college or university. Scholarships vary depending on educational level and amounts awarded. The nominee may be, but need not be, a member of Iota Sigma Pi, depending on the scholarship. The Society also offers professional awards. Awards range from $500 to $2,000. Please contact the address listed below for details. Contact Iota Sigma Pi, Director for Student Awards, Vicki H. Grassian, Department of Chemistry, University of Iowa, Iowa City, IA 52242; 319-335-1392; Fax: 319-353-1115; {www.iotasigmapi.info}; Email: {vicki-grassian@uiowa.edu}.

Legally Blind Eligible For $3,000—$12,000

The National Federation of the Blind is able to offer a broad array of scholarships to applicants who are legally blind and studying full-time in a post-secondary institution in the United States. One scholarship is available to a full-time employee also attending school part-time. One scholarship for $12,000 and three scholarships for $3,000 have no additional restrictions. Twenty-six scholarships are awarded for $3,000. Some have no additional restrictions, although some have female only restrictions and some have field of study restrictions. Contact National Federation Of The Blind, 1800 Johnson St., Baltimore, MD 21230; 410-659-9314; Fax: 410-685-5653; Email: {nfb@nfb.org}; {www.nfb.org}.

Fellowships And Grants For Advancement Of Women In Society

The AAUW provides funds through grants and fellowships to advance education, research, and self-development for women, and to foster equity and positive societal change. Applicants are not required to be members of AAUW. Applicants must demonstrate scholarly or professional excellence and preference is given to women whose interests show a commitment to advancing the welfare of women and girls. Grants to individuals go up to $30,000, and include education. A booklet is available that describes the various programs. Contact American Association Of University Women (AAUW) Education Foundation, 1111 16th St., NW, Washington, DC 20036; 800-326-AAUW; 319-337-1716; TDD: 202-785-7777; Fax: 202-872-1425; Email: {info@aauw.org}; {www.aauw.org}.

SCHOLARSHIPS FOR LUTHERAN WOMEN

Women of the Evangelical Lutheran Church in America (Women of the ELCA) offers scholarships in three different categories. Scholarships for Lutheran Lay Women provides assistance to women of the ELCA in a variety of fields as they return to school after experiencing at least a two year interruption. The Arne Administrative Leadership Scholarship gives financial help to Lutheran women who are pursuing an education to prepare for an administrative position. The Herbert W. and Corrine Chilstrom Scholarship provides assistance to Lutheran women who are in their final year at ELCA seminaries and preparing for the ordained ministry in the ELCA.

Contact Women Of The Evangelical Lutheran Church In America, 8765 W. Higgins Road, Chicago, IL 60631-4189; 773-380-2730; 800-638-3522, ext. 2730; Fax: 773-380-2419; {www.womenoftheelca.org/whatwedo/scholarships.html}.

Musicians Eligible For Awards

The National Federation Of Music Clubs (NFMC) is dedicated to finding and fostering young musical talent. The Federation conducts annual Junior Festivals and offers more than a quarter of a million dollars in state and national competitions.

The awards NFMC offers are numerous. Age limits and categories vary greatly per award. Many awards include performance bookings. Almost all awards require NFMC membership. Contact the NFMC for a chart of competitions and awards. Contact National Federation Of Music Clubs (NFMC), 1336 North Delaware Street, Indianapolis, IN 46202-2481; 317-638-4003; Fax: 317-638-0503; Email: {info@nfmc-music.org}; {www.nfmc-music.org}.

Scholarship For Female Jocks

Women's Sports Foundation offers a scholarship to provide female high school student-athletes with a means to continue their athletic participation as well as their college education. The scholarship offered for this purpose is The Linda Riddle/SGMA Scholarship. The Dorothy Harris Scholarship is offered to provide female graduate students in physical education, sports management, sports psychology or sports sociology with a means to attend graduate school. Contact Women's Sports Foundation, Eisenhower Park, East Meadow, NY 11554; 800-227-3988; Fax: 516-542-4716; {www.womenssportsfoundation.org}; Email: {wosport@aol.com}.

Smart Science Majors Scholarships

The Clare Boothe Luce Program is intended "to encourage women to enter, study, graduate, and teach" in fields where there have been many obstacles to their advancement. These fields include physics, chemistry, biology, meteorology, engineering, computer science, and mathematics. Undergraduate scholarships are generally awarded for two years to a highly qualified female and solely based on merit. Graduate fellowships are awarded to highly qualified women who are doctoral candidates. Contact the Foundation for details. The Clare Boothe Luce Program, The Henry Luce Foundation, Inc., 111 West 50th Street, New York, NY 10020; 212-489-7700; Fax: 212-581-9541; {www.hluce.org}.

$2,000 For Engineering Students

Information Handling Services/SAE Women Engineers Committee Scholarship was established to encourage young women and minority students who are graduating from high school to enter the field of engineering. Applicants must have a minimum 3.0 GPA and be accepted into an ABET accredited engineering program. This $2,000 award will be given for the freshman year only.

In addition, the Society offers over $27,000 worth of scholarships to engineering students at any accredited engineering programs. They also offer scholarships for use at over 50 specific universities. Contact the Society for more information and application deadlines. The Society Of Automotive Engineers, 400 Commonwealth Drive, Warrendale, PA 15096-0001; 724-776-4841; Fax: 724-776-0790; {www.sae.org}.

Up to $10,000 for Aspiring Journalists

The NAHJ Scholarship Fund was established to assist aspiring minority journalists pursuing a career in journalism. Applicants need not be a member of NAHJ, but must be a student enrolled full-time in a college for the entire academic year. Selection is based on academic excellence, a demonstrated interest to pursue a career in journalism and financial need.

High school seniors, college undergraduate or 1st year graduate students pursuing a career in English or Spanish language print, photo, broadcast or online journalism are eligible for a $1,000–$2,000 NAHJ General Scholarship. Current college sophomores are eligible for the $10,000 Newhouse Scholarship Program. Students must be pursuing a career at an English language newspaper. Contact National Association Of Hispanic Journalists, 1000 National Press Building, 529 14th St. NW, Washington, DC 20045-2001; 888-346-NAHJ; 202-662-7145; Fax: 202-662-7144; Email: {nahj@nahj.org}; {www.nahj.org}.

$1,000–$10,000 For Broadcast Journalism Majors

The Foundation sponsors seven different scholarships for students seeking a career in electronic journalism. One of the seven awards is for graduate students only. Award amounts range from $1,000–$10,000. Applicants must be full-time students who have at least one year of college remaining and are officially enrolled in a college. Several of the awards are specific to minorities. The Foundation also offers a variety of internship programs. Contact Radio And Television News Directors Foundation, RTNDF Scholarships, 1600 K Street, NW, Suite 700, Washington, DC 20006-2838; 202-659-6510; Fax: 202-223-4007; Email: {rtndf@rtndf.org}; {www.rtndf.org}.

$6,000 For Women Pursuing Sports Administration

The NCAA offers 16 scholarships to women and 16 scholarships to ethnic minorities who are college graduates and will be entering the first semester of their initial postgraduate studies. Applicants must be accepted into a sports administration or related program. Applicants must be pursuing a career in intercollegiate athletics such as coaching, sports medicine, athletics administration and other careers that provide a direct service to intercollegiate athletics. Each award is for $6,000.

The Degree Completion program is for student athletes who have completed their eligibility for athletics-related aid at a Division I school and are within 30 hours of obtaining their degree. They can be funded five semesters part-time or two semesters full-time. They also offer eight $3,000 scholarships to college juniors majoring in sports journalism. Each year more than $1.7 million in scholarships is awarded. The NCAA also awards a variety of postgraduate scholarships.

Contact The National Collegiate Athletic Association, 700 W. Washington St., P.O. Box 6222, Indianapolis, IN 46206-6222; 317-917-6222; Fax: 317-917-6888; {www.ncaa.org/about/scholarships.html}.

$1,500 FOR MEDICAL AND DENTAL STUDENTS

The CAMS awards scholarships to help qualified candidates, especially of Chinese descent, with financial hardship, to complete their study of research or teaching in the medical science field. This includes either graduate study in medical or dental schools in the U.S.A. or post-graduate medical study or research in schools participating in teaching in medical schools or helping Chinese people abroad. Four to six scholarships are awarded ranging from $1,000–$1,500. Contact Chinese-American Medical Society, Dr. David Wang, Chairman, CAMS Scholarship Committee, 171 E. 84th St., #33B, New York, NY 10028; 212-744-1364; {www.camsociety.org}; Email: {dwang007@yahoo.com}.

Jackie Robinson Foundation

The Jackie Robinson Foundation awards students four-year scholarships of up to $6,000 per year to attend the four-year accredited college or university of their choice. The Jackie Robinson Foundation provides education and leadership opportunities for students of color with limited financial resources.

Contact The Jackie Robinson Foundation, 3 West 35th Street, 11th Floor, New York, NY 10001-2204; 212-290-8600; Fax: 212-290-8081; {www.jackierobinson.org}.

$200-$7,000 FOR PRESBYTERIAN CHURCH MEMBERS

The Presbyterian Church Higher Education Program provides $2 million dollars in grants, loans, and scholarships to students, both undergraduates and graduates, who belong to the Presbyterian Church. Grants range from $200–$7,000 for studies.

One program is for students enrolled full-time and pursuing a medical profession. Other programs are for general studies. Applicants must be members of the Presbyterian Church (U.S.A.), U.S. citizens or permanent residents of the U.S., demonstrate financial need and be recommended by an academic advisor at the institution and by a church pastor. A booklet is available which lists the programs or you may check their website for more information.

Contact Presbyterian Church (U.S.A.), 100 Witherspoon Street, Louisville, KY 40202-1396; 502-569-5776; 888-728-7228, ext. 5776; {www.pcusa.org/financialaid}.

$1,000 For Females With A Love Of Flying

This wonderful fund is offered in remembrance of Nancy Horton who loved to fly! One award of $1,000 is given to the recipient to further the student's flight training. Applicants must be at least 18 years old, have a minimum 3.0 GPA if in school, at least a private pilot, high recommendation from flight instructor, extra flight related activities and, an essay portraying one's love of flight. Contact Nancy Horton "Touch The Face Of God" Scholarship, 4466 N.E. 91st Ave., Portland, OR 97220-5024.

$1,000-$2,500 For Students Studying Real Estate

IREM offers the Brooker Scholarship to increase participation of minorities in the real estate management industry. One graduate level award of $2,500 and two undergraduate-level awards in the amount of $1,000 are given. Applicants must be minority students who are U.S. citizens who have declared a major in real estate or in a related field and have a minimum GPA of 3.0. Students should have completed at least two courses in real estate at the time of application. The deadline for all applications is March 31st.

Contact George M. Brooker Collegiate Scholarship For Minorities, Institute of Real Estate Management, Attn: Brooker Scholarship, 430 N. Michigan Ave., Chicago, IL 60611-4090; 800-837-0706; Fax: 800-338-4736; Email: {custserv@irem.org}; {www.irem.org}.

Roothbert Fund Scholarships

The Roothbert Fund awards yearly grants averaging $2,000–$3,000 and are meant to be supplementary. The main focus of the Scholarship Program is to assist men and women who need financial aid to further their education. Contact The Roothbert Fund, Inc., 475 Riverside Dr., Room 252, New York, NY 10115; 212-870-3116; Email: {mail@roothbertfund.org}; {www.roothbertfund.org}.

Up To $4,000 for Female Medical Students

AMWA Student Members are eligible for a variety of awards from the AMWA. The Wilhelm-Frankowski Scholarship of $4,000 is offered to women medical students attending an accredited U.S. medical or osteopathic medical school. The Janet M. Glasgow Essay Award of $1,000 is presented for the best essay identifying a woman physician who has been a significant mentor and role model. The Carroll L. Birch Award of $500 is presented for the best original research paper written by a student member of the AMWA.

Loans with no interest during medical school are also available. Interest at 7% begins the December after graduation. Contact American Medical Women's Association Foundation (AMWA), 801 North Fairfax Street, Suite 400, Alexandria, VA 22314; 703-838-0500; Fax: 703-549-3864; Email: {info@amwa-doc.org}; {www.amwa-doc.org}.

$2,000 For Geoscience Thesis Work

The Association offers a scholarship program for women who require financial assistance to complete their thesis and to complete a masters or Ph.D. degree in a geoscience field. Applicant must be a woman whose education has been interrupted for at least one year, a candidate for an advanced degree in a geoscience field, and completing their thesis during the current academic year. The scholarship is to be used for typing, drafting, childcare or whatever it takes to finish the thesis. Two $2,000 scholarships will be awarded. Contact The Association For Women Geoscientists, Chrysalis Scholarships, G&H Production Company, LLC, #930, 518 17th Street, Ste. 930, Denver, CO 80202; 303-534-0708; Fax: 303-436-0609, Email: {president-elect@awg.org}; {www.awg.org}.

$5,000 For Training In Field Of Water Supply And Treatment

The American Water Works Association offers The Holly A. Cornell Scholarship to encourage and support outstanding female and/or minority students pursuing advanced training in the field of water supply and treatment. Current master's degree students or students who have been accepted into graduate school are eligible. The scholarship provides a one-time grant of $5,000 to the most outstanding eligible candidate.

The Lars Scholarship is open to any student in a master's or doctorate program in science or engineering. There is a $5,000 scholarship for an M.S. student and a $7,000 scholarship for Ph.D. student. Contact American Water Works Association, 6666 W. Quincy Avenue, Denver, CO 80235; 303-794-7711; Fax: 303-347-0804; Email: {acarabetta@awwa.org}; {www.awwa.org}.

SCHOLARSHIPS FOR JOINING AFROTC

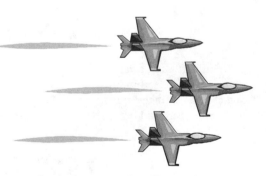

Air Force ROTC offers scholarships to high school seniors and high school graduates. Applicants must have a minimum GPA of 3.0 and minimum SAT scores of 1100, ACT scores of 24. The 2 or 3-year scholarships are offered to in-college students in all majors, but the highest concentration is in science and engineering fields. To qualify, applicants must have a minimum 2.5 GPA for all majors and must hold an AFROTC Professional Officer Course allocation. If accepted for scholarship, students must pass a physical exam and a physical fitness test. Recipients must later serve on active duty to repay obligation. Contact AFROTC for more details. Contact Air Force ROTC, Headquarters AFROTC Scholarship Action Section, 551 E. Maxwell Blvd., Maxwell AFB, AL 36112-6106; 334-953-2091; 866-423-7682; {www.afrotc.com}.

$1,000 For Women Statisticians

The Gertrude Cox Scholarship is open to women who have been accepted into a graduate statistical program. Masters and doctorate students are encouraged to apply for the scholarship. Contact American Statistical Association, 1429 Duke St., Alexandria, VA 22314; 703-684-1221; 888-231-3473; Fax: 703-684-2037; Email: {publicaffairs@amstat.org}; {www.amstat.org}.

Scholarships For Spouse Or Children Of EOD Officer Or Technician

The EOD Memorial Scholarship Application can be viewed at the website below. Applicants must be an unmarried child under the age of 23 years, a widowed spouse who has never been remarried, or a spouse of an EOD officer or enlisted EOD technician of the Army, Marine Corps, Navy, or Air Force who have successfully completed NAVSCOLEOD. Applicants must also be a graduate of an accredited high school and be enrolled in or accepted for enrollment in a full-time undergraduate course of study at an accredited college/university or technical school beyond the high school level.

Money can be used for tuition, books, room, board, and other fees. The amount of the award varies each year. Contact EOD Administrator, P.O. Box 594, Niceville, FL 32588; 850-729-2401; Fax: 850-729-2401; Email: {admin@eodmemorial.org}; {www.eodmemorial.org}.

Presidential Freedom Scholarships

The Presidential Freedom Scholarship Program promotes service and citizenship by students and to recognize students for their leadership in those areas. More than 31,000 scholarships have been awarded to students nationwide. Each high school in the country may select up to two students—juniors or seniors to receive a $1,000 scholarship recognizing outstanding leadership in service to their community. Contact Presidential Freedom Scholarships, 1150 Connecticut Ave., NW, Suite 1100, Washington, DC 20036; 866-291-7700; 202-742-5390; Email: {info@studentservicescholarship.org}; {www.nationalservice.org/scholarships}.

MONEY FOR MIDWIVES TO-BE

The American College of Nurse-Midwives provides scholarships to students in good standing who are enrolled in an accredited midwifery program. For application information contact the office listed below, or use their fax-on-demand system at 202-728-9898 and request document #9001. Contact American College of Nurse-Midwives, 818 Connecticut Ave., NW, Suite 900, Washington, DC 20006; 202-728-9860; Fax: 202-728-9897; {www.midwife.org}.

$500–$2,500 For Ohio Engineering Majors

The Engineers Foundation of Ohio provides a variety of grants ranging from $500–$2,500 for Ohio residents who meet a minimum grade point and SAT/ACT score. These grants are for students who have been accepted into an ABET accredited engineering program. For specific information about the grants and an application, please contact. Contact Engineers Foundation of Ohio, 4795 Evanswood Drive, Suite 201, Columbus, OH 43229-7216; 614-846-1144; 800-654-9481; Fax: 614-846-1131 {www.ohioengineer.com}.

UP TO $2,500 FOR RESPIRATORY CARE MAJORS

The American Respiratory Care Foundation awards grants ranging from $1,000 to $2,500 for students in respiratory therapy programs, both associate and baccalaureate degree programs. Awards generally include travel and registration to the annual conference. One award, the Morton B. Duggan, Jr. Memorial gives a preference to students from Georgia and South Carolina. Contact American Respiratory Care Foundation, 9425 North MacArthur Blvd., Ste. 100, Irving, TX 75063-4706; 972-243-2272; Fax: 972-484-2720; Email: {info@arcfoundation.org}; {www.arcfoundation.org}.

Add Up Your Money Women Accountants

The Educational Foundation for Women in Accounting supports women in the accounting profession. They offer a variety of scholarships ranging from $1,000–$5,000. The Laurels Fund Scholarships are one-year scholarships targeting women who are pursuing advanced accounting degrees.

Women in Transition Scholarship will award up to $16,000 over 4 years and one "Women In Need" Scholarship up to $2,000 per year, and is given to women pursuing an accounting degree. This is for a woman who is in "transition" and was formerly called Displaced Homemaker Scholarship. Contact The Educational Foundation for Women in Accounting, Administrative Office, P.O. Box 1925, Southeastern, PA 19399; 610-407-9229; Fax: 610-644-3713; {www.efwa.org}.

A TOTAL OF $15,000 FOR WOMEN ACCOUNTING MAJORS

Each year the American Society of Women Accountants awards $15,000 in scholarships to women pursuing either a master's or bachelor's degree in accounting. The student can be attending full or part-time. Contact the office listed below for application information. Contact American Society of Women Accountants, 8405 Greensboro Drive, Suite 800, McLean, VA 22102; 703-506-3265; 800-326-2163; Fax: 703-506-3266; {www.aswa.org}.

Money For Human Resource Majors

The Society of Human Resource Management offers a variety of scholarships to undergraduate and graduate human resource majors. Awards range from $1,000–$5,000. Students must maintain a "C" average. Several of the awards are competitions in a research project or essay writing. Contact the office listed below for application information.

Contact Society for Human Resource Management, 1800 Duke St., Alexandria, VA 22314; 703-548-3440; 800-283-SHRM; Fax: 703-535-6490; {www.shrm.org}.

Money For Latinas

MANA, a national Latina organization, provides scholarships to Latinas who have good academic records and financial need. They offer a variety of scholarships. Contact the office listed below for application information. Contact MANA: A National Latina Organization, 1725 K St., NW, Suite 501, Washington, DC 20006; 202-833-0060; Fax: 202-496-0588; Email: {hermana2@aol.com}; {www.hermana.org}.

$2,000–$3,000 For Real Estate Appraisers

The Appraisal Institute offers scholarships to minority students interested in the real estate appraisal field. The scholarship award of $2,000–$3,000 is for undergraduate or graduate degrees in the field. Contact Appraisal Institute, 550 W. Van Buren St., Suite 1000, Chicago, IL 60607; 312-335-4100; Fax: 312-335-4400; {www.appraisalinstitute.org}.

Confederates Unite

If you are a lineal descendant of worthy confederates, you may be eligible for scholarships through this organization. You must have certified proof of Confederate Military Record of one ancestor, and information on how to obtain this information is available. You also need recommendations, a 3.0 grade point average and more. There are several four-year scholarships without restrictions as to schools, major, or state of residency, and others that have some type of restriction. Contact United Daughters of the Confederacy, Scholarship Coordinator, Memorial Building, 328 North Boulevard, Richmond, VA 23220-4057; 804-355-1636; Fax: 804-353-1396; Email: {hqudc@rcn.com}; {www.hqudc.org}.

Count On Accounting

The National Society of Public Accountants awards 43 scholarships per year, ranging in amounts from $500–$2,000. Students must have a 3.0 grade point average and major in accounting at a 2-year or 4-year college. Scholarships are awarded based upon academic excellence and financial need. Contact the Society for application information. National Society of Accountants, 1010 North Fairfax St., Alexandria, VA 22314; 703-549-6400; 800-966-6679; Fax: 703-549-2984; Email: {members@nsacct.org}; {www.nsacct.org}.

AT&T Labs Fellowship Program for Women & Minorities in Science & Tech

Outstanding minority and women students who plan to pursue Ph.D. studies in computers, engineering, and other communications-related fields are eligible to apply for the AT&T Fellowships. The students chosen as fellows will have a mentor assigned to them to help guide them through their studies. The fellowships cover most education expenses, an annual living stipend and more for up to five years of graduate studies. For more information contact AT&T Labs Fellowship Administrator, 200 Laurel Ave. S., Middletown, NJ 07748; 800-FIND-ATT; {www.research.att.com/academic/}.

$500–$1,500 FOR SMART BUSINESS WOMEN

The American Business Women's Association offers a variety of scholarships to undergraduate and graduate business majors, and to students pursuing professional degrees. Awards range from $500–$1,500. Students must be female. Some awards are limited to residents of Anne Arundel County, Maryland. Contact American Business Women's Association, 9100 Ward Parkway, P.O. Box 8728, Kansas City, MO 64114-0728; 800-228-0007; Fax: 816-361-4991; Email: {abwa@abwa.org}; {www.abwahq.org}.

Up to $1,000 for Legally Blind Students

The American Foundation for the Blind offers various support services and scholarships to undergraduate students who are legally blind. Some scholarships are restricted to specific majors; others require a short essay. They also offer several scholarships to students pursuing a Classical Music career. All are based on academic achievement. Contact American Foundation for the Blind, Information Center, 11 Penn Plaza, Suite 300, New York, NY 10001; 800-232-5463; 212-502-7600; Fax: 212-502-7777; Email: {afbinfo@afb.net}; {www.afb.org}.

Money for Smart Business Women

The Business and Professional Women's Association offers a variety of scholarships to women over the age of 25 who are returning to college after a break/delay in their education and plan on pursuing a business career. Some scholarships are intended for use during your junior and senior year only.

The Association considers financial need, academic achievement, recommendations and a personal statement in their decisions. The $1,000 Kelly Services Second Career Scholarship is for women returning to or starting their education due to the death of a spouse or divorce, and is for use during any undergraduate year. The Association may also have loans available. Contact Business and Professional Women's Association, 1900 M St., NW, Suite 310, Washington, DC 20036; 202-293-1100; Fax: 202-861-0298; {www.bpwusa.org}.

$500 for Meteorologists and Atmospheric Science Majors

Interested in a career in the Atmospheric Sciences? The American Geophysical Union offers undergraduate women a chance at $500! Contact American Geophysical Union, American Geophysical Union, 2000 Florida Ave., NW, Washington, DC 20009-1277; 202-462-6900; 800-966-2481; Fax: 202-328-0566; Email: {service@agu.org}; {www.agu.org}.

Up to $4,000 for Nuclear Scientists and Nuclear Engineers

The American Nuclear Society has a large variety of scholarships and research grants available to women who plan to pursue a career in the nuclear sciences. One scholarship awarded each year is reserved for women who are returning to school after a break/delay in their education. All scholarships can be applied for using one application form, which is available on their website. Contact American Nuclear Society, 555 N. Kensington Ave., LaGrange Park, IL 60526; 708-352-6611; Fax: 708-352-0499; Email: {hr@ans.org}; {www.ans.org}.

$5,000 for Smart New York Women

The Foundation has various programs for Jewish female undergraduate students who live in New York, NY. Contact Jewish Foundation for the Education of Women, 135 East 64th St., New York, NY 10021; 212-288-3931; Fax: 212-288-5798; {www.jfew.org}.

$2,000 for Engineering, Math and Science Students

The Brookhaven Institute's Women in Science program targets women who have had their education interrupted due to financial, family, or other problems. Financial need is the primary consideration. Intended for use during your junior or senior year, the scholarship converts to a loan if you do not maintain good academic standing for two consecutive semesters. Contact Brookhaven Women in Science, P.O. Box 183, Upton, NY 11973; 631-344-2425.

$20,000 For SCUBA Divers

Our World Underwater Scholarship Society provides a scholarship to a Scuba diver in North America between the ages of 21 and 25 who wishes to pursue a career which deals with underwater disciplines. The award provides for a year of travel so the recipient can have a variety of experiences related to this field. You can learn about underwater photography, biology, scientific expeditions and more. For more information contact Our World-Underwater Scholarship Society, P.O. Box 4428, Chicago, IL 60680; 800-666-8875 or 630-969-6690; Email: {info@owuscholarship.org}; {www.owuscholarship.org}.

$1,000–$4,000 for Smart Engineering Women

The National Society of Professional Engineers offers several scholarships to graduating high school seniors who are in the top 25% of their class and intend on pursuing a career in engineering. The scholarship is renewable, and requires a minimum GPA of 3.0. Contact National Society of Professional Engineers, 1420 King St., Alexandria, VA 22314-2794; 703-684-2800; Fax: 703-836-4875; {www.nspe.org}.

$1,000 for Smart Journalism Women

The National Federation of Press Women offers several different scholarships, most paying around $1,000, to high school seniors and college undergraduates pursuing a career in journalism. The Federation considers academic achievement, financial need, and potential for success in their decisions. Contact National Federation of Press Women, P.O. Box 5556, Arlington, VA 22205; 800-780-2715; Fax: 703-534-5751; Email: {presswomen@aol.com}; {www.nfpw.org}.

$1,000 for Daughters of Penelope

The Daughters of Penelope offers to members or children of members three different awards ranging from $1,000 to $1,500 for use during your undergraduate years. Academic achievement, financial need and an essay are required. Members of The Maids of Athena are also eligible to apply. For application and information, check with your local chapter first, or the address here. Contact The Daughters of Penelope, 1909 Q St., NW, Suite 500, Washington, DC 20009; 202-232-6300; Fax: 202-232-2140; Email: {ahepa@ahepa.org}; {www.ahepa.org}.

Up to $500 for Activists at CUNY

For women attending any campus of the City University of New York. The Astraea Foundation offers two $500 awards annually to women who demonstrate political and social commitment to actively fighting for gay and lesbian civil rights. For use during any undergraduate year, lesbian sexual orientation is not a requirement—just commitment to lesbian civil rights. Financial need is considered but not required. Contact Astraea National Lesbian Action Foundation, 116 E. 16th St., 7th Floor, New York, NY 10003; 212-529-8021; Fax: 212-982-3321; Email: {info@astraeafoundation.org}; {www.astraea.org}.

$500-$1,000 for Kappa Kappa Gamma Women

If you are a member of Kappa Kappa Gamma and studying social work, special education, or rehabilitation, KKG has money for you!! For application and information, contact Kappa Kappa Gamma, 530 E. Town St., P.O. Box 38, Columbus, OH 43216-0038; 614-228-6515; Fax: 614-228-7809; Email: {kkqhq@kappa.org}; {www.kappakappagamma.org}.

UP TO $1,000 FOR MEDICAL WOMEN

For undergraduate women interested in pursuing a career in clinical healthcare or health administration. Contact American College of Healthcare Executives, One North Franklin, Suite 1700, Chicago, IL 60606-4425; 312-424-2800; Fax: 312-424-0023; {www.ache.org}.

$1,000 for Smart California Women

For undergraduate women studying in any college in California. Must have graduated from a high school in California. Based on financial need, academic achievement, community service, references. Contact Amaranth Fund Awards, California Mason Foundation, 1111 California St., San Francisco, CA 94109.

$1,500 for the Top Ten College Women

Each year, Glamour Magazine looks for the Top Ten College Women in America. Applications are taken during your junior year. Academic achievement, extracurricular activities, community service, personal statement, references and an essay are all considered. For full-time college juniors. Information for next year's contest will be available at the 800 number below.

Contact Glamour Magazine, 4 Times Square, 16th Floor, New York, NY 10036-6593; 800-244-4526; 212-286-6667; Fax: 212-286-6922; Email: {ttcw@glamour.com}; {www.glamour.com}.

A CALL TO ACTION — FOR MONEY!

The Call to Action Essay Contest is for undergraduate women who live in California and are studying business, education, health care, law enforcement or social service. Up to $5,000 is awarded to the winning essay, topic changes yearly. Please write or contact your financial aid office for information. Contact Governor's Conference for Women, A Call To Action, Office of the Governor, 300 S. Spring St., 16th Floor, Los Angeles, CA 90013.

Up to $10,000 for Young Women

Girls Incorporated offers several scholarships and contests to its members, including a national academic scholarship contest worth $10,000. Must be a high school student in grades 11 through 12, under age 19, and a member of Girls Incorporated. Contact Girls Incorporated, 120 Wall St., New York, NY 10005-3902; 800-374-4475; {www.girlsinc.org}.

MONEY FOR AMATEUR ATHLETES

The Amateur Athletic Union provides three scholarships totaling $5,000 to high school seniors who participate in at least one high school sport. You must write an essay on the goals you achieved and the obstacles you overcame in order to reach those goals. For more information contact Amateur Athletic Union, 1910 Hotel Plaza Blvd., P.O. Box 22409, Lake Buena Vista, FL 32830; 407-934-7200; Fax: 407-934-7242; 800-AAU-4USA; {www.aausports.org}.

Money for Women in Oregon

The Oregon State Scholarship Commission manages a large variety of scholarship offers for women who are residents of Oregon. Some of the opportunities for undergraduate women include:

- The Agricultural Women-in-Network Scholarship for college sophomore and junior students attending college in Oregon, Washington, or Idaho. Primarily based on financial need and academic achievement, you must be planning on pursuing an agricultural-related career.
- The Private 150 Scholarship Program, for current college juniors and seniors studying business. The Professional Land Surveyors Scholarship, for use during your junior or senior year. Must be attending any college in Oregon and plan on a career in surveying, cartography, or related careers.

Contact Oregon Student Assistance Commission, 1500 Valley River Dr., Suite 100, Eugene, OR 97401; 541-687-7400; Fax: 541-687-7419; 800-452-8807; {www.osac.state.or.us}.

Money for Women Ministers

For undergraduate women attending college full-time who are preparing for the ministry. Please include SASE with requests for information. Contact Disciples of Christ Church, P.O. Box 1986, Indianapolis, IN 46206; 317-262-8517.

UP TO $1,000 FOR SHEEP

For undergraduate students who are studying agriculture, animal science, veterinary medicine, or animal husbandry and intend on pursuing a career in the Sheep industry. Must be a resident of Oregon. Contact Oregon Sheep Growers Association, 1270 Chemeketa St., NE, Salem, OR 97301; 503-364-5462; Fax: 503-585-1921; {www.oregonsheep.com}.

$500 for Teaching in Oregon

This renewable scholarship is for undergraduate students who plan on teaching in Oregon upon completion of their education degree. The student must attend a public institution in Oregon. Contact Oregon PTA, 531 SE 14th Ave., Room 205, Portland, OR 97214; 503-234-3928; Fax: 503-234-6024; {www.oregonpta.org}.

Over $2 Million
Available for Farmers

There are many different scholarship programs are available to members of the Future Farmers of America. Some programs are available to non-members who are pursuing agricultural-related degrees. Details and applications are available at the website.

Contact Future Farmers of America, Inc., Scholarship Office, P.O. Box 68960, Indianapolis, IN 46268-0960; 317-802-6060; Fax: 317-802-6061; {www.ffa.org}.

$1,000 for Broadcasting in Oregon or Washington

Each year, the OAB offers six $1,000 scholarships; two for graduating high school students and four to students enrolled in two or four year college broadcast programs. For current undergraduate students attending any college in Oregon or Washington who intend on pursuing a career in broadcasting. Academic achievement is the primary consideration. Contact Oregon Association of Broadcasters, 7150 SW Hampton Street, Suite 240, Portland, OR 97223-8366; 503-443-2299; Fax: 503-443-2488; Email: {theoab@theoab.org}; {www.theoab.org}.

Tuition and up to $13,500 for
Smart Graduate Students

The Andrew W. Mellon Fellowship in Humanistic Studies is designed to encourage and prepare students of exceptional academic promise for teaching and scholarship careers in humanistic studies. Students majoring in American studies, art history, the classics, comparative literature, cultural anthropology, english literature, foreign language, history, the philosophy of science, and related majors are welcome to apply. For use at the graduate level of study, this highly competitive and prestigious award grants tuition, fees, and a stipend of up to $13,500 to 80 people yearly. Contact The A.W. Mellon Fellowship in Humanities, Woodrow Wilson National Fellowship Foundation, CN 5281, Princeton, NJ 08543-5281; 609-452-7007; Fax: 609-452-0066; {www.woodrow.org}.

Money for Dietetic Technicians

The American Dietetic Association offers various scholarships to students who are studying dietetics or nutrition, and plan on a career in dietetics. Must be entering your first year of study in an ADA-accredited dietetic technician program. Financial need and academic achievement are the primary considerations. Contact American Dietetic Association, 120 South Riverside Plaza, Suite 2000, Chicago, IL 60606-6995; 800-877-1600; 312-899-0040; {www.eatright.org}.

Up to $1,500 for Dental Hygienists

The Association offers a large variety of scholarships to students who plan on a career as a dental hygienist. Most awards are limited to current college juniors, however some are open to all undergraduate students. Some of their programs target students studying for a certificate in dental hygiene, others target minority students. Applications and information are available at their website. Financial need and academic achievement are the primary considerations.

Contact American Dental Hygienists' Association, 444 N. Michigan Ave., Suite 3400, Chicago, IL 60611; 312-440-8918; Email: {institute@adha.net}; {www.adha.org}.

Money for Internet Teams

Teams of kids can gather together to work on an Internet Project. College scholarships totaling over $1,000,000 are awarded to students, as well as monetary awards to project team coaches and schools. Elementary and secondary students are eligible. For more information check out the website {www.thinkquest.org}.

$2,500 FOR NURSES

The Eight and Forty Scholarship, offered by the American Legion, was established to assist current registered nurses (RN's) who wish to advance their career for positions in supervision, administration or teaching. Students are to have prospects of being employed in specific positions in hospitals, clinics, or health departments on completion of their education and the position must have a full-time and direct relationship to lung and respiratory control.

For more information, contact the address listed below. Contact The American Legion, Attn: Eight and Forty Scholarships, P.O. Box 1055, Indianapolis, IN 46206; {www.legion.org/}.

Up to $10,000 for Handicapped Musicians

This music competition is open to students who are blind, deaf, learning disabled, or physically disabled. An audition tape is required. Check with your local Very Special Arts Organization, or the address below for further information.

Contact Very Special Arts and the Panasonic Electronics Company, 1300 Connecticut Ave., NW, Suite 700, Washington, DC 20036; 800-933-8721; TTY: 202-737-0645; Fax: 202-737-0725; Email: {info@vsarts.org}; {www.vsarts.org}.

Up to $11,000 for Women from Developing Countries

Six awards are available, each up to $11,000 for female students from developing countries. Must show service to women and/or children. Must be 25 years of age or older. Must be planning on returning to your home country within two years. Contact Margaret McNamara Memorial Fund, 1818 H Street, NW, MSN Room H2-204, Washington, DC 20433; 202-473-8751; Fax: 202-522-3142; Email: {familynetwork@worldbank.org}; {www.worldbank.org/yournet}.

UP TO $5,000 FOR
FOOD SERVICE EXPERIENCE

The National Restaurant Association has five different programs available. The Industry Assistance Grants offer up to $1,500 to further the education of those who have at least three years experience in food service. The Undergraduate Scholarships Program offers up to $5,000 to current college sophomores and juniors who have at least a 3.0 GPA. You must also have at least 1000 hours of work experience in the food service industry. Contact National Restaurant Association Educational Foundation, 175 W. Jackson Blvd., Suite 1500, Chicago, IL 60604-2702; 312-715-1010; 800-765-2122; {www.nraef.org}.

$6,000 For The Health Therapy Profession

AMBUCS offers scholarships to students who are in their junior or senior year of a bachelor's program or in graduate school studying physical therapy, occupational therapy, speech language pathology, or hearing audiology. Awards range from $500 to $1,500 annually, with one two-year award of $6,000 being offered. The total amount awarded each year is $225,000. You must fill out the application form online. Contact AMBUCS Scholarship Committee, 3315 North Main St., P.O. Box 5127, High Point, NC 27262; 336-869-2166; Fax: 336-887-8451; Email: {ambucs@ambucs.org}; {www.ambucs.org}.

$1,000 for Oregon
High School Students

Five awards of $1,000 are available through the annual Cascade Policy Essay Competition (Independence Essay Competition). Based on an essay, the topic changes yearly. Private, public and homeschooled students are all encouraged to enter. All high-school age students are eligible to apply, not just college-bound seniors. Contact Cascade Policy Institute, 813 SW Alder, Suite 450, Portland, OR 97205; 503-242-0900; Fax: 503-242-3822; Email: {info@CascadePolicy.org}; {www.cascadepolicy.org/essay.asp}.

Thousands of Dollars for
Students with Norwegian Interests!

The Sons of Norway has several programs available. King Olav V Norwegian American Heritage Fund promotes educational exchange between Norway and North America. For U.S. students, you must demonstrate a keen and sincere interest in the Norwegian heritage. For Norwegian students, you must demonstrate a strong interest in American heritage. To be eligible to apply one must be at least 18 years of age and must study at an institute of higher learning. Most awards are in the range of $250–$3,000.

The Nancy Lorraine Jensen Memorial Scholarship Fund is for women between 17 and 35, who are either members of the Sons of Norway, or employees of NASA/Goddard Space Flight Center. Daughters and granddaughters of members or employees are also eligible to apply. You must be studying chemistry, chemical engineering, mechanical engineering, electrical engineering, or physics. The award pays tuition for no less than 50% for one term and no more than 100% of the tuition for one full year.

Contact King Olav V Norwegian American Heritage Fund, Sons of Norway Foundation, 1455 W. Lake St., Minneapolis, MN 55408; 612-827-3611; 800-945-8851; Fax: 612-827-0658; {www.sofn.com}.

Up to $2,500 for Returning Students

The P.E.O. Program for Continuing Education provides grants to women whose education has been interrupted and who find it necessary to resume studies due to changing demands in their lives. There must be a need for financial assistance with their educational expenses to improve their marketable skills. Must have been out of school for at least a year, must be within the last two years of finishing your degree, must be a citizen of either the United States or Canada. Apply directly with a local P.E.O. Sisterhood chapter. Contact P.E.O. Sisterhood, 3700 Grand Avenue, Des Moines, IA 50312, Attn: Executive Office; 515-255-3153; Fax: 515-255-3820; {http://peointernational.org}.

Money for Graduate Students

Delta Sigma Theta has various programs available to graduate students who have demonstrated a commitment to serving their community. Must have at least a 3.0 GPA. Contact Century City Alumnae Chapter, Delta Sigma Theta Sorority, P.O. Box 90956, Los Angeles, CA 90009; 213-243-0594.

Up to $2,000 for Essays!

Applicants must research and write an essay on a topic to be determined by The Foundation. Applicants must contact The Heritage of America Scholarship Foundation to receive an application form and essay question. Open to current high school seniors, current undergraduate and graduate students. Essays and application forms must be postmarked on or before April 30.

Please include SASE with requests for information! Requests without SASE will not be responded to! Contact Heritage of America Scholarship Foundation, 8222 Thetford Lane, Houston, TX 77070.

Money for Texas Women Returning to School

The Ajay Castro Scholarship for Re-Entering Women provides financial assistance to women from Bexar County, Texas, who have been out of school for at least three years. Must be pursuing your first undergraduate degree, and must be studying a communications-related major. Contact Association for Women in Communications, San Antonio Professional Chapter, P.O. Box 780382, San Antonio, TX 78278; {www.wicsa.org}.

Up to $5,000 for Nevada Women

The Nevada Women's Fund offers a large variety of programs to assist women in Nevada who wish to pursue a college education. Women studying at any academic level are welcome to apply, all programs are based primarily on academic achievement, financial need, and community service. Preference is given to women who are returning to school after a few years break and to single mothers. Most programs are renewable. You must attend college in

Nevada. Contact Nevada Women's Fund, 770 Smithridge Drive, Suite 300, Reno, NV 89502; 775-786-2335; Fax: 775-786-8152; Email: {info@nevadawomensfund.org}; {www.nevadawomensfund.org}.

Up to $3.5 Million for Young Women

The American Young Woman of the Year, a talent and scholarship contest, is for current high school seniors. It's based on SAT or ACT scores, GPA, transcript, interview, physical fitness, talent, poise, and appearance. Contact American Young Woman of the Year Program, P.O. Box 2786, Mobile, AL 36652.

$1,000 for Young Feminists

Spinster's Ink offers an essay contest on "What Feminism Means to Me," for current female high school seniors. Winning essays will also be published in a national magazine. Contact Spinster's Ink, Young Feminist Scholarship, 191 University Blvd. #300, Denver, CO 80206; 303-761-5552; Email: {spinster@spinsters-ink.com}; {www.spinsters-ink.com}.

Money for Arkansas Single Parents

The Arkansas Single Parent Scholarship Fund is open to single parents (of either gender) who wish to begin or continue their higher education. Applicants must reside in a county where a Single Parent Scholarship Fund has been established — you can get a list of counties with this program by contacting the website below or your school's financial aid office. {www.aspsf.org}.

Money for Palo Alto, California Women

Young women who are graduating from any high school in Palo Alto with a 3.0 or higher GPA are eligible to apply. Must be planning on attending a 4-year college or university, must be planning on studying science or a related major. Primary considerations for this award are athletic activities, community service, academic achievement and financial need. Please contact your high school's guidance counselor office or the address below for further information.

Contact Peninsula Community Foundation, 1700 South El Camino Real, Suite 300, San Mateo, CA 94402-3049; 650-358-9369; {www.pcf.org}.

$100 FOR FOLK WOMEN

The Elli Kongas-Maranda Student Prize awards undergraduate and graduate students who submit papers or productions on women's traditional, vernacular, and local culture and/or work on feminist theory and folklore. Contact Elizabeth Nixon Center for Folklore Studies, 226 East Royal Forest Blvd., Columbus, OH 43214-2128.

Up to $1,000 for Women in Hunterdon County, New Jersey

The Mildred Preen Mortimer Women-In-Transition Award is intended to provide financial aid to women in Hunterdon County, New Jersey, who are either returning to school after a break or who wish to pursue a second career. Financial need and desire for financial independence are the primary considerations. Contact Hunterdon Women's Fund, P.O. Box 183, Flemington, NJ 08822.

MONEY FOR BEAUTIFUL AFRICAN AMERICAN WOMEN

This annual competition is open to all African American women, including those who are married and/or have children, are eligible to enter this competition. The competition begins at the state level, winners move on to the national levels. Winners are chosen based on beauty, talent, and personality. There is a $40 application fee and a $550 sponsorship fee. The fees can be paid for by sponsors, fundraising, or by selling subscriptions to "Black America" magazine. Contact Miss Black America Pageant, P.O. Box 25668, Philadelphia, PA 19144; 215-844-8872.

MONEY FOR WOMEN

Open to women from ages 3 to 20 (and men from ages 18–20), the purpose of this program is to "recognize and reward girls who could become tomorrow's leaders." Contestants must never have been married or have a child. In addition to appearance, academic achievement and community service are considered. Pageants are first held on the state level, winners then move on to the national competition. There is a $20 application fee, and a $350 sponsor fee (which can be paid for by an individual's sponsors, family, friends, or through fund-raising.) Contact American Co-ed Pageants, 4120 Piedmont Road, Pensacola, FL 32503; 850-432-TEEN; Email: {nationals@gocoed.com}; {www.gocoed.com/main1.shtm}.

Up to $2,500 for Music Women in Massachusetts

The Madelaine H. Soren Trust Scholarship is available to women music students who have graduated from a Massachusetts high school and wish to pursue their college education in the Boston area.

To apply, contact your high school's guidance counselor or administration office, they MUST nominate you for this program. Direct application is not available. Fifteen awards are made yearly. Contact Boston Safe Deposit and Trust Company, One Boston Place, Boston, MA 02108-4402; 617-722-7341.

Money for Mennonite Women

The purpose of this program is to provide financial support to train emerging women church leaders around the world. Open to women from any country, this program helps with funding training at any level to prepare women for Mennonite church leadership. Training can include workshops for lay women who have very little education as well as course work for high school or college graduates.

Contact Mennonite Women International Women's Fund, 722 Main Street, P.O. Box 347, Newton, KS 67114-0347; 316-283-5100 Ext. 227; 800-794-5101 Ext. 227; Fax: 316-283-0454; Email: {office@MennoniteWomenUSA.org}; {www.mennonitewomenusa.org}.

Money For Graphic Communication Majors

Over 300 awards of up to $1,000 are available annually to students who wish to pursue a career in graphic communications. High school seniors and current college students are eligible to apply. All students must be attending or planning on attending college full-time. Academic achievement and career goals are the primary considerations, although references and extracurricular activities are also considered. All awards are renewable provided a 3.0 GPA or above is maintained. Winners also receive a complimentary membership in the Graphic Arts Information Network. Contact Graphic Arts Technical Foundation, Attn: Scholarship Competition, 200 Deer Run Road, Sewickley, PA 15143-2600; 412-741-6860; 800-910-GATF; Fax: 412-741-2311; {www.gatf.org}.

Money for Talented Deaf Women

Miss Deaf America Pageant Awards. Must be deaf and between the ages of 18 and 28. The main objective of the Miss Deaf America Talent Pageant is ". . . to help us elevate the image and self-concept of deaf ladies throughout the United States. This is not an ordinary contest . . . beauty, poise, gracefulness are desirable qualities, but the biggest point is one's cultural talent performance. Talent is no longer the only thing; the women are judged across a broad spectrum of categories including community service, academics, current events, deaf culture, and more."

Contact National Association of the Deaf, 814 Thayer Avenue, Silver Spring, MD 20910-4500; 301-587-1788; TTY: 301-587-1789; Fax: 301-587-1791; Email: {NADinfo@nad.org}; {www.nad.org}.

Money for Deaf Women

Scholarships are awarded to prelingually deaf or hard-of-hearing students who use speech and speechreading to communicate, and who are attending or have been admitted to a college or university program that primarily enrolls students with normal hearing. Applicants must have had a hearing loss since birth or before acquiring language with a 60dB or greater loss in the better ear in the speech frequencies of 500, 1000, and 2000 Hz.

Only the first 500 requests for applications will be accepted. Applications must be requested between November 1st and December 1st. Contact Alexander Graham Bell Association for the Deaf, 3417 Volta Place, NW, Washington, DC 20007-2778; 202-337-5220; TTY: 202-337-5221; Fax: 202-337-8314; {www.agbell.org/}.

$500 for Communications Women in Maine

This program is open to women of any age who are residents of Maine, and who will be enrolled in a communications or mass communications related college program. Financial need, academic achievement, career goals, and interest in communications are the primary consideration. Contact Maine Media Women, Attn: Jude Stone, Scholarship Committee, RR3 Box 1085, Bridgeton, ME 04009; 207-647-5960.

Money for Navy Wives

The Mary Paolozzi Membership Scholarship is open to women who are wives of Navy personnel and have been members of the Navy Wives Club for at least two years. Financial need is considered. Contact Navy Wives Club of America, P.O. Box 6971, Washington, DC 20032.

$1,000 FOR NAVAL ACADEMY CHILDREN AND WOMEN

Eligible to apply for these scholarships are children of active, retired, or deceased; Navy or Marine Corps officers or enlisted personnel who are or were permanently stationed at the United States Naval Academy complex, children of current full-year members of the Naval Academy Women's Club, children of civilian employees of the Naval Academy and any current member of the Naval Academy Women's Club.

Applicants must be in their senior year of high school, or have graduated from high school, and plan on attending full-time at any 2-year or 4-year college or university, any art school or any technical/trade school. Contact Naval Academy Women's Club, P.O. Box 826, Annapolis, MD 21404; Email: {nawcpres@hotmail.com}; {www.nadn.navy.mil/WomensClub}.

Up to $5,000 for Desert Shield/Desert Storm Veterans and their Spouses and Children

This program provides financial assistance to Veterans of Desert Storm/Desert Shield. Highest preference is given to the children and spouses of men and women who lost their lives while on active duty in these campaigns. At the time of this writing, the schools participating in this program are: University of Arizona, Baylor University, Florida State University, George Mason University, University of Houston, Loyola University of New Orleans, Norfolk State University, Northeastern University, University of Oklahoma, Rice University, Roosevelt University of Chicago, Saint John's University, San Diego State University, Seton Hall University, Southern Methodist University, Texas A&M University, Texas Christian University, Texas Tech University, University of Texas at Austin, and Villanova University. You MUST apply directly with your school; Mobil Corp. does not accept direct applications for this program. Contact The Mobil Corporation Desert Shield/Desert Storm Scholarship Program, Mobil Corporation, 3225 Gallows Road, Fairfax, VA 22037-0001.

Money for Future Homemakers

Family, Career, and Community Leaders of America, Inc. offers members a large variety of scholarship and grant programs. Most are based on a combination of academic achievement, potential for success, community service, volunteer work, service to FCCLA, and career goals. Most programs are applied for directly from your local FCCLA chapter, please check with your local chapter for further information.

Contact Family, Career, and Community Leaders of America, Inc., 1910 Association Drive, Reston, VA 20191-1584; 703-476-4900; 800-234-4425; Email: {natlhdqtrs@fcclainc.org}; {www.fcclainc.org}.

Money for Smart Women

American Mensa offers a variety of essay-based competitions and academic-achievement scholarship programs available through local chapters. Most programs are available to non-members. Please contact your local Mensa chapter (a list of chapters is available at the website) for more information. Contact American Mensa, Ltd., 1229 Corporate Drive West, Arlington, TX 76006-6103; 817-607-0060; Fax: 817-649-5232; {www.us.mensa.org}.

Red River Valley
Fighter Pilots Association Scholarships

This scholarship is available to the dependent sons, daughters and spouses of any member of the U.S. Armed Forces who is listed as killed in action, missing in action, or prisoner of war from any combat situation involving our military since August, 1965. Any dependent child or spouse of any military aircrew member who was killed as a result of performing aircrew duties during non-combat missions and the dependents of any current or deceased Red River Valley Association member are also eligible to apply.

The program has paid out over 900 grants approaching $1,500,000 total since its inception. Individual awards vary depending upon the financial need of the applicant and the cost of their chosen college or university. Academic achievement, financial need, community service, and extracurricular activities are the primary considerations. Contact Red River Valley Fighter Pilots Association, Red River Valley Association Foundation, P.O. Box 1916, Harrisonburg, VA 22801; 540-442-7782; Fax: 540-433-3105; Email: {AFBridger@aol.com}; {www.eos.net/rrva/}.

McDonald's
USA Scolarship Program

The McDonald's National Employee Scholarship Program recognizes and rewards the accomplishments of McDonald's student-employees who are outstanding in their studies, serve their communities and work hard to deliver an outstanding QSC experience for their customers. Every academic year, the McDonald's National Employee Scholarship Program selects one outstanding student-employee from each state and the District of Columbia to receive a $1,000 scholarship. Contact McDonald's Corporation, McDonald's Plaza, Oak Brook, IL 60523; 800-244-6227; {www.mcdonalds.com}.

MONEY FOR HAM RADIO WOMEN

Do you have an interest in ham radios? Have you an amateur or general radio license? Then you might want to check in with the American Radio Relay League. They offer a large number of different scholarships for amateur radio operators, most of which have very few restrictions! Contact American Radio Relay League, 225 Main St., Newington, CT 06111-1494; 860-594-0200; Fax: 860-594-0259; Email: {hq@arrl.org}; {www.arrl.org}.

Up to $2,000 for Hotel Women

The American Express Scholarship Program is offered to students who are currently working at least 20 hours a week at any AH&MA member hotel or resort. Dependent children of current employees are also eligible to apply. Part-time and full-time students attending either a two-year or four-year college or university are eligible to apply. Must be majoring in hotel or hospitality related majors. Work experience, financial need, academic achievement, community service and career goals are the primary considerations.

Contact American Hotel & Lodging Educational Foundation, 1201 New York Ave., NW, Suite 600, Washington, DC 20005-3931; 202-289-3100; Fax: 202-289-3199; Email: {ahlef@ahlef.org}; {www.ahlef.org/}.

$500 for Homeschooled Californians

To be eligible to apply, you must be a resident of California who has been homeschooled for at least 4 years, your parents must be a member of the CHEA. Contact Christian Home Educators Association of California, Inc., Attn: Scholarship Committee, P.O. Box 2009, Norwalk, CA 90651-2009; 800-564-CHEA; Email: {CHEAofCalifornia@aol.com}; {www.cheaofca.org}.

Up to $3,000 for California Real Estate Students

For current California students enrolled at any California two-year or four-year college/university who plan on a career in real estate. Acceptable majors include but are not necessarily limited to: real estate brokerage, real estate finance, real estate management, real estate law and related areas. Also, current realtors in California who wish to pursue advanced education or degrees are eligible to apply. Contact California Association of Realtors, 525 S. Virgil Ave., Los Angeles, CA 90020; 213-739-8200; Fax: 213-480-7724; {www.car.org}.

Up to $2,500 for Architectural Women in California

The Association offers California women who are either residents of California or non-residents attending school in California and are studying architecture the opportunity to apply for several scholarships that they offer. Must be a current undergraduate student. Contact Association for Women in Architecture, 386 Beech Ave., Unit B4, Torrance, CA 90501; 310-533-4042; {www.awa-la.org/default.html}.

Money for Welding Women

Any student intending to pursue a career in welding technology is eligible to apply for the American Welding Society's District Scholarship program. These renewable scholarship awards may be used at any school in the United States with a welding or materials joining program, including technical/vocational schools. Financial need is the primary consideration. Applications are available at the website.

Contact The American Welding Society, 550 NW LeJeune Rd., Miami, FL 33126; 305-443-9353; 800-443-9353; {www.aws.org}.

Up To $3,000 If You Live Near A Tyson Food Plant

If you live near a Tyson Foods plant and are a full-time undergraduate student with at least a 2.5 GPA, you may be eligible to apply for up to $3,000! Those majoring in agribusiness, agricultural related majors, computer science, and other majors are eligible for this renewable scholarship. Contact Tyson Foundation, Inc., 1515 Pioneer Dr., Harrison, AR 72601; 870-743-3000; Fax: 870-391-3340.

Up to $2,000 for
Connecticut Construction Women

For Connecticut residents pursuing a construction-related career. Primary considerations for this renewable award are academic achievement, personal statement, financial need and an interview. Contact Connecticut Building Congress Scholarship Fund, 2600 Dixwell Ave., Suite 7, Hamden, CT 06514-1800; 203-281-3183; {www.cbc-ct.org}.

$1,000 for Hospitality Students

DECA, an association of marketing students and teachers, offers scholarships funded by major corporations such as Safeway, Coca-Cola USA and Hilton Hotels, which provides scholarships of $1,000 for students of hospitality, hotel management. Contact your local DECA chapter for further information, or the website. Contact DECA - Distributive Education Club of America, 1908 Association Drive, Reston VA 20191; 703-860-4013; {www.deca.org}.

MONEY FOR PETROLEUM WOMEN

The Desk and Derrick Educational Trust offers women in the United States and Canada who are studying business, engineering, natural resources or technology related majors and intend to pursue a career in the petroleum industry an opportunity to apply for $1,500. Financial need and academic achievement are the primary considerations. For use during your junior, senior, or graduate years.

Contact Desk and Derrick Educational Trust, 5153 E. 51st Street, Suite 107, Tulsa, OK 74135; Fax: 918-622-1675; {www.addc.org/ET/History.htm}.

Up to $1,000 for Dental Women

The American Association of Women Dentists has several academic achievement-based scholarships available to current junior and senior dental students who are members of the Association. Contact American Association of Women Dentists, 645 N. Michigan Ave., #800, Chicago, IL 60611; 800-920-2293; Fax: 830-612-3067; Email: {info@aawd.org}; {www.womendentists.org}.

Up to $5,000 for Heating,
Refrigerating and Air Conditioning

For students studying electrical engineering, electronics, heating, air conditioning, refrigeration technology, or other majors with intention on pursuing a career in the heating, refrigeration and/or air conditioning industry. Must have at least two years left before graduation, a 3.0 GPA or above, attending a ABET-accredited school, and financial need. Contact American Society of Heating, Refrigerating and Air Conditioning Engineers, Inc., 1791 Tullie Circle, NE, Atlanta, GA 30329; 404-636-8400; 800-527-4723; Fax: 404-321-5478; {www.ashrae.org}.

$1,500 for Safety Engineers

Two awards annually for student members of the American Society of Safety Engineers. Must be attending college full-time with a minimum GPA of 3.0, studying a safety engineering related major, and plan on pursuing a career in safety engineering. Contact American Society of Safety Engineers Foundation, 1800 E. Oakton, Des Plaines, IL 60018; 847-699-2929; Fax: 847-768-3434; Email: {customerservice@asse.org}; {www.asse.org}.

Money for Lutheran Women in Mental Retardation

Interested in a career in service to the mentally disabled? Bethesda Lutheran Homes offers a large variety of scholarships to students in social services, nursing, legal services, special education, health administration, education, therapy, and related majors. Must be an active, communicant member of a Lutheran church. Must be at least a college sophomore.

Please call or write for more information about available programs. Contact Bethesda Lutheran Homes and Services, Inc., National Christian Resource Center, 600 Hoffman Dr., Watertown, WI 53094-6294; 920-261-3050; 800-383-8743; Fax: 920-261-8441; {www.blhs.org}.

Up to $2,000 for Black Nurses

Members of the National Black Nurses Association are eligible to apply for several scholarships that range from $500 to $2,000. Must have completed at least one year of school at time of application and be an African American. Primary considerations are academic achievement, potential for success, references, and involvement in the African American community.

Contact National Black Nurses Association, Inc., 8630 Fenton St., Suite 330, Silver Spring, MD 20910-3803; 301-589-3200; 800-575-6298; Fax: 301-589-3223; Email: {NBNA@erols.com}; {www.nbna.org}.

Money for Michigan Nurses

A maximum of four $500 scholarships are available for sophomores, juniors, and seniors who are residents of Michigan and are attending a college in Michigan. Must be pursuing a nursing degree and have at least a grade of "C" or better. Preference is given to students who plan on working as a nurse in Michigan upon graduation. Application deadline is March 1st.

Contact Michigan League for Nursing, 2410 Woodlake Dr., Okemos, MI 48864; 517-347-8091; {www.michleaguenursing.org}.

Up to $3,000 for Oncology Nurses

A variety of scholarships are available to current registered nurses who wish to further their education and pursue careers as oncology nurses. Some awards are specifically for minority students, others are for current oncology nurses who have contributed to the field of oncology nursing.

Contact Oncology Nursing Society, 125 Enterprise Dr., Pittsburgh, PA 15275-1214; 412-859-6100; 866-257-4ONS; Fax: 877-369-5497; Email: {customer.service@ons.org}; {www.ons.org}.

Up to $1,000 for Logistics

For full-time undergraduate students pursuing a logistics or related major at any four-year college. Must have at least a 3.0 GPA. Contact SOLE-The International Society of Logistics, 8100 Professional Pl., Suite 111, Hyattsville, MD 20785; 301-459-8446; Fax: 301-459-1522; Email: {SOLEHQ@sole.org}; {www.sole.org}.

Up to $5,000 for Composers

The Society offers a variety of contests and competitions for original compositions and musical scores. Some programs are available only to members of the Society. Most require a taped performance of your original music.

Contact American Society of Composers, Authors, and Publishers Foundation, ASCAP Building, One Lincoln Plaza, New York, NY 10023-7142; 212-621-6219; Email: {ascapfoundation@ascap.com}; {www.ascapfoundation.org}.

Up to $3,000 for Parapsychology Students

For undergraduate and graduate students who can show a very strong and serious interest in parapsychology through coursework, research, essays, term papers and dissertations. Students who have only a minor interest are not eligible. Contact Parapsychology Foundation, 228 E. 71st St., New York, NY 10021; 212-628-1550; Fax: 212-628-1559; {www.parapsychology.org}.

MONEY FOR DeMOLAY MEMBERS

Current and former members of DeMolay are eligible to apply. There are no restrictions on what major you are studying. Scholarships are based primarily upon financial need, academic achievement, character and community service. Award amounts vary, but on average are $800. DeMolay members should also check with their local chapter for local scholarships. Contact DeMolay Foundation, 10200 NW Ambassador Dr., Kansas City, MO 64153; Fax: 816-891-9062; 800-DEMOLAY (336-6529); Email: {demolay@demolay.org}; {www.demolay.org}.

Money for Non-Commissioned Officers Association Members

The Non-Commissioned Officers Association offers a variety of programs to its members and their children. Of particular interest is the Betsy Ross Educational Fund, which awards $250 to members who wish to take classes to improve their job skills. Other scholarships are available to spouses and children of members.

Please include a SASE with requests for information. Contact Non Commissioned Officers Association, Scholarship Fund 10635 IH 35N; San Antonio, TX 78233; 800-662-2620; {www.ncoausa.org}.

Up to $13,000 for Jewelry and Gems

The Gemological Institute of America offers high school graduates over the age of 17 a variety of different scholarship programs. All require that the applicant must be in or pursuing a career in the gemology field. Must be attending or planning on attending a school with a Gemological Institute accredited program of study. Contact Gemological Institute of America, Office of Student Financial Assistance-MS#7, 5345 Armada Dr., Carlsbad, CA 92008; 800-421-7250; {www.gia.edu}.

Money for Girl's Club Members

Teenagers between the ages of 14 and 18 who are members of the Girl's Club for at least one year are eligible to apply for scholarships ranging between $2,000 and $8,000. Must apply for this scholarship through your local Girl's Club chapter — direct application is not available. Must have at least a 3.0 GPA in high school. Academic achievement, community service, and leadership potential are the primary consideration. Contact Reader's Digest Foundation, Reader's Digest Road, Pleasantville, NY 10570-7000; 914-244-5370; Fax: 914-244-7642.

Money for Royal Neighbors

Current high school students who have been members of the Royal Neighbors of America are eligible to apply for a variety of scholarships offered worth up to $2,500. Must be under 20 years of age. Primary considerations are academic achievement, service to Royal Neighbors, and community service. Contact Royal Neighbors of America, 230 16th St., Rock Island, IL 61201-8645; 309-788-4561; 800-627-4762; {www.royalneighbors.com}.

$1,000 for Sculpture

For students who have created figurative or representational sculpture. Must include up to 10 photos of your work with application. Contact National Sculpture Society, 237 Park Avenue, Ground Floor, New York, NY 10017; 212-764-5645; {www.nationalsculpture.org}.

Money for Maine Women

The Maine Community Foundation has a variety of programs available to current high school seniors and college undergraduates who are residents of Maine. Most require that you attend school in Maine. Applications are sent to local high schools and colleges every year, so check with your guidance counselor or financial aid office first for information. Contact Maine Community Foundation, 245 Main St., Ellsworth, ME 04605; 207-667-9735; Fax: 207-667-0447; {www.mainecf.org}.

Up to $8,000 for
Non-Traditional Michigan Women

Michigan women who have been out of school for at least four years and plan on attending any campus of the University of Michigan are eligible to apply. Each year, they offer up to 38 scholarships ranging from $1,500 to $8,000. Financial need is the primary consideration. Contact Center for the Education of Women, 330 E. Liberty St., Ann Arbor, MI 48104-2289; 734-998-7080; Fax: 734-998-6203; {www.umich.edu/~cew}.

More Money for Hawaiian Women

Female college juniors, seniors, and graduate students who are residents of Hawaii and have a strong interest in women's studies and commitment to serving women are eligible to apply. Must be attending a four-year college. Contact Kilohana United Methodist Church, 5829 Mahimahi, Honolulu, HI 96821; 808-373-3373.

Money for Vermont Women

The Vermont Student Assistance Corporation manages a large variety of scholarship offers for women (and men) who are residents of Vermont. Awards range from $500 to over $5,000. Requirements vary greatly for individual programs, please contact them and request their free scholarship booklet for Vermont residents. Contact Vermont Student Assistance Corporation, Champlain Mill, P.O. Box 2000, Champlain Mill,Winooski, VT 05404-2000; 802-655-9602; 800-642-3177; Fax: 802-654-3765; {www.vsac.org}.

Money for Louisiana Residents

A variety of scholarships and loans are available for Louisiana residents who are attending college or university in Louisiana. For undergraduate students only. Academic achievement is the primary consideration. Contact Willis and Mildred Pellerin Foundation, P.O. Box 400, Kenner, LA 70063-0400.

Money for Non-Traditional Native Americans

The Association offers several programs to assist Native American single parents or displaced homemakers. Awards are intended to assist with the costs of child care, transportation, and basic living expenses while finishing your education. Primary consideration is financial need. Must have either a certificate of degree of Indian blood or a Tribal enrollment card. Contact Association on American Indian Affairs, Inc., P.O. Box 268, Sisseton, SD 57262; 966 Hungerford Drive, Ste. 12-B, Rockville, MD 20850; 240-314-7155; Fax: 240-314-7159; 605-698-3998; Fax: 605-698-3316; Email: {aaia@sbtc.net}; {www.indian-affairs.org}.

Up to $1,000 for Lutheran Women

The Adult Degree Completion Scholarship Program is available to Lutheran women who are over age 25, full members of the Aid Association, and have an insurance policy or annuity in their name through the Association. Must be pursuing your first associate's or bachelor's degree. Part time students are eligible to apply, however the award will be reduced. Contact Thrivent Financial for Lutherans, 4321 N. Ballard Rd., Appleton, WI 54919-0001; 800-847-4836; {www.thrivent.com}.

MONEY FOR FLIGHT ATTENDANTS

Members and their dependent children are eligible to apply for this scholarship program. Must write an essay, topic changes yearly. Also considered is academic achievement and financial need. Contact Association of Flight Attendants, 1275 K Street, NW, 5th Floor, Washington, DC 20005; 202-712-9799; Email: {afatalk@afanet.org}; {www.afanet.org}.

Money for New Hampshire Women

Residents of New Hampshire are eligible to apply for a large variety of programs offered through the Foundation. Only one application needs to be filled out for consideration of all programs that you may be eligible for. Some programs are restricted to handicapped students, others to those entering the Protestant ministry. For all programs, academic achievement and financial need is considered. Must sign an affidavit certifying that you do not smoke or drink alcohol. Undergraduate and graduate students at both 2 and 4 year vocational schools, colleges and universities are eligible to apply.

Contact New Hampshire Charitable Foundation, 37 Pleasant St., Concord, NH 03301-4005; 603-225-6641; 800-464-6641; Fax: 603-225-1700; Email: {info@nhcf.org}; {www.nhcf.org}.

Money for Asian Pacific Women in Los Angeles

The Asian Pacific Women's Network offers a variety of scholarship and support services to Asian Pacific women who live in the Los Angeles area and surrounding counties and wish to increase their job skills and educational background. Women returning to school after a break due to child rearing or financial difficulties, immigrant women, and refugees are especially encouraged to apply. Financial need is the primary consideration. Contact Asian Pacific Women's Network, P.O. Box 86995, Los Angeles, CA 90014.

Up to $1,500 for Chinese American Women

Current college juniors, seniors and graduate students of Chinese-American background who have at least a 3.0 GPA are eligible to apply for this scholarship. Please include a SASE with requests for information. Contact Chinese-American Educational Foundation, P.O. Box 728, San Mateo, CA 94401-0728.

MONEY FOR
SOUTHERN CALIFORNIAN WOMEN

Current sophomore, junior or senior women with a 3.0 or above GPA and are attending any college in southern California are eligible to apply. Application is done through your financial aid office — you must have your financial aid officer nominate you. Direct application is not available.

Contact College Women's Club of Pasadena, Scholarship Foundation, P.O. Box 452, Pasadena, CA 91102.

Free Money for Short People

The Little People of America offers a scholarship and funding for members (people 4 feet 10 inches and under). The scholarship awards up to $1,500. The George Bock Charitable Trust provides for medical expenses associated with dwarfism and the Kitchen's Travel Fund pays partial expenses for conferences related to dwarfism.

Contact Little People of America, 5289 NE Elam Young Parkway, Ste. F-700, Hillsboro, OR 97124. 888-LPA-2001; 503-846-1562; Fax: 503-846-1590. {www.lpaonline.org}.

Money for Baptist Acteens

Female high school seniors who are Southern Baptists and active in Acteens are eligible to apply. Primary considerations are character, church service, academic achievement, an essay and references. Amount awarded varies depending upon funding availability.

Contact Woman's Missionary Union Foundation, P.O. Box 11346, Birmingham, AL 35202-1346; 205-408-5509; 877-482-4483; Fax: 205-408-5508; Email: {WMUFoundation@wmu.org}; {www.wmufoundation.com}.

$1,000 for African American Church of Christ Women

Undergraduate and graduate African American women who are members of the United Church of Christ and are residents of southern California are eligible to apply. Priority is given to non-traditional women who are returning to college after a break, making a mid-life career change, or starting their college career after age 25. Contact United Church of Christ, Southern California Nevada Conference, 2401 N. Lake Ave., Altadena, CA 91001; 626-798-8082; Fax: 626-798-6648; {www.ucc.org}.

Up to $5,000 for
Rhode Island Women

Rhode Island residents who are current college sophomores and juniors are eligible to apply for the Michael P. Metcalf Memorial Grants. These grants are to support or subsidize non-traditional educational opportunities, such as traveling for educational purposes, public service programs, etc., so long as the experience's primary purpose is to expand your horizons, perspective, and personal growth. Financial need must be established. Primary considerations are thoughtfulness of the proposal, creativity and motivation, and initiative. Contact Rhode Island Foundation, One Union Station, Providence, RI 02903; 401-274-4564; {www.rifoundation.org}.

Money for New Mexico Women

The Albuquerque Community Foundation offers a variety of scholarships. Current high school seniors and undergraduate students who are residents of New Mexico are eligible to apply. For all programs available, financial need is the primary consideration. Amount awarded is based upon need. Contact Albuquerque Community Foundation, P.O. Box 36960, Albuquerque, NM 87176-6960; 505-883-6240; {www.albuquerquefoundation.org}.

$2,500 FOR HOME AND WORKSHOP WRITERS

Current high school seniors, college undergraduates, and graduate level students who have a strong interest in pursuing a career in the "do-it-yourself" market as a writer or journalist are eligible to apply, regardless of declared major.

Contact National Association of Home and Workshop Writers, c/o Frank Brugmeier Company, 7501 Woodstream Terrace, North Syracuse, NY 13212-1921; 315-458-0291.

$1,000 for Lesbians in Louisiana

Louisiana residents who are affirmed and open Lesbians or Gays and 17 years of age or older are eligible to apply. Must be attending any college or university at least three-quarter time. Community service, service to the Gay and Lesbian community, activism, leadership ability or potential and financial need are the primary considerations.

Contact Parents, Families and Friends of Lesbians and Gays, New Orleans Chapter, ATTN: Scholarship Committee, P.O. Box 15515, New Orleans, LA 70175; 504-895-3936; Email: {SmileyHeart5678@yahoo.com}; {www.pflagno.org}.

Money for Massachusetts Baptist Women

Women who are residents of Massachusetts and members of an American Baptist Church in Massachusetts are eligible to apply. Must intend on rendering Christian Service in their chosen major or career, although there is no restriction on what major you may be studying. Primary considerations are academic achievement, financial need, dedication, character and values.

Contact American Baptist Women's Ministries of Massachusetts, 20 Milton St., Dedham, MA 02026-2967; 781-320-8100; Fax: 781-320-8105.

Money for African American Women

African American women who have completed at least one semester or two quarters of undergraduate studies with at least a 2.0 GPA are eligible to apply. Financial need is the primary consideration. Direct application is not available, you must be nominated by a member of the National Association of Colored Women's Clubs. Contact your local Club chapter for further information and to find a potential sponsor to nominate you.

NOTE: This award is offered only during even-numbered years. Contact National Association of Colored Women's Clubs, 5808 16th St., NW, Washington, DC 20011-2898.

Up to $10,000 for New York Women in Communications

Full-time undergraduate and graduate level women who are residents of New York and are studying communications, journalism, speech, broadcasting, and marketing are eligible to apply. Must have at least a 3.0 GPA and be attending a college or university in the New York City region and surrounding counties. Primary consideration is academic achievement and potential for success.

Contact New York Women in Communications, Inc., 355 Lexington Ave., 17th Floor, New York, NY 10017-6003; 212-297-2133; Fax: 212-370-9047; {www.nywici.org}.

Up to $1,500 for Theater Women

Women who have outstanding dramatic talent and need financial assistance to continue their education are eligible to apply. Although preference is given to residents of Massachusetts, there is no restriction on residency. Applications must include recommendations from member(s) of the theatrical profession. Only applications from serious theater arts students of the highest talent will be considered — those with only a passing interest in dramatic arts and theater are not eligible.

Contact Lotta M. Crabtree Trusts, 11 Beacon St., Suite 1005, Boston, MA 02108; 617-742-5920.

$1,000 for Sigma Alpha Iota Women

Sigma Alpha Iota, a national organization for women musicians, offers a variety of scholarships and other support programs to its members. The Undergraduate Performance Scholarship is for outstanding performances in vocal and instrumental music, the String Performance Scholarship is for outstanding string performances, and the Scholarship for the Visually Impaired is for members of the organization who are legally blind and are enrolled full-time in a music-related major. Contact Sigma Alpha Iota Philanthropies, Inc., 34 Wall St., Suite 515, Asheville, NC 28801-2710; 828-251-0606; {www.sai-national.org}.

Starting at $500 for Jewelry Women

Women who are pursuing a jewelry-related career and are enrolled in a program that will enable them to achieve this goal are eligible to apply. Selection is based primarily upon skill in designing or creating unique pieces of jewelry, as determined by submitted photos or drawings of your work. Academic achievement, work experience, recommendations and financial need are also considered. Contact Women's Jewelry Association, 333 B Route 46 W., Suite E215, Fairfield, NJ 07004; 973-575-7190; Fax: 973-575-1445; {www.womensjewelry.org}.

$1,500 for Minnesota Nurses

College juniors and seniors who are either residents of Minnesota or attending college in Minnesota are eligible to apply for these scholarships which are funded by the American Cancer Society. Selection is based on an essay related to the nurse's role in caring for patients with cancer, research or public education on cancer, or a cancer-related subject of your choice. To apply, you do not need to be actually involved in oncology nursing or necessarily plan on a career as an oncology nurse.

Contact Minnesota League for Nursing, 5806 Cambridge St., St. Louis Park, MN 55416-5115; 952-829-5891.

Money for Holistic Women

Nursing students and currently licensed nurses already in the workforce who have a strong interest in furthering their education in holistic health care or alternative health techniques are eligible to apply. Must have been a member of the Association for at least six months. Current nursing students must have at least a 3.0 GPA, financial need and career goals are also considered. Nurses who are already in the workforce are considered primarily on their work experience and interest in holistic health. Contact American Holistic Nurses Association, 2733 E. Lakin Dr., P.O. Box 2130, Flagstaff, AZ 86003-2130; 928-526-2196; 800-278-2462; Email: {info@ahna.org}; {http://ahna.org/home/home.html}.

$1,000 for California Nurses

Women who are already licensed Registered Nurses working in California and wish to return to school to pursue a B.S.N. or graduate degree program are eligible to apply. Must attend school at least half-time and plan on finishing the degree within five years. If the winner doesn't finish their degree within five years, the scholarship reverts to a loan and must be repaid. References, commitment to nursing, work experience and financial need are the primary considerations. This award is renewable yearly depending upon academic achievement. Contact California Nurses Association, 2000 Franklin St., Oakland, CA 94612; 510-273-2200; {www.calnurse.org}.

MONEY FOR HISPANIC NURSES

Hispanic members of the Association who are pursuing diploma or certificate programs in nursing or associate or bachelor's degrees in nursing are eligible to apply. Academic achievement and financial need are the primary considerations. Contact National Association of Hispanic Nurses, 1501 16th St., NW, Washington, DC 20036; 202-387-2477; Fax: 202-483-7183; Email: {info@thehispanicnurses.org}; {www.thehispanicnurses.org}.

Up to $2,500 for Jewish Women in Washington, DC

The Irene Stambler Vocational Opportunities Grant Program is open to Jewish women who are residents of the Washington metropolitan area and need to improve their earning power because of divorce, separation or death of their spouses. Grants may be used to complete an educational or vocational program or start or expand a small business. Contact Jewish Social Service Agency Of Metropolitan Washington, 6123 Montrose Road, Rockville, MD 20852; 301-881-3700; {www.jssa.org}.

Money for Wisconsin Nurses

Residents of Wisconsin who are currently enrolled in any college in Wisconsin and have completed at least half of the requirements needed for their degree are eligible to apply. Applications are available from the financial aid offices at all Wisconsin colleges, please do not write to the address below requesting an application as they do not send applications directly to students. Contact Wisconsin League for Nursing, 2121 E. Newport Ave., Milwaukee, WI 53211; 414-332-6271; {www.cuw.edu/wln}.

$2,000 FOR TRAVEL AND TOURISM WOMEN

The Foundation offers a variety of scholarships to travel and tourism students. For all programs, you must be enrolled full-time in a two or four-year school, have at least a 3.0 GPA, and be majoring in travel and tourism, hotel management, restaurant management, or a related major. You must be intending to pursue a career in the travel or tourism industry. Contact National Tourism Foundation, 546 E. Main St, P.O. Box 3071, Lexington, KY 40508; 859-226-4444; 800-682-8886; {www.ntfonline.org}.

$1,000 or More for Women Grocers

Members of the Women Grocer's of America, along with their children, spouses, employees, and grandchildren are eligible to apply. Must be a college sophomore or above with at least a 2.0 GPA enrolled in a food marketing, food service technology, business administration, business management, agribusiness or related major and plan on pursuing a career in the grocery industry. Hotel/restaurant management and public health majors are not eligible to apply. Contact Women Grocers of America, 1825 Samuel Morse Dr., Reston, VA 20190-5317.

The Gift of Giving for People With Diabetes

The LillyforLife Achievement Award recognizes and celebrates the achievements of people with diabetes of all ages throughout the country. Each winner will receive $1,000 to donate to a diabetes organization of his choice, and have the gift given in his name. Those recognized do not have to be well-known or famous for their accomplishments, but can be everyday people who have done or are doing outstanding things. Contact LillyforLife Award Administrator, Eli Lilly and Company, 1508 E. 86 St., #103, Indianapolis, IN 46240; 888-545-5115; Fax: 317-805-6655. {www.lillyforlife.com}.

Up to $10,000 for Government and Public Policy Women

This year-long fellowship program places women graduate students in Congressional offices to encourage more effective participation by women in policy formation at all levels. Preference is given to women who are studying government, public policy, women's issues or social sciences. Must be a U.S. citizen or legal resident. Send self-addressed, stamped business-sized envelope for information. Contact Women's Research And Education Institute, Congressional Fellowships for Women and Public Policy, 1750 New York Ave., NW; Suite 350, Washington DC 20006; 202-628-0444; Fax: 202-628-0458; Email: {wrei@wrei.org}; {www.wrei.org/fellowships}.

Money for Grand Rapids, Michigan Women

Various scholarship programs are available to female residents of Grand Rapids, Michigan. Preference is given to students currently attending or planning on attending Grand Rapids Community College and intend on transferring to the University of Michigan upon graduation from GRCC. Contact The Grand Rapids Community Foundation, 161 Ottawa Ave., N.W., 209-C, Grand Rapids MI 49503-2757; 616-454-1751; Fax: 616-454-6455; Email: {grfound@grfoundation.org}; {www.grfoundation.org}.

Money for Chiropractic Women

The Association offers several programs to student members who are college juniors or above. Awards are only available at colleges and universities where ICA student chapters are located. Please check with your local chapter for information. Contact International Chiropractors Association, 1110 N. Glebe Rd., Suite 1000, Arlington, VA 22201; 703-528-5000; 800-423-4690; Fax: 703-528-5023; {www.chiropractic.org}.

$2,000 for Graduate Historical Women

The Alice E. Smith Fellowship is open to any woman doing graduate level research in American history. Preference will be given to graduate research on history of the Midwest or Wisconsin. Transcripts, work samples and references are not required nor sought. Four copies of a 2-page letter of application should describe in detail the applicant's current research. Send to State Historian at State Historical Society of Wisconsin, 816 State St., Madison, WI 53706; 608-264-6400; {www.wisconsinhistory.org}.

The Ron Brown Scholar Program

The Ron Brown Scholar Program is a national program helping academically talented and motivated African-American high school students who have demonstrated financial need, social commitment and leadership potential. The Program awards $40,000 towards their college costs. Contact The Ron Brown Scholar Program, 1160 Pepsi Place, Suite 206, Charlottesville, VA 22901; 434-964-1588; {www.ronbrown.org}.

Money for Native American Women in the Humanities

This Residential Fellowship is open to women of Native American heritage who are pursuing academic programs at the graduate level in the humanities or social sciences. Contact D'arcy McNickle Center for American Indian History, Newberry Library, 60 West Walton St., Chicago, IL 60610-3380; 312-255-3564.

MONEY FOR MENTAL HEALTH WOMEN

Open to holders of Ph.Ds, M.D.s, or equivalent degrees who are interested in pursuing careers in mental health services research. Minorities and women are especially encouraged to apply. Fellows will improve their knowledge of public mental health systems and services and increase their theoretical, methodological, and analytic skills during the two-year program. Contact National Association of State Mental Health Program Directors Research Institute, Noel A. Mazade Ph.D, Exec Director, 66 Canal Center Plaza, Suite 302, Alexandria, VA 22314; 703-739-9333.

MONEY FOR CHESS PLAYERS

High school juniors and seniors who excel in academics, chess play and sportmanship are eligible to apply. Primary considerations are an essay regarding how chess has had a positive influence on your life, academic achievement, and recommendations. Contact U.S. Chess Federation, 3054 US Route 9W, New Windsor, NY 12553; 845-562-8350; Fax: 845-561-2437; {www.uschess.org}.

Horatio Alger National Scholarship Program

The Horatio Alger National Scholarship Program is one of the nation's largest college financial aid programs. This program assists high school students who have overcome obstacles in their lives. The Scholarship Program awards 107 college scholarships of $10,000 to eligible students in all fifty states, the District of Columbia and Puerto Rico.

Contact The Horatio Alger Association, 99 Canal Center Plaza, Alexandria, VA 22314;703-684-9444; Fax: 703-548-3822; {www.horatioalger.com}.

Horatio Alger National Scholarship Finalist Program

The Horatio Alger National Scholarship Finalist Program provides financial assistance to students who have exhibited integrity and perseverance in overcoming personal adversity and who aspire to pursue higher education.

The National Scholarship Finalist Program annually awards 200 college scholarships of $1,000 to eligible students in those states where the Association does not offer a state scholarship program.

Eligibility

To be eligible to apply for the Horatio Alger National Scholarship Finalist Program, applicants must meet the following criteria:

- be enrolled full time as a high school senior, progressing toward graduation, and planning to enter college no later than the Fall following graduation;
- have a strong commitment to pursue a bachelor's degree at an accredited institution (students may start their studies at a two-year institution and then transfer to a four-year institution);
- critical financial need;
- involvement in co-curricular and community activities;
- demonstrate academic achievement (minimum grade point average of 2.0); and
- be a citizen of the United States or be in the process of becoming a U.S. citizen.

Horatio Alger Nebraska Scholarship Program

The Horatio Alger Nebraska Scholarship Program provides financial assistance to students in the State of Nebraska who have exhibited integrity and perseverance in overcoming personal adversity and who aspire to pursue higher education.

Funded by Association Member Walter Scott Jr. through the generosity of the Suzanne and Walter Scott Foundation, the Nebraska Scholarship Program annually awards $2,500 scholarships to 100 deserving students from Nebraska.

Eligibility

To be eligible to apply for the Horatio Alger Nebraska Scholarship, applicants must meet the following criteria:

- be enrolled full time as a high school senior, progressing toward graduation, and planning to enter college no later than the Fall following graduation;
- have a strong commitment to pursue a bachelor's degree at an accredited institution (students may start their studies at a two-year institution and then transfer to a four-year institution);
- critical financial need;
- involvement in co-curricular and community activities;
- demonstrate academic achievement (minimum grade point average of 2.0);
- be a resident of Nebraska; and
- be a citizen of the United States or be in the process of becoming a U.S. citizen.

Horatio Alger California Scholarship Program

The Horatio Alger California Scholarship Program provides financial assistance to students in the State of California who have exhibited integrity and perseverance in overcoming personal adversity and who aspire to pursue higher education.

Funded through the generosity of Association Members George L. Argyros and Arthur A. Ciocca, the California Scholarship Program annually awards $2,500 scholarships to 200 deserving students from California.

Eligibility

To be eligible to apply for the Horatio Alger California Scholarship, applicants must meet the following criteria:

- be enrolled full time as a high school senior, progressing toward graduation, and planning to enter college no later than the Fall following graduation;
- have a strong commitment to pursue a bachelor's degree at an accredited institution (students may start their studies at a two-year institution and then transfer to a four-year institution);
- critical financial need;
- involvement in co-curricular and community activities;
- demonstrate academic achievement (minimum grade point average of 2.0);
- be a resident of California; and
- be a citizen of the United States or be in the process of becoming a U.S. citizen.

Horatio Alger Minnesota Scholarship Program

The Horatio Alger Minnesota Scholarship Program provides financial assistance to students in the counties of Anoka, Carver, Dakota, Hennepin, Ramsey, Scott, and Washington in the State of Minnesota who have exhibited integrity and perseverance in overcoming personal adversity and who aspire to pursue higher education.

Funded through the generosity of the Carl & Eloise Pohlad Family Foundation, the Minnesota Scholarship Program annually awards $2,500 scholarships to 42 deserving students from Minnesota.

Eligibility

To be eligible to apply for the Horatio Alger Minnesota Scholarship, applicants must meet the following criteria:

- be enrolled full time as a high school senior year, progressing toward graduation, and planning to enter college no later than the Fall following graduation;
- have a strong commitment to pursue a bachelor's degree at an accredited institution (students may start their studies at a two-year institution and then transfer to a four-year institution);
- critical financial need;
- involvement in co-curricular and community activities;
- demonstrate academic achievement (minimum grade point average of 2.0);
- be a resident of Anoka, Carver, Dakota, Hennepin, Ramsey, Scott, or Washington counties in the State of Minnesota; and
- be a citizen of the United States or be in the process of becoming a U.S. citizen.

Horatio Alger Iowa Scholarship Program

The Horatio Alger Iowa Scholarship Program provides financial assistance to students in the State of Iowa who have exhibited integrity and perseverance in overcoming personal adversity and who aspire to pursue higher education at the University of Iowa. Funds will only be disbursed to those recipients who enroll at the University of Iowa and will not be transferable to another institution.

Funded through the generosity of Association Members John Pappajohn, Marvin A. Pomeraniz, and Henry B. Tippie, the Iowa Scholarship Program annually awards $3,000 scholarships to 100 deserving students from Iowa.

Eligibility

To be eligible to apply for the Horatio Alger Iowa Scholarship, applicants must meet the following criteria:

- be enrolled full time as a high school senior, progressing toward graduation, and planning to enter college no later than the Fall following graduation;
- have a strong commitment to pursue a bachelor's degree at the University of Iowa (proof of enrollment will be required, students may start their studies at a two-year institution and then transfer to a four-year institution);
- critical financial need;
- involvement in co-curricular and community activities;
- demonstrate academic achievement (minimum grade point average of 2.0);
- be a resident of Iowa; and
- be a citizen of the United States or be in the process of becoming a U.S. citizen.

Up to $5,000 for Environmental Public Policy Women

College sophomores and juniors pursuing a career in environmental public policy are welcome to apply for this highly competitive scholarship award. Direct application is not available. Application and nomination forms are sent to colleges annually, if your department chairman or financial aid office does not have information on this program, have your financial aid officer contact the Foundation for information. They also have a highly regarded internship opportunity available. Contact The Morris K. Udall Foundation, 130 South Scott Avenue, Tucson, AZ 85701-1922; 520-670-5529; Fax: 520-670-5530; {www.udall.gov}.

Money for Women in Sports Journalism

Must be studying journalism or communications and intend on pursuing a career in sports journalism. Open to current college juniors only. Scholarships include a six to ten week internship. Minorities are especially encouraged to apply. Contact Sports Journalism Institute, Sports Illustrated, 1271 Avenue of the Americas, New York, NY 10020-1393; 212-522-4044; {http://sportsillustrated.cnn.com}.

Money for Political Science Women in Maryland

Undergraduate women who are residents of Montgomery County, Maryland and studying political science, government, or public administration and attending any college in Maryland are eligible to apply. Send self-addressed stamped envelope for application and complete information. Contact Lavinia Engle Scholarship Foundation, c/o Judith Heimann, 6900 Marbury Rd., Bethesda, MD 20817; 301-229-4647.

Money for Unitarian Women

Limited funding available for active, involved Unitarian women at both the Undergraduate and Graduate level. Some funds are set aside specifically for children of Unitarian ministers. One program, the Ministerial Education Fund, is specificallly for students enrolled in a Masters of Divinity degree program intending on pursuing a career as a Unitarian minister. Contact Unitarian Universalist Association, 25 Beacon St., Boston, MA 02108, 617-742-2100; {www.uua.org}.

$1,000 for Aviation Women in Los Angeles

Three scholarships available to women living in the greater Los Angeles area who wish to pursue a career in aviation. Must be at least 18 years old at time of application. Please include a self-addressed, stamped envelope with requests for information. Contact San Fernando Valley Ninety-Nine's, P.O. Box 7142, Van Nuys, CA 91409; 818-989-0081; {www.ninety-nines.org}.

Up to $10,000 for Texas Women

Several hundred scholarships worth more than $1,000,000 are awarded annually to outstanding high school seniors in the Houston, Texas area. Some funds are also available to students in Texas but living outside of Houston. Most programs are available to students pursuing any major. Must plan on attending college full-time. Contact Houston Livestock Show and Rodeo, P.O. Box 20070, Houston, TX 77225-0070; 832-667-1000; {www.rodeohouston.com}.

Up to $2,000 for Nursing

The Aliene Ewell Scholarship Program offered by Chi Eta Phi is for undergraduate women planning on a career in nursing. Must be recommended by a current member of Chi Eta Phi. Primary considerations are financial need, academic achievement, and potential for success. Contact Chi Eta Phi Sorority, 3029 13th St., NW, Washington, DC 20009; 202-232-3858; {www.chietaphi.com}.

Up to $5,000 for Ethics Women

Scholarship essay contest open to full time juniors and seniors in an accredited four-year college or university. Essay must be on an ethics-based topic, such as "Why are we here and how are we to meet our ethical obligations" or reflecting on an ethical aspect of a public policy issue. The prizes are two at $500, one at $1,500, one at $2,500 and one at $5,000. Please write for more information. Include a self-addressed stamped envelope with requests. Contact Elie Wiesel Prize In Ethics Essay Contest, Elie Wiesel Foundation for Humanity, 529 Fifth Avenue, Suite 1802, New York, NY 10017; 212-490-7777; Fax: 212-490-6006; Email: {info@eliewieselfoundation.org}; {www.eliewieselfoundation.org}.

$2,000 for Women in Technology

The AFCEA offers several scholarship programs for students. For all scholarships, you must be a full-time student attending a 4-year college or university, a U.S. citizen, studying electrical engineering, aerospace engineering, electronics, computer science, computer engineering, physics, or mathematics, and must have a GPA of 3.5 on 4.0 scale or better.

The General John A. Wickham Scholarship accepts applications from current college juniors and seniors. The Ralph W. Shrader Scholarship is for postgraduate students working towards a master's degree in any of the above majors, or communications technology, communications engineering, or information management. At least one scholarship award is set aside specifically for a woman candidate, provided all eligibility criteria is met.

Please include a self-addressed and stamped envelope with information on field of study when writing to request information and application. Contact AFCEA Educational Foundation, 4400 Fair Lakes Ct., Fairfax, VA 22033-3899; 703-631-6149; 800-336-4583, ext. 6149; Email: {scholarship@afcea.org}; {www.afcea.org}.

$1,000 for
Pennsylvania Journalism Women

The Pennsylvania Women's Press Association offers a competitive scholarship of $1,000. To be eligible, one must be a Pennsylvania resident, a print journalism major in a four-year or graduate-level program in a Pennsylvania college or university, and be classified as a junior, senior or graduate student for Fall term. The winner will be selected on the basis of proven journalistic ability, dedication to journalism and general merit. Contact PWPA Scholarship Committee, c/o Teresa Spatara, P.O. Box 152, Sharpsville, PA 16150; 724-962-0990; {www.pnpa.com/pwpa/index.htm}.

$1,000 for Communications
Women in New York

Women who are residents of New York, studying communications, and members or a child of a member of the American Legion Auxiliary, the American Legion Juniors, or the American Legion, any New York chapter. Graduates of Girls State are also eligible to apply. Must be attending or planning on attending an accredited four-year college. Contact New York State Legion Press Association, P.O. Box 1239, Syracuse, NY 13201-1239.

Up to $10,000 for
Education Women in Delaware

This is a renewable scholarship loan program. Current high school seniors or undergraduate college students who are Delaware residents, studying education, and attending any Delaware university are eligible to apply. Must have at least a 2.5 GPA. Must agree to teach in Delaware one year for each year the award was received or pay back the loan. Contact Delaware Higher Education Commission, 820 North French Street, Fourth Floor, Wilmington, DE 19801; 302-577-3240; 800-292-7935; Fax: 302-577-6765; {www.doe.state.de.us/high-ed}.

$1,000 for Vocational Women in Minnesota

Applicant must be a Minnesota high school senior planning to go to vocational school. Selection is based upon financial need, academic achievement, promise of leadership ability, and good character. Students planning on attending a two-year or four-year college are not eligible to apply. Contact Minnesota Federation of Teachers, Scholarship Committee, 168 Aurora Avenue, St. Paul, MN 55103.

Up to $4,000 for Journalism Women

High school seniors who show an interest in a career in the newspaper business, broadcasting, and journalism are eligible to apply. Primary considerations are financial need, academic achievement, character, and potential for success. Contact F. Ward Just Scholarship Foundation, c/o Kennedy, 805 Baldwin Ave., Apt. 308, Waukegan, IL 60085-2359.

Up to $13,000 for Scuba Diving Women

Open to undergraduate women who are certified SCUBA divers and between the ages of 21 and 25. Academic achievement is also considered. Contact Our World Underwater Scholarship Society, P.O. Box 4428, Chicago, IL 60680; 630-969-6690; Fax: 630-969-6690; Email: {info@owuscholarship.org}; {www.owuscholarship.org}.

$1,000 for Clinical Laboratory Technology Women

The Society offers several scholarships to both undergraduate and graduate members. Check with your local chapter first for information. Contact International Society for Clinical Laboratory Technology, 917 Locust St., Suite 1100, St. Louis, MO 63101-1413.

$2,500 for Lesbian Women

Each year, after a highly competitive application process, Legacy awards several $1000 scholarships to outstanding lesbian undergraduate and graduate full-time students. Must have at least a 3.0 grade point average, and demonstrate a commitment or contribution to the lesbian community. Other considerations are financial need, academic performance, honors, personal or financial hardship, and most especially, service to the lesbian community. Further information and applications are available at the website.

Contact An Uncommon Legacy Foundation, Inc., Scholarship Committee, P.O. Box 33727, Washington, DC 20033; 202-265-1926; Fax: 202-265-1927; {www.uncommonlegacy.org}; {Email: scholarships@uncommonlegacy.org}.

Up to $10,000 for Women with Community Service

The Target All-Around Scholarship program is available to both men and women who are current high school seniors and legal U.S. residents. Must be planning on attending any vocational/technical, two-year, or four-year school full-time. Primary consideration is the amount and quality of time you have spent in service to your community as a volunteer. Applications are available every September at all Target stores. Contact Target All-Around Scholarship, c/o Citizens' Scholarship Foundation of America, Inc., One Scholarship Way, St. Peter, MN 56082; 800-537-4180; Fax: 507-931-9168; {www.csfa.org} or {http://target.com}.

Money for Connecticut Women

Current high school seniors who are residents of Waterbury, Connecticut are eligible to apply. Financial need is the primary consideration. Check with your high school counselor or administration office for application and information, or at the address below. Contact Elisha Leavenworth Foundation, 35 Park Pl., Waterbury, CT 06702.

Money for Operating Room Nurses

Scholarship awards covering tuition and fees are available to current Registered Nurses who are members of AORN and wish to return to college to continue or advance their education. Must have at least a 3.0 GPA and attend a four-year college. Graduate students are welcome to apply.

Contact Association of Operating Room Nurses Foundation, Credentialing Division, 2170 South Parker Rd., Suite 300, Denver, CO 80231; 303-755-6304; 800-755-2676; {www.aorn.org}; Email: {custserv@aorn.org}.

$1,000 To Study Farming

Current college sophomores and juniors who are members of or children of members of the Society and plan on studying any agricultural-related major, agricultural engineering, or biological engineering are eligible to apply. Primary consideration is financial need, although academic achievement is also considered. Contact American Society of Agricultural Engineers, 2950 Niles Rd., St. Joseph, MI 49085; 269-429-0300; Fax: 269-429-3852; {www.asae.org}.

$1,000 for Seattle Women in Service to the Homeless

Seven scholarships are available to high school seniors who are residents of Seattle and plan on attending college full-time. Must have a committed interest to the plight of the homeless and have demonstrated community service to the homeless. Financial need, recommendations and an essay are also considered. Contact Windermere Foundation Scholarship, College Planning Network, 171 East Uncas Road N., Port Townsend, WA 98368; 802 18th Avenue, Seattle, WA 98122; 206-323-0624; Email: {seacpn@collegeplan.org}; {www.collegeplan.org}.

Up to $1,500 for Wives of Overseas Active Duty Service Members

Open only to spouses residing with an active duty service member stationed overseas. A grant of up to 50% of tuition for on-base education programs, up to a maximum of $300 per undergraduate term, or $350 per graduate term, and $1,500 per academic year is available. Do not need to be a full-time student. Contact Navy-Marine Corps Relief Society, 4015 Wilson Boulevard, 10th Floor, Arlington, VA 22203-1977; 703-696-4904; Fax: 703-696-0144; {www.nmcrs.org}.

$500 for Graduate Women in Lesbian Studies or Jewish Women Studies

The Graduate Scholarship in Lesbian Studies awards $500 to a student who will be doing research for or writing a master's thesis or Ph.D. dissertation in lesbian studies. The Scholarship in Jewish Women's Studies awards $1000 to a graduate student who is enrolled full-time for the fall semester and whose area of research is Jewish Women's Studies. Contact National Women's Studies Association, University of Maryland, 7100 Baltimore Blvd., Suite 500, College Park, MD 20740; 301-403-0525; Email: {nwsa@umail.umd.edu}; {www.nwsa.org/scholarship.htm}.

Money For Delaware Women Over Age 20

Young women who are at least 20 years old, have graduated high school or achieved a GED, have been accepted to any Delaware two year or four year college, and are residents of Delaware are eligible to apply. Financial need is the only consideration. Contact Fresh Start Scholarship, Wilmington Women in Business, Inc., P.O. Box 7784, Wilmington, DE 19803; Attn: Scholarship Committee; 302-656-4411; Fax: 610-347-0438; Email: {office@wwb.org}; {www.wwb.org/fresh.htm}.

Money for Washington, DC Women in Communications

Current junior or senior female students studying communications, advertising, journalism, public relations, marketing, graphic arts, or a related field are eligible to apply. Must have at least a 3.0 GPA, work experience in communications or related field, active in extra-curricular activities including family obligations, volunteer work, club and organization involvement that show versatility and commitment.

Contact Association for Women in Communications, 780 Ritchie Highway, Suite 28-S, Severna Park, MD 21146; 410-544-7442; Email: {info@awic-dc.org}; {www.awic-dc.org}.

Money for Saginaw, Michigan Women

Each year, the Saginaw Community Foundation awards over 80 scholarships to area high school students and college students. Please check with your high school guidance counselor, college financial aid officer, or the address below for further information.

Contact Saginaw Community Foundation, 100 S. Jefferson, Suite 201, Saginaw, MI 48607; 989-755-0545; Fax: 989-755-6524; Email: {info@saginawfoundation.org}; {www.saginawfoundation.org}.

$1,000 for Culinary Women in Maine

The Maine Restaurant Association offers scholarships to current high school seniors who are residents of Maine and plan on pursuing a career in the restaurant business. Culinary arts majors are also eligible to apply. Primary considerations are financial need and academic achievement. Contact Maine Restaurant Association, 5 Wade St., P.O. Box 5060, Augusta, ME 04332-5060; 207-623-2178; Fax: 207-623-8377; Email: {info@mainerestaurant.com}; {www.mainerestaurant.com}.

Up to $2,500 for Northern Virginia Women

Open to undergraduate women who are 23 years old or over and attending or planning on attending an accredited college or university in northern Virginia. If your planned course of study is not available at any northern Virginia schools, this award may be used at institutions outside of northern Virginia. Primary consideration is financial need.

Contact Junior League of Northern Virginia, 1420 Spring Hill Road, Suite 600, McLean VA 22102; 703-442-4163; Fax: 703-761-4139; Email: {info@jlnv.org}; {www.jlnv.org}.

Scholarships Help Graduate Nursing Students Continue Education

Educational assistance is available to financially needy graduate nursing students residing in the U.S. through the Foundation of the Alumnae Association of the Mount Sinai Hospital School of Nursing, Inc. Contact Foundation of the Alumnae Association of Mount Sinai Hospital School of Nursing, Inc., 1 Gustave L. Levy Pl., New York, NY 10029; 212-289-5575.

National Merit Scholarship Competition from Boeing

Each year Boeing provides scholarships to children of Boeing employees who are selected as National Merit Scholarship winners. Students enter this academic competition their junior year of high school by taking the Preliminary Scholastic Aptitude Test/National Merit Scholarship Qualifying Test (PSAT/NMSQT) in the fall.

To qualify for a scholarship, students should obtain a copy of the *PSAT/NMSQT Student Bulletin* from their high school counselor and make arrangements with their school to take the test in October.

There is no application process through The Boeing Company. All aspects of the awards are handled by the National Merit Scholarship Corporation.

The National Merit Scholarship Corporation may be contacted by writing to:

Department of Educational and Scholarship Services
National Merit Scholarship Corporation
1560 Sherman Avenue,
Suite 200
Evanston, IL 60201-4897
Phone: 847-866-5100

College Funds for Oregon Single Parents

The Ford Family Foundation helps Oregon residents who are single parents, and heads of households, as defined by the IRS. Scholarship amounts vary. They are based upon meeting up to 90% of the student's unmet financial needs—that is the cost of education (tuition, fees, books, childcare if applicable, transportation) minus any federally expected family contribution and other scholarships or gifts.

Students must be high school graduates or continuing college students— seeking a four year's bachelor degree at an accredited, public or private, nonprofit Oregon college or university. For more information, contact the The Ford Family Foundation Scholarship office, 1700 Valley River Drive, Suite 400, Eugene, OR 97401; 877-864-2872; Eugene area: 541-485-6211; E-mail: {fordscholarship@tfff.org}.

More Opportunities from the Generous Ford Family Foundation . . .

The Ford ReStart Scholars Program helps nontraditional students age 25 or over who want to begin or continue an educational program at the postsecondary school level. Applicants must live in Oregon or in Siskiyou County, California. In addition to showing financial needs, they must show their leadership, commitment, history of working responsibly in the job or home. The program intends to meet up to 90% of the student's "unmet financial needs." For more information, {www.osac.state./private.html}.

Help for Oregon's Future Teachers and Nurses

The Friends of Oregon Students Scholarship helps students who are pursuing careers in teaching or nursing. Eligible candidates must: Have a cumulative GPA of 2.5 and be working twenty-plus hours per week while attending college or graduate at least three-fourths time. Preference is given to non-traditional students—for example, those who are older, returning to school or single parents. They also must show volunteer or work experience related to their chosen profession. For information, go to the Oregon Student Assistance Commission at: {www.osac.state.or.us/private.html}.

For Oregon Engineering Students

If you are a high school student interested in a career in chemical, civil, electrical, and industrial or mechanical engineering, and planning to study at an accredited Oregon college in major engineering fields. Look into The American Council of Engineering Companies of Oregon Scholarship. Requirements are available at: {www.getcollegefunds.org}.

Scholarship Opportunities from the American Ground Water Trust

Several scholarships exist for those interested in a career in the field of ground water. The American Ground Water Trust is a not-for-profit membership organization working with volunteers to:

- Protect ground water from contamination.
- Promote the environmental benefits of ground water.
- Provide individuals, educators and legislators with accurate information.

If you have any questions, please call the Trust at 603-228-5444.

Amtrol, Inc. Scholarship

Amtrol, Inc. is a leading manufacturer of water system products.

Eligibility Requirements, Deadline, and Award

- You MUST be a High School Senior intending to pursue a career in a ground water related field.
- Deadline: June 1st, annually
- Award: $1,000 to $2,000

Baroid Scholarship

Baroid is the largest international supplier of drilling and completion fluid products and services.

Eligibility Requirements, Deadline, and Award

- You MUST be a High School Senior intending to pursue a career in a ground water related field.
- Deadline: June 1st, annually
- Award: $1,000 to $2,000

Ben Everson Scholarship
(Claude Laval Corporation)

The Claude Laval Corporation is a leading manufacturer of down-hole camera equipment for the irrigation and water well industry.

Eligibility Requirements, Deadline, and Award

- You MUST be a High School Senior intending to pursue a career in a ground water related field.
- Deadline: June 1st, annually
- Award: $2,500

Flight-Training Scholarship

- Joseph F. Vorbeck Scholarship: Each year four aviation students at the University of Cincinnati Clermont College will receive $2,500 each. The scholarships will go to two outstanding freshman and two outstanding sophomores.

  Clermont College Financial Aid Office at: 513-732-5284.

Scholarships for Women

1. Zonta Amelia Earhart Fellowship Awards. $6,000 grants to women for graduate study in aerospace-related science or engineering.

   Zonta International, 35 East Wacker Drive, Chicago, IL 60601.

2. The Amelia Earhart Memorial Scholarships. Each year, The Ninety-Nines award several Amelia Earhart Memorial Scholarships to qualified 99s (members of at least two consecutive years) for advanced flight training or courses in specialized branches of aviation. Seventeen scholarships were awarded in 1999 that paid for one entire rating or license. The AE awards winners received: 2-Instrument ratings, 2-Commercial licences, 7-multi-engine ratings, 3-Flight Instructor certificates, 1-Airline Transport Pilot licenses, and two B-737 Type Ratings with United Airlines.

   Headquarters at 800-994-1929

3. Women Soaring Pilots Association Scholarships. The scholarships are awarded annually by the Women Soaring Pilots Association (WSPA) to support and encourage aspiring women pilots.

   Sharon Smith, 801 Elsbeth, Dallas, TX 75208; E-mail: {sierray@metronet.com}.

4. National Council for Women in Aviation/Aerospace.

   National Council for Women in Aviation Headquarters.
   800-727-6292; Fax: 630-243-1828.
   E-mail: {pknight@ncwa.com}.

5. Whirly-Girls Scholarships. Annual $4,000 scholarship to a female commercial airplane pilot to obtain an initial or additional helicopter rating.

   Charlotte Kelley, President of the Whirly-Girls Scholarship Fund, Executive Towers 10-D, 207 W. Clarendon Ave., Phoenix, AZ;
   602-263-0190

6. Judith Resnick Memorial Scholarship. $1,000–$5,000 through American Flyers. Must already have a Prvt/Inst. Considered monthly.

   800-233-0808

7.   Jan Jones Aerobatic Scholarship. $1,000 for aerobatic training.

     I.C.A.F., 715 S. Beach, Suite 102, Daytona Beach, FL 32114;
     904-238-5267

8.   Women in Aviation, International Scholarship. Several awards annually that range from $500 to $30,000. Many awards/grants awarded, e.g. Flight Training Magazine, Women in Aviation, International Achievement Awards, SimuFlite Maintenance Scholarship, etc. All applications must include three recommendation letters, 250-word descriptive essay, resume, copies of all aviation licenses and medical certificates, last three pages of your pilot logbook; deadline December 12.

     Women in Aviation. 937-839-4647

9.   Women Military Aviators, Inc. (WMA) Scholarship. One scholarship of $2,500. Applicant must be a woman interested in an aviation career to pursue an FAA (or equivalent private pilots rating or advanced ratings). Award based on financial need as well as on goals and aspirations; deadline June 3.

Index